Laurentian upland of low hills and many lakes

LANDFORMS OF THE UNITED STATES

BY ERWIN RAISZ

Reprinted through the courtesy of Blaisdell Publishing Company,
a division of Ginn and Company.

Scale

Miles

Kilometers

GEOLOGY /

A SURVEY OF EARTH SCIENCE

A SURVEY

GEOLOGY /
OF EARTH SCIENCE

Edgar Winston Spencer

CHAIRMAN, DEPARTMENT OF GEOLOGY

WASHINGTON AND LEE UNIVERSITY

with drawings by ELIZABETH HUMPHRIS SPENCER

THOMAS Y. CROWELL COMPANY

NEW YORK / ESTABLISHED 1834

PREFACE

THIS BOOK is a nonmathematical introduction to geology and related earth sciences. No previous background in science is assumed. The treatment is based primarily on the classical subject matter of physical and historical geology. However, introductions to astronomy and meteorology are included for use where needed in earth science courses. Although these chapters may be omitted, they should at least be assigned as outside reading because they are designed to emphasize the relationships between geology and these fields of study. The book is intended for use in one semester survey courses in geology for liberal arts students and secondary school teachers, or it can be used with outside readings as the basis for a two semester course. A supplementary reading list is included for this purpose.

In the preparation of an introductory book such as this the author must be guided in his selection of topics and their treatment by certain perspectives determined by his own view of what is important. In this book an attempt is made to present as balanced a coverage of subject matter as is consistent with the other objectives of the book. These are:

to provide some historical perspective of the development of scientific ideas. The first chapter deals with the historical development of man's view of the earth in space. This chapter demonstrates the evolution of scientific thought and shows how it can be influenced by the society in which the scientific work is conducted. Similar treatment is used in the study of matter, the origin of the geologic time scale, and geosynclinal theory.

to point out the interrelationships between the various scientific disciplines. These interrelationships become clear in the consideration of the origin of the earth and of its character as a planet, and in the interactions between the oceans, the atmosphere, and the land, and are pointed up in the study of the interior of the earth, of the theory of evolution, and of the nature of matter.

to demonstrate the variety and types of approaches used by scientists—the scientific methods. These are seen through historical development and in descriptions of modern methods of analysis. The extent of the variety of these methods will become clear when the student compares modern methods of investigating the magnetic field, the solar system, or the earth's interior with those used to decipher the history of ancient climates, Precambrian history, or evolution of life.

to emphasize the state of our progress in the study of the earth. In this regard the student should be made aware of the vast store of knowledge which has been built up in the past and the significant ideas which have been derived from this record. Certainly no man can claim to be liberally educated who has not considered the origin of the Earth and the Solar System, the possible origins of life, and the theory of evolution, or looked at human history with the perspective gained by an appreciation of geologic time.

to point up the unsolved problems of the present, the controversies of today, and some probable directions of future study. No student should ever leave a geology course today with the feeling that the study of the earth is complete. He should leave convinced that this is a vital field in which many of the most challenging and significant questions are yet to be answered.

Edgar Winston Spencer
March, 1965

NOTE TO THE INSTRUCTOR

THIS BOOK IS DESIGNED to allow for considerable flexibility in its use. If the course is designed as an earth science course or for training of earth science teachers, Part I, which covers selected aspects of astronomy, and Part III, which covers topics of meteorology, should be used.

The first three parts may be omitted if the text is used for a one semester survey course in geology. In this case it will be advisable to assign Part IV, The Oceans, after Part V, Matter, Minerals, and Rocks, so the student will have some knowledge of processes of sedimentation before studying sedimentary environments. This order may be found desirable even in earth science courses.

Throughout the text scientific terms have been placed in italics where they appear for the first time or where they are most fully defined and described. For this reason no glossary is needed. The definition for a term can be found through the index. In the last few chapters names of some classes and phyla, and informal names which are not ordinarily italicized have been italicized where these groups are first described.

A series of shaded relief and geologic maps is included at the end of the book along with a selected list of references. Footnotes through the text refer to these maps. A few sample questions are included with the maps. It is anticipated that the teacher will prepare other questions on the maps when this is desirable.

E. W. S.

ACKNOWLEDGMENTS

MY SINCERE THANKS go to those students, colleagues, and friends who have contributed ideas about teaching geology to liberal arts students or have assisted directly in the preparation of the manuscript and illustrations for this book.

I wish to thank Dr. Edward Turner for reading the chapters devoted to astronomy and making suggestions concerning their organization and presentation; and Llewellyn Smith for giving a critical appraisal of the entire manuscript from an undergraduate student's point of view. I am especially grateful to Philip Winsor for editing the manuscript with patience and care, and to Tinsley Crowder for his devoted effort to make the manuscript clear to students without science backgrounds. The critical reading of the galley proof by Dr. Ernest H. Muller is also gratefully acknowledged.

For the illustrations I am most grateful to my wife, who prepared most of the line drawings. Photographs and other illustrations have been acknowledged where they appear in the text. I especially wish to acknowledge the help of Dr. G. A. Cooper and the staff of the United States National Museum, and the United States Weather Bureau, for their help in securing photographs.

In deep gratitude for her work in preparing the illustrations and for her encouragement during the writing of this book, this book is dedicated to my wife, Elizabeth Humphris Spencer.

E. W. S.

CONTENTS

I / THE PLACE OF EARTH IN THE UNIVERSE

II / PLANET EARTH

III / THE ATMOSPHERE

IV / THE OCEANS

V / MATTER, MINERALS, AND ROCKS

VI / SURFACE FEATURES OF THE EARTH

VII / STRUCTURE AND INTERIOR OF THE EARTH

VIII / ANALYSIS OF EARTH HISTORY

IX / SKETCHES FROM GEOLOGIC HISTORY

X / HISTORY OF LIFE

I /

THE PLACE OF EARTH
IN THE UNIVERSE

Historical Development of Man's View of the Place of Earth in the Solar System

MAN'S CONCERN WITH THE SUN, MOON, planets, and stars most certainly had its beginnings in the early days of his history. He used moonlight to hunt by and in time learned to use the positions of the stars as a guide to directions. Changes in position of the sun and moon allowed an estimate of the time of the day or night. When agricultural society began to develop, man found it increasingly important to be able to predict seasonal changes with accuracy so that he could plant seed at the proper time. With the rise of commerce, even more accurate methods of keeping time and determining direction became necessary. Thus man's concern with the "Solar System" grew from practical considerations. However, considerable religious significance came to be attached to the celestial bodies. Lacking control over nature, man recognized the benefits he derived from the heat and light of the sun, and the light of the moon. It was natural to assume that these magical bodies might be the source of good or perhaps evil in the world. We know a little about the role of the Solar System in early man's mythology. To what extent he attained any measure of scientific understanding of the Solar System in these most primitive times we can only guess. The oldest written record comes to us from Babylon.

A fragment of the Babylonians' knowledge of the stars has been found preserved in a large number of tablets uncovered in excavations of the ancient cities of Mesopotamia. These tablets indicate that the positions and movements of the sun, moon, and stars had been carefully recorded in early Babylon. It is even probable that the Sumerians had accumulated a large body of observations before the time of Babylon. The Babylonians, whose astronomy was well developed by 1000 B.C., tried to find mathematical formulae which could be used to predict future movements of the celestial bodies. This mathematical approach differs strikingly from the geometrical models used later by the Greeks, particularly in that the Babylonians made no attempt to understand what happened to the sun, moon, or stars after they had set below the horizon. As late as the fifth century B.C. the Egyptians, whose astronomy depended heavily on that of Babylon, believed that when the sun set it was carried in a boat across a sea stretching from the western to the eastern horizon, where it began its ascension the next day. Apparently the Babylonians were more interested in accurate predictions than in obtaining an understanding of why the celestial bodies performed as they did. The time of many religious festivals was determined by the moon. Therefore the phase and position of the moon were of particularly great, importance. The moon, therefore, rather than the sun, was the basis of the early calendar—a most unfortunate choice, as we shall see.

It will be easier to follow the course of development of ideas concerning the Solar System if the observations available to the Babylonians and early Greeks are clearly in mind. Let us try to put ourselves in the positions of these early observers, remembering, of course, that no accurate maps were available. They would see essentially what the reader might observe over a long period of years of careful observation without a telescope.

1. The land is bounded by the sea—a vast flat-appearing surface. Overhead the stars appear to be fixed in a large hemispherical shell. (Without instruments man would not perceive that these stars are at different distances.)

2. The celestial sphere moves. In the Northern Hemisphere the stars in the northern sky can be seen to rotate around a particular region or star—today the North Star, Polaris. As seen by an observer looking north, the rotation of the stars is counterclockwise. As the night passes stars disappear along the western horizon and others appear along the eastern horizon.

3. The sun and moon are obviously not fixed to the celestial sphere because they move in relation to the stars. As the moon moves, it can be seen to block out a view of the stars behind it.

4. The sun provides a most useful marker of direction, time, and season. It rises on the eastern horizon, follows a path across the southern sky (as seen in the Northern Hemisphere), and sets along the western horizon. The path varies with the time of year. Only on two days a year, the *equinoxes*, does the sun rise in the due east and set in the due west, but its highest position on each day of the year marks the direction of due south (Fig. 1–1). At this point in the day a post erected in the open will cast a shadow due north. The shadow will be longest in winter when the sun rises south of east, follows a low arc, and sets south of west. In the summer the arc is higher, the sun rises and sets north of east and west, and the shadow cast by the post is shorter. The length and direction of the shadow make it possible to tell the time of day roughly, and the length of the shadow at noon is an indication of the time of year. The position of sunrise varies along the eastern horizon, but the shifting position of successive sunrises forms a systematic movement. A *year* is the time required for the position of sunrise to move from its northernmost point to its southernmost point and then back to its northernmost point again.

5. Early civilizations gave names to particular patterns of stars, called *constellations*. They named them for animals and legendary humans, and we have kept the same names on our modern celestial maps, sometimes changing the name to suit our own experience. Thus Polaris is at the end of the tail of Ursa Minor, the little bear, which we have also named the Little Dipper. We will see certain patterns of stars sweep counterclockwise around the pole star which stands still and marks due north.

Just as the sun's path varies from season to season, the celestial sphere shifts. The positions of the stars in relation to one another remain fixed, but, as the seasons change, the particular pattern of stars directly overhead at midnight is very slightly different each night. It takes one year for the cycle to be complete. Stars that set on the western horizon at a particular time on one day will set a few minutes earlier the next day. It appears that the celestial sphere is moving in its arcuate path slightly faster than the sun. It is just enough faster, in fact, for the celestial sphere to make one extra complete revolution each year.

The difference in the rate of movement of the sun and stars showed the ancients that the two were moved by different agents or "gods." The sun's movements can be thought of as having two components. One of these is the daily path from the eastern to the western horizon, paralleling the movement of the stars; the second is a much slower movement backward through the star pattern. This track of the sun through the star pattern is called the *ecliptic*.

6. Certain stars, the early observer would note, do not remain fixed in the pattern of stars but instead seem to move independently through the celestial sphere. The Greeks called these stars "wanderers," the root of our name for them, *planets*. Five planets—Mercury, Venus, Mars, Jupiter, and Saturn—are visible to the naked eye. Mercury and Venus are very bright, and neither appears far from the sun. They move back and forth in front of or behind the sun and can be seen only at sunrise or sunset. Mercury, closer to the sun than Venus, is hard to see. Venus is known both as the "evening star" and the "morning star." For many years it was thought to be two different planets.

Mars, Jupiter, and Saturn can be seen to wander within a narrow belt very close to the sun's path across the celestial sphere. Like the sun and the moon, planets move through the star pattern, but at different rates. The belt containing the paths of the sun, moon, and planets through the star pattern is called the *Zodiac*. Early astrologer priests divided the zodiac into twelve parts, after the twelve lunar months of the year, each named for a prominent constellation. The paths of some of the wandering stars appear very erratic and no doubt caused early observers to wonder at their odd behavior. These paths were the sources of much superstition. They are looped, as viewed against the star pattern (Fig. 1–2). When the path of one of these planets, Mars, Jupiter, or Saturn, makes such a loop, the planet moves slower and slower to the east among the stars, then stops and moves westward with the stars, comes to a second stop, and then progresses eastward again. Mars requires about two years to make its complete looped path through the zodiac. Jupiter takes about 12 years and Saturn takes nearly 30 years.

7. To the observer standing on the earth, the moon and sun appear to be of similar size. It is not surprising that early viewers thought it

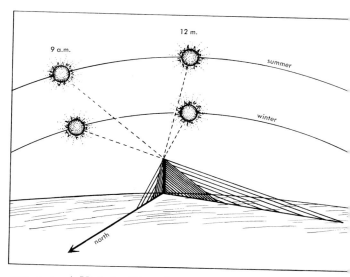

FIG. 1–1. / *High position of sun marks north. The post casts a shadow of different length at different times of day and at different seasons. At high noon the shadow points north.*

FIG. 1–2. / *A planet describes a looped path when viewed against a star background.*

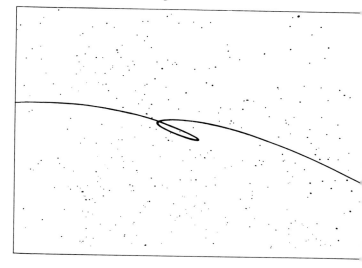

probable that the movements of these two bodies would be directly related in some way. The moon, like the planets, follows a path close to that of the sun as viewed against the star pattern. About every 27⅓ days returns to a given position with respect to the star pattern. However, 29½ days elapse between two successive new moons or two full moons. Thus approximately thirty days make up a *lunar (synodic) month*. Twelve of these months are nearly a year. This approximate coincidence of the length of twelve synodic months with the year (the length of the year being defined by the sun's position in its path) led the Babylonian astronomers to base their calendars on the synodic month. This unfortunate choice resulted in problems which plagued the accuracy of the calendars for literally thousands of years. The difference between a year composed of 12 synodic months and one based on the sun's position is about 10 days.[1]

[1] It is obvious that a calendar which accumulates an error of 10 days per year will not long be useful as a guide for agricultural purposes. Unfortunately the Mesopotamians' religion and culture were so intensively centered upon the moon that they chose to make a number of shifts of days rather than give up the moon as a basis for their calendar.

One method used by the Babylonians was based on the fact that 235 synodic months are very nearly 19 years. Thus by having 12 years with 12 lunar months and 7 years with 13 lunar months a nearly satisfactory solution was reached.

Because the length of the astronomical year is not an integral multiple of day lengths, no calendar based on days will come out exactly. The astronomical calendar is about 11 minutes less than 365¼ days.

Julius Caesar introduced the leap year system in 45 B.C. By this system a fourth year of 366 days is introduced into the calendar every four years. This calendar was used until 1582. By that time the 11 minute error each year had added up to nearly 10 days. Pope Gregory XIII ordered a correction by dropping 10 days and changing the calendar so that in certain years which would have been leap years the extra day would not be added. These years are found as follows—if a leap year ends in two zeros then it is counted as a leap year only if the figures preceding the zeros are divisible by four. The Gregorian calendar is still in general use today.

Ancient Greeks' View of the Solar System

THE BABYLONIANS WERE NEVER TRUE SCIentists, as the term is defined in modern times, because they never were concerned with explanations of what their data signified. They were willing to go on compiling data, essentially time graphs for the sun and moon, without consideration of the relationships between the bodies they observed in the sky. The most significant advances in man's view of the universe sprang out of a monastic brotherhood founded in one of the Greek colonies in southern Italy about 550 B.C. by Pythagoras, a Greek philosopher and mathematician, who attained such stature that his followers considered him divine. His studies were concerned with nature, astronomy, geometry, music, and arithmetic. The Pythagorean theories of geometry will be familiar to all who have studied plane geometry. He believed that the universe is constructed on the basis of harmony—meaning an orderly adjustment of the parts in a complex pattern. Pythagoras sought order in music and was successful in finding a numerical solution, which he then applied to the entire universe. This gave rise to the theory that "all things are numbers." The Pythagoreans looked for order or harmony in the movements of the planets and the sun and moon. Their search led to a system of astronomy much as we know it today. The orbits of the planets, sun, and moon against the fixed-star pattern were conceived as circular orbits. The different rates of movements of the planets were seen as an indication of their distance from the earth. Thus Mercury was in the closest orbit, then, at increasingly greater distances, Venus, the sun, Mars, Jupiter, and Saturn (Fig. 1–5).

The Pythagorean brothers are credited with suggesting that the earth is a sphere. The fact that other celestial bodies could be seen to be spherical suggested that for reasons of symmetry the earth also might be spherical. They argued that an earth of any other shape would fall in on itself. The concept did not gain wide acceptance until the time of Plato (428–348 B.C.), who argued that the sphere was the most perfect shape for a body and hence the earth, at the center of the universe, must be a sphere. Aristotle (*ca.* 340 B.C.) pointed out a more convincing argument: during an eclipse of the moon, when the earth comes into a position directly between the sun and moon, the shadow cast by the earth on the moon is circular. He also pointed out that a man who travels a short distance northward or southward will find a changed star pattern. Another Pythagorean view is that the main influence of the universe must come from the center and that the center must be a great fire. Since the earth was not a fire it must not be at the center but must revolve about the center (at a rate of once every 24 hours), along with the sun, moon, and planets. It remained for Heraclides in the fourth century B.C. to dispense with the concept of the central fire and perceive rather that the earth rotates on its axis once each 24 hours.

The Greek mathematician Eudoxus, a student of Plato, who had also studied in Egypt and Babylon, made the first serious attempt to explain the intricacies of planetary motion in terms of uniform circular motions. The system he devised was one of concentric spheres nested around the earth at the center. A separate system of spheres then represented motions of the sun (3 spheres were needed), moon (3), each of the five visible planets (4), and the celestial sphere (1). In a mechanical model which Eudoxus built to illustrate his theory, each sphere turns on an axis supported by holes in the next outside sphere. In this way the axis of each sphere could be differently oriented. Then by selecting the correct direction for the axis and the correct uniform rate of spin for each sphere, the observed facts of planetary motion could be reproduced. This hypothesis of Eudoxus proved to be simple and workable, and received the support of Aristotle. However, it soon became obvious that the model did not explain all observed movements and the addition of more and more spheres introduced increasingly complicated problems. Further, the theory failed to explain why planets change in brightness. According to the model the planets remain at fixed distances from the earth, and yet the brightness of Mars is seen to change markedly.

FIG. 1–3. / *Schematic diagram of the Solar System. Distance relationships, of course, are not accurate.*

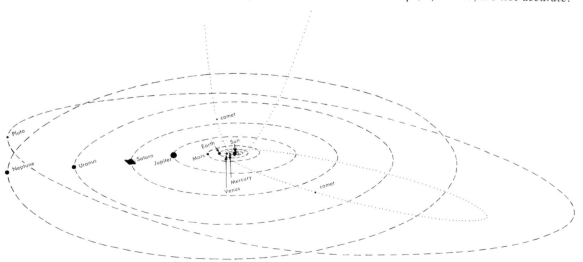

Heliocentric Theory—A Forerunner of the Modern Heliocentric Theory

HERACLIDES (375–310 B.C.) SUGGESTED that the earth itself rotated on an axis once every 24 hours and that the center of revolution of the planets was the sun. Aristarchus of Samos (about 280 B.C.) is credited with taking this idea to its logical conclusion. It is likely that at first he envisioned the planets as moving in orbits around the sun, and the sun, in turn, as moving in an orbit around the earth—a view revived by Tycho Brahe nearly 2,000 years later. But Aristarchus came to adopt the heliocentric theory—the view of the sun as the center of the universe, with the earth and the other planets moving in circular orbits around it. Aristarchus concluded that the stars must be very far away from the earth, in terms of comparative distances in the Solar System, because they do not appear to change position in relation to one another during the year as the earth moves in its orbit.

Aristarchus also made the remarkable discovery of the approximate scale of the Solar System. He realized that at the moment when the moon's surface is half light and half dark, lines connecting earth, sun, and moon form a right triangle (Fig. 1–4). Thus if the angle moon-earth-sun (angle ABC) can be measured, the ratio of the distance from the earth to the sun to the distance from the earth to the moon can be calculated. The distance to the moon could then be calculated by comparing the radius of the moon to the radius of the shadow of the earth on the moon during eclipse. Thus the ratio of the radius of the moon to the radius of the earth could be established. Eratosthenes in the third century B.C. had made an estimate of the earth's diameter, using a method we shall examine later. Thus Aristarchus was able to estimate the distance and size of the moon, sun, and the radii of the orbits of the planets. He calculated the sun's distance at about five million miles (compared with the modern estimate of 93 million). The greatest weakness in this method lay in the difficulty in determining the exact moment to measure the

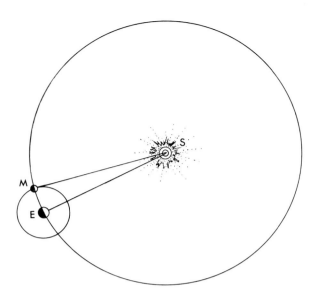

FIG. 1–4. / *Aristarchus' method of determining the distance from the sun to the earth.*

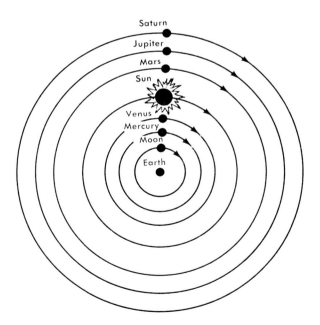

FIG. 1–5. / *Geocentric Solar System.*

angle between the moon, earth, and sun. Aristarchus was off by about 2⅝ degrees. He may have recognized certain problems his theory presented. Among these is the fact that the seasons are of different lengths. If the earth's orbit were circular, the seasons would be equal in length. (Today we know the earth's orbit is an ellipse.)

After Aristarchus, Greek astronomy made few truly significant advances. The heliocentric theory was abandoned in favor of epicyclic theories which again envisioned the earth at the center (Fig. 1–5). The Greeks could not bring themselves to abandon the idea of circular orbits in favor of elliptical orbits, and the known motions of the Solar System could not be completely explained by epicyclic theories. The most outstanding work with epicycles was done by Ptolemy (120 A.D.) whose ingenious mathematical constructions made it possible for him to approximate the features of elliptical motion by a compounding of circular movements.

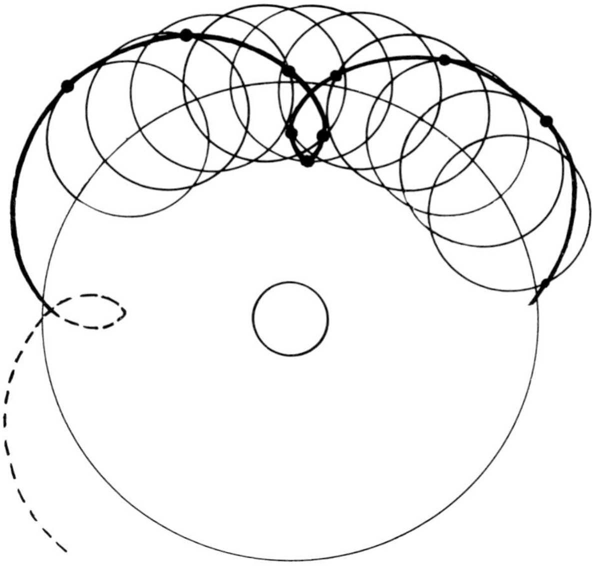

FIG. 1–6. / An Epicycle. Motion of this type was proposed to explain the looped paths of planets, and thus was needed in geocentric models.

The Size of the Earth

THE IDEA THAT THE EARTH IS SPHERICAL was universally accepted in Greece by the time Aristarchus made his efforts to discover the size of the Solar System. In making his calculations he figured the distances to the moon and sun in terms of the diameter of the earth.

A remarkably accurate estimate of the size of the earth was made by Eratosthenes about 230 B.C. He observed that at noon in midsummer a vertical stick at Syene (Aswan) did not cast a shadow, while at the same time a vertical stick at Alexandria did cast a shadow. If the stick at Syene is considered to be in a truly vertical position, the shadow cast by the stick at Alexandria indicates that the sun there is displaced by 7° 12′ from the vertical (Fig. 1–7). It was either known or assumed that Alexandria and Syene are on the same longitude (Alexandria is due north of Syene). If the distance from Alexandria to Syene could be accurately measured, the circumference of the earth,

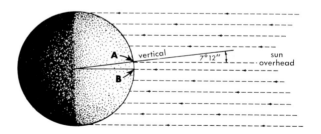

FIG. 1–7. / Eratosthenes measured the diameter of the earth by observing the angle a vertical pole made with the incident sunlight at A which was a known distance from B where no shadow was cast. The angle between A and B at the center of the earth is 7° 12″, the same as the angle between the vertical and the sun. Through knowledge of this angle and of the distance A–B, the radius of the earth could be calculated.

and in turn its diameter, could be calculated. Eratosthenes determined that the earth's diameter was 7,850 miles, which is only 70 miles less than it is estimated to be today.[1] Many modern astronomers have doubted the accuracy of Eratosthenes' calculations, and some have thought that by good fortune he may have incorporated some compensating errors in them.

The Long Lull

FOLLOWING THE DEATH OF ARISTARCHUS, the idea of an earth-centered Solar System returned to the fore, and the outstanding astronomers of the next three hundred years tried to explain planetary motions in terms of epicycles. Ptolemy, who lived around 120 A.D., was the last astronomer to produce important work (and it is more important for its ingenuity than for its findings) for the next 1,400 years. This period was marked by many important changes in the world—the fall of the Roman Empire, the separation of eastern and western Europe from each other, with a near cessation of scientific communications between them, and most significantly the rise of Christianity. Most of the Christian scriptures were written by Hebrews —a people who had not been scientifically oriented. These writings, including especially the Book of Genesis, contained scientific ideas which the Greeks would have considered naive. The Bible was interpreted quite literally by leaders of the early Christian Church. Certain passages in Scripture seem to imply a flat earth, so the Greek concept of a spherical earth was discarded, and the earth was conceived of as a flat surface above which the sun and stars followed a daily journey from the east to the west horizon and then returned to the east just below the horizon—a conception the Greek astronomers had abandoned a thousand years earlier. However, though Greek science was dead for a time, it was not lost. The ideas of the Greeks were preserved in their writings, and were undoubtedly influential in the scientific revolution

[1] Eratosthenes gave the distance in "stadia." There is some disagreement over the actual length of this measure, so he may have been much further off.

which followed the Reformation. Outstanding among the new scientists was Copernicus.

Return to the Sun-Centered (Heliocentric) Theory

BY THE TWELFTH CENTURY A.D. EUROPEAN scholars were again studying the products of Greek science and philosophy. Thomas Aquinas (1225–74) merged Greek philosophy with Christian theology in his new philosophy. During the 1,400 years between Ptolemy and Copernicus astronomy was kept alive in the Near East. European students of astronomy in 1500 had access both to the epicyclic earth-centered theories of Ptolemy and to the writings of Aristotle, which embraced the concentric spheres of Eudoxus. The vast difference in these two systems undoubtedly impressed the young Nicolaus Copernicus (1473–1543), whose work laid the foundation for the modern conception of the Solar System. The Ptolemaic system had been kept alive in the Near East, but there was dissatisfaction with the accuracy of predictions obtained by astronomical calculations based on it. As we have seen, even the length of the year was in question.

Copernicus objected to the nonuniform motion of the Ptolemaic epicycles. He also returned to the idea of a rotating earth. Ptolemy had rejected this idea, reasoning that if the earth were rotating, a body thrown into the air would lag behind, which did not occur in actuality. Copernicus, however, correctly reasoned that the motion of the rotating earth would be imparted to the object and that consequently there would be no lag.

Copernicus sought a simple arrangement of circles for planetary movements in which each body would move at a uniform rate and from which the observed movements could be deduced. This marked a return to the idea of Aristarchus. However, unlike Aristarchus, Copernicus was able to prove through calculations that the motion of celestial bodies could be represented by uniform circular movements in a sun-centered solar system (Fig. 1–8).

Unfortunately, it later became clear that the heliocentric system of Copernicus was unable to predict planetary movements more accurately than Ptolemy's system. The uniform movements which appealed so much to Copernicus had to be abandoned. But acceptance of the hypothesis that the earth rotates on an axis and revolves about the sun, as do the other planets, made it ultimately possible to explain the apparent motions of the stars, the flattening of the earth at the poles, the tides, the tradewinds, and the behavior of the gyroscope.

Kepler's Laws of Planetary Motion

FRANCIS BACON (1561–1626), GALILEO Galilei (1564–1642), and Tycho Brahe (1546–1601) were all contemporaries of Johannes Kepler (1571–1630) at the end of the Renaissance. Tycho Brahe, whose observatory was located at Copenhagen, made a vast contribution to astronomy through his improvements in observational techniques. Although astronomical telescopes were not yet available, he measured planetary motions with far greater accuracy than had ever been achieved before. Kepler, a German colleague of Tycho, continued the observations after Tycho's death and began to analyze the large quantity of data which had been collected. Kepler was convinced of the validity of the heliocentric hypothesis, and he constructed a model showing the geometrical relations between the planets (Fig. 1–9). This model marked an interesting point in the history of scientific exploration, but it added little to man's understanding of the Solar System.

The great contribution of Kepler lies in his discovery of the planets' elliptical paths. Kepler found it impossible to fit Tycho Brahe's data on the orbit of Mars into the single uniform circular motion of the Copernican System. Copernicus would not have been aware of the discrepancy because his observational data were not sufficiently refined. After years of effort to find a solution, Kepler realized that the substitution of an elliptical path for a circular orbit would remove the necessity of thinking in terms of epicyclic movements (Fig. 1–10). Thus a simple scheme could replace a more complicated one and the first of Kepler's laws of planetary motion was introduced: "All planets move in elliptical paths, with the sun at one focus of the ellipse."

This law by itself is not sufficient for an accurate prediction of planetary motion because it does not allow prediction of the time at which a certain planet will be at a given point on the ellipse. Kepler set to work to try to find a means of making this prediction, and in time came to recognize a second law of planetary motion, known as the *law of equal areas:* during any given time interval, the imaginary line connecting a planet and the sun sweeps over the same area. It can be shown mathematically that if the speed and distance of a planet from the sun are known at any given time, it is possible to predict its speed in traveling any other distance in an elliptical orbit.

Even after these two great achievements Kepler was not completely satisfied with his understanding of planetary movement. Like the ancient astronomers, he was convinced that there should be some simple unifying principle by which the motions of the planets might be related. Finally, after many trials, he did indeed find such a principle. Kepler's third law of planetary motion states that the period of one complete revolution of a planet about the sun squared equals a constant (with the same value for all planets) multiplied by the cube of the mean radius of the elliptical path; or, in a mathematical formula $T^2 = KR^3$. Constant K could be derived, since the period T of the earth equals one year and the distance of the earth from the sun, R, was known to be 93 million miles.

Kepler now set about constructing accurate tables of planetary motion. If any one thing sets Kepler's approach apart from that of his predecessors, it is his emphasis on mathematical relations to supplement the older, geometric models.

Galileo Galilei (1564–1642), like Kepler, was firmly convinced of the accuracy of the Copernican system. The two men were also sim-

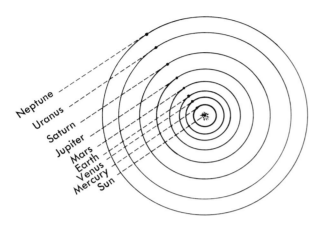

FIG. 1–8. / *Copernicus' model of the Solar System.*

ilar in their emphasis on mathematics. Galileo was the first astronomer to use a telescope for astronomical observation. In 1610 he reported the presence of dark spots on the sun and of mountains and seas on the moon, and the fact that Venus, like the moon, goes through phases. He also observed that Saturn has bulges, and he saw four of Jupiter's twelve satellites. This last observation is particularly significant, because the system composed of Jupiter and its satellites was clearly one in which the revolution was not around the earth, and in Galileo's time the Church still held to the doctrine of an earth-centered universe.

In 1616 Galileo was warned by the Inquisition to stop teaching that the sun is the center of the Solar System, on the ground that such a belief was clearly in conflict with the Bible. Seven years later a friend of Galileo's was made Pope and Galileo apparently considered himself safe. In 1632 he made some final changes in a manuscript which he then published as *Dialogue on the Great World Systems*. In this volume he set forth his support of the Copernican view of the universe so clearly that the work could not be overlooked by the Church. Gali-

leo's heresy was studied by a special commission and the astronomer found that he must either admit his error and plead for mercy or suffer torture, condemnation, and death, as did Giordano Bruno in 1600 for his views on the universe. Galileo decided to admit his error. He was placed under home arrest, a prisoner of the Inquisition. His book was placed on the *Index Expurgatorius* along with books of Copernicus and Kepler, and he was forced to recite his abjuration, part of which follows:

I must altogether abandon the false opinion that the sun is the center of the world and immovable and that the earth is not the center of the world and moves. . . .

Therefore, desiring to remove from the minds of your Eminences, and of all faithful Christians, this vehement suspicion justly conceived against me, with sincere heart and unfeigned faith I abjure, curse, and detest the aforesaid errors and heresies and generally every other error, heresy, and sect whatsoever contrary to the Holy Church. . . .

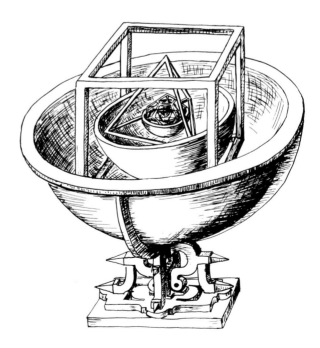

FIG. 1–9. / *Kepler's model of the Solar System. Planets occupied paths in the spheres only.* (*After Kepler.*)

Newton and the Law of Gravitation

SIR ISAAC NEWTON (1642–1727) LIVED AT a time when science was flourishing. Gilbert was making great contributions to the understanding of magnetism; Huygens was exploring the nature of light and of centripetal force, was experimenting with the pendulum clock, and had invented the reflecting telescope; Roemer had measured the speed of light; Hooke was studying and formulating principles of elasticity; and Agricola had written his famous book on mineralogy.

Until the time of Newton, astronomers had been chiefly concerned with the problem: "What paths do the planets follow?" Now their concern turned to another question: "What forces must act on a body to make it move in an elliptical orbit?" In Newton's famous book *Principia* he set forth the mathematical explanations of the forces of gravitational attraction between bodies and applied these to the motions of the planets, comets, the moon, and the tides. He showed that by postulating that all bodies in the universe exert forces of gravitational attraction on one another he could derive the motions of all bodies in the Solar System.

He established first that any body moving in accordance with Kepler's second law, the law of equal areas, must be acted on by a central force. Thus, since it had been shown that each planet did in fact move in accordance with Kepler's second law, the net force on each planet must be directed toward one focus of the elliptical path. Newton went beyond this to establish the magnitude of the force as well as its direction. And he was able to show that the force upon each planet must at any moment be inversely proportional to the square of the distance from the center of the body (if it is spherical) to the focus of the ellipse. The question of the origin of this force remains. Newton saw in the attraction of objects on the earth to the earth the solution—all objects attract one another with a gravitational force. Thus, he reasoned, the central force on a planet was the

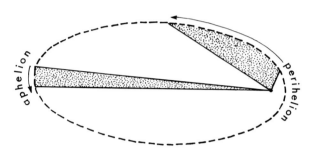

FIG. 1–10. / *An ellipse. Kepler discovered that planets traveling in elliptical paths sweep out equal areas (shaded) in equal periods of time. Thus a planet at perihelion must travel more rapidly than one at aphelion.*

gravitational attraction to the sun. In similar manner the force on the moon must be the gravitational attraction between the earth and the moon. Newton decided that the magnitude of the force must be proportional to the masses of the two objects, and thus the law of universal gravitational attraction which he developed becomes

$$F = \frac{KM_1M_2}{R^2}.$$

The value of the constant, K, was later established by Cavendish (1731–1810).

Newton tested his theory by using these hypotheses to calculate the period of revolution of the moon about the earth. He calculated a value of 27 days, compared with the actual value of 27⅓ days, and this result showed that he was on the right track. He extended his principle of gravitation to the planets and successfully derived Kepler's third law. Thus a theoretical basis was laid for the experimental results of Kepler.

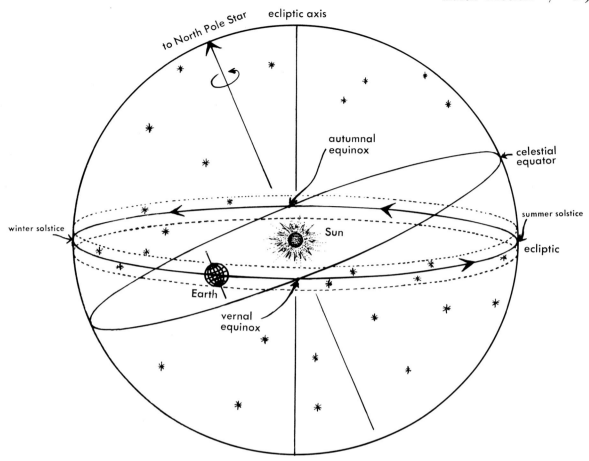

FIG. 2–4. / *Relationships between the ecliptic, the earth's equator, and the solstices.*

One of the best means of demonstrating the rotation of the earth is the freely swinging pendulum, known as the Foucault pendulum. In 1851 the French physicist Foucault used a large iron ball suspended on 200 feet of wire to demonstrate how such a pendulum can prove the earth's rotation. The wire was attached so that there was little friction. When the pendulum is set in motion the plane of oscillation slowly turns in relation to the floor. This relative motion is actually due to change of the direction of the ground. Because every point on the surface of the earth completes a full rotation in the same amount of time, the velocity of points on the surface depends on latitude (zero at the poles, a maximum at the equator). Thus in the Northern Hemisphere points north of the pendulum move eastward slower than those south. This type of motion would be most pronounced

if the pendulum were set up at the pole. There would be no deflection if the pendulum were set up on the equator. Movement of the pendulum in relation to the floor is clockwise in the Northern Hemisphere, counterclockwise in the Southern Hemisphere.

A proof of rotation similar to the Foucault pendulum is the observed deflection of objects moving horizontally. Imagine a projectile fired due north from some point in the Northern Hemisphere. Two components of motion are given the projectile when it is fired—one northward by the gun and one eastward due to the velocity of the movement of the ground under the gun. This bullet moves northward and hits on the surface of the earth, but not due north of the gun. Instead it appears deflected to the east, because the target has been rotating eastward more slowly than the gun. Had the pro-

FIG. 2–5. / *View of the earth's path around the sun viewed from over the Northern Hemisphere. Note that the earth is farther away from the sun in summer than in winter in the Northern Hemisphere.*

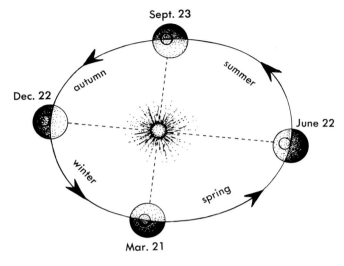

Sept. 23

autumn

summer

Dec. 22

June 22

winter

spring

Mar. 21

FIG. 2–6. / *Precessional motion of the earth. The earth gyrates slowly like a spinning top.*

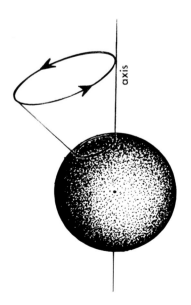

axis

jectile been fired due south it would have fallen behind its target to the west. Thus, regardless of the orientation of the gun, the projectile is deflected to the right in the Northern Hemisphere. Similar analysis will show that the deflection is left in the Southern Hemisphere. We shall see later how this is related to movements in the atmosphere and oceans.

The earth completes one full rotation in a period that is just a few minutes less than 24 hours. In order to check the accuracy of the speed of rotation it is necessary to time other periodic events that are independent of the earth's rotation. Such events are the transit time of Mercury as it crosses the sun, or the revolution of satellites of one of the planets. These observations do indeed indicate that rotation of the earth is not constant. A steady slowing amounting to about one-thousandth of a second per century has been detected. In addition, there are fluctuations in the period of rotation that run as high as 30 seconds. These are thought to be related to small changes in the diameter of the earth due to internal expansions and contractions.

Wandering Poles

WHEN SCIENTISTS LEARNED TO TAKE very precise measurements of latitude, they detected that the latitude of any given point experiences slight variations. Apparently this may be due to a continuous movement of the exact position of the axis. This movement is somewhat irregular, but it is roughly circular. Measurements so far indicate that this wandering takes place within a circle whose radius is approximately 40 feet.

Revolution of the Earth

THE ANNUAL MOTION of the earth in its orbit around the sun may be used with equal effectiveness to prove that the sun revolves annually about the earth. Other evidence is now available to prove that it is the earth, not the sun, that revolves. Let us examine this evidence.

ABERRATION OF STARLIGHT. An English astronomer, James Bradley, discovered that there is an annual periodic change in the direction of movement of each star as seen by an observer on earth. What the observer sees is an apparent displacement of a star in the direction in which the earth is moving. The same effect is seen in the case of a man with an umbrella walking in the rain. If the man is still, the raindrops fall and appear to fall vertically around him. But if he walks very fast the rain will appear to fall at an angle from the direction toward which he walks. The fact that a star appears to be displaced first in one direction and then in another can be explained if it is understood that either the star moves or the earth revolves. Stars situated near the plane of the earth's orbit appear to oscillate while those near the pole travel in circular patterns. This is best explained through the conception of a revolving earth.

Parallax of a star. A second line of proof of the revolution of the earth lies in the ease with which the concept explains annual parallaxes of stars. Parallax (Fig. 2–7) is observed because all stars are not at the same distance from the earth. As the earth follows its path around the sun, closer stars appear to oscillate in relation to those farther away. So minute is this oscillation that it was not detected until 1838 and not measured until the early part of the twentieth century. The parallax effect has proven useful in determining distance to stars.

Precessional earth motion. The third major type of movement of the earth is a very slow conical movement of the axis of the earth around the pole to the ecliptic. Earth's axis is inclined 23½° to the pole of the plane in which the earth revolves. If the earth were not rotating, the gravitational attraction of the sun and moon would soon bring the equator of the earth into the plane of the ecliptic. Because the earth is spinning on its axis, it acts like a top in motion and resists a change in the orientation of its axis. The net effect is to produce a wobble. This slow conical movement of the axis is called earth's *precessional motion*. The period of the completion of this motion is about 26,000 years. It follows that a precessional motion of

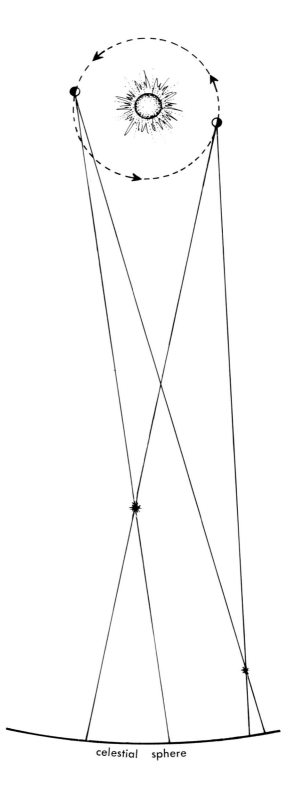

celestial sphere

FIG. 2–7. / *Parallax effect.*

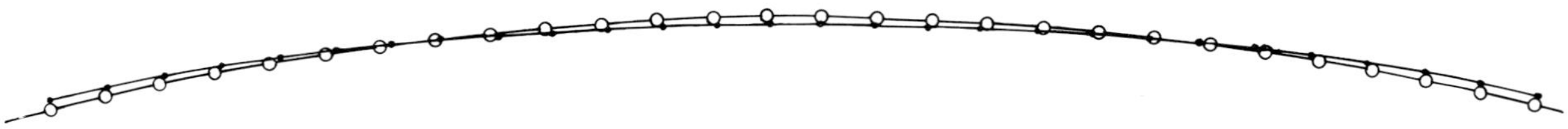

FIG. 2–8. / *Orbits of the earth-moon system around the sun.*

the axis means a precessional motion of all points on the earth, including the equator. Since the direction of precession of the axis is westward, both the equator of the earth and the celestial equator, which is a projection of earth's equator, shift slowly west. The orbit of the earth remains unaffected by this movement, so the ecliptic remains stationary. It follows that the points of intersection of the celestial equator and the ecliptic (the equinoxes) move westward slowly. Thus precession of the earth's axis means necessarily a precession of the equinoxes. If we remember now that the projection of the vernal equinox on the celestial sphere is one of the main astronomical reference points, it is apparent that this precession is very important. It is the cause of a constant displacement of all measurements of right ascension, and is responsible for the fact that the signs of the Zodiac do not coincide with the constellations for which they are named. The Zodiac is a band of the celestial sphere, 16° wide, which contains the ecliptic and the paths of most of the planets and the moon. It was divided into 12

parts of 30° length, marked off beginning from the vernal equinox, and each part was named for a constellation. Because this division was made about 2,000 years ago the displacement, due to precession, has been significant.

Geology of the Moon

MAN'S DEVELOPMENT OF ROCKETS AND HIS exploration of the moon with the intention of eventually placing a man on its surface have focused attention on lunar geology (Shoemaker, 1964). The nature of the moon's surface, the natural processes taking place there, and the types and quantities of materials making up its crust, are all vital questions that have direct bearing on the success or failure of projected moon visits. Some of these questions will probably remain unanswered until a man is placed on the moon; answers to others have long been known.

The best known features of the moon are

FIG. 2–9. / *Illumination and phases of the moon. Direction of sunlight is from left to right.*

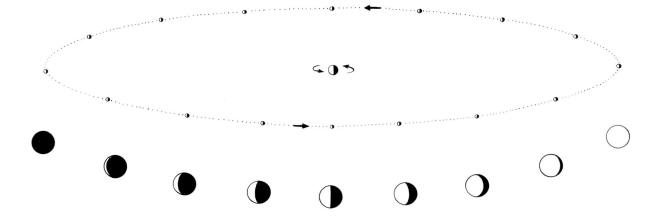

its size and motions. Its radius is about one-quarter that of the earth, and its mass is close to 1/82 that of the earth. This points up one striking comparison—the low density of the moon. Its average density is about 3.3. This is very close to the density of the earth's crust, 2.7, but it is significantly below the average for the earth as a whole, 5.5. One consequence of the moon's low density is a weak gravity field, approximately one-sixth that of earth. Thus it would be easy for a man on the moon's surface to jump fifteen to twenty feet high, or to lift objects which would weigh several hundred pounds on earth. A rocket would require a much lower escape velocity to leave the moon than to leave the earth.

To the geologist, the low density of the moon has many highly significant effects. Most important of these is the absence of an atmosphere. There are no clouds, nor has an atmosphere of any type been detected. Just as the earth's gravity field is not strong enough to hold hydrogen and helium, the moon cannot retain oxygen, nitrogen, carbon dioxide, or even heavier gases such as xenon and krypton. If the moon ever had an atmosphere, at some early stage, it was lost rapidly, or if gases gradually escaped from the interior of the moon as they are now escaping from the interior of the earth, they were lost into space.

The importance of the earth's atmosphere becomes clear when a comparison is drawn between the earth and the moon. Ocean waters are condensed water vapor. In the absence of an atmosphere ocean water would evaporate and be lost. Thus all processes associated with the oceans and the interchange of materials between the ocean, the atmosphere, and the land would stop. In the absence of an atmosphere there would be no chemical weathering of rock and mineral materials, no organic life of the type we know, no blanket of insulation to moderate temperatures. The side of the moon receiving solar radiation has an estimated temperature in excess of 212° F. The side in the dark is approximately −240° F. Geological processes of erosion and weathering, which are so effective on earth, are largely inoperative on the moon.

There are no glaciers, no running water, ground water, wind erosion, or oceanic processes of shoreline erosion, at least on the portions of the moon that receive sunlight and probably on the entire surface. This would leave primarily processes of mass wasting and thermal expansion and contraction as active processes of erosion and degradation. In addition, the moon's surface has been affected for millions of years by the rain of small and large meteorites. The impact of these bodies together with effects of volcanic activity have been important in shaping the moon's surface. It is obvious from the surface features of the moon that other processes either are acting or have been acting in the past.

The moon offers a varied and interesting surface. It can be seen in considerable detail with good telescopes. The big telescopes permit distinction of objects of as little as 50–100 yards in size. In 1964 the *Ranger 7* spacecraft obtained excellent photographs of a portion of the moon's surface. The closest of these was taken only 1,600 feet up from the surface and allowed resolution of objects only a few feet in diameter. Lunar atlases and geologic maps have been prepared from photographs, and techniques have been developed which permit close approximation of the size of features on the surface. The features seen in this way include vast, nearly flat plains, called *maria* (singular, *mare*) or seas, long ragged mountain ranges with peaks reaching as much as twenty to thirty thousand feet high, faults, fracture systems, rilles, craters from which rays may radiate for as much as 1,000 miles, and other markings interpreted as results of the flow of crustal material.

The maria are vast areas that seem nearly featureless when viewed through a small telescope. They appear as darker areas on most photographs; however, when viewed through a large telescope with oblique lighting, many small-scale features are evident. These features have been described by Elger (1895):

. . . many low bubble-shaped swellings with gently rounded outlines, shallow trough-like hollows, or, in the majority of them, long sinuous ridges.

The ridges are called *wrinkle ridges*. The features observed on the maria are consistent with the long-held view that the maria are essentially "seas of frozen lava." It must be borne in mind that since there are few processes of erosion, such features remain essentially unchanged. They could be literally billions of years old. Faint outlines of what are probably old craters appear in the maria.

Mountains found surrounding the maria are very unlike mountain belts on earth. Those on earth are generally belts of folded sedimentary rocks which have been intruded by molten rock and altered. Certain regular forms associated with them are missing in the lunar mountains. There is no evidence of folding. Instead, masses of rubble can be observed. On the other hand, moon mountains are like those on earth in that they display many faults and fracture systems. Along some of the faults there have been great displacements, as in "Straight Wall," a fault scarp about sixty miles long and over a thousand feet high. The origin of these mountains is little understood. Some have suggested that they are composed of material splashed out of the maria. However, it is possible that they were formed by some long-continued volcanic activity. Almost certainly the moon was largely molten at one time, and probably it passed through a stage of considerable explosive volcanism.

Other prominent features on the moon's surface are the long narrow channels, called *rilles*, which are found both within and outside the maria. These channels have steep sides, as much as a thousand feet deep, and extend for hundreds of miles. Apparently they cut across all other features, which suggests that they were the most recently formed of all the moon's features. Some of the rilles end in craters, and many of them are lined with small craters. Rilles may be comparable to graben fault structures, which are down-dropped blocks of the earth's crust.

Probably the most intensively studied features on the moon are the craters. Many scientists feel that these hold significant clues regarding many other aspects of the moon's history, its formation, and the origin of other features of its surface. There are two opposed views concerning the formation of the craters:

one, that they are splash features formed by the impact of meteors or comets on the moon at a time when its surface was molten or nearly molten; the second, that they were formed during the degassing of the interior of the moon by explosions of gases forcing through the surface of molten or semi-consolidated materials.

Neither theory has been conclusively proved at this time. The variety of the craters' shapes suggests that both modes of formation may have been involved. There are no volcanic or meteorite craters on earth of a size even close to that of the largest on the moon. Nor are there nearly as many craters known on earth as the more than thirty thousand known on the moon. The craters are by no means all alike. They vary in size, shape, and relation to rilles, maria, rays, and other features. The small ones on the maria have a bubble-like form. The larger ones measure over a hundred miles in diameter. Many have nearly smooth floors which may or may not be broken by a central hill or crater. Their sides are typically steep and ragged cliffs. Many of them have terraced walls which create the impression of step-fault patterns.

The moon's craters have undergone various types of morphological statistical analysis. One of these considers the relation between the number of craters of each size and their diameter. When this relation is plotted, a smooth curve is obtained. This suggests that the craters may have a single mode of origin. Most of the craters are under ten miles in diameter. Approximately 18 per cent of these small craters have central peaks, but a third of the larger ones have these features. These central peaks are also much more common among the youngest craters. About three-fourths of the young large craters have a central peak. Other studies have been concerned with the shape of the craters. Craters occur in at least two common shapes.

FIG. 2–10. / Surface of the moon. (Courtesy of Mt. Wilson and Palomar Observatories.)

One is like a bowl, with smooth sides rising up toward the surrounding wall. The other, characterized by steep walls, is like an inverted truncated cone. The shapes have been compared with theoretical impact models, with craters formed by meteorite impact on earth, and with craters formed by explosion of atomic bombs underground. Unfortunately, the results are inconclusive. Some moon craters closely resemble volcanic craters in shape; others are more like meteorite craters. The *Ranger 7* photographs show that there are many very small craters, and that these have smooth rather than rough sides. One interpretation accounts for the smoothness by attributing it to the effects of long-term meteoritic impact. These impacts would act to reduce old rugged shapes through a process somewhat analogous to sandblasting.

Those who favor the volcanic origin of the craters point to their appearance, and to their seemingly nonrandom distribution. Many small ones are aligned along rilles and other faultlike features. Faults would be logical loci for volcanos, since these would provide lines of easy access for lava and gases coming from within the moon. Even some of the larger craters are apparently aligned with one another. In 1958, after many years of observation, a Russian astronomer, Kozyrev, detected gaseous emanation from one moon crater named Alphonsus. This was a most significant discovery, as it proved conclusively that the moon is not a completely dead body, and that volcanism is and undoubtedly has been an active process there. Features interpreted as lava flows have been recognized on the *Ranger 7* photographs.

Some of the most striking yet perplexing features are the raylike projections which radiate out from young craters. In a few instances these extend as much as 1,000 miles. They have a somewhat lighter color, possibly due to powder or dust-sized materials along them, and they have very low relief, standing only a little higher than the surface about them. Their form is that of radial tension fractures like those formed in a brittle substance by point impact or domical uplift.

History of the Moon

BY THE APPLICATION OF TECHNIQUES of photogeology a geologic map of the moon has been prepared. It has been possible to distinguish several periods of activity by observing crosscutting relationships. Probably the most distinctive dividing line in the history of the moon was the formation of the maria. Thus events are often referred to as premaria or postmaria. The major stratigraphic systems recognized thus far, arranged in chronological order starting with the youngest, are:

COPERNICAN PERIOD. The Copernicus crater has been selected as the type example of the features of this period. It has bright rays, terraced walls, a built-up rim, and indistinct radial ridges.

ERATOSTHENEAN PERIOD. These craters are similar to Copernicus, but the rays are indistinct.

PROCELLAREAN PERIOD. The period of formation of the maria.

IMBRIAN PERIOD. Included here are craters filled or partially filled by maria materials. This was the time of formation of one of the major mountain ranges, the Apennines, which are located on the west side of Mare Imbrium and which contain some three thousand peaks in a range three hundred miles long.

PRE-IMBRIAN PERIOD. Features that formed before the Apennines and related mountain systems.

The origin and early history of the moon are not known. A popular notion is that the moon was derived from the earth. According to this hypothesis, the earth was rotating at a very fast rate. A day's length at that time was five hours, as compared with the present twenty-four. This would produce a much greater equatorial bulge than we presently observe. If there were tidal distortions due to the sun, with a period that was just that required for resonance with the earth's pulsations, then the forces generated might be great enough to cause a portion of the earth to become separated from the rest. Proponents of this hypothesis point to the Pacific Ocean as the place from which the moon came, and they argue that the density of the moon, 3.3, is very close to the density of the earth's crust, 2.7. An alternative speculation is that the earth and moon were formed essentially simultaneously according to one of the nebular hypotheses discussed in the next chapter.

Motions of the Moon

THE COMPLEXITY OF THE MOTIONS of the moon prevented early astronomers from understanding them. A fundamental fact which they did not comprehend was that the moon moved in an orbit around the earth while the planets moved around the sun. They were also unaware of the precessional motions caused by the proximity of the earth to the moon.

The movements of the moon may conveniently be broken into several components:

Revolution of the earth–moon system around the sun.

Monthly revolution around the center of mass of the earth–moon system.

The moon's rotation about its axis.

The orbits of the earth and moon around the sun are very close, but not parallel. Both bodies move together around the sun in one year and the two mutually revolve in a little less than a month. This gives rise to a slightly wavy path—the orbit of the center of the earth is not quite the same as the orbit of the center of mass of the earth–moon system. Imagine the earth and moon connected by a rigid rod. The center of mass is the point along that rod at which the two would be counterbalanced. This point lies 2,900 miles from the center of the earth in the direction of the moon—still within the earth. Despite the revolution of the moon about the earth, orbits of both are concave toward the sun (Fig. 2–8).

Revolution of the Moon around the Earth

IT IS POSSIBLE TO REFER to the angular distance from one body to another by means of its ascension (measured in the celestial equator). This measure is commonly used to define the position of the sun in relation to the moon (Fig. 2–3). When the angle between the sun and moon (right ascension) is 90°, the moon is said to be in *quadrature*; when the angle is 0°, the two are said to be in *conjunction*; and when the angle is 180°, they are said to be in *opposition*.

The Moon's Phases

MOST APPARENT of the phenomena associated with the movement of the moon around the earth is the constantly changing amount of illumination received on earth from the moon. The moon simply reflects light; in no way is it an original source of light. The light of the moon is primarily that coming from the sun, although a small portion is reflected to the moon from the earth. At all times the sun's light falls upon one half of the moon's surface —one full hemisphere. As the moon revolves, varying amounts of this sunlit hemisphere are visible to us (Fig. 2–9). At conjunction the dark side is toward us and the moon is *new*— that is, entirely invisible. As the moon moves on in its orbit, part of the illuminated side becomes visible, until at quadrature we see one half of the sunlit hemisphere, the *first quarter*. At opposition the moon is *full*, and then the phases pass in reverse order back to new moon. The time taken for this cycle, as was discussed earlier, is called the *synodic month* (29½ days). The synodic month differs from the *sidereal month* (27⅓ days), time between successive conjunctions of the moon's center with any given star. This difference is about one extra sidereal month per year. From the earth the moon continually falls behind the sun when the paths of the two are compared from day to day. The degree of this retardation depends on the angle between the moon's path and the horizon near the observer. It averages about 50 minutes per day in the middle latitudes, where most of the world's population lives, and each day (or night) the moon rises about 50 minutes later.

The moon's apparent path against the celestial sphere (when stars are reference points) is inclined to the ecliptic about 5°. It intersects the ecliptic at two points called *nodes*. The position of these nodes is not constant, but instead

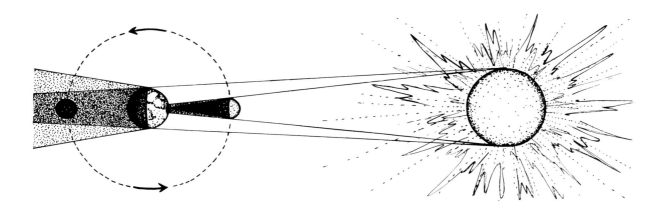

FIG. 2–11. / *Schematic showing conditions giving rise to eclipses.*

moves westward along the ecliptic at a rate which allows each node to complete a revolution along the ecliptic once in 18.6 years. That is the time between two successive moments when the moon is seen to have exactly the same star background pattern.

Rotation of the Moon

IN ADDITION TO revolving around the earth and sun, the moon rotates on its axis. It happens that the period of this rotation is $27\frac{1}{3}$ days—the same as the period of revolution about the earth, therefore the same side of the moon always faces the earth. The moon also makes a slight rocking motion called *libration*. The axis of the moon tips first toward the earth and then away from it by $6\frac{1}{2}°$ every two weeks. The moon also appears to rock east-west by $7\frac{3}{4}°$. This arises because the moon does not revolve around the earth at a perfectly uniform rate. (Kepler's laws explain why the moon travels with varying speed in different parts of its elliptical orbit.)

Eclipses

MOVEMENTS OF THE MOON in relation to the earth and sun provide opportunities for the shadow of the earth to be cast on the moon (an eclipse of the moon) and for the moon to blot out the light from the sun (an eclipse of the sun). Eclipses occur either when the moon is full or new. Because the path of the moon is inclined $5°$ to the ecliptic, eclipses do not occur every month. Usually the moon passes either north or south of the sun at conjunction. Only when the moon is very close to one of the nodes of its orbit can an eclipse occur. This happens twice each year, but never at the same time in the year, because the position of the nodes is not constant. The conditions during an eclipse are illustrated in Fig. 2–11. Periods of eclipse have taught us much about the sun. Likewise the circular shape of the earth's shadow on the moon during eclipse was one of man's first proofs that the earth was not flat but spherical. An eclipse may be either total or partial, depending on the paths of the earth and moon in relation to the sun and, during solar eclipses, the point of observation from the earth. The eclipse of the sun is called *total* when the umbra, Fig. 2–11 (the shadow of the moon), falls on earth. The eclipse is said to be *annular* if the umbra does not fall on the earth's surface.

The Sun

THE CENTRAL FIGURE IN OUR SOLAR SYSTEM, the sun, is of great importance to us not only because it provides the heat necessary for life and for many earth processes, but because it is the nearest star. Undoubtedly the origin of the earth is closely tied to that of the sun. The sun's proximity to us provides us with invaluable evidence about the universe. The development of the spectroscope provided an opportunity for a new field of astronomical investigation. It gave us a means of studying composition of stars and gases penetrated by light from stars.[1]

The spectrum of the sun is a continuous spectrum with dark bands called *Fraunhofer* lines. The solar spectrum has wavelengths that range from 3,000 to 10,000 angstroms (1 angstrom = 10^{-8} cm). By comparison, the human eye is sensitive to wavelengths in the range of 4,000 (violet) to 8,000 angstroms (red). Very short wavelengths are absorbed by earth's atmosphere. We can be thankful for this, for if we were not so protected from the intense ultraviolet wavelengths, life as we know it would be impossible. The bright part of the solar spectrum is produced by radiation from the sun. This radiation comes from a great variety of different elements. In a very simple way we

may describe the radiation as resulting from the collision of atoms, which causes them to become excited and to emit energy in the form of light of a particular wavelength, producing a bright line spectrum. Atoms of each element emit radiations of particular wavelengths and thus have characteristic colors. For this reason the spectrum can be used for chemical analysis. The continuous spectrum results when a gas at high pressure becomes so hot that some elements lose their electrons, and these collide with other atoms. This happens in the sun and in other stars. If light from a star passes through a cooler gas consisting of atoms that are not broken down, some of the light will be absorbed by the atoms of the cooler gas. The particular wavelengths absorbed are exactly those that the gas would radiate if it were heated. The spectrum thus produced has a bright background with dark gaps. This is the way the spectrum of the sun appears (Fig. 2–12). Elements differ in their power to absorb their particular wavelengths; this absorption depends on temperatures as well. Thus spectral analysis provides an indication of chemical composition, temperature, and density of the hot gases that produce the spectral lines, and, simultaneously, of the composition of cooler outer atmospheres of the star.

The principal elements recognized in solar spectral analysis are shown in Table 1 below:

TABLE 1 / *Composition of the Sun's atmosphere. The more abundant elements are listed below in the order of their abundance (after Unsöld, 1950).*

Hydrogen
Helium
Oxygen
Iron
Nitrogen
Magnesium
Silicon
Carbon
Sulphur
Aluminum
Sodium
Calcium
Nickel

[1] A simple spectroscope consists of a prism of glass or some transparent mineral and two telescopes. Light from a source such as the sun or a star enters one telescope and is directed onto the prism through a narrow slit located at the focus of the objective. Here the light entering the prism is refracted and broken into its component wavelengths. The second telescope is used to view or photograph the spectrum thus produced. If the light consists of a single wavelength (single color) the spectrum will be a line of that color. White light appears as a band ranging from violet at one end to red at the other; such a band is called a *continuous spectrum*. If one wavelength is absent a *dark line* will appear at the appropriate place in the spectrum. A *bright line spectrum* is one which consists of a limited number of bright lines against a dark field. The source of such lines is a body (usually gas) radiating a limited number of wavelengths. The wavelengths are characteristic of the elements making up the gas. A dark line spectrum results when the continuous spectrum is broken by dark lines. These dark lines result from absorption of certain wavelengths by a gas (atmosphere) between the source and the observer; they indicate the composition of the intervening gases.

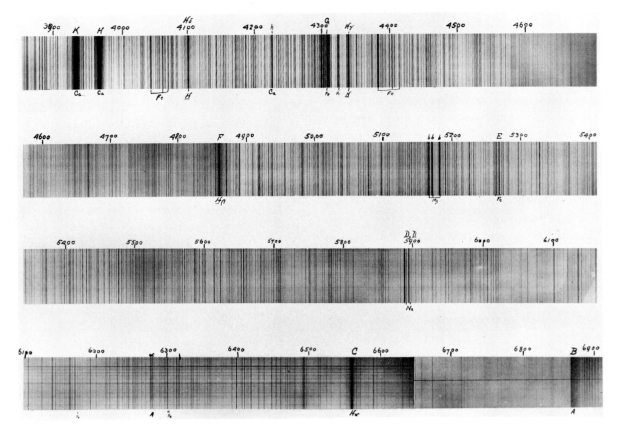

FIG. 2–12. / *Solar spectrum, photographed with 13-foot spectrograph. (Mount Wilson and Palomar Observatories.)*

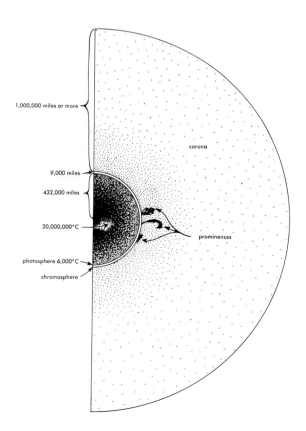

FIG. 2–13. / *The solar atmosphere.*

By far the most abundant element is hydrogen. It is about ten times as abundant as the next most abundant element, helium, and these two elements together are hundreds of times more abundant than all others combined. Many other stars are similar to the sun in composition, but stars with much larger proportions of certain elements are known.

Solar Atmosphere

THE SUN IS SURROUNDED by three vast envelopes of gases (Fig. 2–13). The inner envelope, which extends for about 9,000 miles out, is called the *photosphere*. Temperatures here are in the range of about 6,000 degrees absolute. Beyond the photosphere is the *chromosphere*, with temperatures in the range of 5,000–35,000 degrees absolute. The chromosphere gradually blends into the *corona*, which extends for nearly a million miles out. Temperatures in the inner part of the corona are in the range of several hundred thousand degrees, and reach perhaps nearly 1,000,000 degrees before beginning to drop off. The corona is shown dramatically in photographs taken during solar eclipses (Fig. 2–14). One of the most striking facts about the solar atmosphere is the temperature variation: first it drops, then rises rapidly, and then drops again farther out.

As early as the 1860's man had learned that helium is a principal constituent of the solar atmosphere. During solar eclipses huge cloud-like, arch-shaped protrusions called *prominences* can be seen to emerge far out from the surface of the sun, at times extending well into the corona (Fig. 2–15). It was in the spectrum of

FIG. 2–14. / *The sun's corona. This thin gaseous layer of the sun is not normally visible except when the moon covers the photosphere during total eclipses. In this photograph the corona is shown at a time of little sunspot activity. During greater sunspot activity the corona is extended farther out and it is more nearly circular. Parts of the corona extend over a million miles above the photosphere, and even in its most dense parts the corona is only about one million-millionth of the density of the earth's atmosphere at sea level. (Photo by courtesy of Yerkes Observatory.)*

FIG. 2–15. / *Prominence on sun. This large, active prominence is about 140,000 miles high. It was photographed in the light of calcium. These explosions occur above the photosphere in the lower part of the corona. (By courtesy of Mount Wilson and Palomar Observatories.)*

these prominences that helium was first discovered—before it was known on earth. Helium was particularly difficult to isolate on earth because it becomes a gas at −269° C. and as a result of its extreme lightness it is not held to earth by gravity. Helium does not produce spectrum lines except at very high temperatures. An indication of the high temperatures in the inner corona was found in the eventual explanation of certain spectral lines which did not fit those of any known element. At first they were thought to be produced by some new element, but they were later shown to be produced by atoms of iron and calcium from which a large number of electrons had been removed. These electrons are lost from the atoms because of the very high temperatures and consequent violent collisions.

Sunspots

GALILEO REPORTED DARK SPOTS on the surface of the sun in 1610, but only since 1843 have they been carefully studied. Their behavior is well known, though rather poorly understood. The number of these spots, known as sunspots, is highly variable. The spots often occur in pairs, individual spots lasting from a few days to several weeks. A sunspot begins as a mass of black specks which gradually come together, forming a large dark area from ten thousand to a hundred thousand miles in diameter. Even the small sunspots are larger than the diameter of the earth. Sunspot activity reaches a maximum once every eleven years. During the eleven year cycle the spots start at latitudes of about 40° north or south of the solar equator and gradually drift toward the equator. When sunspot activity reaches its peak they are about 15°–20° from the equator. Before the spots reach the equator their activity dies down. Successive observations of the sunspots show that the sun rotates (Fig. 2–17).

Strong magnetic fields are now known to be associated with the centers of the sunspots. It is well-known that periods of sunspot activity cause interference with radio transmission on earth. Magnetic fields are also thought to be associated with solar prominences. These magnetic fields are believed to arise near the surface of the sun just below the photosphere. One explanation is that where gases of the sun are in violent convection, part of the mechanical energy is converted into magnetic energy. This energy then forms a magnetic field, which rises out of the photosphere into the corona and discharges, creating a prominence. In such a prominence, or solar flare, high-speed particles are blasted out into space, heating the solar atmosphere.

The Sun's Interior

STARS, such as the sun, differ from planets, their satellites, and other smaller bodies in the universe in that their extreme size creates pressures in their interiors so great that the material of which they are composed cannot exist as solids or liquids. It was known even in the 1800's that solids and liquids can withstand only limited pressures before they break down into gases. The size, mass, and composition of the sun are known. It is possible to derive from these values the density of the sun, the force of gravity at its surface, the pressures in its interior and even the temperatures, derivation of which is beyond the scope of this treatment. The values show that the force of gravity at the sun's surface is nearly 30 times that on the earth's surface, and the temperature at the center of the sun is on the order of 15 million degrees absolute. At temperatures and pressures on the order of those in the sun's interior, atoms break down; the gases are thus electrons and nuclei of atoms. We have seen that the temperature of the photosphere is 6,000° absolute. Such a great temperature difference between the surface and the interior of the sun sets up convection. The granular appearance of the sun's surface (Fig. 2–16) is probably due to the outlines of areas of convection, in which heat and energy are brought to the surface of the sun. An infinitesimally small amount of this heat reaches the earth.

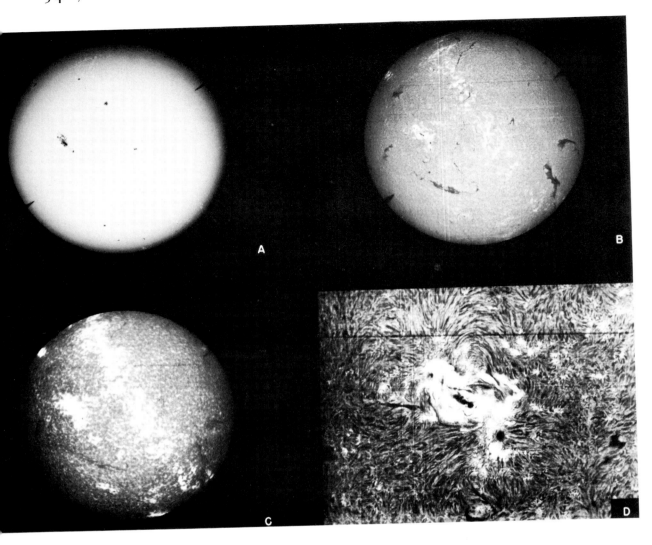

FIG. 2–16. / *Four views of the sun, September 15, 1949. a) ordinary photograph, b) hydrogen (Hα), c) calcium spectroheliogram, d) enlarged hydrogen spectroheliogram. (Courtesy of Mount Wilson and Palomar Observatories.)*

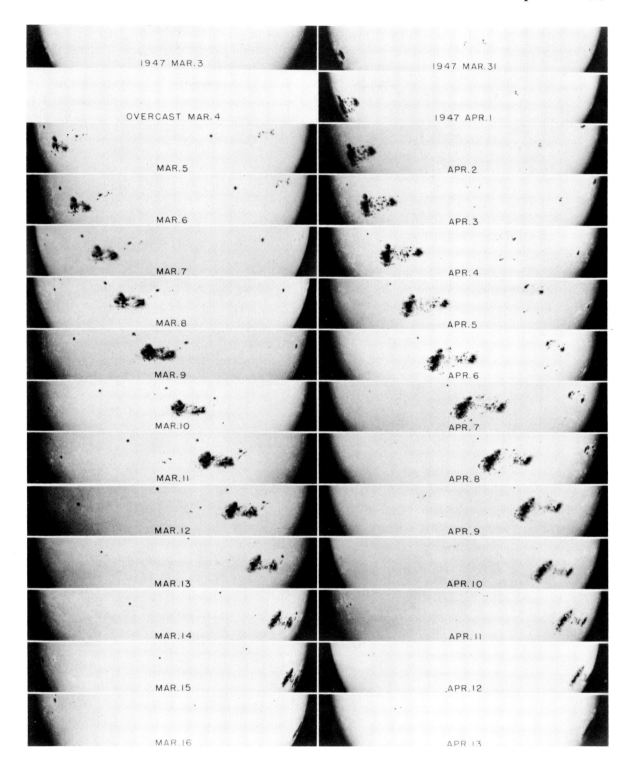

FIG. 2–17. / Twenty-seven photographs of the great sunspot of 1947 as it was carried twice across the disk by the sun's rotation. (Courtesy of Mount Wilson and Palomar Observatories.)

The Planets

Motion of the Planets

WITH THE DEVELOPMENT of the telescope, the five planets recognized by ancient astronomers, Mercury, Venus, Mars, Jupiter, and Saturn, were supplemented by three newly discovered planets, Uranus, Neptune, and Pluto. Acceptance of the Copernican view of the Solar System added the earth to the list. In addition to these large bodies, there are a number of smaller bodies, called *asteroids*, which follow planet-like paths around the sun.

The planets' paths are relatively simple, at least by comparison with that of the moon, and have a number of characteristics in common:

1) The orbits of all the planets are nearly circular.
2) The orbits lie close to the plane of the ecliptic. (With the exception of Pluto, no planet's orbit is ever more than 8° from the ecliptic.)
3) All of the planets revolve from west to east, the same as their direction of rotation.

The period of revolution and mean distance of each planet are shown in Table 2 below. Note the very great range, from 88 days for Mercury to 248 years for Pluto.

Mercury and Venus, the two planets closer to the sun than the earth, have very different apparent motions from those farther away than the earth. Both planets have periods of revolution of less than a year. To the observer on the earth, they appear to oscillate east and west, back and forth, in front of and behind the sun, and to exhibit phases similar to those of the moon (Fig. 2–18).

The outer planets, by comparison, have longer periods of revolution and do not show all of the phases we see for the moon, Venus, and Mercury. They appear either to be full or nearly full (Fig. 2–19).

Mercury

THE CLOSEST of the planets to the sun is Mercury. The ancient Greeks believed that Mercury was two different planets because in the early morning it appears in the east and at sunset it appears in the west. This planet travels in an elliptical path that follows the ecliptic very closely. The path of Mercury is more elliptical than that of any other planet except Pluto. It appears to the observer on earth that it takes 116 days for Mercury to complete one revolution about the sun, but the time is actually 88 days. The difference is due to the earth's revolution.

The diameter of Mercury is about 3,000 miles, and its mass is about four times that of the moon. Though Mercury is the smallest of the planets, its density is greater than that of

	MASS EARTH = 1	RADIUS (MILES)	DENSITY	MILLIONS OF MILES FROM SUN	PERIOD OF REVOLUTION Sidereal	Synodic
Sun	332,000.	432,000	1.4			
Mercury	0.05	1,500	5.1	36	88 days	116 days
Venus	0.81	3,800	5.0	67	225 days	584 days
Earth	1.	3,950	5.5	93	365 days	
Mars	.11	2,100	3.9	141	687 days	780 days
Jupiter	318.	43,500	1.3	483	12 years	399 days
Saturn	95.	36,000	.7	886	29 years	378 days
Uranus	14.6	15,500	1.3	1,783	84 years	370 days
Neptune	17.3	16,500	2.2	2,793	165 years	367 days
Pluto	.03	4,000	2.?	3,666	248 years	367 days

TABLE 2 / The Solar System.
The mass of other bodies in the Solar System is given in relation to the mass of the earth.

any of the others. If Mercury is similar in composition to the earth, it must contain a high percentage of some metal such as iron or nickel. Mercury is known to complete a full rotation on its axis in a period of 88 days. Since its rotation and its revolution are identical in duration, the same side of the planet faces the sun all of the time. The side constantly facing the sun must be extremely hot and the other side undoubtedly very cold. This would not be the case if Mercury had an atmosphere, because the atmosphere would tend to hold the heat just as the earth's atmosphere does. However, although we can see the surface of Mercury with a telescope, we can detect no clouds or other evidence of an atmosphere. Its relatively small mass probably gives it a gravitational field too weak to hold an atmosphere against the tremendous pull of the sun. The surface of the planet which the telescope reveals to us is somewhat similar to that of the moon.

Venus

VENUS, the earth's closest neighbor in space, is the first planet man has closely investigated by means of rockets. On December 14, 1962, the surface of Venus was scanned for 35 minutes by a variety of specially designed instruments mounted on *Mariner II*. The instruments on *Mariner II* were designed to send back to earth information on the magnetic field, on temperature, and on the composition of Venus' atmosphere, and various other technical data. Scientists have speculated that life might exist on Venus, but information gathered during the *Mariner II* space probe makes this possibility seem remote, if not nonexistent. The atmosphere was found to contain little water vapor or oxygen, but large quantities of carbon dioxide. Astronomers have long known that Venus has a thick cloud cover. This cloud cover produces what is called the "greenhouse effect"— that is, the clouds let the heat from the sun in and tend to hold it. Consequently, temperatures near the planet's surface are about 800° F. The cloud cover is on the order of 10 to 20 miles thick, and hovers at a height of 45 miles

above the surface. These clouds apparently contain large amounts of hydrocarbons. The *Mariner II* space probe found no evidence of rotation, nor of any magnetic field, nor of a radiation belt surrounding the planet such as the Van Allen belt now known to surround the earth.

Mars

NO PLANET has attracted more popular attention than Mars. This interest arises from the long-held hope that Mars is inhabited by some form of life. The chief basis for this hope is the canal-like patterns observed on the planet's surface. However, observations with modern instruments fail to confirm this hope. Mars has an atmosphere, but its clouds, unlike those surrounding Venus, are not thick, nor do they cover the entire surface. The hypothesis that life exists on Mars, as it does on the earth, is supported by several other observations—Mars rotates on its axis at nearly the same rate as the earth; the axis is inclined to the ecliptic at nearly the same angle as earth's axis; white polar caps develop during winter, suggesting snow or ice caps, which in turn suggest water vapor in the atmosphere, and during the spring these caps disappear. The spectrum of light reflected from Mars is similar to that reflected by certain earth plants. It is generally felt that life of some sort may well exist on Mars, but that this life is probably plant matter of a rather primitive sort. The planet is too cool and its atmosphere too sparse to sustain advanced forms of life as we know them.

Jupiter

JUPITER STANDS OUT among all the planets in several respects. It is by far the largest, having a volume nearly 40 per cent greater than all the other planets combined, and a mass nearly two and a half times as great as the combined weight of the others. It has a dozen satellites, remarkable surface coloration, and emits strong radio signal bursts. Most recently it has been discovered to have a belt of deadly radiation ex-

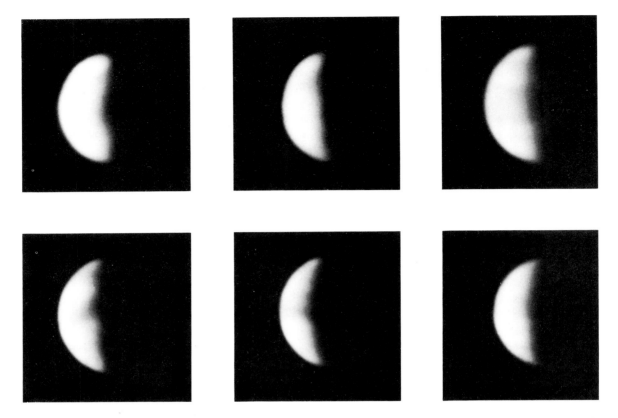

FIG. 2–18. / *Venus, six photographs taken with a 100-inch telescope. (Courtesy of Mount Wilson and Palomar Observatories.)*

tending some thirty thousand miles out from its equator. Jupiter is the closest of the outer group of planets, which are distinguished by their larger size and lower density. In the case of Jupiter, this lower density is due to its composition, which is largely hydrogen and helium.

The surface features of Jupiter have long been known to man. At the present time there is a large red spot on the surface. This was first recognized by Robert Hooke in 1664. Although this spot, which is 30,000 miles long and 7,000 miles wide, was apparently absent between 1713 and 1831, it has been present since. It has undergone changes in color—ranging from brick red and pink to a greenish white. The cause of this variation has been attributed to organic chemical compounds. In addition to the spot, the surface of the planet is characterized by changing patterns of color oriented in belts roughly perpendicular to the axis of the planet. Usually there are four such belts which undergo changes

in width and color—the colors are varying shades of reddish browns and greens. These belts are thought to be rapidly moving streams of clouds. Estimates of the rate of movement of these clouds are as high as twenty thousand feet per minute, over 200 miles per hour.

Jupiter has a short period of rotation, about ten hours. This fact, combined with its great size, means that the surface near the equator is moving at a rate of nearly twenty-eight thousand miles per hour. As a result, the planet is distinctly flattened at the poles.

Jupiter's atmosphere is known to be composed of hydrogen, helium, methane, and ammonia. In recent years there has been considerable controversy over the relative amounts of each, but the most widely held view at present is that the proportions are approximately those found in the sun. About 80 per cent of Jupiter's mass is hydrogen. The interior of the planet is unknown, but the pressures should be great enough to squeeze the hydrogen near the center into a hydrogen metal. Some have estimated that the planet may even have a well-defined hard surface. This surface is estimated to have a temperature of about 1,000 degrees Fahrenheit. Over this surface several layers of gases are postulated. Of these layers, the closest to the surface would be water vapor. Farther out there would be clouds containing water, clouds containing gaseous ammonia, then ammonia clouds, and finally clouds composed of ice crystals of ammonia.

Radio bursts from Jupiter have attracted much attention recently. These bursts occur only when certain areas of the planet face the earth. They have been attributed to volcanic activity within the interior of the planet, and more re-

cently it has been suggested that they are related to the magnetic field. In this case the radio waves are thought to be generated when high-speed electrons from radiation belts (probably similar to the Van Allen belts) move down along magnetic lines of force into the planet's atmosphere. Neither the magnetic field nor the radiation belt is centered about the planet's axis, as are those of the earth.

Saturn

THE RINGS which surround it give Saturn the most distinctive appearance of any planet. Three flat rings of matter circle the planet in the plane of its equator. The exact composition of these rings is unknown; one speculation is that they

FIG. 2–19. / *Mars, Jupiter, Saturn, and Pluto. The first three are photographed with 100-inch telescope; Pluto with a 200-inch telescope. (Courtesy of Mount Wilson and Palomar Observatories.)*

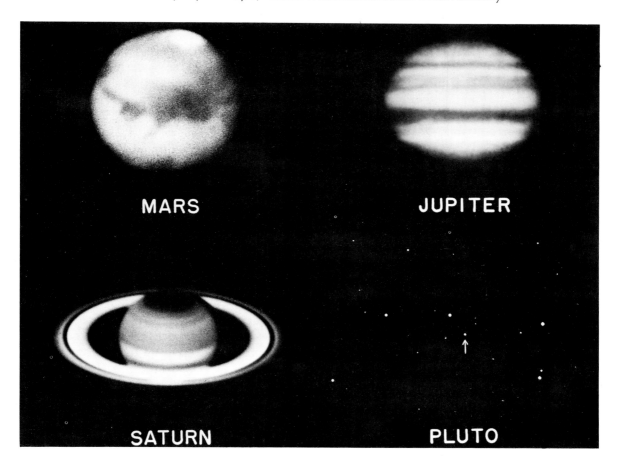

MARS

JUPITER

SATURN

PLUTO

are composed largely of small, widely spaced ice crystals.

The main body of the planet is somewhat similar to Jupiter in that it has marked color patterns. The regions near the poles have a greenish tint, and the equatorial regions are yellowish.

Uranus, Neptune, and Pluto

RELATIVELY LITTLE is known about these three planets, other than the data on their distances from the sun, periods of revolution, orbits, size, and mass, which are given in Table 2. Uranus was discovered by accident, but Neptune and Pluto were discovered only after an extensive search for bodies which had been postulated to explain discrepancies in the motions of other planets. Because of their great distance from the sun all three of these planets must be very cold. Telescopes of even the highest power reveal little surface detail. Uranus and Neptune have a greenish tint, while Pluto is yellowish. Spectra of Uranus and Neptune indicate the presence of methane and ammonia in their atmospheres. Unlike the other planets, Pluto has a highly inclined and eccentric orbit which at times brings it closer than Neptune to the sun.

Meteorites

"SHOOTING STARS" HAVE CAPTURED THE IMagination of man since early times. Their origin is still unknown, though numerous ideas have been advanced to explain them, but they have yielded a considerable body of information. Recently they have been studied with increased interest, for they may well hold invaluable answers to many questions about the formation of the Solar System.

Meteorites are bodies of stone and metal that fall through the atmosphere and strike the earth. *Meteors* are presumably identical bodies which burn up before they hit the ground. The bright fiery trail seen coming from one of these bodies originates through frictional heating of

its surface as it passes through the atmosphere at speeds estimated to range from six to thirty-five miles per second. Burning starts at approximately seventy-five miles above the earth's surface. Small meteors are completely burned, and many of these may be no larger than peas. The larger meteorites have surfaces sculptured by this burning, but in the few cases in which they have been examined shortly after hitting the surface they have been cold to the touch. This is due to the extremely low temperatures of the bodies in space, and the short duration of the burning, which is only surficial.

Composition of meteorites is variable. Most people associate the massive nickel-iron bodies, called *siderites*, with all meteorites, but in actuality meteorites are more commonly stony bodies. Those called *stony meteorites*, or *chondrites*, are composed of aggregates of the minerals olivine and pyroxene (see Chapter 11). There are also many meteorites of intermediate composition. Thus the range of composition is from all nickel-iron (usually 90 per cent Fe, 10 per cent Ni) to all olivine-pyroxene. Also there are bodies composed of naturally formed glass, called *tektites*, that may have come from outside the earth. The relative abundance of the two main types, nickel-iron and stony, depends on the way the count is made. Stony meteorites resemble igneous rocks so closely that it is easy to see why nickel-iron bodies are more often found. This is not the case, however, when the meteorite is seen to fall. There have been over fifteen hundred observed falls. Over 90 per cent of the meteorites actually seen to fall are stony.

The largest known meteorite fell in southwest Africa. It is composed of nickel-iron, measures nearly twelve feet in diameter, and weighs an estimated sixty tons. The stony meteorites are small by comparison. The largest of these weighs slightly over a ton. Those of intermediate composition may weigh up to two tons.

When a large meteorite hits the surface of the earth, the impact sometimes forms a small crater. In other cases the meteorite explodes, forming an explosion crater. The famous meteor crater of Arizona is an example of an explosion crater. It is over four-fifths of a mile in diameter and 600 feet deep. Fragments of nickel-iron have been found both in and around the crater. The meteorite struck relatively flat-lying sedimentary strata. These have been deformed locally around the edges of the crater, so that they are steeply inclined away from the crater, as would be the case after a near-surface underground explosion. Some of the sand has been fused, and an unusual variety of silica, formed only under extreme pressure, has been found. In 1908 such an explosion in Siberia flattened forests over many hundreds of acres. The body that exploded is known as the Tunguska meteorite.

Meteorites are particularly interesting to geologists and astronomers because they are thought to provide one of our best clues to the relative abundance of elements in the Solar System. It seems probable that in examining a meteorite we are looking at material that formed at the time of the origin of the Solar System. Further, meteorites are possibly fragments of a disintegrated planet. In Chapter 22 the nature of the interior of the earth is discussed. It will be noted there that the density of the earth's core is approximately that of a nickel-iron alloy, and it is generally thought now that the outer mantle of the earth is a rock composed of olivine and pyroxene. The composition of meteorites certainly supports these views regarding the earth's interior, especially if it can be shown that they originated within the Solar System. Meteors are thought to travel in elliptical paths within the Solar System, and either to overtake the earth or to be overtaken by it as their orbits cross.

The age of meteorites has been studied through a number of radioactive dating methods (discussed in Chapter 27). Results consistently indicate that the crystallization of the minerals within the meteorites occurred approximately four to four and a half billion years ago. This is likewise considered the likely age of the earth.

Numerous ideas have been advanced to explain the origin of meteors. The most popular and consistently held view is that they are fragments of a disrupted planet. The main problem involved in this view is what caused the planet to break up. This "planetary body" would have formed under processes similar to those that formed the earth and other planets. A likely process of formation is the slow accretion of small, cool fragments. As the planet grew it became subjected to internal heating, which caused melting and gravity separation of the principal materials. In this way the nickel-iron became segregated from the olivine-pyroxene. The mantle materials became further differentiated and altered through volcanism. Ultimately the planet broke up. Its fragments cooled and then became broken into smaller sizes by collisions.

Comets

COMETS PROVIDE ONE OF THE MOST SPECtacular heavenly displays. Until almost the eighteenth century they were considered to be omens of impending disaster. The English astronomer Edmund Halley first computed the orbits of a number of comets and showed that they were a part of our Solar System and that they travel in very elongate elliptical orbits around the sun. On the basis of his calculations, he predicted the approximate period, 75 years, of one particularly spectacular comet, which is now known as Halley's Comet (it will be visible again in 1986). The orbit of Halley's Comet carries it out to a position between Neptune and Pluto. We have learned much from its most recent passage. In 1910 it passed between the earth and sun, and the earth passed through its tail without any observable effect.

Comets are much more numerous than most people realize. An average of five or six are seen each year, but many of these are too faint to be seen by the unaided eye.

Some facts about the nature of comets are generally accepted, even though we do not know how they originally were formed. A typical comet consists of a *nucleus* of frozen gases at temperatures close to absolute zero. As the nucleus moves toward the sun the ice crystals begin to evaporate. The gases formed in this way radiate out from the nucleus, forming a *coma*. Radiation pressure from the sun moves the gas particles and crystals away from the sun, thus forming a long, tail-like projection. This tail always tends to point away from the sun, even as the nucleus moves in that part of its orbit nearest to the sun. The head of a comet is often tens of thousands of miles in diameter, and the tail may extend tens of millions of miles out, but both are so rarefied that they have densities less than the most perfect vacuums on the earth. Even so, the light coming from them is partially reflected and partially due to a fluorescent effect caused by absorption of ultraviolet rays which are then re-radiated in visible wavelengths. Analysis of these wavelengths reveals the presence of oxygen, nitrogen, carbon, and hydrogen. If the processes acting in comets are correctly interpreted, they are slowly disintegrating each time they come close to the sun and will eventually disappear.

Evolution of the Solar System

A NUMBER OF IMPORTANT THEORIES HAVE been advanced to explain the evolution of the Solar System. Certain basic facts about the Solar System, in addition to the data given in Table 2, must be accounted for in any satisfactory hypothesis:

1. The mass of the Solar System is concentrated in the sun, which contains about 99.8 per cent of the total mass. The nine planets contain the remaining .2 per cent.
2. The planets move in orbits about the sun. These orbits, except for that of Pluto, lie approximately within a single plane.
3. Most planets rotate about axes, and in the same direction.

FIG. 2–20. / Head of Halley's Comet, May 8, 1910. 60-inch telescope. (Courtesy of Mount Wilson and Palomar Observatories.)

4. The direction of rotation about the axis is the same as the direction of revolution of the planets about the sun.

5. The planets are spaced in a regular pattern composed of two groups. The inner group includes Mercury, Venus, the earth, and Mars. The outer group includes Jupiter, Saturn, Uranus, and Neptune, much larger planets, and Pluto, the smallest planet.

6. About 98 per cent of the angular momentum of the Solar System is concentrated in the planets.

The principal theories advanced to explain the origin of the planets may be classified in two groups. All theories have in common the idea that the planets evolved from the sun. In one group, material was pulled out of the sun by an external force, such as gravitational pull, which was the result of the dynamic encounter or near collision of our sun with another star. The second group holds that the planets became isolated masses of matter as the material of the Solar System condensed into the sun.

Dynamic Encounter Theory

THE THEORY THAT THE PLANETS WERE formed as a result of the near collision of the sun and another star was first proposed by the French philosopher Buffon in 1749. It was later elaborated by Chamberlin and Moulton. These theories propose essentially that as another star approached our sun tremendous tides, or filaments of hot gases, were set in motion on the surface of the sun, and that as the star passed these arms of gas were pulled out from the sun and given a rotational motion. After the star was gone, the gaseous matter in these arms condensed into solid material and gradually drew together to form planets. The size of the planets was determined by the amount of matter distributed at various distances from the sun. Because the two arms would probably be very similar in size and shape, it would be logical

FIG. 2–21. / Comet Cunningham, December 21, 1940. Photographed with 5-inch aperture Ross lens. (Courtesy of Mount Wilson and Palomar Observatories.)

to expect that similar-sized planets would form at similar distances from the sun. Thus, this theory explains the occurrence of pairs of planets of approximately the same size at about the same distances from the sun. Such pairs are Mercury and Mars, Venus and the earth, Jupiter and Saturn, and Uranus and Neptune. The rotation of the arms of gas would also account for the concentration of angular momentum in the planets rather than in the sun itself.

At the present time this theory has fewer followers than it has had in the past. Among the important objections to it are that the gases drawn out from the sun might be expected to disperse throughout space rather than to condense into planets. Furthermore, the chances that another star would come close to the sun are extremely small, and there is no evidence to suggest or prove that such an approach ever actually occurred.

The Nebular Hypothesis

THE FIRST NEBULAR HYPOTHESIS WAS advanced by Kant and Laplace about 1796. It was the most generally accepted hypothesis for more than a century, when it was supplanted by dynamic encounter theories. According to the nebular hypothesis, the Solar System evolved from a single, large, flat, rotating nebula that extended out beyond the position of the most distant planet. As this nebula contracted, its mass became increasingly concentrated toward the center, and the speed at which it rotated slowly increased. As the velocity increased, the gravitational attraction exerted by the mass upon the material around its equator became insufficient to provide the necessary centripetal force to contract the outer rim of the disc further. As a result, a ring of matter was left while contraction of the remaining, inner matter continued. In this manner successive rings of matter were left behind the contracting mass. Subsequently the material within each ring was drawn together, forming the planets and their satellites. The formation of the satellites from the planets was essentially similar to the forma-

tion of the planets from the sun. Thus this theory accounts for similar directions of rotation of planets and most of their satellites. The theory also leaves the planets within about the same plane of rotation, and does not require any special conditions for the development of planets in this Solar System that might not be expected in other Solar Systems as well.

The theory was refuted when it was learned that the angular momentum of the Solar System is concentrated in the planets and not in the sun. This is not compatible with the idea that the mass of matter rotated more rapidly as it condensed. Since the original theory was advanced, much theoretical work has been done on the nature of the turbulence in rotating and contracting clouds of gas and dust. These advances have led to the formulation of new theories which nonetheless bear similarities to the original hypothesis of Kant and Laplace.

In 1944 a German physicist, C. F. von Weizsacker, proposed a modification of the nebular hypothesis. In the von Weizsacker theory the sun was conceived of as a hot, concentrated, central mass radiating light and heat, much as it is presently doing. A thin, flat, rapidly rotating cloud of matter encircled the sun's equator. This disc of material consisted primarily of hydrogen, helium, and a small amount of heavier elements. The temperature of this matter was about the same as that of present-day planets at varying distances from the sun. Radiation from the sun drove off hydrogen and helium. Heavier elements left behind collided with the escaping hydrogen and helium, and angular momentum was transferred to them. This accounts for the concentration of momentum in the planets. Eddy-like vortices formed, and these became sites of local accumulations of matter which slowly cooled and became the planets. This theory explains why the inner and outer groups of planets differ in density and size. Temperatures would decrease out from the sun in the postulated disc of material, as more material could condense in the outer parts than in the inner parts. Lighter-weight material would be driven out. Thus we find the inner planets are small and dense, whereas the outer planets are large and have low density.

One of the most popular hypotheses in recent years was devised by Gerard Kuiper. Kuiper visualizes a slightly flattened and slowly rotating disc-shaped solar nebula bulging out from the equator of the sun. In composition this cloud is similar to the sun and contains mostly hydrogen and helium with small amounts of heavier elements, but the disc and the sun itself are thought of as being cool. The disc, containing about a tenth the mass of the sun, finally becomes internally unstable and breaks up into smaller concentrations called *protoplanets*. The amount and type of material in each protoplanet are the natural result of the original distribution of material within the solar nebula when it became internally unstable. Within each protoplanet heavier elements tend to settle toward the center, and lighter particles and gases remain in the outer shells. After the formation of the protoplanets the sun contracted and started to radiate. This radiation drove off the atmospheres from the closer and smaller planets, which means there must have been a great reduction in the original amount of matter in the planets.

The Universe

The Milky Way—Earth's Galaxy

THE DISTRIBUTION OF VISIBLE STARS IN THE sky is not random. The greatest concentration falls in a belt known as the Milky Way. With a telescope we can see that often what appears to our naked eyes to be an individual star is actually a vast cluster of stars called a *galaxy*, comparable in size to our Milky Way, which is itself a galaxy. The distances between these galaxies and the earth can be estimated by methods we shall presently examine. The closest of these galaxies is about 2.2 million light years away.

The Milky Way Galaxy is shaped like a disc, with spiral arms and a globular center probably similar to Andromeda (Fig. 3–1). The Milky Way is in the order of 80,000–100,000 light years in diameter and an estimated 10,000 light years thick at the thickest points. The Solar System is located about 30,000 light years from the center. Our galaxy consists of our

FIG. 3–1. / A *Spiral nebula in* Andromeda, *seen edge on. Photograph with 60-inch telescope. (By courtesy of Mount Wilson and Palomar Observatories.)*

Solar System, an estimated 100,000 other stars, vast clouds of gases and dust, called nebulae, and interstellar clouds, far more diffuse, of gas and dust.

Stars

ALTHOUGH STARS LOOK REMARKABLY ALIKE, they differ greatly in luminosity, in distance from the earth, and in their spectra. Some appear to be single stars but are actually great star clusters (Fig. 3–7); others are two stars which rotate about one another; still others are bright clouds of gas and dust.

Stellar Spectra

SPECTROSCOPY HAS PROVED to be one of the most useful techniques for studying the sun and other stars. As early as 1924 the spectra of over two hundred thousand stars had been obtained and catalogued. From this compilation it was soon discovered that almost all of these spectra could be arranged in an orderly sequence. This sequence is broken up into seven classes labeled O, B, A, F, G, K, and M.

Class O stars are the hottest. In these the lines of helium, oxygen, and nitrogen are ion-

the Milky Way. The dust is generally thought of as small crystals of ice or other frozen gases.

The spectra of stars may be taken through even the denser portions of nebulae. Gases present give absorption lines in the spectra from the stars. Thus we know that nebulae are composed of sodium, calcium, and hydrocarbons. Hydrogen has also been detected by means of radioastronomy. Their composition is strikingly similar to that of stars. This and other evidence points to the probability that the stars might have formed from nebulae. Under certain conditions of temperature, stars in the nebulae not only illuminate it but produce a bright line spectrum. The lines thus produced are lines of hydrogen, helium, nitrogen, and oxygen.

The name *planetary nebulae* is given to certain clouds which are small and more or less round. Some of them resemble smoke rings. These are usually found to be slowly expanding, and are thought to be the product of the explosion of a supernova.

Luminosity

THE LUMINOSITY, the quantity of light emitted, of stars has become of great concern to us, because a number of important characteristics and measurements have been found to be related to it, including stellar distances, mass,

FIG. 3-3. / NGC 1952 "Crab" Nebula in Taurus. Messier 1. Four 100-inch photographs in infrared, red, yellow, and blue. (By courtesy of Mount Wilson and Palomar Observatories.)

and radii. In the time of Ptolemy a scale of six magnitudes of brightness was established, which provided a rough way of classifying stars according to their apparent visual brightness. The twenty brightest stars were called stars of the first magnitude. Later it was discovered that stars of the first magnitude were about a hundred times brighter than those of the sixth magnitude.

The apparent magnitude of a star obviously depends on its distance as well as its actual luminosity. It is known from experiment that the apparent brightness of a point source of light is inversely proportional to the square of its distance. Therefore, if we know the apparent magnitude of a star and its distance from the earth, we can calculate the apparent brightness that star would have if it were at some other distance. By this means it is possible to compare stars by calculating their luminosity at some given distance. The distance selected is 10 parsecs (32.6 light years). At this distance the sun would be a star of fifth magnitude and thus much less bright than many of its companions in the Milky Way.

Hertzsprung-Russell Diagram

FIG. 3-5 SHOWS a plot of luminosity against spectral types for some seven thousand stars located close to the sun. One of the interesting features of this plot is that the distribution is

INFRARED λ7200-λ8400

nonrandom. There is a main sequence of stars that fall on the curve across the center of the diagram. In addition there is a concentration of points above the main sequence (giants and supergiants) and a few isolated stars below the main sequence (white dwarfs—hot, but small stars with exceedingly high density). This diagram has proved to be one of the mainsprings from which astronomy has advanced in modern times.

Stellar Density

UNDERSTANDING OF OUR GALAXY or any other would be greatly promoted by a knowledge of the density of stars of different types. Such a study has been made for the vicinity of our sun

YELLOW λ5200-λ6600

with very interesting results. For a given volume of space there are very few giant stars, but many faint stars. (For each giant of magnitude 5, there are hundreds of thousands of fainter stars.) From this we infer that even the telescope cannot give us a true representation of the types and numbers of stars that exist in a given region of space. The giants, of course, are visible at far greater distances than the fainter stars.

Determining Stellar Distances

THERE ARE FOUR methods of determining the distances to stars and galaxies. Each of these is used to determine successively greater distances than the preceding one, and each is based on the assumption of the accuracy of the information obtained by its predecessor. The four involve the use of trigonometry, luminosity, Cepheid magnitudes and periods of oscillation, and, finally, the brightness of whole galaxies.

TRIGONOMETRIC OR PARALLAX METHOD. Careful observation of a close star will demonstrate that as the earth moves in its nearly circular path about the sun, the star appears to change position with respect to the background of stars at greater distances. If the direction to the star is measured at various points in the earth's orbit it will be found to vary. The diameter of the earth's orbit is known, the angle between the earth, the star, and the sun can be measured, and the distance is then the side of a triangle. Distances to stars are so great in relation to the size of the earth's orbit that only relatively close stars can be measured in this way. This distance is a function of the angle and is measured in parsecs. (One parsec is the distance to a body that would appear to vary through one second or arc, a distance of 3.26 light years.) Actually, the closest star is 1.3 parsecs away. This method can be used for the closest 10,000 stars.

BLUE λ3100-λ5000

LUMINOSITY AS A MEASURE OF DISTANCE. The use of parallax is limited by the capacity of the telescope. Most stars in our galaxy are so far away that the parallax is too slight to be measured accurately. As we have seen, it is possible to determine the absolute magnitude of a star and its spectral type. These can then be plotted on the Hertzsprung-Russell diagram. A sample of about 10,000 stars whose distances can be determined by trigonometry define a distinct curve on the Hertzsprung-Russell diagram. For these 10,000 stars we know their apparent magnitude, spectral type, distance, and therefore their *absolute magnitude*, the apparent magnitude they would have at a distance of 10 parsecs. As we know, the spectrum and apparent

FIG. 3–4. / *Nebulosity in* Monoceros. *Situated in south outer region of NGC 2264. Photographed in red light with a 200-inch telescope. (By courtesy of Mount Wilson and Palomar Observatories.)*

magnitude of a distant star may be determined. The star is then compared with a star with a similar spectrum whose distance is known. From its spectral type the absolute magnitude or luminosity of the distant star is estimated. A distance relation exists between the apparent and absolute magnitude of the star. Thus if the apparent and absolute magnitude can be estimated, its distance can be estimated.

CEPHEID VARIABLES. Certain stars, known as Cepheid variables, change in brightness periodically. The periods tend to be very constant, varying from about one day to as long as 45 days. The increase in brightness is rapid. They are yellow supergiants with very high luminosity, which accounts for their prominence. Actually, these stars are much less numerous in proportion to other types of stars than they appear to be. To the average person, the best known of the Cepheid variables is the polestar, Polaris.

The period of the change in brightness of Cepheids has been plotted against their apparent magnitude. In one study it was shown that the same relationship exists between period and absolute magnitude as between period and apparent magnitude. Thus once it became possible to determine the distance to one Cepheid by one of the previously discussed methods, the distance to all others could be calculated if their periods and apparent magnitudes could be determined. Fortunately, the distances calculated in this way could be checked for a large number of Cepheids by determining their distances through luminosity and the Hertzsprung-Russell diagram.

Cepheids are bright enough to allow measurements throughout the Milky Way and even as far as a few close galaxies.

The fourth method is used exclusively for determination of distances between galaxies. In this method the whole galaxy is treated as a single star. Other galaxies are so distant that all of the stars in them can be considered at essentially the same relative distance. About a thousand galaxies are close enough so that their distances may be measured by the Cepheid method and a modification of it which can be

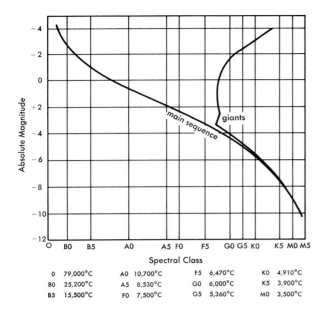

FIG. 3–5. / *Hertzsprung-Russell diagram. This is a plot of absolute visual magnitudes against spectrum types. The sample is taken from the Milky Way.*

used to measure distances up to about 25 million light years. This sample is large enough to permit another relation to be observed—the relation between the total brightness of a galaxy and its distance. If we assume that all galaxies of similar type have the same total brightness, then we must conclude that their apparent magnitude is a function of their distance.

Galaxies

MAN'S KNOWLEDGE OF THE UNIVERSE HAS progressed far enough to give him a degree of understanding of the structure not only of the Solar System and the Milky Way but of other galaxies as well. Estimates based on the range of the largest telescopes suggest that millions of galaxies exist. The closest of these is Andromeda (Fig. 3–1), which is thought to be similar to the Milky Way. The gases and dust clouds from which stars are probably formed lie far out from the center. In the central portion old stars tend to be more prominent. Among these

the relative abundance of giants accounts for the brightness of the central portion. In recent years a halo of hot gases has been discovered surrounding Andromeda, and similar halos are seen to surround other large galaxies. Radiation from these halos is in the wavelength range of X-rays. High-speed electrons also occupy these halos and appear to be deflected by the magnetic fields of the galaxies, producing radio waves. These radio waves provide us with one of the best tools for studying galaxies—radio-astronomy.

Not all galaxies are shaped like Andromeda. In fact, a great variety of types, or sequences, of galaxies have been identified and classified. The classification devised by Edwin Hubble distinguishes three main types of galaxies on the basis of their shapes. These are ellipses, spirals with curved arms, and spirals with a central straight, barlike concentration (Fig. 3–6). These three main sequences account for over 90 per cent of all known galaxies. The remainder are irregular and not classifiable into types.

Most galaxies seem to fit into a pattern of continuously varying characteristics. This in itself suggests that galaxies are not formed at random, but are related by physical conditions of formation and perhaps by historical evolution through the three types. One evidence of this is the varying speed of rotation in the different types of galaxies. Spherical galaxies have little rotation, but presumably some of the flattened galaxies have rapid rotation.

If the sequential variation in the character of galaxies leads us to suspect that they have undergone evolution with time, we must ask how such evolution could take place. In the case of spiral galaxies, it is known that gases and dust are more prominent in the spirals than in the center. The belief that new stars form from this material is supported by the observation of hotter blue stars in the spirals and older red giants in the central region. Unless some theoretical process of formation of gas and dust can be devised, the amount of gas in a galaxy must change with time, and this in turn will affect the rate of formation of new stars.

Photographs of some galaxies seem to show

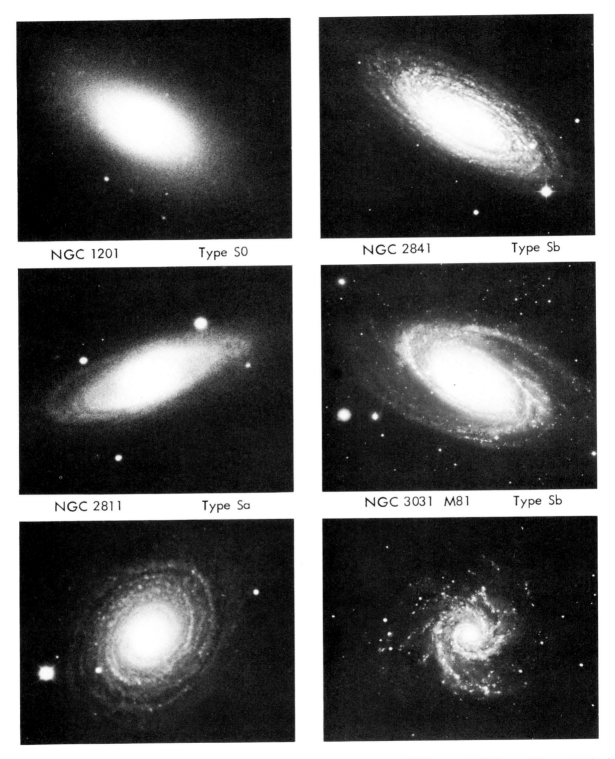

NGC 1201   Type S0

NGC 2841   Type Sb

NGC 2811   Type Sa

NGC 3031 M81   Type Sb

FIG. 3–6. / *Classification of normal galaxies. (By courtesy of Mount Wilson and Palomar Observatories.)*

two galaxies passing through one another. This does not mean that stars of the two collide, because the interstellar distances are so vast that a number of galaxies could pass through one another at the same time without collision. What might happen is that gases of the two would collide, become hot, "evaporate," and perhaps leave both galaxies. The loss of this gas would halt the formation of new stars. In time such a galaxy might be expected to lose its spiral structure and become more or less spherical in shape. This conjecture does not explain the entire observed sequence. At the present time there is no completely satisfactory explanation. Radioastronomy has shown the great elliptical galaxies to be particularly active emitters of radio waves. This suggests that these galaxies are involved in some very active physical processes.

Origin of the Universe

ONE OF THE ULTIMATE QUESTIONS OF science is, "How did the universe originate?" Most scientific theories on this question fall into two highly contrasting general groups known as the *evolutionary theory* and the *steady state theory*.

Evolutionary Theory

THE IDEA THAT the universe originated in one "central" place of space, that all matter was there at one time, and that since that time this matter has been expanding and evolving, is supported by spectral studies. As the largest telescopes scan space they detect what appears to be a rather homogeneous distribution of galaxies. These galaxies are found to be in motion. Studies of the spectrum of light from each galaxy reveal that the lines of the spectrum are shifted toward the red end. This is interpreted to mean that the galaxies are moving away from us. It is further observed that as the distance to a galaxy increases, the velocity of its movement away from us increases as well. This prompts the generalization that the farther a galaxy is away the greater its velocity. Some of these velocities are estimated to be in the range of one-third the speed of light, or about 62,000 miles per second. The simplest way to envision the expansion and the observed effect of all galaxies moving away from us, aside from assuming that we are at the center of the universe, is to imagine that all of the galaxies are represented by dots on a balloon. As the balloon expands the dots all move away from one another and out from a central region.

It appears possible (within the limits of error in the observations) that the paths of the galaxies might intersect if projected backward, and that all of the galaxies would arrive back at their point of origin at about the same time. Although estimates of that time differ greatly (anywhere from 6 to 15 billion years), they are each consistent within the same order of magnitude, which is rather remarkable when we consider the inherent potential errors in measuring the distances of such far-off bodies. Assuming that this theoretical reversal is indeed a possibility, then all of the matter in the universe was "created" in some one region of space. In such a vast nebula temperatures would be exceedingly high, and atoms as we know them would be stripped of their electrons. The formation of elements would be yet to come. There would be convection in this mass, and then for some unknown reason it would begin to break up and expand as though exploding. Convection cells would form and move apart, to cool eventually and condense into clouds of atoms; these clouds in turn would condense into stars. In this hypothesis, the different types of galaxies represent different stages in the evolution of these initial vast convection cells. Matter in space is thus becoming more and more dispersed as the galaxies move apart.

Steady State Theory

IN THE ABSENCE of a large body of observations confirming predictions based on a particular theory, it is normal scientific procedure to look for other theories which explain present observations as well, if not better. So it is not

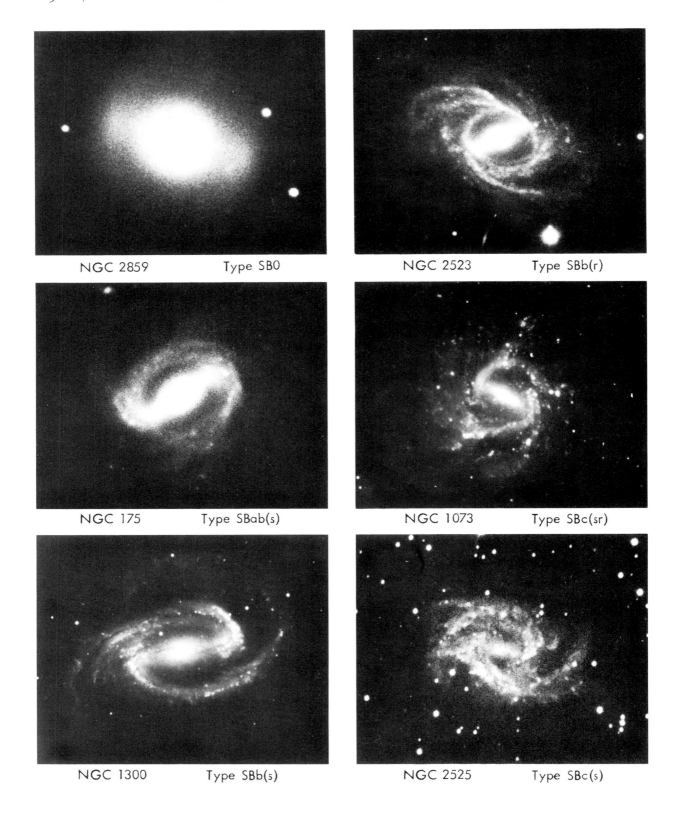

NGC 2859   Type SB0

NGC 2523   Type SBb(r)

NGC 175   Type SBab(s)

NGC 1073   Type SBc(sr)

NGC 1300   Type SBb(s)

NGC 2525   Type SBc(s)

surprising that theories other than the "evolutionary theory" are being considered at present. If all of the matter of the universe did pass through a high temperature–high pressure phase it would be hoped, though not necessarily expected, that some evidence of this might be found. No such evidence is known, and many of the observations on which the "evolutionary theory" are based can be explained by an alternative theory—the steady state.

Those who support the steady state hypothesis point out the possibility that new matter may be created constantly in the universe in a process something like the known production of electrons from gamma rays. The rate at which matter is created, according to this theory, is so slow as to be virtually undetectable—on the order of a few atoms per year per cubic mile.

The idea of an expanding universe is not abandoned in the steady state hypothesis, but unlike the concept in the "evolutionary theory," the average density of matter in space remains constant. As matter is moved out of a given volume of space through expansion, new matter is created to replace it. Matter, then, is not confined to galaxies, but also exists in space. It also follows from this argument that space would appear to be the same throughout all time. From the intergalactic matter diffuse clouds originate and condense into galaxies of new stars. Galaxies, in this theory, undergo evolutionary changes from the time of their origin until they disintegrate.

The conclusion that the number of galaxies in a given volume of space has remained constant has provided one of the ways of testing the steady state hypothesis. We know of galaxies because we see light from them and receive radio waves from them. Because the speed of light is finite (186,000 miles/sec), time is required for the light to travel from one place to another in the universe. The light from many of these galaxies left them as much as half a billion years ago. Waves from other sources have taken over a billion years to reach us. Present observations tell us what those bodies were like at the time the light or radio waves left them. Since sources are available at different distances, we are presented with a way of comparing the density of space at different times. Dr. Martin Ryle, who has made a study of this concentration, has shown that on the basis of his sample of sources the density of galaxies in space has in fact decreased with time. If this is a representative sample it eliminates the steady state hypothesis. Supporters of the steady state suggest that either the volume of space from which the sample was taken is not large enough to be representative or that the sample itself is not large enough.

It is hoped that future studies in radio-astronomy will shed some light on this problem. One of the critical tests will be the demonstrations of the nature of the space between galaxies. The steady state hypothesis contends that matter forms there. The evolutionary theory of the universe does not ascribe any particular characteristics to this space. The arguments between these two schools of thought will undoubtedly provide extremely stimulating intellectual debates during the years ahead.

FIG. 3–7. / *Classification of barred galaxies. (By courtesy of Mount Wilson and Palomar Observatories.)*

II /

PLANET EARTH

FIG. 4-1. / *Some of the common minerals. (Courtesy of the U.S. National Museum.)*

quartz crystals

feldspar

hornblende crystals in cleaved calcite

calcite

4/

Introduction to Geology

WHILE THE EARTH'S PLACE IN THE SOLAR System is of primary importance, the earth scientist is more directly concerned with the solid earth, its interior and surface, the great bodies of water that cover nearly three-fourths of its surface, and the surrounding envelope of gases—the atmosphere. The study of life is the province of biology, but plants and animals are an integral part of many earth processes and cannot be disregarded in a study of the earth. Fossils are an important part of the rock record; they have provided the basis for unraveling a large portion of the earth's history, and study of the fossil record is a traditional field of geology.

Unlike the study of mathematics, physics, and, to some extent, chemistry, in the study of the earth there is no widely accepted system of approach which treats at first simple and then increasingly complex problems. The earth may be viewed by the astronomer as a planet of a certain size, shape, and density, involved in an established pattern of movements. The geologist is concerned with these, but he sees the earth more in terms of the materials which compose it, the shape of its surface, the nature of its interior, the natural processes acting in and upon it, and its history. It is the historical as-

pect of geology that sets it apart most distinctly from other physical sciences. Mathematics, physics, and chemistry, as well as biology, are applied to the study of the earth, but time is frequently an important element in natural processes acting on the earth. The geologist is continually confronted with historical perspective in his concern for the origins and the evolution of changes which have led to the present state of the earth. The earth must be considered in terms of complex interrelations of particular configurations of materials and natural processes leading to changes through time. Quantitative analysis is being applied increasingly in a broad spectrum of research into earth problems, but the large number of variables, complex interrelationships in nature, and the size and time factors make rigorous quantitative analysis difficult and sometimes impossible. Because the various fields of earth science are so interrelated, none can be satisfactorily treated independently of all others. Ideally, the student needs a background in the other natural sciences and in other fields of geology before starting the study of any earth problem. However, this is clearly impossible. The purpose of this chapter is to put at your disposal some of the most

FIG. 4-2. / *Typical specimens of igneous* (*top and bottom left*), *sedimentary* (*top and bottom right*) *and metamorphic* (*opposite*), *rocks.* (*Sedimentary rocks by courtesy of the U.S. National Museum.*)

pertinent facts and concepts of geology, and to provide a general framework for what follows in succeeding chapters.

Materials

CHEMICAL ELEMENTS OCCUR NATURALLY on earth as organic compounds in animal and plant tissue, oil, and coal, or as inorganic compounds called *minerals* (Fig. 4–1). These minerals occur sometimes in a pure form, but more generally as *rocks*, which are usually aggregates of minerals. By far the most common chemical elements in the earth are oxygen, silicon, aluminum, iron, magnesium, calcium, sodium, and potassium. These are combined in such common minerals as *feldspar* $(KAlSi_3O_8)$, *quartz* (SiO_2), *mica* $(KAl_2(OH,F)_2AlSi_3O_{10})$, *hornblende* $(Ca_2(Mg,Fe)_5(OH)_2(Al,Si)_8O_{22})$, *calcite* $(CaCO_3)$ and *olivine* $((Mg,Fe)_2SiO_4)$.

Rocks and their component minerals are known to form in three main ways—through crystallization from molten masses within the earth (*igneous rocks*); by settling out (*sedimentation*) and consolidation from water, ice, or air, as is the case with sediment in oceans and lakes, sand dunes, volcanic dust, and glacial deposits (*sedimentary rocks*); and through *metamorphism*, a process which alters igneous or sedimentary rocks by high temperature, stress, pressure, or chemically active fluids (forming *metamorphic rocks*) (Fig. 4–2). Igneous rocks composed of minerals rich in silicon and aluminum are called *sialic* rocks; an example is *granite*, whose component minerals are quartz, mica, and feldspar. When magnesium is more prominent the igneous rock is called *simatic*; an example is *basalt*, composed of olivine, hornblende, and feldspar. Most sedimentary rocks are shale, sandstone, limestone, or mixtures of these. Metamorphism of limestone produces marble; sandstone is transformed to quartzite; and shale under high stress is transformed into slate, under other conditions, into schist.

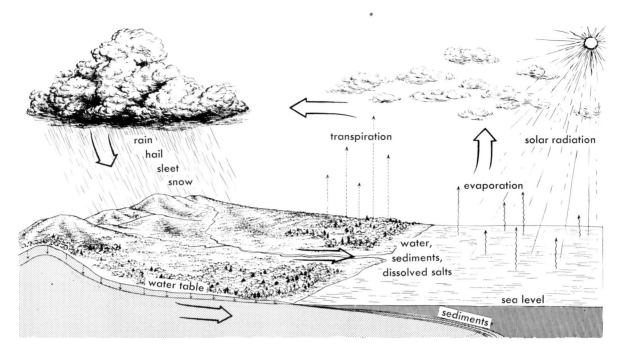

FIG. 4–3. / *The hydrologic cycle. Water is an important agent in bringing about change near the surface of the earth. This is possible because it is recycled through the oceans, atmosphere, and land. Solar radiation causes evaporation of water from the oceans. Plants release water vapor directly into the air by transpiration. This water vapor then moves through the atmosphere until conditions favorable for precipitation as rain, hail, sleet, or snow occur. Then the water falls to the earth. The runoff carries sediment in streams and erodes the land. That water which seeps into the earth moves much more slowly through the soil and bedrock promoting solution and decomposition of rock. The broken sediments and dissolved solids are carried by the runoff and ground water into the ocean where they are deposited as sediments on the sea floor. Then the cycle is complete.*

Hydrologic Cycle

THERE IS A CONTINUAL INTERCHANGE OF material between the atmosphere, oceans, and land surface. The interchange of water is known as the *hydrologic cycle* (Fig. 4–3). Solar radiation evaporates water from the oceans. This water becomes water vapor in the atmosphere, and later condenses and falls back to earth as rain, snow, or sleet. This precipitation may bring about erosion on land through glaciation or stream action, it may dissolve soluble rocks, or it may be absorbed by and become involved in chemical reaction with minerals of rock or soil. Eventually the water, along with sediment and dissolved substances, finds its way into the ocean, and the cycle is complete.

The hydrologic cycle is but one example of the interplay of the air, oceans, and land. The earth's rotation, the shape of the ocean basins, and the density of sea water all affect ocean surface currents. The currents influence the temperature and moisture content of the overlying air masses, and these air masses are governing factors in climates. Climates are important determinants of rock weathering and soil development, which in turn help influence the types of land forms developed. Such chains of interdependence are a common characteristic of the natural processes of the earth.

FIG. 4–4. / *The origin of a mountain glacier as seen in this view of part of the White Mantle Range, Knight Inlet, British Columbia. (Photo by courtesy of the Royal Canadian Air Force.)*

Gradation

NATURAL PROCESSES ACTING ON AND within the earth are constantly shifting, altering, and rearranging the materials of the earth's crust. Where rocks come in contact with the elements of the atmosphere, mechanical and chemical reactions take place which lead to the decomposition and breakdown of the rocks and the formation of soil. Taken as a group, these processes acting on the earth's crust are called *weathering.*

Both weathering products, soil and the consolidated or semiconsolidated rock beneath, are subject to the effects of various geomorphic agents such as running water, glaciers, wave action, ground water, and wind (Figs. 4–4 through 4–12). Each of these agents brings about erosion, transportation, and eventually deposition of earth materials through a complex of natural processes peculiar to itself. The over-all effect of these agents is a shifting of materials from higher to lower places on the earth. These forces can collectively be called processes of *degradation.* Each of the geomorphic agents brings about erosion through different processes, and the methods of transportation and deposition differ. Thus, where one of these dominates, the land surface gradually assumes a shape that is characteristic of that geomorphic agent. Because each

FIG. 4–5. / *Lower Falls, Yellowstone River. Waterfalls occur along many rivers which have not yet become adjusted to recent changes in their courses. The drainage patterns in many parts of the world have assumed their present configuration during the Pleistocene either as a result of glaciation, diastrophism, or volcanism within the Pleistocene. (Photo by courtesy of the Union Pacific Railroad.)*

FIG. 4–6 (*far left*). / *Stream dissection of flat-lying beds of a plateau. This is an early stage in the dissection of this plateau. Later the divides will be narrowed and the valley will become wider. (Photo by courtesy of the U.S. Air Force.)*

FIG. 4–7 (*left*). / *High mountains in China eroded by running water. Mass wasting and running water combine to dissect mountains as shown here. (Photo by courtesy of the U.S. Air Force.)*

FIG. 4–8 (*left, bottom*). / *Dust storm in New Mexico. "The day had been relatively calm with light wind from the southeast. The dust storm rolled in on a very light wind, but about 15 minutes later a regular hurricane struck which lasted about 30 minutes. Visibility was zero, and tightly closed rooms were filled with fine choking dust." Dust is so light that it remains in suspension in the air. (Photo by courtesy of the U.S. Soil Conservation Service.)*

FIG. 4–9 (*right, top*). / *The Big Room of Carlsbad Caverns, New Mexico. This photo shows evidence of two stages in the history of the cave. First the cavern was formed through solution of the limestone by underground waters. Then began deposition of massive columns and pointed stalactites of calcium carbonate. (Photo by courtesy of the New Mexico State Tourist Bureau.)*

FIG. 4–10 (*right, bottom*). / *Details of landslide topography near Ouray, Colorado. (Photo by courtesy of the U.S. Geological Survey.)*

FIG. 4–11. / *Weathering and mass wasting in high mountains result in the slow breakdown and eventually reduction of such features. (Photo by the author.)*

agent is different, it becomes possible to recognize the landforms and the character of the deposits formed through each agent, even though that agent is no longer acting.

If the earth were affected only by processes that tended to reduce its surface, it would long since have obtained a nearly flat and featureless surface. The main factors in keeping portions of the earth high are *igneous activity*, the production of rock melts, and *diastrophism*, movements of the crust (Figs. 4–13 through 4–17). Igneous activity includes *volcanism*, through which volcanoes are built and vast outpourings of lava take place. Hundreds of recently active volcanoes are known, and one of the most extensive of the lava plateaus is the Columbia River plateau of the northwestern United States.

Carefully surveyed level lines across large areas of continents reveal that parts of the continents are even now being elevated in relation to other parts. Diastrophism may act slowly, as in this almost imperceptible uplifting, or violently, as in the Alaskan earthquake of 1964. Rock strata near the top of the Grand Canyon are composed of sediments that today form only in the oceans, and these sediments contain fossils of animal groups that today live only in the oceans. Marine fossils are found in the rock units near the top of Mt. Everest, nearly thirty thousand feet above sea level. These are but a few bits of the mass of information indicating that the crust of the earth is not as stable as it appears. The crust is sometimes warped over a large area, elevating some portions and depressing others. In addition, certain long belts

FIG. 4–12. / *Ground fractures. These fractures opened in the ground near a fault scarp which resulted from the Montana earthquake of August, 1959. (Photo by the author.)*

of the crust have been strongly deformed so that the rocks there are folded, broken by faults, and uplifted to form high mountain belts. The nature of the deformation is such that it could be produced only by great stresses within the crust. Rocks subjected to great stress and lying at great depths behave quite differently from rocks at the earth's surface. Under the high confining pressures and at the high temperatures of the earth's interior, rock loses its brittleness and flows. This flowage is apparent in the deformed rocks found in the cores of uplifted mountains which have been dissected by weathering and erosion. The behavior of rocks under such conditions gives us an indication of the nature of the earth's interior.

FIG. 4–13. / Kilavea flank eruption (eruption on rift zone), Hawaii, 1960. Fountains about 200 feet high throwing new spatter onto the ramparts they are building around the erupting rift. (Courtesy of U.S. Geological Survey.)

The Interior of the Earth

MOST OF WHAT WE KNOW OF THE EARTH'S interior comes from indirect observations. In exposed cores of mountain ranges we can examine rocks which have been at depths of several miles; a few mines penetrate a mile or more deep; and a few oil wells have been drilled to depths of four or five miles. However, these distances are slight when compared to the earth's diameter, and we have no direct information about the interior of the earth below the crust. Such information as we do have is gained chiefly through *seismology*, the study of shock waves which have traveled through the earth from earthquake foci, and through measurements of the gravity and magnetic fields of the earth. Based on the known depths within the earth at which changes occur in the velocity and character of shock waves, a number of important zones have been recognized. The closest of these to the surface is called the *M* or *Mohorovičić discontinuity*, and it is used to delineate the base of the *crust* of the earth. The crust is deepest under mountain ranges, and deeper under continents than ocean basins. Velocities of the shock waves through the continents suggest that the composition of the continents is similar to that of sialic rocks such as granite. The ocean

FIG. 4–14. / A composite volcano in Japan. (Photo by courtesy of Japan Air Lines.)

basins appear to be underlain by simatic rocks like basalt. The differences in composition and level of the continents and ocean basins seem to be related to the density of the rock types. Sialic rocks are less dense than simatic rocks. This suggests that the crust is more or less "floating" on the top layer of the interior of the earth—the *mantle*.

If such floatation is indeed the case (and it is borne out by many lines of evidence), then the rocks of the mantle must be able to "*flow*." Of course this flowage is not like that of most familiar liquids, but more like that of asphalt, which appears to be a solid but behaves as a plastic or highly viscous liquid. The lower limit of the mantle is defined by another zone of seismic discontinuities. Below the level of about 1,800 miles, the outer boundary of the core, only those shock waves are transmitted that are capable of moving through liquid. This has led to the conclusion that the earth has a liquid core. The density of this core is so great that only a few materials as we know them at the surface of the earth could form it. The most probable of these is a nickel-iron compound like that commonly found in meteorites.

FIG. 4-15. / *Belt of folded mountains in Africa (Atlas Mountains). Deformation and uplift of the crust of the earth is one of the main factors in maintaining parts of the crust high. Already these mountains have been deeply dissected. Note the erosion products of the mountains which lie on the flanks of the ridges. (Photo by courtesy of the U.S. Air Force.)*

FIG. 4-16. / *A sharp downward pitch in an anticline on the west side of the Big Horn Mountains in Wyoming. Folded structures of this nature indicate the magnitude of forces which deform the earth. (Photo by courtesy of the U.S. Geological Survey.)*

Gross Features of the Earth's Crust

IN THE CHAPTERS THAT FOLLOW, THE PROCesses that cause erosion of the earth and those that are responsible for maintaining parts of the crust at high elevation in spite of erosion will be discussed in detail. Before turning to the study of this balance between upheaval and erosion, let us get firmly in mind the major framework of the crust.

Continents and Ocean Basins

THE MOST OBVIOUS as well as the most important divisions of the crust are the continents and the ocean basins (Fig. 4–18). These differ in many respects and are separated by zones of transition which have different characteristics from those of either the continents or the ocean basins. Among the most striking differences between the continents and the ocean basins are the following:

1. The elevation of the continents is, on the average, almost half a mile above the level of the present-day seas, but the average depth of the ocean floors is almost three miles beneath the surface of the waters. Thus there is a difference of about 3½ miles in surficial elevation between the two (Figs. 4–19 and 4–20).

2. The thickness of the crust is strikingly different under oceans and under continents. Measuring from the ocean's surface, the crust in the ocean basins is between 8 and 10 km. thick, while it is about 20 km. thick under the continents, reaching a maximum under some mountains, where its thickness may be as great as 40 km.

3. The crust under the oceans has a bulk composition that differs from that under the continents. Almost the entire continental crust is thought to be sialic, but the oceanic crust contains a thin layer of sialic material and in some places none at all. The minerals of the oceanic crust are those that make up basalt, and are thus simatic.

FIG. 4–17. / *Uplifted wave-cut terrace. Epeirogenic deformation of the crust often elevates portions of the sea floor as it has here along the California coast where a wave-cut terrace has been uplifted. (Photo by the author.)*

4. The products of igneous activity under the oceans are different from those under the continents in that extrusions and intrusions under the oceans tend to be basaltic in composition, whereas those in and on the continents tend to be more granitic in composition.

5. Even the processes of erosion and deposition are strikingly different, due to the various properties of the fluids directly in contact with the lithosphere on the continents and under the oceans. These fluids are, of course, the atmosphere and the oceans.

6. In general, the continents may be considered the sites of the most rapid erosion, while the ocean basins are primarily sites of deposition.

7. The variety of factors involved in the erosion and decay of rocks is greater on continents than in oceans.

While the ocean basins and continents have

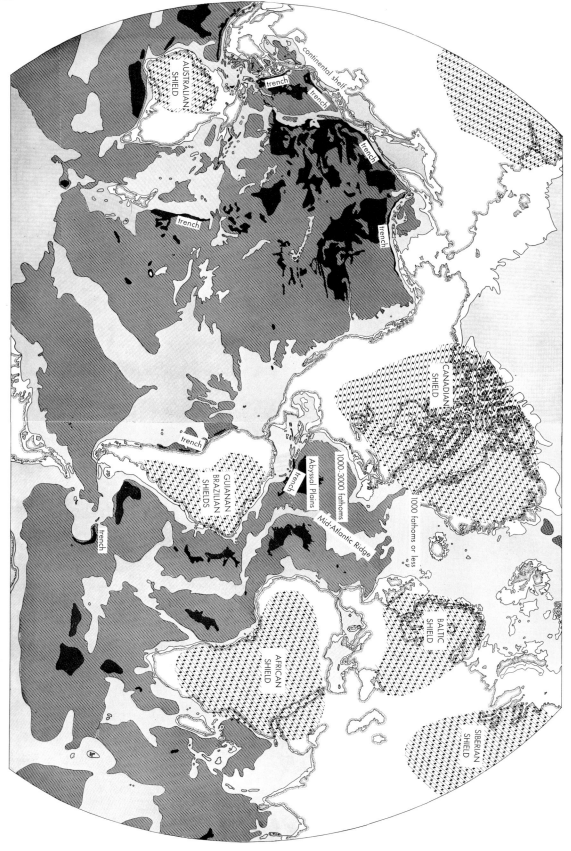

AUSTRALIAN
SHIELD

continental shelf

trench

trench

trench

trench

trench

trench

CANADIAN
SHIELD

trench

GUIANAN
BRAZILIAN
SHIELDS

Abyssal Plains

1000-3000 fathoms

1000 fathoms or less

Mid-Atlantic Ridge

trench

BALTIC
SHIELD

AFRICAN
SHIELD

SIBERIAN
SHIELD

many striking differences, there are some respects in which they are rather similar. Each has broad plain areas that are nearly flat. Both have high mountain ranges that extend for thousands of miles. Just as there are high mountain peaks like Everest (30,000 feet) on continents, there are trenches nearly 38,000 feet deep in the oceans. Both peaks and trenches are extremes of relief that make up a relatively small amount of the total area.

It is possible to make further subdivisions of the crust, distinguishing a vast number of unique crustal segments, but for the purpose of general discussion the definition of six types of crustal segments is sufficient.

Continental Shields

EACH CONTINENT CONTAINS a large and usually centrally located segment composed mainly of crystalline igneous and metamorphic rocks of Precambrian age, more than 600 million years old. Although these regions, known as continental shields, were unstable in the Precambrian time, today they are the most stable portions of the continental crust, having few earthquakes and no young, folded mountain belts.

Folded Mountain Belts

THE YOUNGEST of the folded mountain belts are physiographically high regions like the Appalachians, Alps, Rockies, Pyrenees, Andes, Himalayas, and Urals. All belts that have been deformed since the Precambrian fall into the category of folded mountain belts even if they are no longer high. They are characterized by folded and faulted strata, the presence of igneous intrusions along their axial zones, past or present earthquakes, unusually thick sequences of sedimentary rocks, linear patterns, and long-term instability.

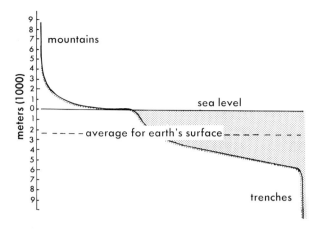

FIG. 4–19. / *The distribution of elevations in various parts of the earth. The vertical scale is elevation. The horizontal scale is surface area of the earth.*

FIG. 4–20. / *A plot of the percentage of the earth's surface at each elevation. This is one of the most conclusive demonstrations of the great differences in level between ocean basins and continents. (After Bucher, 1933.)*

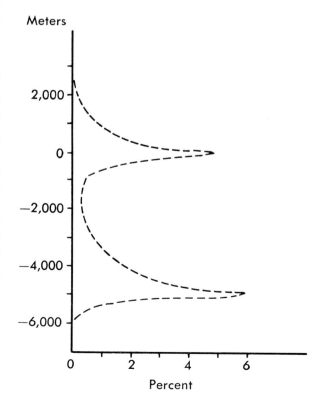

FIG. 4–18. / *Map of the world.*

Continental Shelves

THE CLASSIC EXAMPLE of a continental shelf is the eastern margin of the United States. Where exposed above sea level, the continental margin is relatively flat; this nearly level topography extends out under the ocean as far as one hundred miles in a few places, before it breaks away in a steeper slope leading down into the depths of the ocean basins. The shelves are transition zones between the continents and the ocean basins. Seismic work in the shelf zone has been less successful in revealing the subsurface structure than has the work in the deep oceans or on the continents because the structure of the transition zone is complex. Most of the major streams extend onto the shelves in the form of submarine canyons.

Island Arc Systems

THESE ARE THE LEAST stable portions of the crust. Here earthquakes of great intensity are concentrated, and here also occurs most of the earth's volcanic activity. Where the islands have been cut by erosion, great intrusions are found. The island arcs form arcuate patterns, with the convex side toward the ocean basins, the Aleutian Islands being the classic example. Off the islands are the deep and narrow submarine trenches which contain the greatest deeps of the oceans. Most of the island arcs today are located around the margin of the Pacific Ocean.

Deep Oceanic Crust

AT DEPTHS of around 18,000 feet are found the flattest portions of the crust, large expanses known as the *abyssal plains*. Beneath these plains the structure of the crust, as now known, is rather simple. There is a thin veneer of modern unconsolidated sediments, or, in some places, a thin section of consolidated sediments. Beneath these sediments are, first, layers of basalt and then at a shallow depth of about 10 kilometers, the base of the crust. Like the shields, the abyssal plains are very stable portions of the crust at present. Their history, whether stable or unstable, is for the most part unknown to us.

Midocean Ridges

THE OCEAN basins are not entirely flat, featureless plains, but instead present a highly varied topography. Certainly one of the most prominent features is the midocean ridges. These ridges are comparable to the Rocky Mountains, and they are culminated by a few peaks that rise as islands above the sea. Of these ridges, the Mid-Atlantic Ridge is the best known. It has a relief of over twenty thousand feet above the adjacent abyssal plains. Most of the samples collected from this ridge show it to be volcanic material of basaltic composition. This is borne out by the fact that all of the islands projecting above water are volcanoes. One notable feature of the midocean ridges is a rift zone along their crests, where apparently the ridges have been pulled apart by stresses within the crust.

Geologic Time

GEOLOGY IS A YOUNG SCIENCE. THE MAN who is considered the "Father of Historical Geology," William Smith, lived in the early nineteenth century. The geologic time scale we use today was first applied in 1833, but absolute dates (in terms of years) have been added to parts of it only in the last few years. The sequence of events in the earth's history had been worked out in considerable detail long before the advent of radioactive dating techniques for determining the age of rocks and minerals. Among the guideposts in the early studies of the earth's history was the recognition that many of the sedimentary rock units had great lateral extent and that they had been deposited in seas in the distant past. The simple observation that, where these stratified deposits were found in a succession, the younger layers rest on older layers provided one of the first "laws" of geology, *the law of superposition*. Many of these strata were known to contain fossils. William Smith demonstrated that each stratum contained certain characteristic fossils by which

TABLE 3 / **Modern Geologic Time Scale** (*modified after Kulp, 1961*).

Era	Period	Time Between Periods
CENOZOIC	QUATERNARY	8500 *Years*
	TERTIARY	63 *Million Years*
MESOZOIC	CRETACEOUS	135 *Million Years*
	JURASSIC	181 *Million Years*
	TRIASSIC	230 *Million Years*
PALEOZOIC	PERMIAN	280 *Million Years*
	CARBONIFEROUS (Pennsylvanian) (Mississippian)	
	DEVONIAN	345 *Million Years*
	SILURIAN	405 *Million Years*
	ORDOVICIAN	425 *Million Years*
	CAMBRIAN	500 *Million Years*
PROTEROZOIC } ARCHAEOZOIC } PRECAMBRIAN		600 ± *Million Years*

it could be recognized and distinguished. This observation made it possible to correlate strata over long distances despite missing or buried intervening sections. The unraveling of the earth's history had begun.

In devising the geologic time scale, a major division was established between the stratified rocks which contain fossils, and the igneous and metamorphic rocks which are complex, poorly stratified or unstratified, and unfossiliferous. The stratified rocks were gradually classed in order of their age. The various periods of time were given names of the localities where rocks of that age were first discovered or where they were well exposed. Numerous problems beset the geologists in this task. There is no place on Earth where a complete, unbroken sequence of sedimentary rocks of all ages can be found. In order to define the sequences that compose geologic time it was necessary to *correlate* rock units over long distances. A large portion of the stratigraphic section was discovered in Great Britain, and accordingly the early periods took British names, but later portions of the time scale were found in and named for such places as the province of Perm in Russia and the Jura mountains of France (see Table 3).

Strata are rarely unbroken in sequence. Breaks in the sequence, called *unconformities*, are common, and below these breaks the strata are often tilted or folded. The tilted or folded strata were eroded before the overlying sediments were deposited. The early students of the stratigraphic record were much impressed by these breaks. Because they appeared often at about the same position on the time scale in widely separated areas, they were attributed to "world-wide" periods of deformation. When it was found that very different groups of fossils characterized the rocks above and below certain of these breaks, even greater emphasis was given to their significance. The main division of the time scale into eras was based largely upon such breaks and changes in fossil types found in rock units above and below them. Thus, the major divisions on our scale are from youngest to oldest:

CENOZOIC—modern types of life (mammals are the most advanced group)

MESOZOIC—middle types of life (dinosaurs are prominent among the fossils)

PALEOZOIC—early life (fossils are primarily invertebrates)

PROTEROZOIC—beginnings of early life (worms, sponges, algae)

ARCHAEOZOIC—the most ancient rocks devoid of fossils (no fossils, or only most primitive types, such as algae)

These major divisions are further subdivided into the *periods* named for localities where strata of that age were first described. Within the sequences of each of these periods there are many strata. The basic name applied to a mappable stratum or rock unit is *formation*. Later, as the methods used to unravel the history of the earth are discussed, it will become apparent that some of these early concepts of geological time divisions were not exactly true. The process of refining knowledge is fundamental to the scientific method, and never ceases.

A major "breakthrough" in geology came with the application of radioactive decay theory to the dating of minerals. Because the radioactive compounds decay and form other materials at a uniform rate, and because the end product of this decay is often a mineral or element that remains unchanged with time, it is possible to determine the absolute age of certain minerals and, indirectly, the rocks and fossils with which they are associated. The carbon-14 method is probably the most widely known of these, but it is applicable only to the last fifty thousand years. Other decay sequences, particularly uranium to lead, rubidium to strontium, and potassium to argon, are useful in dating rock millions and even billions of years old. The oldest rocks described at this time are 3.3 billion years old.

The Geochemical Cycle

As a RESULT OF GEOCHEMICAL PROCESSES, the crust is constantly undergoing change. It is possible to depict in a general form all of these processes acting in and on the crust, along with the products of their action (Fig. 4–21). Taken as a whole, they form an unending cycle. Magma, molten rock, may be intruded into the crust from the interior of the earth. As the magma cools, it crystallizes to form igneous rocks, and in crystallizing releases gases, which become part of the earth's atmosphere, and water, which remains in the earth or enters the atmosphere or oceans. Igneous rocks are the original source of all forms of rock. The igneous rock is attacked by chemical agents within the crust or uplifted until it is exposed to weathering at the surface. Decomposed rocks and the remains of decaying plants and animals (composed of materials released by the weathering of this rock) make up the unconsolidated sediments typical of the earth's surface. By compression these sediments may be transformed into sedimentary rocks. These, in turn, may be eroded and weathered to form more sediments, or altered by heat, pressure, and fluids to form metamorphic rocks. If extreme heating is present, the metamorphic rocks melt, forming secondary magma. Ultimately the secondary magma may harden into igneous rocks, and the cycle begins again.

Energy for Earth Processes

STREAMS FLOWING FROM HIGHER TO lower parts of the continents of the world carry billions of tons of rock, soil, and debris with them. Moving glaciers gouge out the sides of mountains. Rocks exposed near the surface are almost constantly under attack by agents tending to decay and break them down. Volcanoes pour forth lavas and throw out huge blocks of rock. Whole sections of the crust of the earth are buckled and folded as mountain systems

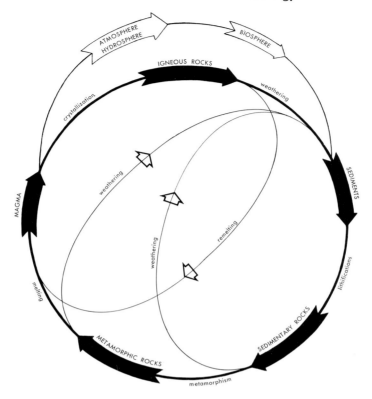

FIG. 4–21. / *The geochemical cycle. It is possible to depict in a general form all of the processes, and their products, acting in and on the crust of the earth. The crust is constantly undergoing change as a result of these processes. Most of them require the expenditure of great quantities of energy which are supplied from the sources discussed in the text. The crust is not a closed energy system. That is, energy is supplied to it and is lost. Heat energy may be introduced in the crust along with molten rock, magma, from the interior of the earth. This magma crystallizes to form igneous rocks. As the magma cools, gases are produced which go to make up the earth's atmosphere and oceans. Life sprang from the oceans. The remains of decaying plants and animals along with the decayed and decomposed rocks make up the unconsolidated sediments typical of the earth's surface. These sediments may be compressed, dried out, compacted, and thus transformed into sedimentary rocks. These may then be eroded and weathered to form more sediments or they may be altered by heat, pressure, and fluids to form metamorphic rocks, those which have undergone a change of form. If heating is excessive, the metamorphic rocks melt to form secondary magma and the cycle is completed.*

slowly rise. To sustain these processes, great sources of energy must be available in and on the earth's crust.

The crust is not a closed energy system; that is, it receives energy from outside sources and also loses and uses up energy (it is not, in fact, used up, but is converted into a stable form and is not used again, or its reuse is delayed for a very great time). (A closed energy system may constantly reuse energy from within the system itself. The closed system often uses and reuses its energy in many forms, but it neither receives nor loses energy outside the system.)

One relatively satisfactory definition of energy is "the ability to do work." Work is the overcoming of a resistance for some distance, as when a weight is carried up a flight of steps. Work is done to overcome the resistance of the force of gravity on that weight through the vertical distance between the bottom and top of the steps. The energy that sustains this work arises through a mechanically produced arrangement of matter. It is one of several forms of energy, and differs somewhat from the other forms, i.e., thermal energy, such as is possessed by a hot body, and chemical energy, which is involved when a chemical reaction takes place between two compounds.

Mechanical Energy

THE MECHANICAL ENERGY possessed by bodies is of two sorts. Energy possessed by a body in motion is called *kinetic energy*. Once a body is set in motion, it has a tendency to remain in that state of motion until something happens to it—until some force acts upon it to change the state of motion. When a force acts on the body in motion, some form of work is performed, or the kinetic energy is converted into thermal energy. Water in motion, such as that in streams or breaking waves, has kinetic energy. This energy is expended in part by the transportation of rocks, soil, and other matter. When water flowing over a waterfall hits the bottom of the falls, it has a large amount of kinetic energy, much of which it expends in breaking up the rocks it hits and in undercutting the falls. It appears that the water suddenly has obtained more energy at the bottom of the falls than it had at the top. Actually a transformation in the type of energy has taken place. At the higher elevation the water had potential energy because of its position. A block of rock has *potential energy* if it occupies an elevated position, regardless of whether it is suspended at the top of a hoist or buried in the top of a mountain. Both have the potential of accomplishing work if they are freed and move down under the force of gravity. In our example of the waterfall, the potential energy of the water was partially converted into kinetic energy, which was in turn partially used in breaking the rocks and partially retained in the continued flow of the water.

So far, we have said that kinetic energy is the energy of a body in motion, and potential energy is the energy imparted to a body by its elevated position. There is a second form of potential energy, that contained by a body as a result of its arrangement of matter, as in a coiled spring. The crust of the earth has potential energy from position because of the downward pull of gravity against it. This potential energy of position may be transmitted into parts of the crust as stress, which is potential energy like that of a spring. If this stress suddenly causes an earthquake, the potential energy becomes kinetic energy in the resulting motion. This kinetic energy acts until it has done all the work for which it has the capacity, or until it is overcome by an opposing force.

Chemical Energy

THE OTHER FORMS of energy are *thermal* and *chemical*. A heated body possesses the ability to accomplish work with consequent loss of heat. Likewise, certain chemical reactions may take place between substances with the evolution of heat energy, *exothermic reactions*.

Chemical energy is involved in all chemical reactions. A chemical reaction that liberates thermal energy is an exothermic reaction. On the other hand, an endothermic reaction absorbs heat, converting it into the chemical energy required for the reaction. Since a great variety of chemical reactions take place within the crust and on its surface, many in weathering, chemical energy is a very important force in the crust. All chemical changes are accompanied by a change in the energy of the system involved, either by the absorption or liberation of energy. These changes may be manifest through development of thermal energy, heat, mechanical energy, as in the pressure of a gas, by radiant energy, light, or as electrical energy.

First and Second Laws of Thermodynamics

ENERGY IS NEITHER created nor destroyed. It may be transformed from one type of energy into another, but it is not lost. Therefore, it would appear that a certain quantity of energy was initially present in the universe. Since the origin of the universe this energy has been exchanged from one body to another and transformed from one type to another. This particular feature of energy is expressed in the physical law of the *conservation of energy:* Energy can be converted from one form to another, but it can never be created or destroyed; or, stated in another way, the total energy of an isolated system is always constant. A special aspect of this is the *first law of thermodynamics:* When a given quantity of work is completely converted into heat, an equivalent amount of heat is produced; and conversely, when heat is transformed into work, a definite quantity of work is produced. Thus this first law is a statement of the principle of conservation of energy. The *second law of thermodynamics,* as stated by Clausius, is: "It is impossible for a self-acting machine, unaided by any external agency, to convey heat from one body to another at a higher temperature; or, heat cannot of itself pass from a colder to a warmer body."

The conversion of thermal energy to mechanical and chemical energy is very important in earth processes. Consider our Solar System as a whole. Radiant energy from the sun comes to the earth, making possible many natural processes including life, and it propels the hydrologic cycle. Gradually this thermal energy is becoming less available, since according to the second law of thermodynamics each reaction takes place with a movement of heat from hot to cooler bodies. In a sense, then, the free energy available for the fundamental earth processes is slowly diminishing.

The law of the conservation of energy and the second law of thermodynamics are two of the most important laws of science. All the natural processes may be reduced to simple physical or chemical processes, which may be considered in terms of the energy transformations that characterize them. Thus these laws provide a basis for unifying the diverse natural processes into a single coherent picture.

Energy Sources

WE MUST DISTINGUISH BETWEEN ULTI-mate and immediate sources of energy. The ultimate source of the energy content of the uni-verse is unknown to us. But we can discern the immediate sources of energy responsible for certain processes. It is possible for us to see that there are certain primary sources from which most of this energy springs.

Solar Radiation

OF THE SOURCES OF ENERGY on the earth, none is more important than the solar radiation received each day. Without solar radiation, life as we know it would disappear. The oceans would freeze, and the continents would become covered by snow and ice, as the temperature fell toward absolute zero ($-273°$ centigrade). There would be no rain, and rivers would cease to flow. Erosion would almost halt as running water ceased to transport erosion products across the surface.

The amount of thermal energy coming to the earth each year amounts to about $6{,}800 \times 10^{20}$ calories. This heat is partially held to the earth by our atmosphere, which forms a blanket of insulation over the earth. Because the moon does not have an atmosphere, extremes of temperature exist on its surface. Most of the solar radiation coming to the earth is used to evaporate water; but some is absorbed by the earth, and a small amount is needed in the process of photosynthesis of plants.

That part of the solar radiation used in evaporating water is transformed from thermal energy to mechanical energy. The evaporated water forms water vapor in the atmosphere. This water vapor possesses great potential energy by virtue of its high position above the earth. It condenses to form rain, and this falls back to earth. Some of the rains fall on the high continents, and the potential energy is converted to kinetic energy as the waters collect, erode the ground, transport matter, and bring about chemical reactions with the rocks.

Gravity

THE FORCE OF ATTRACTION between all masses, and in particular the force that pulls masses toward the center of the earth, may be considered as the main source of potential energy. It is this force that causes the ocean water carried into the atmosphere as water vapor to return to the earth. The force of gravity makes possible the conversion of potential energy into kinetic energy by exerting a continuous force on the water and maintaining it in motion until it reaches the oceans. Gravity is responsible for the mass movement of rock debris and soils down slopes. It is the driving force behind glaciers. Without it very little erosion would be accomplished. Rocks might decay to form soils, but even this is questionable since it is largely the interaction between the atmosphere and the rocks that brings about decay, and the atmosphere is held to the earth by gravitational attraction.

Heat from the Earth's Interior

IN THE DEEP MINES at Butte, Montana, and in the diamond pits in South Africa, temperatures of the ground are found to increase with depth. The rate of increase near the surface is about 1° centigrade for each 100 feet of descent. The temperatures at the bottom of the mines at Butte reach 140° Fahrenheit, and fresh cool air must be blown into the mine to protect the men working there. If the rate of increase in heat, known as the *geothermal gradient*, continued to rise, it is obvious that the temperatures found at great depths in the earth's interior would be exceedingly high; they would, in fact, approach the temperature of the sun's surface. It seems almost impossible, however, that the center of the earth is actually this hot, and there is geologic evidence supporting the belief that the gradient is not a constant rate all the way down. Records from deep wells support this belief, and geologists have observed that rocks once buried at specific great depths have not been altered as they would have been if the temperatures had been as great as would be the case with a constant geothermal gradient. Nevertheless, the temperatures in the earth's interior are high. Seismic evidence indicates that beyond a depth of about 1,800 miles the interior is probably hot enough to be a liquid.

There is still much uncertainty as to how much of this internal thermal energy makes its way to the surface, but it is estimated to be barely sufficient to raise the temperature of the surface one degree, if that much. Studies of the heat flow through the earth's crust are in progress, and within a few years we may expect some answers. Probably solar radiation alone would be sufficient to maintain most processes now acting at the surface. The particular importance of internal heat is found in the geologic processes taking place within the earth. Most important of these are deformation of the earth's crust, which is almost certainly connected with internal heat energy, and the generation of magma.

Earth's Rotation

THE EARTH'S ROTATION provides a source of mechanical energy. The most important of the effects of this energy is the maintenance of the earth's form. As a rotating body, the earth tends to maintain its somewhat pear-shaped form against the pull of external bodies such as the moon and the sun. The gravitational attraction of the moon not only causes tides in the oceans, but pulls the solid crust of the earth out toward it as well, creating a very slight bulge. Because the earth rotates, a frictional drag is created between the solid earth and the fluid media, water and air, which are in contact with it. This sets wind and water currents in motion and imparts kinetic energy to them.

Energy from Changes of State— Chemical Reactions

MOST CHEMICAL REACTIONS that take place under falling temperatures are *exothermic*. An example of such a reaction taking place in the earth is the crystallization of masses of molten rock. Through this process the heat energy released can accomplish more work—and perhaps contribute toward the melting of more rock. Other reactions take place between the constituents of the earth's *lithosphere*, the solid crust, *hydrosphere*, the watery envelope, *atmosphere*, the gaseous envelope, and *biosphere*, the sum total of the organic life on earth.

III /

THE ATMOSPHERE

FIG. 5–1. / *Lightning. (Photo by Noel M. Klein, U.S. Weather Bureau.)*

5

Nature and Composition
of the Atmosphere

THE TERM ATMOSPHERE IS APPLIED TO THE gaseous envelope that overlies the land and oceans of the earth. The three are intimately connected through exchange of materials and through processes in each that affect the others. The true nature and extent of the atmosphere is not yet completely known to us. Probing with rockets and satellites in the past few years has greatly extended our knowledge, particularly of the upper parts of the atmosphere. Atmospheric phenomena such as the aurora, twilight effect, reflection of radio waves, appearance of meteorites, and, most prominent of all, weather, emphasize the diversity of processes acting in the atmosphere.

The atmosphere consists primarily of nitrogen, oxygen, argon, carbon dioxide, hydrogen, and water vapor. These gases are held to the earth by the force of gravitational attraction, which pulls atoms of the gas down toward the surface. Thus the density of the atmosphere is greatest at the surface and decreases upward; over half of the atmosphere lies below 18,000 feet. It extends out at least several hundred miles, but how far beyond that is not known. At distances of 75 miles over the earth, meteorites become hot and burn primarily through

frictional drag in the atmosphere. The aurora extends out over 400 miles.

Although it appears possible that the atmosphere extends out over 20,000 miles, our attention will be directed mainly toward that part of it close to the earth. Gases are sensitive to temperature and pressure variations, which exert considerable influence upon the amount of water vapor air will contain and upon movements of air masses both vertically and horizontally. Pictured as simply as possible, the atmosphere is a blanket of air in which density (pressure) decreases with increased altitude and in which large-scale movements are related to the rotation of the earth. The sun is the primary source of heat. However, to achieve any real understanding of atmospheric phenomena as we experience them at the earth's surface we must also consider such factors as:

1. Effects of differential heating of the earth's surface.

2. Interrelationships between temperature, pressure, and composition of air.

3. Influences of the shape of the land surface.

4. Interactions of oceans and air over them.

The effect of these varied factors is to break

up the "blanket" into masses of air differing in temperature, pressure, and composition. These masses then move in response to the general pattern of atmospheric circulation caused by the earth's rotation and local pressure and circulatory conditions.

Divisions of the Atmosphere

THE ATMOSPHERE HAS BEEN DIVIDED INTO a number of different layers according to temperature variations, behavior of radio waves, and composition (Fig. 5–2). These different layers are known as the *troposphere* (up to about 10 miles), *stratosphere* (10–20 miles), *ozonosphere* (20–30 miles), and *ionosphere* (above 30 miles).

TROPOSPHERE. The troposphere is the dense layer of air close to the surface. The height of this layer varies with latitude and with the season. It is highest at the equator and in summer, and lowest over the poles and in winter. Its height is about 25,000 feet over the poles, but it attains heights of 60,000 feet over the equator. In the troposphere the temperature of the air decreases with increased altitude. Because of the difference in heights at various latitudes, temperatures near the top of the troposphere over the equator are lower (by up to 50° F.) than those over the poles. Moisture and dust from the earth are limited to this layer, as are almost all of the effects we know as weather. The upper limit of the troposphere, called the *tropopause*, is the highest point at which most clouds form. Certain narrow belts of high speed winds, which, collectively are called *jet streams*, are located in the zone of contact between the troposphere and the stratosphere.

STRATOSPHERE. Throughout the troposphere, temperature decreases with elevation. Where this steady decrease ceases there is a stable, stratified layer known as the stratosphere, about 10 miles in thickness. A certain type of cloud known as a mother-of-pearl cloud occurs commonly within the stratosphere; these clouds

mark the absolute upper limit of all cloud activity. A temperature reversal takes place in the stratosphere, but although the upward decrease in temperature is halted, temperature does vary with latitude in the stratosphere, (Fig. 5–2).

OZONOSPHERE. Overlying the stable-temperature layers of the stratosphere there is a layer about 10 miles thick in which ozone is concentrated. Temperatures increase upward through this layer, at a rate of about 16° F. per mile. This increase in heat is caused by the fact that the ozone present in this layer absorbs ultraviolet solar radiation. Were it not for this absorption, most forms of life could not exist on earth. A decrease in the effectiveness of this layer would afflict human beings with intense sunburn and blindness.

IONOSPHERE. The atmosphere above the ozonosphere is composed of several ionized layers (D, E, F1, F2) of very rarified air that extend upward hundreds of miles. These layers are collectively known as the ionosphere. The layers are recognized by the variations in electrical properties. Radio waves are reflected from different parts of the ionosphere. Long radio waves are reflected back to earth from the "D" layer; medium and high frequency (medium and short) waves are reflected from the "E" layer; short wave radio waves are reflected from the "F1" layer, particularly in the daytime; and the "F2" layer reflects short waves, especially at night. Auroral displays take place in the ionosphere at distances from about 70 miles up to three or four hundred miles.

Temperature changes are a notable feature of the ionosphere. In the lowest part of the ionosphere a reversal takes place, and temperatures, which have risen steadily with altitude in the ozonosphere, drop into the range of —100° F., at a distance of 50 miles from the earth's surface. Then, higher in the ionosphere, another reversal occurs, and temperature increases from that point out, possibly reaching temperatures of 1,300° F. at about 2,000 miles.

That these layers within the ionosphere are

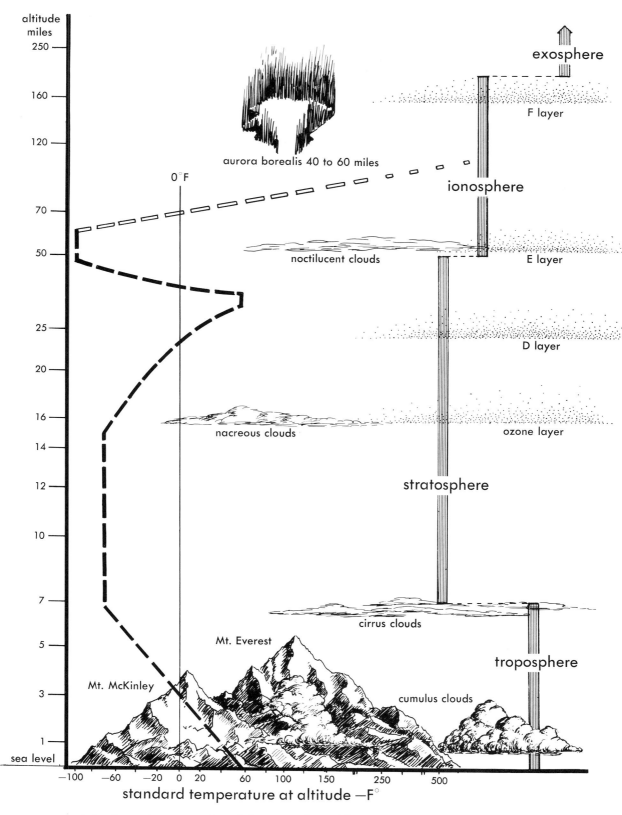

FIG. 5–2. / *A schematic cross section of the atmosphere. (Courtesy of Pratt and Whitney Aircraft Co.)*

closely related to solar activity is shown by the disappearance of "D" and "E" layers at sunset. During periods of solar flares almost all medium and high frequency radio communication stops because of absorption of these waves in the "E" layer.

Properties of Air

ROBERT BOYLE (1627–1691) WAS AMONG the early students of gases. He was the first to show how changes in the volume of a gas affected pressure in that gas. He established that any decrease in volume causes a proportional increase in pressure if the temperature is kept constant (PV = a constant).

Later Jacques Charles (1746–1823) and Joseph Gay-Lussac (1778–1850) demonstrated the relationship between volume and temperature of gases. They showed that pressure in a gas which is being heated remains constant only if volume is increased (V/T = constant). These two laws were later combined into a single statement known as the *"General Gas Law"* (PV/T = a constant). If a body of gas of any given composition is altered by changing its volume, temperature, or pressure, there will automatically be adjustments in the other two variables. That is to say, if temperature of an air mass is increased either volume or pressure or both will increase. If temperature of the gas is decreased then either volume or pressure or both will decrease. If volume of a gas is increased then either pressure decreases or temperature increases or both. If volume of a gas is decreased then either pressure increases or temperature decreases or both. If pressure of a gas is increased then volume decreases or temperature increases or both. If pressure of a gas is decreased then the volume increases or temperature decreases or both.

Weight of the Atmosphere

EVANGELISTA TORRICELLI (1608–47) performed an interesting experiment to demonstrate the weight of air. He was interested in creating a vacuum. To do this he took a long glass tube, one end of which was closed. This was filled with mercury and then inverted, and the open end was placed in a cup of mercury. The level of the mercury in the tube rapidly dropped to a point where it stabilized. When it was stable the column of mercury was 30 inches above the level of the mercury in the open cup. This was the first barometer. The force holding the mercury up in the tube was the pressure of the atmosphere on the open surface of the mercury in the cup. The amount of this pressure was later shown to be 14.7 pounds per square inch at sea level. Because this pressure is exerted by a gas it has no direction (unlike the pressure of a weight tied to a string), and behaves like hydrostatic pressure. The weight of air decreases upward as the air becomes less dense. At 18,000 feet the density is about half that found at sea level, and accordingly the pressure is 7.5 pounds per square inch. The weight of air in the atmosphere depends on the relative percentages of the various elements of which it is composed. It is notable that a cubic foot of water vapor weighs less than a cubic foot of dry air—moist air is lighter than dry air. This is because a molecule of water vapor is lighter than a molecule of any other gas normally found in the atmosphere. Since moist air is lighter than dry air, when the air gains moisture the barometric pressure goes down.

Heat Transfer

ALMOST ALL of the heat of the atmosphere is derived from the sun, and that comes to us as solar radiation—electromagnetic waves. Without going into the various concepts on the physical nature of radiation, let us examine some of its characteristics. These electromagnetic waves may be visualized as sinuous waves of varying lengths but constant velocity, ranging from cosmic rays through X-rays, ultraviolet rays, visible light, and infrared rays to radio waves. Their lengths vary from one-thousand-millionths of a centimeter to a thousand million centimeters. Solar radiation received on earth falls largely in the range of the visible spectrum, but includes some ultraviolet and some infrared radiation. These various lengths of radiation are transmitted, absorbed, and reflected in varying amounts by different materials. For example, visible radiation will be transmitted through glass, water, or air; X-rays will go through most metals; cosmic rays will penetrate deeply into rock. On the other hand, longer rays such as infrared rays cannot penetrate glass. That part of the radiation that falls on an object but is not transmitted through it is either reflected or absorbed. Absorbed radiation is converted into some other form of energy and used. This energy may be used by the body to generate some different length of radiation or to heat itself, or it may be used in a process such as condensation or some chemical reaction. We have already seen how absorption of ultraviolet radiation by ozone in the ozonosphere is followed by a rise in temperature.

The unit of measure used to describe a quantity of heat is the calorie. One *calorie* is the amount of heat required to raise the temperature of one gram of water from 15 to 16 degrees centigrade. The amount of solar radiation reaching the outer edge of the atmosphere where the sun's rays hit vertically is an average of 1.9 calories per square centimeter per minute, and is called the *solar constant*. Even if a spot on the surface of the earth actually receives only a fraction of this amount, a tremendous amount of heat energy is available at the surface for various processes such as evaporation and plant growth. Of course, radiation reaching the earth is only a minute part (an estimated one-billionth) of the total solar radiation.

The amount of solar radiation that actually reaches any point on the earth's surface is highly variable. It depends on the distance of the earth from the sun, the length of the day, the angle of incidence of the sun's rays, and the amount of clouds, dust, and water vapor in the atmosphere. Clouds, dust, and water vapor greatly affect the amount of absorption and reflection of radiation. Of these, water vapor is particularly important as an absorber of energy; clouds are good reflectors; and dust may cause scattering of the radiation. The distance of the earth from the sun varies because of the earth's elliptical path. The earth is some three million miles closer to the sun in January than it is in July. Although more radiation therefore reaches earth in January than in July, summers in the Southern Hemisphere are not hotter than in the Northern Hemisphere primarily because of the moderating influence of the greater bodies of water in the Southern Hemisphere. Changes in the length of the day and the angle of incidence of the sun's rays on a given place are due to the inclination of the earth's axis to the plane in which it revolves about the sun (Fig. 2–4).

Heat Balance

TREMENDOUS QUANTITIES of heat from the sun reach the outer edge of the atmosphere. Of this an estimated one-third is reflected and scattered in the atmosphere and never reaches the earth's surface. Another third is absorbed by the atmosphere, and the remaining third is absorbed by the earth. It is obvious that this absorption rate by the atmosphere and the earth could not continue long unless there were some processes by which heat could be lost. Radiation is the principal of these processes. Long heat waves in the infrared range are emitted by the earth itself and by dust and water vapor in the earth's atmosphere.

Because various substances reflect, absorb, and transmit radiation differently, certain selective effects are to be expected. If the air contains a large amount of water vapor, as in a humid climate, water vapor will tend to absorb infrared radiation from the sun during the day. Shorter wavelength radiation will go through the clouds and be absorbed by the earth, which will later give off part of this energy as infrared radiation. At night clouds will absorb and hold the long wavelength radiation from the earth, and the temperature range during the day and night will thus be small. In an arid climate, where the air is dry, the earth will heat up during the day, but this heat will readily be lost at night, since there is little moisture in the atmosphere, and temperatures will drop. As we have seen, since the moon has no atmosphere, extremes of temperature exist on its surface.

Naturally the amount of solar radiation absorbed depends on the character of the earth's surface at a given place. Ice and snow are excellent reflectors and cut down on the amount of radiation absorbed; dark-colored soils are better absorbers than light-colored ones. Water is a good reflector—though not as good as ice or snow. Energy absorbed by water serves to evaporate the surface layers, or else to penetrate and warm the water beneath. Several times as much heat is required to raise the temperature of water as is needed to raise the temperature of a similar amount of dirt or rock. This accounts for the moderating effect of large bodies of water. They gain and lose heat slowly by comparison with adjacent land.

Of the solar radiation reaching the earth, most is absorbed, but a part is reflected. Of the absorbed part, most goes back into the lower atmosphere through radiation of long wavelengths. Transfer of heat is accomplished by conduction and convection. *Conduction* is the passing of heat through matter. A good conductor passes heat through with very little loss by absorption; a poor conductor passes little heat through. Rocks are poor conductors of heat; this accounts for the small amount of heat reaching the surface of the earth from the interior. For the same reason, heat from the surface is not conducted down from the earth's surface into the interior. However, the layer of air in contact with the earth may be heated by conduction, but since air also is not an efficient conductor, this effect is of minor importance. Convection is of far greater significance. *Convection* is the transfer of heat through movement and mixing in a differentially heated fluid. When air near the ground surface becomes warm as a result of absorption or conduction, it begins to expand and become lighter or less dense, and consequently it rises. As it ascends, air which is cooler and more dense moves in under it. In accordance with the general gas law, the air that has risen and expanded undergoes a drop in temperature. Convection is thus important in the development of thunderclouds and in the general transfer of heat in the lower atmosphere.

Temperature

TEMPERATURE IS SIMPLY A MEASURE OF heat. The three best-known scales are centigrade, Fahrenheit, and absolute. Fahrenheit is the scale in most general use by the public, while the centigrade and absolute scales are used mainly by scientists. On the centigrade scale water freezes at 0° and boils at 100° (1 atmosphere of pressure). On the Fahrenheit scale water freezes at 32° and boils at 212°. It is easy to convert these two by the following formula: the number of degrees centigrade equals ⅝ of the number of degrees Fahrenheit, minus 32; and, conversely, the number of degrees Fahrenheit equals ⅞ of the number of degrees centigrade, plus 32. On the absolute scale zero is set at −273° centigrade, and the degree is an identical unit to that used in the centigrade scale. Fahrenheit and centigrade are abbreviated F. and C., respectively, but absolute is abbreviated K., in honor of Lord Kelvin (1824–1907).

Vertical Temperature Gradient

IT WILL BE OBVIOUS that in the troposphere the rate of change of temperature with an increase in elevation is highly variable. It varies with the time of day or night, weather conditions, time of year, and latitude. In spite of all these variable factors, it is still possible to arrive at an average figure: approximately 3.5° F. per thousand feet change in elevation. This is known as the *normal* or *vertical lapse rate* and it accounts for our common experience of finding mountain tops cooler than the plains or lower country, other factors being the same. Occasionally the temperature increases, instead of decreases, with elevation, due to various conditions. This is known as a *temperature inversion*—a not uncommon atmospheric phenomenon.

Adiabatic Changes

THE GENERAL GAS LAW provides an excellent key to variations in temperature, pressure, and volume in a gas. In analysis of air in the atmosphere, the only significant variable that is not taken into account in this law is the change in composition of the air due to varying amounts of moisture (water vapor) and consequent decrease of other constituents. Omitting this last variable for a moment, we see from the general gas law that when dry air rises, pressure on it decreases, and volume is expanded. This expansion requires expenditure of energy, in this case heat energy, so the temperature of the air falls. Experiments show that the rate of drop is 5.5° F. per thousand feet of rise. Such a change is called an *adiabatic change*, which means that it takes place without the addition or loss of heat from the outside. It is due solely to the pressure change. This standard rate of temperature drop of 5.5° F. per thousand feet is called the *dry adiabatic rate*.

Now consider what happens when air has water vapor in it. As the air mass rises, it cools at the dry adiabatic rate until water begins to condense out of the gas. Remember that heat is needed to evaporate water, and heat is given off when water condenses. The effect of the addition of this heat to a cooling mass of air is to lower or retard the adiabatic rate so that it is only about 3° F. per thousand feet and is then called the *wet adiabatic rate*. This rate is more variable than the dry adiabatic rate because it depends on the amount and form of the condensed moisture, and also on whether that moisture is held as the air mass rises or whether it is dropped out.

Stability–Instability

AN AIR MASS may be considered stable when it tends to resist change successfully. A stable condition arises when the air is perfectly stratified, with the most dense air at the bottom and successively less dense layers above. Such stability might occur when the bottom layer has more density on account of its temperature (cold air being more dense than hot air) or its moisture content (dry air being more dense than moist air). If the air mass closest to the earth is colder than that above it, a temperature inversion exists. If this colder air is elevated it becomes still colder, and thus more dense, and *settles back*. In this case the rate of decrease of temperature with elevation is less than the dry adiabatic rate. Thus a stable condition exists when the temperature gradient is less than the adiabatic rate.

Instability occurs when a mass of air is easily moved. This would happen in the case of thunderstorms, brought about when one area on the ground becomes warmer than surrounding areas. Local warming of the air causes the density of the air to decrease so that the air rises. It continues to rise until stability is reached. Instability is often accompanied by precipitation because the air becomes saturated with moisture. As the warm air rises the temperature drops until moisture condenses. When condensation does occur, heat is liberated and instability is increased. How far this process can go is obviously limited by the amount of moisture available in the air.

Moisture in the Air

IT IS ALREADY ABUNDANTLY EVIDENT FROM the preceding sections that the amount of moisture in the air has important influences on behavior of air. Now we should turn to the condensation of that water vapor and conditions under which clouds, frost, dew, fog, snow, ice, and rain form. The capacity of air to contain water vapor depends on the temperature of the air (Fig. 5–2). How much moisture the air actually does contain depends on other factors as well as on temperature. Hot air in deserts seldom has much water vapor in it. Availability of water vapor depends on the amount of water on the ground surface and on rates of evaporation and transpiration by plants. The amount of water vapor in the air is generally also a function of altitude. On the average, air over a mile high has about half the amount of water vapor of air at sea level.

The amount of moisture in the air may be specified in several ways. *Absolute humidity* is the actual weight of water vapor per unit volume of air; it is usually expressed as a certain number of grains per cubic foot or grams per cubic meter. *Specific humidity* is the actual weight of water vapor per unit weight of air. This might be expressed as grams of water vapor per kilogram of air. Specific humidity is used more in reference to the upper atmosphere. Probably the most familiar term to the general reader is *relative humidity*. This is the ratio of the actual amount of water vapor in the air to the amount of water vapor the air can contain at a given temperature. A relative humidity of 80 per cent means that the air at its present temperature contains 80 per cent as much water vapor as it is capable of holding. Generally, some form of precipitation occurs when the relative humidity reaches close to 100 per cent, but air can become slightly supersaturated. This normally happens only when the air is still and there are very few dust particles to serve as nuclei for condensation.

It follows that if the amount of moisture in the air is a function of temperature, then, provided there is water vapor present, it will begin to condense out of the air if the temperature is lowered sufficiently. The temperature to which a given mass of air must be lowered in order to start condensation is called the *dew point*. If this temperature is below freezing, then the first moisture to condense will become ice or frost.

Dew

THE PROCESS RESPONSIBLE for the formation of dew is the same that causes droplets of water to form on the outside of a glass filled with ice or on surfaces of a refrigerator. Whenever the temperature of an object is at or below the dew point of air surrounding it, moisture begins to condense on the object. What we generally call dew is the moisture that forms on grass and leaves. They become cooler than the surrounding air because they radiate their heat; air immediately above the ground within a few inches is cooled by conduction, and consequently the temperature at the surface may be reduced to the dew point. This is likely to happen only if the air is quiet. Wind would disrupt cooling of the air near the ground and probably prevent it from becoming cool enough.

Frost

IF THE DEW POINT is below freezing, then frost forms instead of dew. Frost is actually a mass of tiny ice crystals. Like dew, frost forms only under relatively stable air conditions. Cool air, being more dense than warm air, sinks. It tends to move down the sides of a valley and to accumulate in the bottom. Thus frost may form even when the temperature of the air in general is well above freezing. Most people have noticed frost on the inside of windows in a house in winter. This may happen even when room temperature is in the sixties. Because of the tendency of cool air to move downward, orchards are often successful on the valley sides but not on the valley floor. The term "killing frost" is applied if the frost is heavy enough to destroy crops.

Condensation in the Air

BOTH DEW AND FROST are forms of condensation that occur on the surface of plants or inanimate objects. They do not form in the air and "fall" onto the ground, as does precipitation. What form precipitation takes depends on the amount of moisture in the air, the amount of movement and turbulence, and particularly the temperature and its rate of change. Condensation in the free air requires some type of nucleus about which the water may condense. These nuclei may be dust particles blown into the air from the ground or from volcanoes, but the most effective types of nuclei for condensation are those substances which absorb moisture, called *hygroscopic materials*, such as smoke and salt spray. In tests over wide areas there appear to be sufficient nuclei of condensation present almost all of the time for condensation to occur if the relative humidity is close to 100 per cent.

FIG. 5–3. / *Advection fog seen from above on Mt. Wilson, California. Cirrostratus clouds are above. (U.S. Weather Bureau.)*

FIG. 5–4. / *Hailstones that fell at Stegal, Nebraska, July, 1958. They had been carried thirty miles by automobile before the picture was taken. (U.S. Weather Bureau.)*

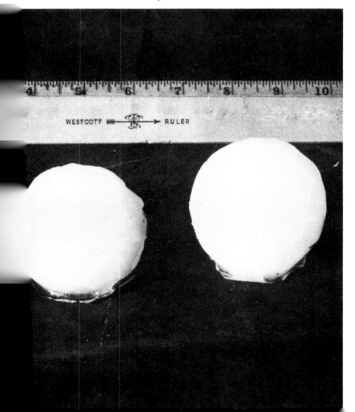

Fog–Haze

FOG IS COMPOSED OF microscopically small drops of water (in the range of .1–.01 mm.). There are several classifications of fog. If the drops are small enough and dispersed enough so that objects within about a half mile or more are visible, the fog is known as *haze*. If smoke and fumes are mixed with a fog, it is called *smog*. If the drops are large enough to fall, it is called a *mist*, or a *drizzle*. The conditions under which these types of fog form are so similar that they will be treated together. Fog is usually classified according to its density and effect on visibility.

Light fog—objects visible at ⅝ mile
Moderate fog—objects visible between ⁵⁄₁₆–⅝ mile
Heavy fog—objects visible between ⅕–⁵⁄₁₆ mile
Dense fog—objects visible less than ⅕ mile

Fog may form under the same conditions which cause dew or frost. The main difference is in the greater thickness of the layer of air that is cooled when fog forms. *Ground fog* is most likely to form when there is a very slight turbulence that mixes and cools a zone of air from several feet to over a hundred feet thick. This turbulence is due to cooling at night and the consequent temperature inversion.

Temperature inversion, such as that responsible for ground fogs, may take place at high altitudes, especially in the winter, when cold air may lie close to the ground below warmer air. This temperature inversion may occur at elevations from a few hundred to several thousand feet. The fog that forms is actually a low cloud, which may build down from the inversion toward the surface of the ground. Such fogs are common in Europe when Arctic air moves into the continent and stagnates there. Fog over industrial areas can be particularly dangerous, since it can become mixed with smoke containing toxic fumes.

Fogs may also form when warm moist air moves in over cold surfaces such as ice, snow, or cold water. These fogs are apt to become very thick if the air is moving and the surface is so cold that great quantities of the warm, moist air

FIG. 5–5. / *Ice on wires resulting from an ice storm. (Photo by W. J. Larcey, courtesy of U.S. Weather Bureau.)*

FIG. 5–6. / *Snowflakes, showing the hexagonal crystal patterns. (U.S. Weather Bureau.)*

may be cooled below the dew point. Such fogs are called *advection fogs* (Fig. 5–3). These are common in the North Atlantic Ocean near the Gulf Stream, where warm, moist air from over the Gulf Stream is moved over cold water on either side.

Evaporation fogs can form when a cool layer of air becomes saturated as a result of evaporation from warmer water. This might happen when warm rain falls through a cool layer of air or when a layer of cold air moves over a warm body of water. This type of fog is most common when one mass of air moves over or under another of a different temperature.

Precipitation

PRECIPITATION OCCURS in a wide variety of forms, from rain, mist, and drizzle to snow, hail, and sleet. While mist and drizzle are simply very light forms of rain, hail has quite different properties. *Rain* consists simply of drops of water that condense on nuclei of smoke, dust, or other matter suspended in the air. *Hail* is composed of nodular-shaped masses of ice that are built up in successive concentric layers and may become as large as a baseball (Fig. 5–4). *Snow* forms when condensation occurs in air that is below the freezing temperature, usually 20° F. or less. Snow takes the form of flakes which are individual crystals of ice having a hexagonal crystal pattern (Fig. 5–6). *Sleet* is the name applied when rain freezes while it falls, forming small particles. The term is also applied to *freezing rain* and mixtures of rain and snow. When conditions permit freezing rain to fall, ice storms are likely to ensue. Glazes up to several inches thick may then form, causing tremendous damage (Fig. 5–5).

As is the case with dew, frost, and fog, precipitation may occur whenever a mass of air is cooled until it becomes saturated. Conditions which make this possible are:

1. *convection*
2. *orographic uplift*—movement of an air mass over a mountain
3. *overriding*—movement of a warm air mass over a cold air mass

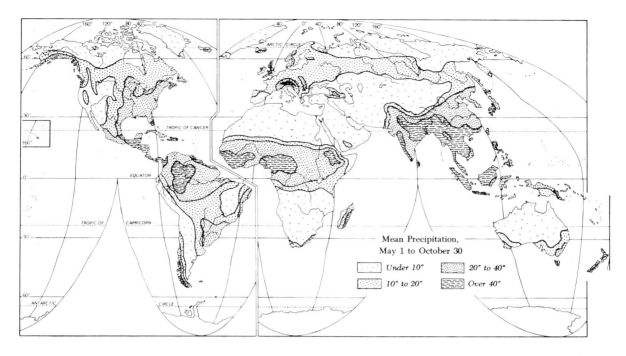

FIG. 5–7. / *Top: World distribution of precipitation in summer. The heaviest precipitation is received in the tropical and subtropical areas largely north of the equator. (Drawing by Donald T. Pitcher. From Miller and Langdon,* Exploring Earth Environments, *used with the kind permission of the authors.)*

FIG. 5–7. / *Bottom: World distribution of precipitation in winter. The heaviest precipitation is received in the tropical areas south of the equator. Note the relatively low precipitation in northern Africa, Asia, and interior North America. (Drawing by Donald T. Pitcher. From Miller and Langdon,* Exploring Earth Environments, *used with the kind permission of the authors.)*

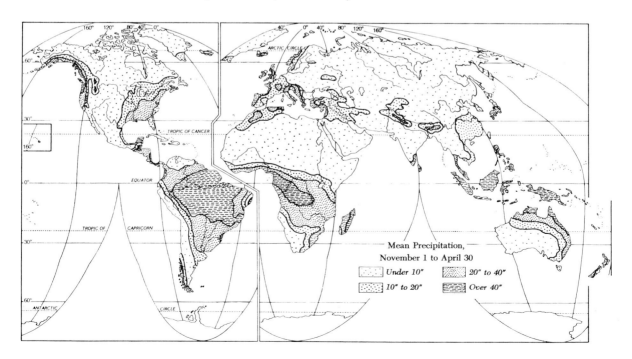

4. *invasion*—movement of a cold air mass in under a warm air mass
5. *cyclonic activity*—convergence of winds and overlap
6. mixing of two masses of air of different temperature

The amount of precipitation received in various parts of the world has a great range. Fig. 5–7 shows the average distribution of rainfall over the surface of the earth in winter and in summer. What this map does not show is how much of that precipitation may come down at one time. Some of the records for precipitation are 46 inches in one day, recorded at Baguio in the Philippine Islands, and 131 inches in one week, 366 inches in one month, and 1,041 inches in one year, all recorded at Cherrapunji, India. The U.S. Weather Bureau measures the amount of rainfall on the basis of the depth of water in a cylinder 8 inches in diameter. The Weather Bureau has found that the amount of snow or sleet necessary to make one inch of rain ranges from about 6 to 18 inches.

Clouds

ALTHOUGH CLOUDS occur in great variety, they may be classified rather simply in terms of several basic types. These types are called *cirrus* (curl), *cumulus* (heap), and *stratus* (layer). Mixtures of two of these are called by both names, such as cirro-cumulus or cirro-stratus (Fig. 5–8). The prefix *alto* may be added to indicate an intermediate altitude for cloud types that are normally at a lower elevation. The name *nimbus* is also used in connection with cumulus (cumulo-nimbus) and stratus (nimbo-stratus) to indicate that the cloud has considerable precipitation associated with it. Photographs of a number of cloud types are shown in Fig. 5–8.

Cirrus clouds have a distinct feathery form. They are normally the highest clouds, ranging from 20,000 to 40,000 feet. All cirrus clouds are composed of ice crystals. Precipitation is not associated with them, but high cirrus clouds, particularly in the middle latitudes, may

FIG. 5–8. / *Various clouds.* (U.S. Weather Bureau, see Weather Bureau publications for complete list of cloud-types.)

a. Cirrus unicinus

b. Altocumulus floccus

c. Altocumulus lenticularis

f. Altocumulus opacus

d. Clouds along a mild cold front

e. Stratocumulus

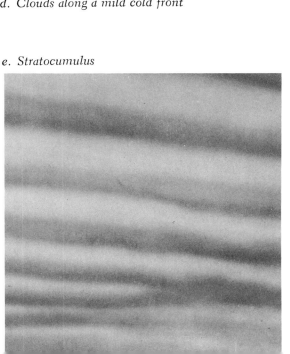

g. Altocumulus translucidus

h. Cumulus congestus, a thunderstorm cell in its
   early cumulus stage.

i. Altocumulus cumulonimbogenitus

precede the arrival of a storm—sometimes by one or more days.

Cumulus clouds occur at all altitudes and are noted for their woolly appearance. They have a flat base which marks the elevation at which the dew point is reached. Convective conditions promote their growth. Thunderstorms, which are associated with cumulo-nimbus clouds, may have vertical development from very low to exceedingly high altitudes. Altocumulus clouds and the normal cumulus clouds generally denote fair weather. They occur on warm to hot days in summer when the air is moderately moist. Although they are not usually forerunners of major storms, they may develop into cumulo-nimbus clouds with great turbulence.

Stratus clouds are those with great lateral extent. They frequently cover the sky from horizon to horizon. Most of them are relatively low, and sometimes they are so close to the ground that they form fogs. They have a rather flat base marking the altitude of condensation, and quite frequently they give rise to heavy precipitation. When the bottoms of these clouds are scalloped they are called strato-cumulus.

j. Cumulo-nimbus. The top of this cloud is over 45,000 feet. (U.S. Air Force.)

6

Movement of Air

BEFORE TURNING TO THE GENERAL PATTERN OF planetary circulation it will be helpful to consider further some of the relations between temperature, pressure, and the movement of air. One such relationship has already been mentioned—convection of air as a result of differential heating of the surface of the ground. The warm air becomes less dense, rises, and is replaced at the ground by cooler air. Another way to look at the convection of air is to consider what happens to the pressure. As the heated air begins to rise, the atmospheric pressure is reduced at the ground surface, allowing cooler, denser air all around to press in under the warm, rising air. Pressure in a gas or fluid has no direction—it exerts an equal amount of force in all directions. Gas will expand to fill any container in which it is placed, and the pressure within it will be uniform in all directions. The atmosphere differs from this container in that its dimensions are so great that the force of gravitational attraction varies from its base near the surface up to its upper edge. Therefore the density and pressure in gases of the atmosphere vary with altitude. At any given altitude the pressure is the same on the average, other factors being equal. However, the other factors are not usually equal. Actually we find that the pressures at one place on the earth are likely to change from hour to hour, that pressure is not likely to be the same in adjacent areas, and finally that the average pressure changes from season to season. These pressure changes are due to the movement of air masses. Movement of the air is prompted by the rotation of the earth, and by differences in temperature which create differences in density and thus in pressure.

Variations in pressure may be described in terms of a *pressure gradient*, which means simply the rate of change of pressure with distance. When referring to a particular pressure gradient, we should clearly indicate which direction is intended, since distance may be vertical, horizontal, or in any other direction. Normally we consider only horizontal or vertical variations in pressure gradients because these two may be combined to give an accurate picture of the pressure in all directions. The simplest and most meaningful way to depict a horizontal pressure gradient is on a map. Lines connecting points of equal pressure, called *isobars*, are drawn on the map. The gradient may then be determined between any two points by dividing the difference in their respective pressures by the distance between them. Note particularly that this is a horizontal gradient, so that all pressure data must be taken at the same elevation. The distribution of a particular pressure is not represented by a line, but by a plane called an *isobaric surface*. This plane can be perfectly flat if the air is quiet and evenly stratified. More commonly it will be curved or bent.

Atmospheric pressure at a given place is the weight of the overlying atmosphere pressing down on that place. Thus, if there is an area of high pressure close to an area of low pressure, there will be a tendency for the high pressure air to move into the area of low pressure and bring about equilibrium. When this movement takes place in an essentially horizontal plane it is called *wind*. Examples of winds equalizing areas of different pressures are the well-known sea breeze and land breeze.

The *sea breeze* is the wind that usually blows from the sea toward land. During the day the land is warmed more than water. The warmed air rises and expands, forcing the isobaric surface over the land upward. Air flows from the upper part of the expanded air out toward the ocean. This flow causes pressure over the land to be reduced. The air layer close to the surface of the water then moves toward the lower pressure area immediately over the land, thus causing the sea breeze. This effect is normally confined to a layer of air no more than a thousand feet thick. At night the conditions are exactly reversed. The land cools more rapidly than the water, so the air over the land cools and becomes denser than the air over the water. The wind then blows from the land toward the ocean and is known as the *land breeze*.

Planetary Circulation

The general pattern of atmospheric circulation on the earth as a whole is of great importance in determining local climates and weather conditions; however, it is not the only determinant. Omitting local considerations, what factors are of importance in determining large-scale movements within the atmosphere? Certainly the difference in the amount of solar radiation reaching the earth at different latitudes and times of year must be significant in that this difference brings about unequal cooling of the blanket of air. Polar regions remain significantly cooler all year long, and if other factors were not important, this phenomenon alone would create a movement of air masses out of the polar regions toward the equatorial low pressure areas, where they would converge, become warmer, rise, and then move back toward the poles, where they would again become cool, sink to the surface, and retrace the cycle.

This simple pattern is interrupted and modified by the general distribution of land and water areas. Since the continents warm more than adjacent oceans in the summer, there are resulting movements of air similar to the sea and land breezes but on a much larger scale. It is just these movements—large-scale seasonal change in direction of winds between continents and adjacent oceans—that create *monsoons*. Monsoons are most prominent in southern Asia, equatorial Africa, and, to a lesser extent, in Australia. Along the eastern coast of North America a similar effect is seen, in the reversal of the direction of the prevailing winds, which are southern (from the Gulf of Mexico and the Atlantic) in summer and northern (from Canada) in winter.

It is perhaps needless to say that there are other complicating factors in the general atmospheric circulation. These include seasonal variations in the amount of solar radiation received at any latitude, presence of great mountain masses interrupting circulation in the lower layers, existence of large-scale ocean currents causing temperature and moisture variations in air over various parts of the ocean, and the deflective effect of the earth's rotation, known as the Coriolis effect. This last factor is of particular importance because it influences the movements of all air masses throughout the earth's atmosphere.

FIG. 6–1. / *Aerial view of cumulus clouds. (U.S. Weather Bureau.)*

Coriolis Effect

THE CORIOLIS EFFECT is the deflection of objects moving on the earth independent of its surface. There is a certain amount of frictional drag between the earth and the atmosphere, so that air is not completely independent of the earth's surface, but the frictional drag is small enough so that the deflection becomes important in atmospheric circulation. One of the easiest ways to visualize the Coriolis effect is to imagine a set of four cannons, one at each pole pointing toward the equator, and two at the equator pointing toward the opposite poles. Because of the rotation of the earth, shells that are loaded in guns at the equator are moving in an easterly direction at the rate of movement of all objects on the earth at the equator. Shells in the guns at the poles are not moving except to turn around once each day. Let us then assume that all of the guns are fired at once. The four shells start out in north and south paths along lines of longitude. The shell fired from the gun at the north pole travels south, but while it is in the air the earth continues to rotate from west to east beneath the path of the shell, so that it lands on a longitude line that is west, or to the right, of the line along which it was fired. The shell that was fired north from the equator moves in response to both the muzzle velocity and the eastward movement of the gun. The shell is deflected increasingly to the east as it travels north, because it is moving into latitudes where the velocity of the earth's surface is progressively decreasing. Thus both shells followed paths of deflection to the right. The same reasoning will show that deflections in the Southern Hemisphere are always to the left.

To apply the Coriolis effect to the movement of air, assume that you stand with your back to the wind in the Northern Hemisphere. The wind will be deflected to your right. This effect does not alter the velocity of the wind— only its direction. The Coriolis effect must be considered in the light of the other determining factors in circulation. If pressure differences alone determined the direction of movement, then the direction of the wind would be perpendicular to lines of equal pressure, the isobars. But just as soon as the air is set in motion, it is deflected by the earth's rotation into a curved path. As soon as it begins to follow a curved path another effect becomes active. This third factor is centrifugal force. Its effect is observed when an object is whirled on the end of a string, and when drops of water are thrown off by a turning wheel. Centrifugal force tends to move the object out away from the center of revolution. To understand how these factors combine, assume there is a high pressure area. The air movement will tend to be directed out away from the center. In the Northern Hemisphere the movement of the air will be deflected to the right, and winds will move in an arc or circle clockwise around the "high." In the case of a low pressure area, the air will be pushed in toward the center of the "low" by the adjacent highs, but as soon as the air starts moving it will be deflected to the right and thus will follow a counterclockwise direction around the "low" (Fig. 6–2).

General Pattern of Circulation on Earth

CONVECTION CELL MODEL. Patterns of temperature and pressure distribution as observed over the earth are shown in Figs. 6–4 and 6–5. These patterns of pressure distribution and prevailing winds have long been explained in terms of a convection cell model such as that shown in Fig. 6–3. This model has served as a relatively satisfactory explanation of the observations. Planetary circulation is explained according to this model as follows:

Along the equator there is a prominent and persistent belt of low pressure known as the *doldrums*. Winds in this belt are light to calm. Year-round heating of the earth's surface is greatest in this belt. Cooler and denser air moves toward the equatorial belt from both north and south. Consequently, the doldrums are characterized by convergence and uplift of air masses. The winds that flow toward the equator from both sides of the doldrums are deflected by the

Coriolis effect and blow from the northeast and southeast. The *trade wind belts,* in which the prevailing winds blow from east to west, are located here. They start at about 25° latitude north and south. They arise at these latitudes rather than farther north and south apparently because of the nature of the movement of the air that rises in the doldrums. This air flows, at high altitudes, north in the Northern Hemisphere and south in the Southern Hemisphere. Like all moving air masses, these are deflected. By the time the high air currents reach 25°–30° latitude they have been directed east instead of north or south; consequently air accumulates at those latitudes and builds up high pressure cells. These high pressure belts at 30°–35° north and south are known as the *horse latitudes* or subtropical high pressure belts. Here air from high altitudes sinks to the surface and builds up pressure. In the horse latitudes wind is variable to calm, but the building up of pressure causes movements of air out of this belt, both northward and southward. The movements toward the equator are called the *trade winds,* and the movements toward the poles in either hemisphere are called the *westerly wind belts.* The direction of these winds is also governed by the Coriolis effect. In the Northern Hemisphere the northward-moving air from the horse latitudes is deflected to the east, giving rise to westerly winds. In the Southern Hemisphere the deflection is to the east also. These movements are directed generally toward the subpolar low pressure belts. A low pressure belt is well defined in the Southern Hemisphere between latitudes 60°–70°, where the belts form over water. In the Northern Hemisphere there are several large continental land masses at this latitude and pressure tends to build up over these, but a low pressure cell is found over the North Atlantic in this lattitude. Both poles are areas of high pressure, and cold air masses moving out of these along the earth's surface are important determinants of weather.

Flaws in this convection theory are now being found as a result of recent studies of the upper atmospheric circulation; however, no entirely satisfactory alternative has yet been ad-

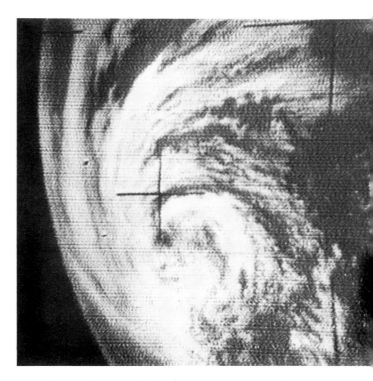

FIG. 6–2. / *Counterclockwise movement around a low. This is a view of hurricane Liza as seen by Tiros III, July 19, 1961. (U.S. Weather Bureau.)*

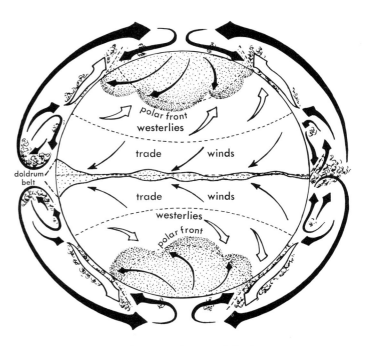

FIG. 6–3. / *Classical convection model of atmosphere circulation.*

FIG. 6–4. / *Pressure distribution in January.* (U.S. Weather Bureau.)

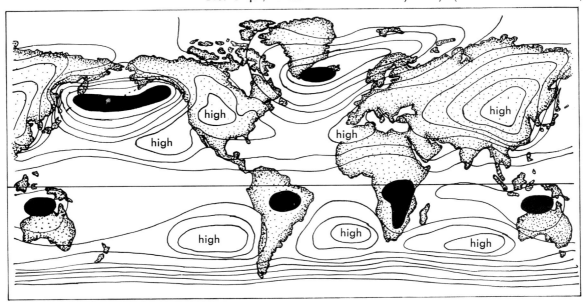

FIG. 6–5. / *Average January temperature.* (U.S. Dept. of Agriculture.)

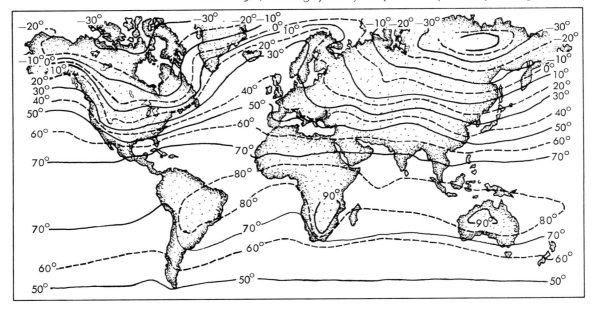

vanced to replace the convection model. Wind directions and magnitudes in the upper atmosphere are not exactly those predicted in the convection model.

Many meteorologists favor an explanation of planetary circulation known as the *eddy theory*. These eddys are large cyclonic and anticyclonic whirls of the middle latitudes and waves in the westerlies of the upper part of the troposphere.

It is postulated that the eddys form as follows: differential heating of poles and equator initiates a large scale convection, but the rotation of the earth prevents poleward movement of the hot equatorial air. As a result, a high temperature gradient is created in the low latitudes. It has been established both theoretically and experimentally that a uniformly rotating fluid will become unstable at some critical temperature with the result that wave patterns form in the original flow pattern. Thus these waves superimposed on convectional patterns due to differential heating may provide a highly satisfactory explanation.

Movement of Air at High Altitudes

WE HAVE ALREADY CONSIDERED transfer of air at a high altitude from the equatorial belt toward the poles. At these altitudes (between one and two miles) the pressure distribution is much simpler than near the surface. High pressure dominates in high altitudes over subtropical latitudes because of the upward movement of air. In polar regions, low pressure prevails, because of the cold temperature and consequent sinking of air. Thus the picture of air movement at high altitudes is very simple: from the equator up, then toward the poles, and down.

Jet Stream

NEAR THE UPPER CONTACT of the tropopause there is a narrow belt of high-speed wind known as the *jet stream*. This current was not well known until the Second World War, when bombers encountered, at certain latitudes, extremely high winds at altitudes of 30,000 feet. Since then these winds have been studied in detail. So far we know that they vary in altitude, position, and speed, and with the seasons; they are known in both hemispheres and can be considered in each hemisphere as forming one overall stream. Wind velocities of as much as 400 miles per hour are known in the streams. Their altitude varies from a low of 20,000 feet to slightly above the tropopause at 60,000 feet. The exact mode of origin of the jet streams is still somewhat uncertain; however, they do appear to be associated with the contact of dry, cold air from the poles with warmer, humid air of the tropics. It is well established that the jet streams and the eddy currents associated with them are important influences on surface weather such as cold waves, blizzards, and other cyclonic phenomena.

Movements of Air Masses—Fronts

MANY METEOROLOGICAL PHENOMENA are associated with the movement of masses of air. Cold fronts, warm fronts, and the storms and clear weather associated with them are topics of everyday conversation. They are of great importance to agriculture, commerce, and all types of transportation.

The *air masses* to which we refer are very large bodies of air that are fairly homogeneous horizontally with respect to temperature and moisture content. Such masses of air are most likely to develop over large expanses of either land or water, where they can gradually assume fairly uniform temperature and moisture conditions. One of the most prominent source areas for cold air masses is northern Canada and the Arctic Ocean. Warm air masses develop over the Gulf of Mexico, the Caribbean Sea, and in the eastern Pacific. It is common practice to describe air masses by names based on the approximate latitude of origin, such as Arctic, polar, tropical, and equatorial air masses. The first two are similar, as are the latter two. Air masses may also be described as continental or maritime and warm or cold. Because of the higher density of cold air, cold air masses are high pressure cells, warm air masses are low pressure cells. Once an air mass has developed it moves in the general pattern of atmospheric circulation. The advancing margin of such a moving mass is called a *front*. Fronts are active because they are the lines of contact of air masses with different properties and different directions of motion (Fig. 6–8).

Along a *cold front* cold air moves in over warmer ground. Along a *warm front* warmer air moves in. We have seen in the discussion of general circulation that cold air masses move toward the equator from both poles and are deflected to produce easterly winds. Westerly winds bring warm subtropical air masses into high latitudes, where they come in contact with the polar air masses moving in the opposite direction. Where these two different masses of air traveling in essentially opposite directions come in contact, a drag arises along the fronts where

FIG. 6–6. / A map of the Northern Hemisphere with cloud pictures taken by Tiros I superimposed on a conventional analysis showing the contours of the 500-mb pressure surface. The map gives an approximate idea of the air flow at about 3 miles above sea level and shows numerous waves in the westerly wind belt. (Courtesy of the U.S. Weather Bureau.)

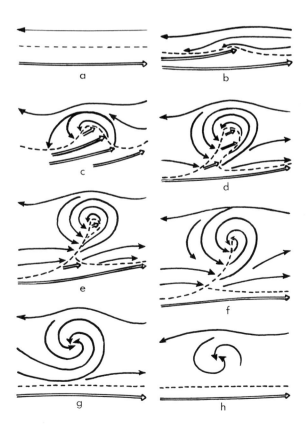

their opposing motions slow them down. Vilhelm Bjerknes, a Norwegian meteorologist, has presented one of the probable explanations of what happens along these fronts (Fig. 6–7). The Bjerknes explanation is illustrated in Fig. 6–9, which shows a sequence in the development of activity along a front. As a result of the drag between the two air masses, a broad undulation, or "wave," occurs in the front. Warm air gradually pushes farther into the cold air in a counterclockwise direction, riding up over the cold, more dense air. As the embayment of warm air increases in size, cold air begins to move in behind and under the warm air until all of the warm air is forced up, producing an *occluded front*. (An occluded front is one in which warm air is present, but only at a distance above the ground, which is then covered with cold air.) The movements in the cycle create a counterclockwise air flow—essentially a large eddy current.

The following definition of the term "cyclone" is taken from the *Weather Glossary of the United States Weather Bureau*, 1946:

A circular or nearly circular area of low atmospheric pressure around which the winds blow counterclockwise in the northern hemisphere and clockwise in the southern.

The word "cyclone" was first used in 1855 by Henry Piddington as the generic term for all circular or highly curved wind systems, but it has since undergone modifications in two directions. In the first sense, the term tropical cyclone is used to designate the relatively small, very violent storm of tropical origin known as a hurricane and a typhoon. . . . In the second usage of the word, an extratropical cyclone, also called a low or a depression, is the name given to a low-pressure system of much greater size and (usually) less violence, frequent in middle latitudes. Unlike the tropical cyclone . . . , it may cause precipitation and cloudiness over many thousands of square miles.

FIG. 6–7. / In the above diagram the sequence, a, b, c, d, etc., shows the formation of a wave disturbance (a and b) on the boundary between a cold and warm current; development of a cyclone (c and d); occlusion (e and f); and dissipation (g and h). (U.S. Weather Bureau.)

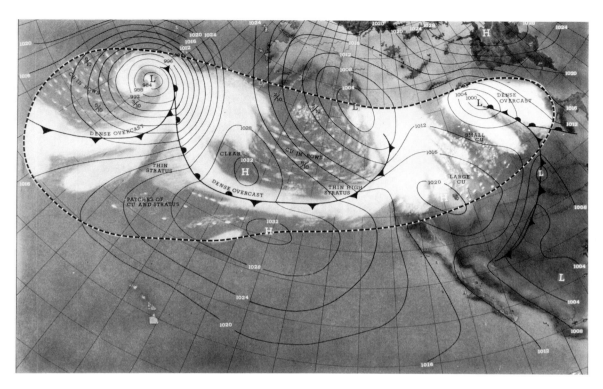

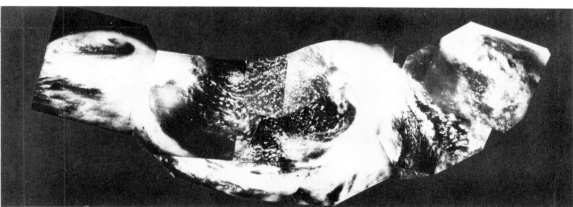

FIG. 6–8. / *The top illustration presents the cloud pattern associated with the fronts and pressure systems extending over North America and the northern Pacific, May 20, 1960. At the bottom is the mosaic of Tiros photographs of the area that served as a model for the above illustration. (Courtesy of the Weather Bureau.)*

The structure and weather associated with a frontal cyclone are depicted in Fig. 6–10. Inhabitants of North America are familiar with the movement of one front after another across the continent through the winter months, as polar air masses move out of the Arctic region and encounter warmer air from the south and east.

In cyclones such as the one described in Fig. 6–8, both a warm front and a cold front are present. The two are quite different. Along the advancing cold front, cold air, being more dense, moves under the warmer air, but frictional drag at the ground may retard the front at the ground level so that a tongue-like mass of cold air projects into the warm front not

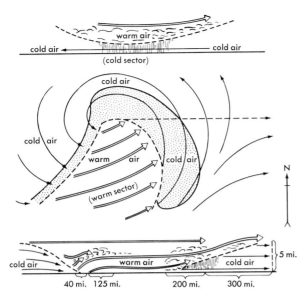

FIG. 6–9. / Idealized extratropical cyclone formed by the process illustrated in Fig. 6–7 with vertical east-west cross sections through the northern part (above) and southern part (below). (After Bjerknes.)

FIG. 6–10. / Types of occlusions. If the cold air in the rear is colder than the cold air in advance, the cold front will push under the air ahead of the front. This is called a "cold front type occlusion," top, and is accompanied by precipitation near and behind the surface front. If the cold air in the rear is not as cold as the air being overtaken, it will slide upward over the cold air in front. This condition is called a "warm front-type occlusion," middle, and generally produces precipitation in advance of the surface front. If there is little or no difference in temperature between the two cold air masses a "neutral-type occlusion," bottom, results. In this case precipitation occurs along the front and the low pressure system dissolves. (U.S. Weather Bureau.)

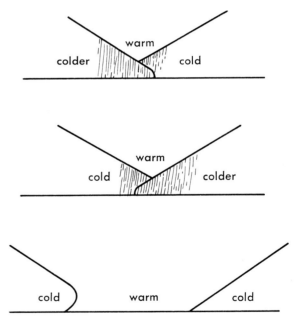

far above the ground, even for a distance of as much as a hundred miles or more. Near the ground the cold front appears steep, often marked by cumulo-nimbus clouds, which bring lightning storms, heavy rain or snow, hail, and occasionally tornadoes. Along the warm front, warm air rides up over the colder air at a low angle. A warm front is normally wider than a cold front. Fogs, light rain, or ice storms are likely.

Because cyclones can form in the absence of polar fronts, there must be other ways besides the wave theory of Bjerknes by which they may be generated. The jet stream seems a most logical source. A great deal of cyclonic activity is found along the margin of the jet stream, particularly on the side toward the equator. Cyclones are likely to form whenever the jet stream lies above a frontal zone.

Special Types of Storms and Winds

A NUMBER OF PARTICULARLY VIOLENT OR at least prominent weather conditions arise in association with fronts. These include thunderstorms, tornadoes, ice storms, blizzards, "nor'-easters," hurricanes, and typhoons. There are, in addition, a large number of very special winds. Details about them can be found in the selected references at the end of this book.

Thunderstorms

THESE ARE AMONG the most common types of storms in the United States. The thunder from which the storm takes its name is incidental to it, but not always its most prominent feature. A cumulo-nimbus cloud formation is characteristic of a thunderstorm, along with thunder, lightning, rain or hail, and strong winds of short duration (Fig. 6–11). The path of a local storm is likely to be only a few miles wide and extending with time perhaps over a path a few tens of miles in length.

A thunderstorm develops through convective processes. In the early stage there may be only one main updraft, caused by excessive heating of the air near the surface and consequent expansion and upward movement. In this up-draft cumulus clouds develop. As surface air is raised it is cooled at the dry adiabatic rate, until at the dew point condensation begins, a cumulus cloud forms, and rain starts to fall. The air continues to rise but cooling now proceeds at the wet adiabatic rate. At this stage downdrafts form in the cloud. These result from drag of the falling rain. They start to form near the base of the cloud formation and to build upward. The original single cell is modified through the addition of more convective cells. In the mature stage the cumulonimbus cloud is composed of many closely adjacent updrafts and downdrafts. These clouds may extend to heights of many thousands of feet, and some are even known to have exceeded 60,000 feet. The storm begins to die down only when the updrafts bringing moist air are cut off by the downdrafts. At this stage rain begins to fall off, the cloud begins to disperse and evaporate, and the storm is over. Thunderstorms of this sort may occur as rather isolated clouds or all along a front where warm air is lifted over colder masses.

Hail is most commonly developed in con-

FIG. 6–11. / *Thundercloud, or cumulonimbus. (U.S. Weather Bureau.)*

nection with thunderstorms. According to one of the most popular theories of hail formation, snow flakes or clumps of coalesced snow form above the freezing zone in the cloud. They fall through a layer in the cloud that contains supercooled water droplets. When the snow comes in contact with the water it immediately freezes to it, and a pellet of ice and snow forms. If this pellet is then caught in one of the strong updrafts, it is elevated back through the supercooled layer where another ice layer is added. This process may be continued time and time again until the ball is too heavy to be carried back up. Hail may also grow through the formation of small pellets which then fall low enough to be covered with a layer of rain and then are uplifted until the layer freezes.

FIG. 6–12a. / *Tornado, Peshawar, India, 1933.* (*U.S. Weather Bureau.*)

Tornadoes

THERE IS STILL some debate about the causes of tornadoes, but the effects and conditions under which they form are well-known. They occur along cold fronts where differences in air temperature between warm air before the front and cold air behind it are great. Tornadoes have the shape of extended cones (Figs. 6–12a and 6–12b). Within this cone air moves in a spiraling, counterclockwise direction and rises very rapidly, sometimes carrying heavy objects hundreds of feet upward. Within the cone pressure drops very low. This accounts for the explosive effect when a tornado passes over a closed house —the walls are blown out because the pressure within the house suddenly becomes drastically high in comparison with the pressure outside. Winds around the center may reach velocities of several hundred miles per hour. These features combine to make the tornado, or "twister," particularly dangerous to life and property. Fortunately, tornadoes are not more than a quarter of a mile in diameter and they rarely touch the ground for distances of more than twenty miles. The average tornado lasts only a few minutes, very rarely more than ten. When tornadoes occur over water they are called *waterspouts.*

It is obvious that the tornado is set in

FIG. 6–12b. / *A tornado at Hartner, Kansas, June, 1929.* (*U.S. Weather Bureau.*)

motion by a rapid rise of warm and humid air along a cold front, but what causes this rise is not completely known. Some observers have pointed out that the rate at which the temperature of the rising air drops is very low because the air is moist. With these low rates of cooling, air may rise to very great heights before a stable condition is reached. This prolonged updraft could cause the tornado. Other observers suggest that tornadoes may result when a break occurs through the tonguelike overhang of the cold front, allowing a violent updraft with resulting spiraling motion. In the United States, tornadoes are most common in the central states, where warm, moist air moving northeast from the Gulf and Caribbean meet cold fronts moving south out of the north.

Tropical Cyclones

TROPICAL CYCLONES are called hurricanes, baguios, typhoons, or simply cyclones. All of them arise under similar conditions in low pressure areas in the tropics. When a low pressure center forms and begins to move, it follows a westward path in the direction of the prevailing winds. The typical cyclone is a vast (300–600 miles in diameter), symmetrical, rotating storm (Fig. 6–14). Around the center, winds blow in a counterclockwise direction in the Northern Hemisphere, clockwise in the Southern Hemisphere, commonly reaching velocities of 200 miles per hour. The center is a calm central core ten or more miles in diameter. Pressure in the core, or eye, is exceptionally low (often less than 28 inches of mercury). As in tornadoes, there is an upward spiraling of air which may extend from the surface up to six or seven miles. Motion of air in cyclones is very similar to that of water in a tub with an outlet in the center; however, the storm as a whole moves, at a rate of 10–15 miles an hour. They tend to move westward with the winds until, in the latitudes of the westerlies, they start to move eastward. Unlike the frontal storms previously considered, cyclones are not associated with sharp changes in temperature. They tend to be very nearly circular, with temperature, clouds,

FIG. 6–13. / Houses overturned and smashed by a hurricane at Buzzards Bay, Mass. (U.S. Weather Bureau.)

FIG. 6–14. / Counterclockwise motion shown from view high above Typhoon Ida. (Courtesy of the U.S. Air Force.)

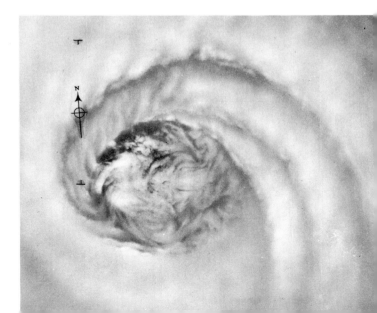

precipitation, and pressure symmetrically distributed. The steepness of the pressure gradients accounts for their high wind velocities.

Cyclones originate in a region of warm, moist air. In the doldrums, very light winds move from east to west. A wavelike front appears in these winds and from this wave a cyclone may develop. The exact causes of these waves are not well understood, but most cyclones do not appear to originate less than 5 degrees away from the equator (Figs. 6–17 and 6–18). It has been suggested that the Coriolis effect may be important in their formation. They do not tend to form over cool water such as the South Atlantic and eastern South Pacific. Warm, moist air tends to favor low pressure and convection. Once there is a drop in pressure, air starts moving in a circular path, and upward convection begins. Condensation of moisture in the convection updraft increases the speed of rotation.

Many meteorologists consider it likely that the jet stream plays an important role in the formation of cyclones. Waves of polar air moving at very high altitudes in the jet stream system do sometimes sweep down into the low latitudes. The movements of these waves in a northeasterly direction could produce a drag effect on the tropical air and set it in motion.

Most Atlantic tropical cyclones form in late summer and autumn. The paths most frequently followed are illustrated in Fig. 6–17. As a storm approaches the eastern coast of the United States, pressure begins to drop in the areas near its path. As the storm approaches pressure steadily drops. The lowest pressure recorded will mark the time at which the storm is closest. As the storm approaches, winds gradually in-

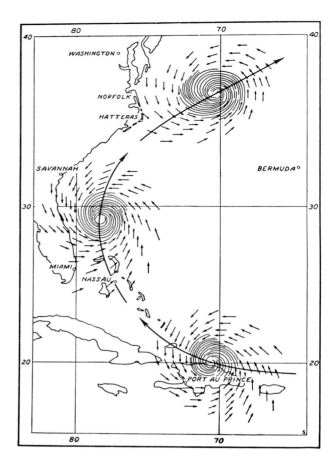

FIG. 6–15. / *Track and wind system of a hurricane. The winds are depicted here as they are directed, momentarily, about the center of a progressing cyclone. As experienced at the earth's surface, over which the cyclone passes, the winds are the resultants of progressive and cyclonic movements. (U.S. Weather Bureau.)*

FIG. 6–16. / *Tide record at Montauk, N.Y. during Hurricane Carol, August 27 to September 2, 1954.*

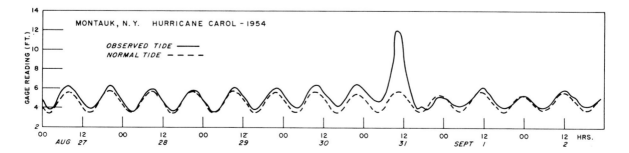

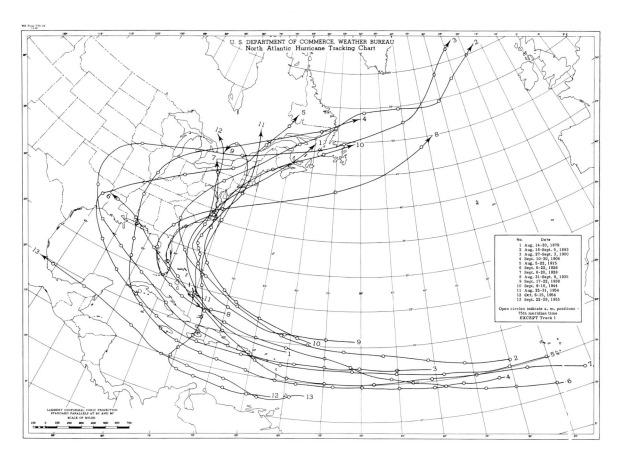

FIG. 6–17. / *Tracks of some devastating North Atlantic hurricanes. (U.S. Weather Bureau.)*

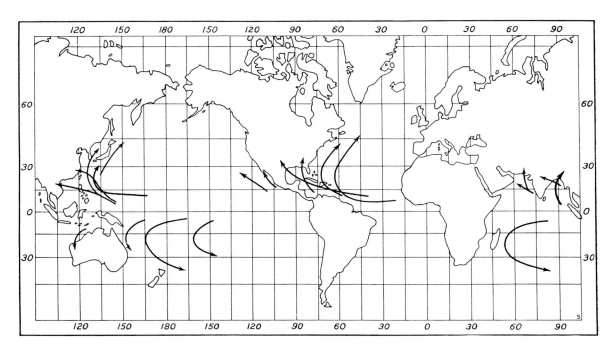

FIG. 6–18. / *Principal world regions of tropical cyclones. Arrows indicate general areas of occurrence and direction of motion. (U.S. Weather Bureau.)*

crease and come from a northeast direction. If the storm passes east of the observer, the wind direction will shift from the northeast to the north, then from north to northwest, and finally to west.

Optical Phenomena in the Atmosphere

REFRACTION OF SUNLIGHT IS RESPONSIBLE for a number of the most colorful atmospheric displays. Sunlight is white, but when it passes through a glass prism, it is bent and split into its component wavelengths, which correspond to different colors. Light is also refracted when it passes through layers of air of different densities. When change in density is very gradual, the bending of the light is too diffuse to produce a separation of light into its component colors, but the path of light is bent, making objects appear to be slightly displaced. This bending makes it possible to see the sun, moon, and stars when they are actually slightly below the horizon.

Light is bent down on entering more dense air. Thus light entering the upper atmosphere at an angle is bent in an increasingly curved line toward the surface. One result of this is to increase the time between sunrise and sunset. In the lower latitudes this increase amounts to only a few minutes per day, but toward the poles it makes the summer sun visible 24 hours per day, even when in actuality it is slightly below the horizon at night. This same bending accounts for the apparent flattening of the sun and moon when they are close to the horizon. Light from the lower margin of either body is refracted more than light from the top due to the slight difference in the angle at which light from the two areas enters the atmosphere.

Other phenomena caused by refraction are twinkling of stars, mirages, rainbows, and halos. The *twinkling* effect can be produced by slight movements of layers of air that have different densities. Similar movements can cause distant objects to be indistinct to an observer on the surface even when the air is clear of dust.

Mirages, which have the effect of making things appear to be where they are not, are always fascinating but can have tragic consequences. The condition favoring a mirage is a strong temperature contrast between adjacent layers of air (Fig. 6–19). Light passing through one layer is reflected from the other so strongly that images are also reflected. The mirage is called *"inferior"* when the image appears below the real object. This happens when a thin layer of hot air is overlain by cooler air. The image of clouds may be refracted so that they appear to be a pool or lake of water. Such images are commonly seen on paved roads and flat deserts in any part of the world. Objects seen in this way are inverted. Mirages also occur when cold air is overlain by warmer air. In this case the image appears above the actual object and is called a *"superior"* mirage. It is possible sometimes to see the object, an inverted image of it above the object, and even a second image, right side up, above the inverted image.

Rainbows are produced by refraction of light through drops of rain. On entering the drop, light is refracted and broken into various wavelengths which travel by different paths through the drop. Most of the wavelengths are refracted again as they pass out of the drop (Fig. 6–20), but some of the wavelengths will be reflected back through the drop and then refracted as they re-enter the air on the same side from which the light originally entered. In order to see the colors produced in this way, the observer must be located between the sun and the raindrops. If the sun is more than 42 degrees above the horizon no rainbow is possible, for reasons explained in Fig. 6–20. Two concentric rainbows are sometimes visible. These are formed by double reflection of light within raindrops before it is refracted back into the air.

Halos are often seen surrounding the sun and the moon. This effect is produced when rays of light pass through a thin, high cloud layer composed of ice crystals. Light is refracted and appears to form arcs or circles around the sun or moon. Rings with a radius of 22 or 46 degrees are most common.

Scattering of Light

THE ATMOSPHERE CONTAINS large quantities of extremely fine dust, smoke, and other particles. Many of these particles, as well as the molecules of gas in the atmosphere, have diameters which are less than the wavelengths of light passing through them. In this situation light may be selectively dispersed or scattered. It has been found that the atmosphere will scatter light of different wavelengths to correspondingly different degrees. Blue wavelengths are scattered almost 10 times as much as red wavelengths. For this reason, the sky appears blue when penetrated by sunlight nearly perpendicular to the earth's surface, but becomes red or yellow when the light travels through a greater thickness of atmosphere at sunrise and sunset. Increased amounts of dust and other light-scattering particles over deserts and industrial centers account for the spectacular red sunsets to be seen in those areas.

Diffraction is the bending of light around a corner. This occurs when light passes *particles* of a size similar to that of the wavelengths of the light. Diffraction accounts for the appearance of a diffuse light-colored aureole, called a *corona*, that may be seen encircling the sun and moon when sunlight or moonlight passes through a cloud of water drops. The effect is different from the refraction effect which produces halos. In refraction the light is broken up and each wavelength is reflected at an angle. In diffraction the light is not broken up and reflected, only bent gently in its path, each wavelength bending near particles of the required size.

Twilight is the combined effect of scattering, diffraction, and reflection of sunlight from the upper atmosphere. These effects may pro-

FIG. 6–19. / A *mirage in Death Valley.* (U.S. *Weather Bureau.*)

duce a lightening of the sky before dawn or after sunset for as much as one or two hours while the sun is actually below the horizon. Some light is visible even when the sun is about 18 degrees below the horizon, which marks the limit of *astronomical twilight.* There is generally not enough light for outside work if the sun is more than 6 degrees below the horizon, the limit of *civil twilight.* The amount of time required for the sun to move between 6 degrees or 18 degrees below the horizon and the horizon depends on the angle of the sun's path with the horizon, which varies with latitude and season.

FIG. 6–20. / *Refraction in a raindrop giving one and two rainbows. Light coming in as shown at the right is refracted, reflected inside the raindrop, and refracted back out to produce the primary rainbow. When light strikes the raindrop as shown at left there are two internal reflections. The emerging light is so directed that a secondary rainbow outside the primary one is formed.*

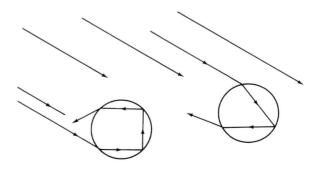

7 /

Climate

CLIMATE MAY BE THOUGHT OF AS THE SUM total of the weather at a particular place over a period of time. Such a definition immediately raises a number of difficult questions. The most difficult of these is: "How do we go about arriving at a total weather picture?" We might start by trying to summarize the various factors of which the weather is composed, such as temperature, pressure conditions, precipitation, and wind direction. But these alone do not determine the weather at a given location. A number of local weather phenomena are associated with mountains, with coasts, and with almost every other topographic setting. Continental phenomena differ from oceanic phenomena, and even within the oceans the different currents cause a variety of water temperatures and a consequent variety of weather characteristics. Once all of the variables have been enumerated, the question arises: "How should we consider them in their proper relation to one another?" In the case of temperature alone, one way of summarizing the relevant data is to take the average temperature of a given place over a period of time, yet two places with an identical average temperature may actually be very different. The temperature of one may have a very low range, staying near the average all year, whereas the temperature of the second may run to extremes, high and low, and only on rare occasions hover near the average. It would certainly be misleading to classify these two locations together. The large number of variables suggest the possibility of an extremely large variety of combinations, each of which may be considered a separate climate.

From this we can see why a number of different climate classification systems are in use. For most purposes it is useful to have a relatively simple system of classification. But before taking up any of these classifications, it will be most helpful to summarize some of the more important factors or elements which influence climate. The chief effects of each of these can be delineated if we assume, for the purpose, that some or all of the other variables are constant. A list of these factors should include at least the following:

Solar climate
Temperature
Pressure variations
Precipitation

In addition, the climates of specific locations are related to such factors as the position of the area in relation to large bodies of water and mountain barriers, elevation, prevalence of cyclonic storms, prevailing wind directions, and ocean currents.

Solar Climate

Solar climate is the climate that would result from the influences of solar radiation if the earth had no atmosphere. There is no doubt that solar radiation is the most important determinant of the earth's climates. The amount of energy received in this way is tremendous, in spite of the fact that the amount of heat indicated by the solar constant (1.9 calories/cm²/minute) is never actually obtained, because the solar constant is based on the assumption that the atmosphere is absent. It is also calculated on the basis of radiation perpendicular to the earth's surface, a condition possible only in the tropics. Variation in the angle of incidence of sunlight on the earth's surface is one of the most important factors influencing solar climate. This angle varies with the season, due to the inclination of the axis of the earth to the plane of the ecliptic, as was illustrated by Fig. 2–4. A second important climatic factor is the duration of sunlight, which allows a wide range of values for the total amount of solar radiation received at any given point. The duration of sunlight varies from zero to 24 hours per day, depending upon latitude and season. A third factor is variation in the distance of the earth from the sun due to the earth's elliptical path. This distance varies by about three million miles.

So far, we have disregarded the effects of the atmosphere in our consideration of solar radiation; however, the thickness of the atmosphere has an important bearing on insolation. The atmosphere is thickest at the equator, but because the sun's rays pass through the atmosphere at a high angle here, they pass through less atmosphere than those at higher latitudes that penetrate the atmosphere obliquely. The light rays are absorbed, scattered, diffracted, and become more diffused as they pass through increasingly greater thicknesses of air. All of these effects vary not only with latitude, but with the time of day as well, since the sun's angle with the horizon will strongly affect the amount of radiation striking the earth.

Temperature

Since solar radiation is the prime determinant of temperature distribution, we may expect that variations in mean annual temperatures reduced to sea level would be due primarily to differences in latitude (Fig. 7–1). But when this world picture is examined in detail, the importance of other factors in determining temperature becomes apparent. Chief among these are effects of oceans and ocean currents, and major differences in the continental as opposed to the oceanic influences. Continents have greater extremes of temperatures, while oceans are moderating influences. Certain ocean currents are particularly effective in influencing temperature over parts of the oceans and adjacent land. Warm waters of the Gulf Stream, for example, are responsible for the relatively warm temperatures in the waters of the North Atlantic, extending far up along the coast of Norway. Waters at the same latitude on the western side of the Atlantic average nearly 20 degrees lower.

Pressure and Wind

World distributions of pressure systems are given in Fig. 6–4. Again we find basic differences related to latitude and to oceans and continents, but the picture as a whole is very close to that which we might theoretically predict for a rotating body. There are low pressure belts at the equator, high pressure cells in the horse latitudes, subpolar low belts, and polar

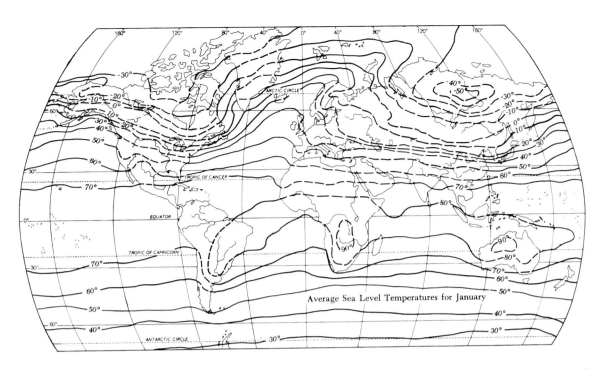

FIG. 7–1a. / *Average January temperatures of the world, reduced to sea level. The northern continental masses are much colder than the corresponding oceanic latitudes. The area with the coldest average January temperature lies near Verkhoyansk in northeastern Siberia. The warmest areas are in Africa and Australia. (Drawing by Donald T. Pitcher. From Miller and Langdon,* Exploring Earth Environments, *with the kind permission of the authors.)*

high pressure cells. Large-scale interruptions in this simple picture are due to differential heating of the lands and oceans. For this reason, the picture in the Southern Hemisphere, where the greater area of water dominates, is simpler than that in the Northern Hemisphere. Land areas tend toward high pressure in the winter and low pressure in the summer. This seasonal difference is an important determinant of the monsoon climate of southern Asia.

Precipitation

PRECIPITATION IS ANOTHER FREQUENTLY used criterion of climate classifications. Mean annual precipitation by itself can create a very misleading picture, because there are such great variations in the form, the frequency, and the variability of precipitation. Precipitation occurs only after the dew point is reached. Pressure and wind are the principal agents whereby air masses are moved into conditions in which the

dew point may be reached. The largest source of moisture is the ocean, and the proportion of this source that is lost through evaporation is determined by insolation, the temperature of the water, and the rate at which air masses are moved over it. Thus all of these factors in the production of precipitation are closely interrelated.

In the equatorial belt, temperatures are high and the air moves slowly over the oceans, taking up large amounts of moisture. Where this warm, moist air is blown onto land, there are large amounts of rainfall. If mountains are near the coast, very great quantities of rain will fall on their windward slopes.

The source of the trade winds is the dry air that settles into the horse latitudes from high altitudes. The trade winds tend to flow from cooler to warmer latitudes, thus little rain is usually associated with them. Consequently the world's largest desert areas, the Sahara, Arabian, Australian, and Kalahari, all fall within belts of trade wind circulation. The horse latitudes

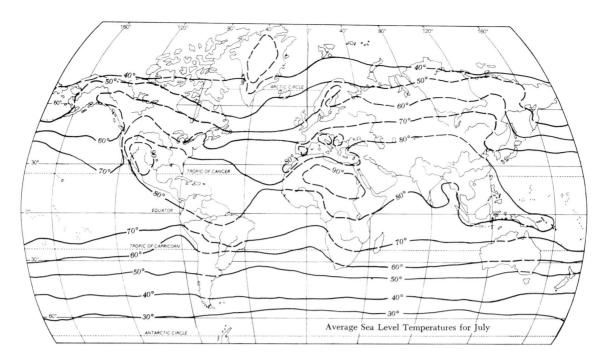

Average Sea Level Temperatures for July

FIG. 7–1b. / *Average July temperatures of the world, reduced to sea level. The warmest areas are found on the major land masses of the Northern Hemisphere. Notice the gradual decrease in temperature over the oceans in the Southern Hemisphere from the equator to the Antarctic continent. (Drawing by Donald T. Pitcher. From Miller and Langdon,* Exploring Earth Environments, *with the kind permission of the authors.)*

are dry because dry air here settles back to the surface. This air moves partly into the trade wind belt and partly into the belts of prevailing westerly winds. Though the air is dry as it settles, it picks up moisture from the ocean. That moving into cooler latitudes is more likely to reach the dew point than that moving toward warmer areas. This is borne out by observation, and in the belt of the prevailing westerlies, the west coasts of the continents are usually rainy, although if these coasts are mountainous the eastern slopes of their mountains are likely to be dry.

In the polar regions temperatures drop so low that only a small amount of moisture can be held in the air, and precipitation and evaporation are both low.

Köppen Classification of Climates

THE MOST WIDELY USED SYSTEM OF classification of climates is that devised by Wladimir Köppen in 1918 and later modified by Trewartha. This system is quantitative and may be applied with more objectivity than some other systems allow. The chief components of the Köppen system are temperature and precipitation, considered both on a monthly and on an annual basis. The system, like all others, has certain shortcomings; climatic areas which in actuality are quite different are sometimes classified together.

In the Köppen system a series of letter combinations denote a symbol for each climate. The first letter indicates one of the five major climates:

A: Tropical climates where mean temperature in the coldest month is above 64° F.
B: Dry climates where evaporation exceeds precipitation.
BW is the arid or desert climate.
BS is the semiarid or steppe climate.
C: Humid middle temperature climates where winters are mild, with no mean monthly

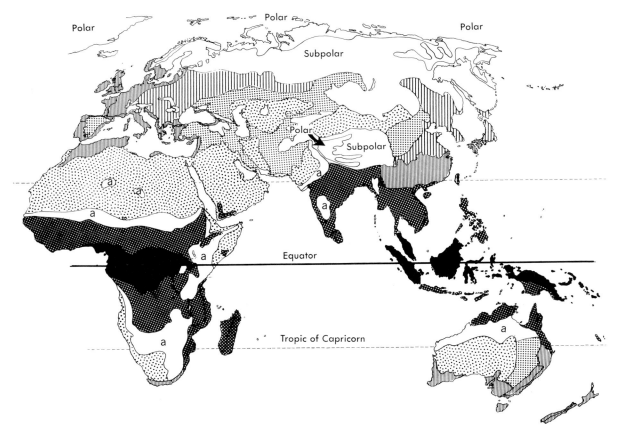

FIG. 7-2. / *Climatic regions of the world.* (*Modified after a map by Koeppe, courtesy of A. J. Nystrom Company.*)

temperatures below 27° F. and at least one month has average temperatures above 50° F.

D: Humid microthermal climates where winters are long and cold, but summers are long enough to permit some agriculture. Temperatures are similar to those in C, but the average temperature of the coldest month is below 27° F.

E: Polar climates where no monthly average is above 50° F.

The second letter in the Köppen formula goes one step further in providing details about the temperature:

a—warm summers, warmest month above 72° F.

b—cool summers, warmest month below 72° F.

c—short, cool summers, less than four months above 50° F.

d—long, cold winters, coldest month below 36° F.

A third letter is given to indicate the amount of precipitation:

f—no dry season
g—dry summers
w—dry winters
m—dry winters with monsoon rain in summers.

By using two or three of these letters a reasonably accurate impression of the climate can be given.

Koeppe Classification

ANOTHER USEFUL CLASSIFICATION AND ONE somewhat more simplified than the Köppen system is that devised by Dr. Clarence Koeppe (Fig. 7-2). It demonstrates a different approach to the problem of climate classification. The purpose of any classification is to provide a simple way of representing a complex body of

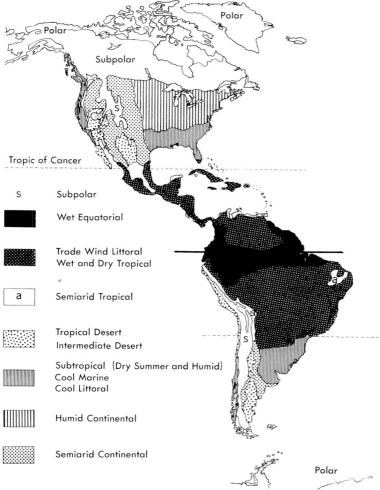

S — Subpolar

■ Wet Equatorial

▨ Trade Wind Littoral
Wet and Dry Tropical

a — Semiarid Tropical

Tropical Desert
Intermediate Desert

Subtropical (Dry Summer and Humid)
Cool Marine
Cool Littoral

Humid Continental

Semiarid Continental

data. Closely similar climates are grouped in such a way that they can be compared and contrasted with other groups. The Koeppe· system is a genetic classification; climates are grouped together when areas of similar geographic position have essentially the same climatic characteristics. The sixteen groups in this classification are briefly outlined below. See Fig. 7–2 for their locations.

WET EQUATORIAL CLIMATE: The general location of this climate is the low pressure doldrum belt, about 10 degrees of latitude in width. All of the months are warm and moist with temperature averages above 70° F. (with the exception, naturally, of the mountainous areas). The sun is always high in these latitudes, with the peaks of insolation at the equinoxes being matched by unusually wet periods. Rain is likely to occur almost every day and to accumulate to 60 inches or more per year. Thunderstorms are

common; ordinarily, however, the wind is calm to slight, except in times of tropical cyclones.

TRADE WIND LITTORAL CLIMATE: Climates of this type are located along the eastern coastal, or *littoral*, margins of continents in the trade wind belts. These regions are long from north to south and relatively narrow from east to west, their dimensions being determined by the basic north–south alignment of topographic features supplying the relief necessary to bring about rainfall through uplift of the air masses. In these belts trade winds blow steadily in autumn and winter. The mean annual temperatures are above 70° F., but they vary with latitude as well as altitude. There is normally more than 35 inches of rainfall distributed fairly evenly throughout the year, but the amount is highly variable (Hawaii sometimes has 200 inches). The maximum rainfall comes in autumn. Monsoons are found in these latitudes, and they may interrupt the trade winds, giving rise to a dry season and a wet season. Cyclones are common.

WET AND DRY TROPICAL CLIMATES: The wet and dry tropical climates are located on the poleward sides of the wet equatorial climate. Solar heating reaches a maximum twice a year, at times very close together, producing one long, warm period. Most of the rain is concentrated in the one period when the doldrum belt expands into the region. During the remainder of the year trade winds influence the weather and there is little rain. The location of these climates is also influenced by cold ocean currents that extend close to the equator along the west coasts of South America and Africa. Average annual temperature is above 70° F., except in regions influenced by the monsoons. Highest temperatures are reached just before the summer rains. Rainfall is highly variable, with at least 35 inches average and sometimes several hundred inches in the monsoon areas. Winters are always dry with little or no rainfall.

SEMIARID TROPICAL CLIMATE: On the poleward sides of the wet and dry tropical climates are the semi-arid tropical climates. Typically these are located in continental interiors, especially on plateaus, and are usually adjacent to deserts. In the summer the semi-arid tropical climate is on the outer edge of the doldrum belt, and in the winter it is influenced by the trade winds or the calm of the horse latitudes. Some areas are semiarid because of cold ocean currents or the rain-shadow effect of adjacent mountains. Temperatures average above 70° F. There is often a double period of high temperature, but rainfall is low—between 10 and 35 inches, most of which falls in the summer months.

TROPICAL DESERT CLIMATE: Most climates of this type are located in the horse latitude belts of high pressure, but some occupy continental interiors or leeward coasts in the trade wind belts. Annual temperature averages 70° F. or more, but the daily temperature range is great, with rapid radiation of heat at night. In the day temperatures may often reach 120° F. or more. Rainfall is very low, averaging less than 10 inches per year with a maximum in the winter, usually.

DRY SUMMER SUBTROPICAL CLIMATE: This climate is sometimes known as the Mediterranean type. It is characterized by average monthly temperatures above 45° F. in the coldest month and below 75° F. in the warmest. The range is between 10 and 40 degrees, varying from a low near the coasts to a high in the interior portions. Rainfall is normally under 35 inches per year, but its range is great, 10 to 90 inches, depending on the amount of relief and the position in relation to the coast. Summers are dry. The winter wet season is generally mild, but it may be accompanied by freezing temperatures when cold fronts move in. Tropical cyclones sometimes come into these regions, which are mostly in the horse latitudes where high pressure dominates summer weather.

HUMID SUBTROPICAL CLIMATE: Climates of this type are found on the eastern margins of continents in middle latitudes. High pressure over the oceans in summer promotes movement of air inland, as in the eastern section of the United States. Strong cyclonic storms in the winter, with a rapid succession of warm and cold fronts, are characteristic of this area of the United States, but not of another region with this climate, the eastern coast of China, which is dominated in the winter by cold Arctic air. The mean temperature in the coldest month is above 40° F., and the warmest month averages from above 70° to 80° F. Precipitation ranges from 35 to 60 inches per year, or sometimes more, with no really dry months. Tropical cyclones are common in autumn, and tornadoes occur during the spring in this climatic region of the eastern United States.

COOL MARINE CLIMATE: This climate is found on the western margins of continents, in the regions of the prevailing westerlies. The influence of the westerlies is interrupted only by intense cyclonic activity in winter. Warm ocean currents in these latitudes tend to keep the temperatures in winter higher than is usual for these latitudes. The average temperature of the coldest month is 30°–45° F., and the warmest month averages about 60° F. Range of temperatures is small, 15°–35° F. Precipitation is heavy with averages of 35–60 inches, much of which may fall as snow because the maximum precipitation occurs in winter. Extremes of annual rainfall are close to 200 inches.

COOL LITTORAL CLIMATE: This climate is located in the high middle latitudes, where marine and continental influences are essentially balanced. The mean temperature in the coldest month is under 40° F., and averages in the warmest month may reach 60°–70° F. Precipitation is in the range of

25–60 inches, and is rather evenly distributed throughout the year in Europe, but this is not true of all regions of the cool littoral climate. New Zealand has a winter maximum, and Japan a summer maximum. Typhoons influence areas of Japan, bringing excessive rainfall in brief periods of time.

HUMID CONTINENTAL CLIMATE: This climate is found primarily in the interiors of continents in middle latitudes of the Northern Hemisphere. There is a large range of temperature, with the coldest month often averaging below freezing and sometimes even below 0° F., but at least three months have averages above 60° F. In spite of the humidity that characterizes this climate, the precipitation is not excessive, falling in the range of 16 to 50 inches per year. Cyclones, with accompanying cold and warm fronts, influence the climate in winter, and thunderstorms are common in summer.

SEMIARID CONTINENTAL CLIMATE: This climate is located in the interior of continents in middle latitudes where there is a mountain barrier cutting off moisture supplies. Like the humid continental climate, the semiarid continental climate has a large range of temperatures, but annual precipitation rarely exceeds 16 inches. Although most of this falls in the summer, the pattern of distribution is erratic; some areas of semiarid continental climate may receive no rain in some years. Prolonged periods of drought contribute to dust storms, which often come in the winter.

INTERMEDIATE DESERT CLIMATE: When there is consistently less than 6–12 inches of rain in a portion of a region of semiarid climate, the area is classed as an intermediate desert climate.

MARINE SUBPOLAR CLIMATE: This climate is found in the northern middle latitudes along coasts with high mountains nearby. Ocean waters tend to moderate the temperatures, producing a somewhat smaller range than might be expected for the latitude. Average temperatures are under 30° F. for several months, and at least one month has an average temperature over 50° F. Precipitation varies greatly. The regions are affected by frequent cyclonic activity in fall and winter, and fogs are common.

MODERATE SUBPOLAR CLIMATE: This climate is found primarily in mountains such as the Rockies, the Alps, and the Sierra Nevada, where winters are not quite as cold as in the continental interiors in the subpolar latitudes. Temperatures are similar to those in the marine subpolar climate, but precipitation is in the range of 25–40 inches, distributed throughout the year.

EXTREME SUBPOLAR CLIMATE: Temperatures average below 30° F. for five or more months in the subpolar continental interior regions where this climatic type occurs. Most of these regions are located from the Arctic Circle to about 48° N. in North America and 30° N. in Asia, where the high altitudes contribute to the low temperatures. Summer temperatures may reach an average of 50° F. or more for one month, and extreme ranges are a common characteristic. Precipitation is concentrated in the summer months, and the annual average is usually below ten inches. Cold air masses so dominate the climate that little moisture can be held in the air.

POLAR CLIMATE: The polar circles approximately define the boundaries of this climatic zone. Average temperatures never rise above 50° F. for any month, too low to permit growth of forest or agricultural crops. The regions are characterized by ice caps and tundra.

IV/

THE OCEANS

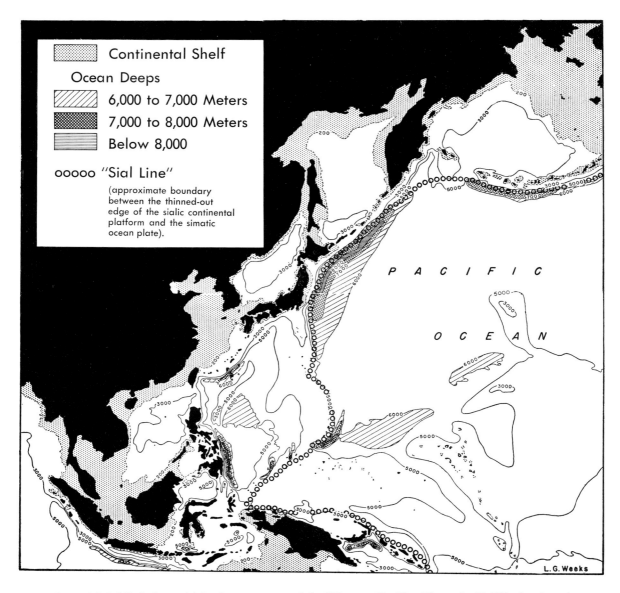

FIG. 8–1. / *Mobile belts and island arc systems of the Western Pacific.* (*From L. G. Weeks, Am. Assoc. Petrol. Geol., Bull., v. 36, No. 11.*)

Ocean Waters and Processes

Shape and Structure of Ocean Basins

THE CONTINENTAL MARGINS MARK THE zone of transition from continental crustal structures to the deep-ocean basins. Just as the structure of continents is not perfectly uniform, all ocean basins are not identical, but generalizations can be made concerning certain aspects, such as depth to the Mohorovičić discontinuity, the composition of the rocks, and the average elevation, which appear to hold true for all continents and oceans. In this sense, continental margins are zones of change—from high elevations to great ocean depths, from great depths to the Moho under continents to shallow depths under oceans, and from sialic to simatic compositions (Fig. 22–1).

Regardless of what criteria are chosen for classifying continental margins, there are several different types. Some margins are characterized by island-arc systems (Fig. 8–1). Others are sites of young, folded mountain belts. The most common type of continental margin is a shallow shelflike extension from land, which slopes off into deeper water at some distance from shore. These continental margins usually have three parts which are based on the configuration of the ocean floor—shelf, slope, and rise (Fig. 8–3).

The *continental shelf* is a shallow, gently sloping surface of low, local relief. It has a slope of about 1 in 1,000, so slight that you would not perceive its slope if you were standing on it. The shelf is rarely more than 100 fathoms (600 feet) deep at its outer margin, and frequently less. Its outer edge is marked by a sharp increase in slope. The width of the shelf ranges from as little as a few miles to more than 200 miles. On the west coast of Florida the shelf is as wide as the state. Shelves are extremely important geologically, because they are sites of deposition for large quantities of material eroded from the parts of continents above sea level. Shallow waters provide excellent places for living organisms, for they receive sunlight and have an abundant supply of food. For this reason, shelves also receive large quantities of sediment deposited by organisms. Most of these sediments are composed of lime.

The *continental slope* is steeper, 3° to 6°, as compared with the 1:1,000 of the shelf, but the slope is still hardly enough to be detected

FIG. 8–2. / *Schematic cross sections, showing postulated steps in evolution of island arc. 1 shows juxtaposed contrasting crustal plates, with lower density plate hydrated only to a certain depth (corresponding here with 500° C.). 2 shows initial thickening and magma generation, and corresponds with spilite-keratophyre phase. 3 shows formation of trench and rise, and development of highly faulted surface of rise. 4 is section across Puerto Rico (largely after Talwani et al., 1959), with additional local complication of subsidiary fault slice beneath trench, and strike-slip fault south of island platform. 4A is same, without vertical exaggeration. (From T. W. Donnelly, A. A. P. G. Bull., v. 48, 1964.)*

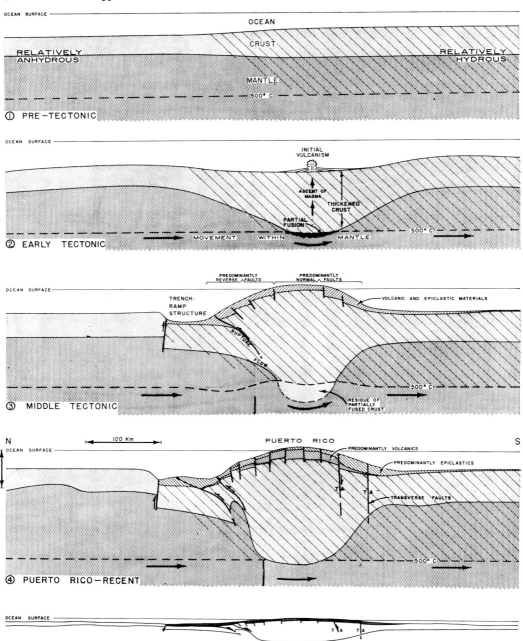

visually. On most diagrams showing continental margins vertical dimensions are greatly exaggerated, so that the slopes appear much steeper than they actually are. In spite of the relative gentleness of the slope, the depth of the ocean floor drops from about 100 fathoms to between 800 and 1,800 fathoms before the slope gives way to the rise. Slopes vary in width, but are generally much narrower than either the shelf or the rise.

The *continental rise* is the name given to the province between the slope and the deep, flat, abyssal plains of the ocean basins. Usually a marked decrease in slope occurs at the beginning of the rise, but there may be no change whatsoever. The rise ranges from a few feet to more than 100 miles in width and is characterized by slopes between 1:1,000 and 1:700, almost as gentle as the slope of the continental shelf.

Since the margins of the continents mark transition zones of crustal structure, they are extremely important. Profiles of the crust under the margins reveal three general features:

A thick, lens-shaped body of sediment and sedimentary rock beneath the continental rise,

A discontinuity in crustal structure at the base of the slope, and

A wedge-shaped mass of unconsolidated sediments beneath the continental shelf.

Examples of some cross sections of continental margins are illustrated in Fig. 8–4.

Island Arcs

AMONG THE MOST INTERESTING and active segments of the earth's crust are the arcuate volcanic islands, the *island arcs*. While the shields, continental margins, ocean floors, and even young, folded mountains and mid-ocean ridges have been relatively stable for long periods of time, the island arcs are the sites of the greatest instability known anywhere on earth. Nowhere in the crust are more processes in action at the present time. The island arcs make up a portion of the continental margins. Most of them are located in the Pacific Ocean, where

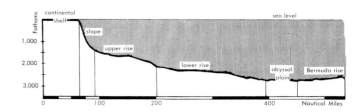

FIG. 8–3. / *A typical profile of the sea floor off the northeastern U.S. (After B. C. Heezen, Geol. Soc. Am., Special Paper 65.)*

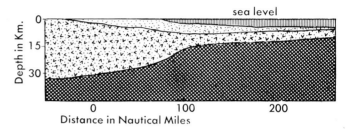

FIG. 8–4. / *Cross section across the continental margins near Cape May, New Jersey. (Worzel and Shurbet.)*

they almost form a rim around the entire northern, western, and southern margins. Others are located in the Atlantic, especially in the Caribbean Sea. The largest arcs include:

Aleutian Islands arc, extending from Alaska to Kamchatka
Kurile Islands arc (Kamchatka to Japan)
Japanese arc
Philippines arc
Indonesian archipelago, Sumatra through Java to North Guinea
Solomon Islands arc
New Hebrides arc
New Caledonia arc
Kermadecs and Tonga Island arcs
Sandwich Islands arc
West Indies arc.

General features of the island arcs are familiar to us. Their pattern on a map is so striking that even the most casual observer must note their peculiar arcuate arrangements. The fact that large earthquakes are more common in the island arcs has provided excellent means of studying the crustal sections near the arcs. Many studies have been made of the gravity field over the arcs and have yielded most im-

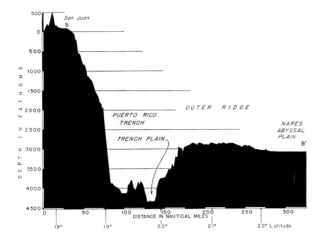

FIG. 8–5. / *A profile of the Puerto Rico Trench. (From Maurice Ewing and B. C. Heezen, 1955.)*

pressive results, as have other geophysical studies. The weakest link in our knowledge about the arcs comes from a lack of field studies of local geologic features in the arcs. This is understandable, because most of the islands are located in the tropics and, as a consequence, are covered by jungles and are usually fringed by reefs concealing their margins. Many are also covered with thick lava flows.

Unique features of the arcs that are common to all arcs include:

1. The islands form an arc that extends for 100 miles or more. These arcs are almost invariably convex, bending toward the deep-ocean basin. Most of the arcs end when they intersect a second arc.

2. Arcs are marginal to continents. They are situated where the continental crust comes into contact with the oceanic crust. That this is the case in the Pacific is shown by the difference in the composition of lavas coming out of volcanoes on the island arcs, which is andesite (intermediate between rhyolite, the composition of granite, and basalt), and differs from that of volcanoes in the central Pacific, which is basaltic.

3. Trenches associated with island arcs contain the greatest depths found anywhere in the oceans, extending as deep as 38,000 feet below sea level. Some of the trenches have flat floors similar to the abyssal plains (Fig. 8–5). The trenches are all located on the deep-ocean side of the island arcs.

4. Large negative gravity anomalies are invariably found over the deep-sea trenches. The negative anomaly means that the force of gravity over the trench is less than would be predicted for a theoretical homogeneous earth. Therefore there is a deficiency of mass in the section of the earth beneath the negative gravity anomalies.

5. Most island arcs are sites of volcanic activity. The composition of their surfaces appears to be largely volcanic rocks, and although volcanic activity occurs elsewhere on earth the arcs are the most active zones of volcanism on earth today.

6. Belts of intense seismic activity parallel the arcs. Almost all deep-seated earthquakes with focus depths of 700 km. occur in the arcs, and shallow earthquakes are also heavily concentrated along them. If the positions of earthquake epicenters[1] and depths are plotted, it is found that the deepest earthquakes are on the continental side, and that the more shallow ones are aligned in a position approximately parallel to the bottoms of the trenches. This line of earthquake foci is inclined about 50 degrees toward the continents, and is generally thought to be a major fault along which ocean basins and continents are moving in relation to one another (Fig. 8–6).

7. The largest and youngest intrusions of molten rock are found in the arcs.

8. There is no evidence of the Precambrian basement of metamorphosed rocks which dominates the shields and is exposed in the cores of folded mountains.

9. Arcs are sites of active deformation within the crust. They may be the initial stages of the formation of mountain systems.

10. Most of the arcs are not directly connected with the continents, but are separated by shallow seas which in several cases are more than 100 miles wide.

Deep Oceanic Crust

The continental rise slopes gradually to depths of about 1,800 fathoms, and here the floor of the ocean basin is found. On the basis of topography, at least three major types of

[1] Point on ground surface vertically above origin of the earthquake.

ocean floor can be recognized: the abyssal floor, oceanic rises, and seamounts.

The *abyssal floors* or *plains* are more or less the midocean counterparts of the mid-continent great plains of North America. They are flat— much flatter, in fact, than the plains of Kansas, Oklahoma, or the Dakotas. Abyssal plains have been found in all oceans. However, they do not occupy central parts of the oceans. In the North Atlantic there are four plains, two on either side of the Mid-Atlantic Ridge (Fig. 8–7). They are found off coasts which do not have marginal trenches, and thus are not found in association with island arcs. Abyssal plains have total relief of only a few feet. They are irregular in shape, and are found in a great range of sizes up to widths of several hundred miles. Margins of abyssal plains are frequently marked by greater relief, consisting of isolated hills which project above the extremely flat surface. These may well represent topographic features being slowly buried by sediment in the plains.

Oceanic rises are large areas that are neither isolated seamounts nor parts of midocean ridges. They rise a few hundred fathoms above the level of the surrounding abyssal floor. Such rises are found around Bermuda and in the South Atlantic, Indian, and Pacific oceans.

Seamounts are isolated mountain-shaped rises which usually protrude more than 500 fathoms above the ocean floor. Many extend to the surface, where they stand as islands. Seamounts are found on oceanic rises and on midocean ridges as well as on abyssal floors. Most seamounts appear to be remnants of volcanoes, having the general shape of volcanoes and being covered by ash and volcanic debris; indeed, some are still active.

Abyssal plains and oceanic rises are seismically inactive. Crustal sections obtained in these provinces indicate the following structure:

a layer of water 1,800 fathoms deep,

between one-half and 1 km. of unconsolidated sediment and sedimentary rocks, and

oceanic crustal rocks (basalt) 3 to 4 km. thick

Midocean Ridges

THE MIDOCEAN ridge is one of the longest and most continuous features of the crust of the earth. The existence of a Mid-Atlantic ridge (Figs. 8–8 and 8–9), has been known for many years, but its true extent under the oceans was discovered only in 1958. This ridge runs the length of the North Atlantic, South Atlantic, Indian, and South Pacific oceans. It is more than 40,000 miles long (Fig. 8–10).

A rift valley runs along the crest of the ridge throughout most of its extent. This shows up as a notch or cleft on most profiles. The valley is as much as 1,000 fathoms lower than peaks on either side, and the two sides are 20 to 30 miles across. This rift appears to be a down-dropped section of the crust, bounded on either side by faults. This feature exists not only on the crest of the Mid-Atlantic Ridge; there is positive evidence of its existence at many other

2 miles
4 miles
6 miles
8 miles
10 miles
12 miles
14 miles
16 miles
18 miles

magma generated along a fault

FIG. 8–6. / *Hypothetical cross section showing the generation of magma by the frictional heat along a fault. Temperatures increase with depth at a rate of about 1 degree centigrade per 100 feet near the surface. Thus rocks at a depth of several miles are normally hot, but not hot enough to melt.*

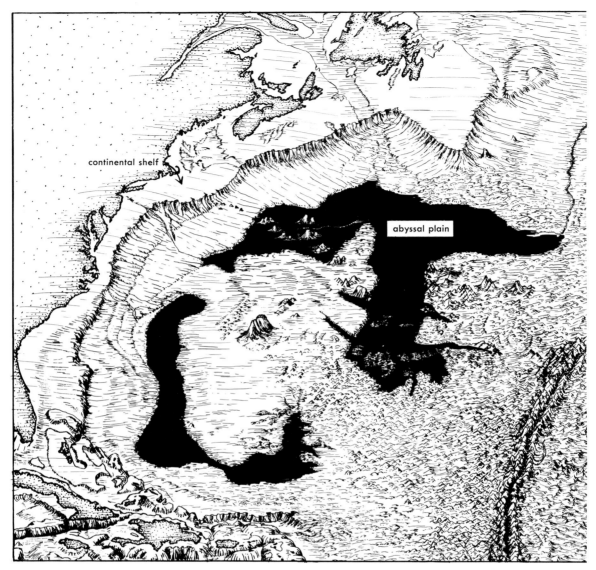

FIG. 8–7. / *Physiographic diagram of the North Atlantic Ocean Basin.* (*Redrawn after B. C. Heezen, Geol. Soc. Am., Special Paper 65.*)

places along the midoceanic ridges, and it is possible that this rift zone follows the mid-oceanic ridges around the world. If it does, it may be of profound significance, since a rift of this sort could be created by the crust of the earth being pulled apart as a result of tension within the crust.

The mid-ocean ridge is the center of much seismic activity. When epicenters of oceanic earthquakes are plotted, they form two striking patterns. One is associated with island arcs, and the second is a very narrow zone along the crest of the mid-ocean ridge. Many epicenters fall in, or on edges of, the rift valley along the crest of the ridge.

Rocks dredged, cored, or exposed along the Mid-Atlantic Ridge are igneous and volcanic, and most are basaltic in composition. The samples include such rocks as olivine gabbro, serpentine, basalt, and diabase (see Part V). The same is true of the rocks dredged from flanks of mountains in the Pacific.

Crustal structure of the Mid-Atlantic Ridge is known only through scattered seismic profiles. In general it consists of:

.5 km. of sediment,

3 km. of rock through which shock waves travel with a velocity of 5.1 km./sec., approximately that of basalt, and

a substratum of velocity 7.3 km./sec.

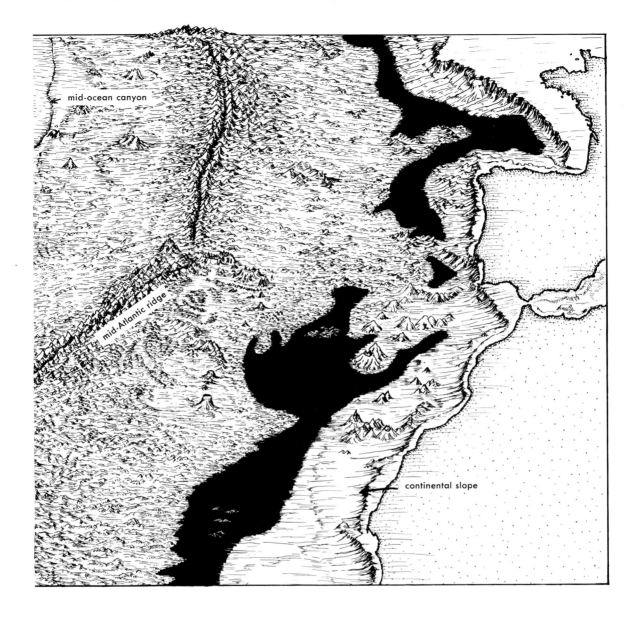

mid-ocean canyon

mid-Atlantic ridge

continental slope

Movements of Surface Waters of the Oceans

CIRCULATION OF OCEAN WATER NEAR THE surface has long been of interest and importance to man. Study of ocean currents began soon after the first attempts at navigation on the seas, but the complexity of the movements of water even near the surface is such that there are still many unanswered questions.

Factors in Surface Water Movement

FIG. 8–11, WHICH ILLUSTRATES the important surface currents of the oceans, clearly indicates that oceanic currents do not have a simple ex-

planation. Anyone who is familiar with the sea is well aware of the great variety of its moods. It is sometimes whipped into huge waves by storm winds, and at other times it is quiet and calm. Twice daily it responds to the gravitational pull of the sun and moon as tides come and go. Many factors play important roles in the movements of the seas. Most important of these are:

1. slope of the surface of the ocean,
2. wind blowing over the water,
3. density variations within the water,
4. the Coriolis force,
5. gravitational attraction of the moon and sun (see *tides*), and
6. configuration of the ocean floor.

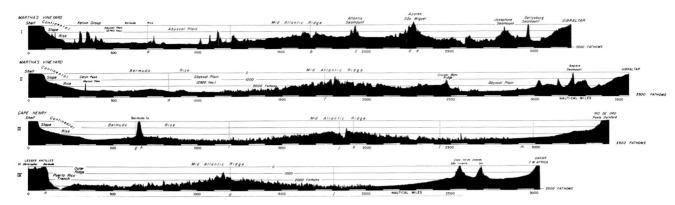

FIG. 8–8. / *Profiles of the Atlantic Ocean sea floor. Note the great vertical exaggeration of the scale, 40:1. (From B. C. Heezen, Special Paper 65, Geol. Soc. Am.)*

Slope of the Surface of the Ocean

At one time ocean currents were attributed largely to the fact that the surfaces of the oceans of the world are not at exactly the same level. For example, the Gulf of Mexico is nearly seven inches higher than the Atlantic on the opposite side of the Florida peninsula. Some such differences appear to be relatively constant, while others are transient. Since there is much more rainfall in equatorial regions than in middle and higher latitudes, water tends to pile up near the equator, elevating the surface. Where ocean currents drive water into bays or gulfs, the surface tends to be elevated. The same effects are produced by tidal currents, which

FIG. 8–9. / *Profiles of the ocean floor. The top record was made during a crossing of the Mid-Atlantic Ridge. The 2200 fathom line is indicated. The lower profile is across the continental rise west of St. Nazarre, France. (From B. C. Heezen, Geol. Soc. Am. Special Paper 65.)*

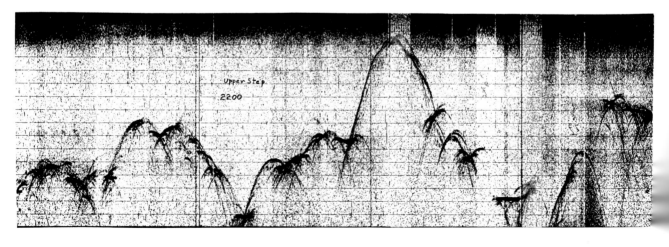

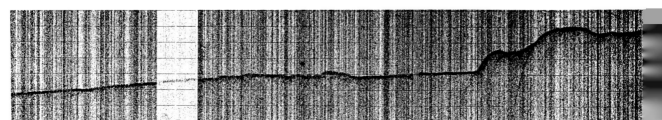

push water into embayments. In all these instances the level of the ocean is raised differentially, and compensating movements of the surface are initiated to restore the level. A perfectly level surface is never obtained. Instead, a balance is reached so that the rate of movement away from elevated areas is approximately equal to the rate of movement toward them.

Effects of Wind in Contact with Water

WHEN A STRONG WIND blows across a body of water, waves are set in motion on the surface and a wave current in the direction of the wind is generated. Wave currents are often attributed to frictional drag of wind on the surface of the water. A very strong wind is required to start this motion if the wind is moving in a smooth and steady flow, but usually enough turbulence is involved in wind motion to create eddies, minor updrafts, and irregularities in the flow pattern of air over the water surface. These in turn initiate depressions and rises in the surface of the water. Once such motion is started, only a slight wind is needed to continue the action. If the wind is consistently from one direction it exerts a more or less continuous pressure on one side of the wave, tending to push it along. As the wind passes the crest of the wave it exerts a pull, a form of suction, on the other side. In this manner wave currents in the oceans are established where wind directions are consistent. This is particularly important in trade wind belts of the tropics and along the equator, where wind directions are predominantly from east to west. In middle latitudes westerly winds set up a drift of currents from west to east.

Density Variations within the Water

VARIATION IN DENSITY of sea water is one of the most important factors in the circulation of the water of the deep seas. It is important to a lesser degree in determining movements near the surface. Density of sea water is highly variable. It varies with salt content (amount of dissolved solids in solution) and with tempera-

Legend
➤ Mid ocean ridges
⌁ Ocean depths less than 1500 fathoms
◗ Land

FIG. 8–10. / The midocean ridges. To view the Pacific Ocean invert the page. This ridge is continuous for about forty thousand miles. It is a few hundred miles wide and from 10,000 to 30,000 feet high above the ocean floors. Near the crest of this ridge there is a fault scarp along which the crust is ruptured and pulled apart slightly. (From J. T. Wilson, Am. Scientist, v. 47, No. 1.)

ture (cold water is more dense). Such variations are the result of four factors: evaporation, which concentrates salts; precipitation, which tends to dilute sea water; heating and cooling of surface waters; and inflow of waters from the continents. Effects of these variations in density are closely tied in with the Coriolis force.

Coriolis Force

G. G. CORIOLIS, a French mathematician, first demonstrated that any object in motion on a

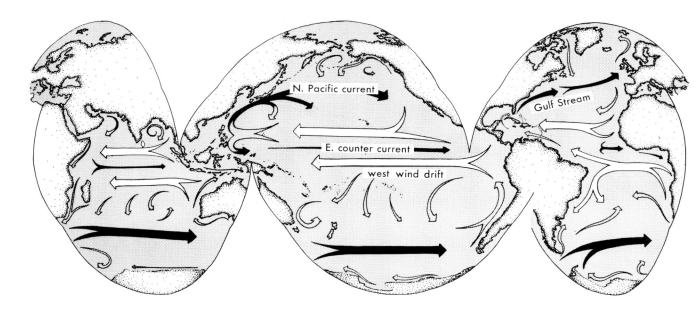

FIG. 8–11. / *Surface currents. (Modified after Sverdrup, based on Goode Base Map No. 201HO. Adapted by permission from* The Oceans: Their Physics, Chemistry, and General Biology, *by H. V. Sverdrup, Martin W. Johnson, and Richard H. Fleming. c 1942. Prentice-Hall, Inc. Reproduced by permission of the Department of Geography, from the Goode Base Map Series, copyright by the University of Chicago.)*

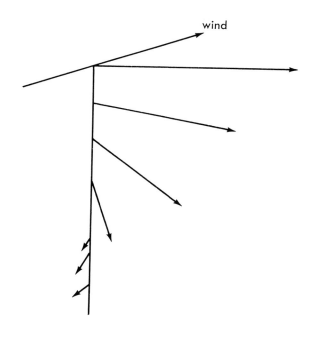

FIG. 8–12. / *Current deflection due to Coriolis effect. Currents set up by wind currents are deflected to the right in the Northern Hemisphere. The amount of the deflection and the velocity of the resulting currents vary as shown with depth. (After Ekman.)*

rotating sphere is subject to a force that tends to deflect it. As we have seen, on the earth the Coriolis force deflects objects in motion to the right in the Northern Hemisphere and to the left in the Southern Hemisphere. This force, although small, affects all objects in motion on the earth's surface. In most cases the force is so small that it has little effect, but in wind and water movements the other forces acting on them are so slight that the Coriolis effect is noticeable. It is at a minimum along the equator, where the ocean currents follow most closely wind direction, and increases toward the poles. As a consequence of this force, surface-water motion in the Northern Hemisphere is generally along a path 45 degrees to the right of prevailing wind directions in the open sea (Fig. 8–12).

When water of increased density rises to the

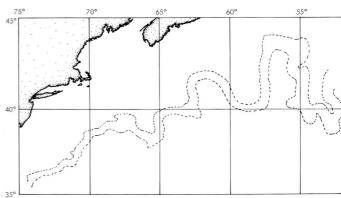

FIG. 8–13. / *Schematic representation of the Gulf Stream, showing its general meandering pattern. (After Strommel.)*

surface from the depths of the ocean, or develops from increased evaporation, it will tend to be concentrated to the right of the prevailing current direction in the Northern Hemisphere and to the left in the Southern Hemisphere.

Configuration of the Ocean Floor

THE SHAPE OF THE OCEAN BOTTOMS and of the coasts of continents provides a framework within which the other factors operate. Surface movements are confined within this framework and deflected by it. For this reason, surface movements in the Southern Hemisphere, which has very little land area, are much simpler than those in the Northern Hemisphere, which is irregularly broken up by odd-shaped continental masses making up four-fifths of all the land on the earth.

In the Southern Hemisphere the west-wind drift causes prevailing surface currents to follow a simple circular pattern flowing from west to east. The only obstacle is the narrowness of the passage between South America and Antarctica, which constricts the currents. In the Northern Hemisphere the equatorial currents follow the equatorial drift from east to west, but in the Atlantic these currents are broken up and deflected north and south by the eastward protrusion of South America.

Ocean Currents

THE COMPLICATED DETAILS OF MOVEMENT of surface water in the oceans can be reduced to a relatively simple picture. Surface currents flow from west to east in what is called the *west-wind drift* in the middle latitudes of both Northern and Southern Hemispheres in all oceans. Along the equator, currents flow from east to west in the equatorial drift of the Atlantic, Pacific, and Indian oceans. Between the prevailing westerly drifts and the equatorial drift, currents are deflected to the right in the Northern Hemisphere and to the left in the Southern Hemisphere. Where islands or irregular coast lines lie in the paths of these currents, they are deflected both right and left in streamlined patterns around the land.

In the Atlantic the northern equatorial current flows from east to west across the Atlantic. It strikes the northern coast of South America and is deflected to the north, where it flows through the Caribbean and into the Gulf. In the Gulf of Mexico warm water is backed up and augmented by flow from the Mississippi River. Here the well-known *Gulf Stream* flows from the Gulf through the strait between Florida and Cuba at the rate of almost three miles per hour. This segment, known as the Florida Current, flows northward along the southeastern coast of the United States, where it is joined by currents that have been deflected to the northern side of the Caribbean Islands. This stream of warm, northward-moving, equatorial water is as much as 50 miles wide and well over 1,000 feet deep. It follows a meandering course at times, and is occasionally broken up into several threads flowing in a braid-like pattern (Fig. 8–13). At about the latitude of Washington, D. C., the stream moves farther from the coast. Part of it diverges as the North Atlantic Current flows eastward almost all the way across the Atlantic. It is broken up off the western coast of Europe and split into two parts; one moves southward back toward the equator, and the other moves northward along the coast of Norway.

A second important current along the eastern coast of North America is the *Labrador Current,* which flows southward from the Arctic Ocean between Greenland and Labrador. It is largely broken up south of Newfoundland where it mixes with the Gulf Stream, which has continued to flow northeast after forming the North Atlantic Current.

Along the western coast of North America the principal current is the *North Pacific Current,* which flows from west to east and impinges on the coast at the state of Washington. Here it is split; one part is deflected northward to form the *Alaska Current* along the coast of Canada and southern Alaska. The other component is deflected to the south to become the *California Current,* which continues to move southward and eventually rejoins the equatorial drift.

Tides

Tide is the name applied to the daily rise and fall of sea level. Even in ancient times it could be seen that there was a relation between tides and the phases and position of the moon in its orbit. As men learned to measure the *period* (time between successive stages), *range* (variation in level of the water surface), and variability of tides from time to time and from place to place, they came to recognize the complexity of the causes of the earth's tides. It has long been clear that the two dominant factors are gravitational forces, due primarily to the attraction between the moon and sun and the oceans, and the hydrodynamic behavior of ocean waters confined by the shape of the ocean basin and subjected to disturbing forces which set the water in motion. Yet even today tidal observations cannot be completely explained by tidal theory. An appreciation of the variability of tides will be gained by study of the charts

(Fig. 8–14), which show fluctuations of sea level at various coastal points over a period of time. Note that there are variations in period, range, and number of tides per day, as well as variations over longer spans of time.

Effects of Gravitational Attraction

Pliny the elder (23–79 a.d.) is credited with being the first to document the relation between the tidal ranges and the phase and position of the moon. Nearly 1,600 years later, Sir Isaac Newton developed a theory which explained this relationship in terms of gravity.

The sun and moon are the two bodies of the Solar System which exert great attraction on the surface water of the earth. Although it is 93 million miles away, the sun is such a massive body that it exerts nearly 167 times as much attractive force on earth as does the moon. Therefore it seems unlikely that the moon should be more closely linked to tidal phenomena. Yet this is the case, and the reason is that the attraction of the moon for water on opposite sides of the earth differs to a much greater extent than does that of the sun. Water on the side toward the sun or moon is eight thousand miles closer to it than water on the opposite side. The eight thousand miles makes a significant difference in the distance to the moon (238,860 miles), but only a very little difference in the distance to the sun (93 million miles).

To understand how the earth's tides are affected by the gravitational attraction of the moon and sun, let us assume that the earth is a rotating and revolving sphere covered to a uniform depth with water. The moon's attraction will pull this water in two bulges on opposite sides of the earth, one toward the moon and the other directly away from it. We have already seen that the moon and the earth revolve about a common center of gravity. If it were not for this revolution the moon would be pulled to the earth. Similarly, if the moon and earth were held in fixed positions, in relation to each other, there would be only one large bulge of water, and that would extend out to-

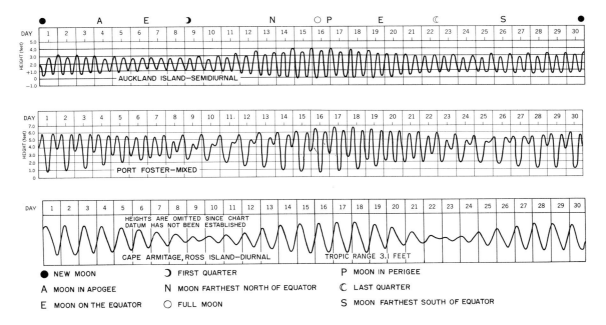

● NEW MOON ☽ FIRST QUARTER P MOON IN PERIGEE

A MOON IN APOGEE N MOON FARTHEST NORTH OF EQUATOR ☾ LAST QUARTER

E MOON ON THE EQUATOR ○ FULL MOON S MOON FARTHEST SOUTH OF EQUATOR

FIG. 8–14. / *Examples of diurnal, semidiurnal, and mixed tides. (From U.S. Navy Hydrographic Office, "Oceanographic Atlas of the Polar Seas.")*

ward the moon. But in the case of a stable system of two bodies in revolution about a central point, the forces of attraction between the two bodies must be counterbalanced by opposed centrifugal force. The amount of the centrifugal force is constant and is directed in the opposite direction from the gravitational forces (Fig. 8–15). The gravitational forces on the earth vary from place to place depending on the distance from the moon. Thus two tidal bulges would occur on our model earth with a uniform hydrosphere—one on the side toward the moon, where the force of attraction exceeds the centrifugal forces, and a second on the opposite side, where the centrifugal forces exceed the force of attraction. It happens that the two forces are close but not exactly equal in strength. This gives rise to a slightly higher bulge on the side toward the moon. The effects of the sun are similar in character, but slightly less than half as strong as those of the moon. The sun and moon do not at most times lie on a straight line with the earth, and the two effects are usually out of phase. Because of all these considerations, certain components of observed tides can be predicted and explained in terms of the movements of the sun and moon.

1. There should be two high tides and two low tides each day due to the earth's rotation about its

FIG. 8–15. / *Tide-producing forces. The heavy solid arrows depict centripetal forces acting on the earth which are equal in magnitude everywhere, but gravitational attraction of matter on earth to the moon varies as indicated by the barbed arrows.*

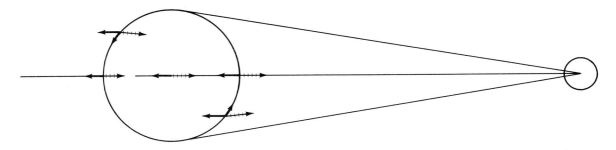

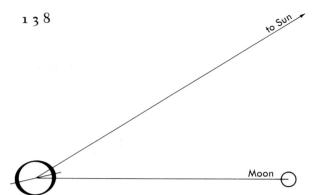

to Sun

Moon

FIG. 8–16. / *Conditions causing lagging tides, the high tide arrives after the meridian passage of the moon, are shown. Lines pointing directions to the sun and moon and high tides are indicated. Note that the line connecting the high tides lags behind and does not coincide with the line to the moon.*

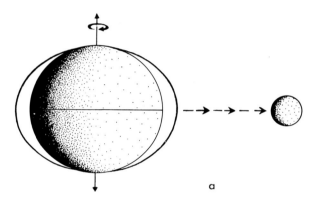

a

FIG. 8–17a. / *The moon is shown directly over the equator. Under this condition the height of the tide is essentially a function of latitude.*

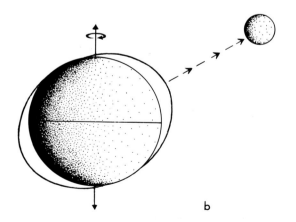

b

FIG. 8–17b. / *Here the moon is shown out of the plane of the equator. Under this condition there will be unequal tides at any given latitude. One of the tides will be much higher than the other.*

axis. Actually the interval between high tides is normally 12 hours and 25 minutes, the slight difference being due to the revolution of the moon around the earth. Thus the high tides occur about fifty minutes later each day. These high tides are retarded by the moon, but they do not normally coincide exactly with the passage of the moon overhead (that is, over a given meridian). There is a certain amount of frictional drag which usually causes the tide to arrive at any spot later than the passage of the moon. This interval is known as the *lunitidal interval*. It varies greatly from place to place, but for a given locality it is relatively constant.

2. When the sun and moon lie in line with the earth, as at the times of new and full moons, the attraction of the two bodies are cumulative, and unusually high tides, called *spring tides*, result. The name has no relation to the season. When the sun and moon are located at right angles to the earth (quadrature), the tide-producing forces act at right angles, tending to cancel each other out and giving rise to unusually low tides, called *neap tides*. Both of these conditions occur twice each month. When the sun and moon approach alignment with the earth the resultant tidal bulge may arrive a little before the passage of the moon overhead, and the tide is said to be *priming*. After the passage of the moon out of line with the sun the bulge will tend to be retarded, and the tide is said to be *lagging* (Fig. 8–16).

3. The orbit of the moon is inclined to the ecliptic (the path of the earth around the sun) by about 5 degrees. The earth's orbit is inclined by 23½ degrees to the plane of the equator. Thus the moon is over the earth's equator twice a month, but its path takes it as far as 28½ degrees above and below the equator at times. When the moon is directly over the equator the two daily tides are about equal in range (*equatorial tides*), but when the moon is far out of the plane of the equator great differences in the range of the two daily tides occur, as is indicated in Fig. 8–17. Such tides are called *tropical tides*.

4. The distance to the moon varies because the moon's path around the earth is elliptical. Gravitational attraction varies inversely with the square of the distance. Thus tides vary with the position of the moon in its orbit. The amount of variation due to this cause reaches about 20 per cent.

5. Similarly, a slight amount of tidal variation may be related to the varying distance to the sun as the earth moves in its elliptical orbit around it.

All five of these factors bring about variations in tides, and in addition each of these varies with a given period. At times the effects of two or more of these factors are cumulative; at other times they tend to cancel one another out.

Hydrodynamics of the Oceans

MANY TIDAL OBSERVATIONS cannot be reconciled with the gravitational theory. On the Pacific coast of North America, for example, where the direction of the coastline is essentially north–south, high tides tend to sweep from south to north. High tides normally come to Cape Flattery in northern Washington three hours later than they do at San Diego. Similar wavelike motions, as if the tide were a long wave striking the shore at an angle, are found elsewhere and cannot be directly related to the rotations and revolutions of the earth, sun, and moon. Another significant situation is found in the Society Islands of the South Pacific. Here high tides come at high noon and midnight while low tides come at 6:00 A.M. and 6:00 P.M. Tidal behavior here is apparently related to the attraction of no body except the sun, the area seeming totally immune to the attraction of the moon. Both of these effects can be explained in terms of hydrodynamic principles.

If a container of water is periodically tilted, *standing waves* will be set up. The size, period, and number of these waves will depend on the size and shape of the container and the depth of the water. In a standing wave certain points along the wave remain static while the other points oscillate. In a three dimensional container the static points, called *nodes*, may be a line, or under certain circumstances a single point, about which the wave moves. As early as 1900 the oceans were divided into oscillating areas. This division was made in such a way that the observed differences in time of arrival of high and low water at opposite ends of an area would be about six or twelve hours. Since then the view of the oceans as complex systems of standing-wave oscillation has become well established.

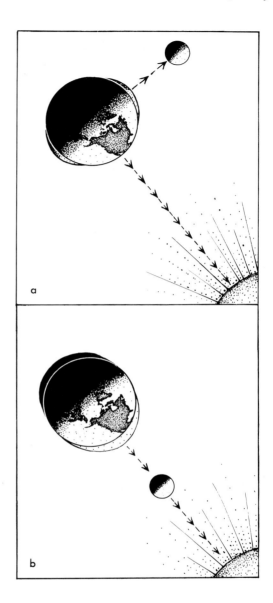

FIG. 8–18a. / *Conditions depicted are those caracteristic of quadrature when the moon is at right angles to the line connecting the sun and earth. At this time tides tend to be unusually low.*

FIG. 8–18b. / *At conjunction the effects of the sun and moon on the tides are additive. Unusually high tides occur under these conditions.*

The tidal phenomena along the Pacific coast and in the Society Islands can be explained by the concept of standing waves. The islands must lie close to a node of a standing wave whose period is about equal to that of the semi-daily tides produced by the moon. Oscillating standing waves of the sort envisioned could not be simple standing waves because they are subjected to gravitational influences and exist in water on a rotating earth. The oscillating standing waves move in a more or less circular motion, called *amphidromic*, around the nodes. The motion can be likened to that of a liquid in a cup which is first tilted back and forth, creating a standing wave, and then swirled around so that the standing wave moves in a radial motion about the center of the cup. Radial lines, called *cotidal lines*, may be drawn from a node to connect points that experience high tides at the same time. These tides are not equal in range because they are at different distances from the node. The cotidal lines sweep counterclockwise in the Northern Hemisphere and clockwise in the Southern Hemisphere. One of the best documented instances is in the North Sea (Fig. 8–19). The Pacific Coast tides are borne by such an amphidromic standing wave reaching Cape Flattery, Washington, three hours after it passes San Diego.

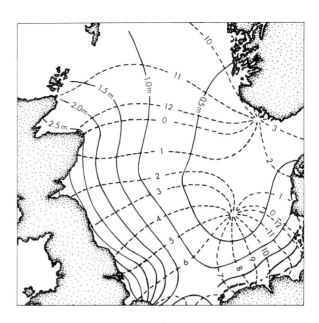

FIG. 8–19. / *North Sea Cotidal lines. The solid lines connect points that have equal tidal range. The dashed lines show successive times of arrival of high tides. (After Admiralty Manual of Tides.)*

Effects of Tides

Most points on the world's sea coasts are affected by tidal movements. Some typical tidal ranges are nine feet at Boston, six feet at New York, two feet at Key West and Galveston, and twenty feet at London. At certain locations, as in the Bay of Fundy, even higher ranges are known. The effects of tides in restricted portions of the coasts and in rivers along a coast having high tides may be pronounced. As the tide approaches the coast it creates a horizontal current, called the *flood*, which moves into bays and rivers and continues upstream great distances in some instances. The Hudson River, for example, is affected by tides as far as 130 miles upstream at Troy, where the tidal range of the river is five feet. In a number of rivers

where tidal ranges are particularly high the movement of the water takes the form of a turbulent wave, called a *tidal bore*, which moves with high velocity. The tidal bore formed on the Amazon River is sixteen feet high and moves

FIG. 8–20. / *Theoretical wave form seen in cross section. The movement of water beneath the wave surface dies out at a depth equal to about one-third of the wavelength. Particles of water in the wave move in slightly elliptical paths.*

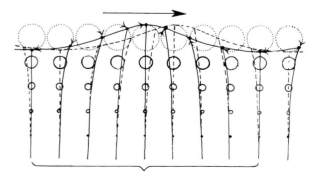

at a velocity of 12 knots. Tidal currents are effective agents of marine erosion, keeping fine sediment in suspension and preventing its deposition. For this reason tidal bores help scour and shape the channels of the streams in which they are found.

Waves

ALTERATION OF SHORE OR SEASCAPE BY marine agents is accomplished mainly by waves and by the currents set up by wave motion. Most ocean waves are elongated humps separated by irregular troughs. Wave motion is started by variations in atmospheric pressure due to turbulence in the air and frictional drag. Once motion is started, waves are propagated in the direction of the prevailing wind. They become aligned approximately perpendicular to wind direction, and in parallel rows if the wind is continuously from the same general direction. Where the air is turbulent, waves are short and choppy—they may change direction of motion or die out altogether.

Fig. 8–20 shows a model of a theoretically perfect wave. This model is approximated very closely in nature by many of the waves that move toward the seacoasts. Waves are not necessarily continuous over a long distance. In profile the wave is a sinuous, curved surface. The top of the wave form is called the *crest*; the depression between two crests is the *trough*. The distance between two crests or two troughs is called the *wave length*. The vertical distance between the top of a crest and the bottom of a trough is the *wave height*. The time required for a crest to progress one wave length is called the *period* of the wave motion.

If you have ever watched a cork bob up and down on a water surface you know the nature of the movement of water in a wave. Water does not move along with the wave form; if it did, seas would be impassable to most surface vessels (Fig. 8–21). Instead water travels in a nearly circular path. At the crest of a wave, motion is in the direction of the wave's movement, but in the trough motion is in the opposite direction. Beneath the surface of the wave, the motion of the water is also almost circular, but the size of the orbits decreases with depth until at a depth equal to about half of the wave length the motion is negligible. Below this depth wave movements have no effect either in the water itself or on the ocean bottom. A submarine sub-

FIG. 8–21. / *U. S. Coast Guard Cutter in high waves. (Courtesy of U.S. Coast Guard.)*

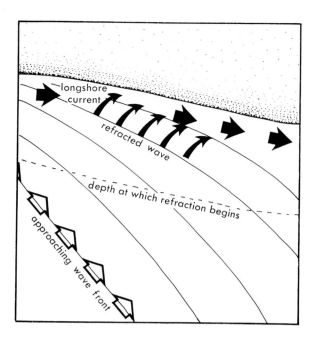

FIG. 8–22. / *Refraction of incoming wave fronts. The refracted waves do not come in perpendicular to the shore line. For this reason a component of movement is set up along the shore. The longshore current is indicated by the heavy black arrows.*

FIG. 8–23. / *Refraction of incoming waves along a rugged shore. Contours of the sea floor are indicated by dashed lines. The energy possessed by the wave at the position first shown is equally distributed along the wave, but as the wave front is bent the energy is spread over areas of varying sizes. Thus a much larger portion of the wave's energy is dissipated on the headlands than along an equal distance of bay shore.*

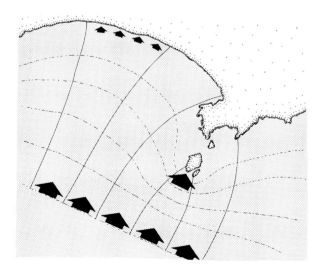

merged to this depth may experience no movement even if violent storm waves occur on the surface. However, wave lengths of some *swells* (wind-generated waves which have advanced into regions of weaker winds or calm) and storm waves are great—several thousand feet—and these can be felt on the bottom at depths of more than 1,000 feet.

Bending of Waves toward Shore

IF THE COAST is oblique to the direction of wave movement, the waves are bent, or *refracted*, so that they tend to approach the shore perpendicularly. The wave is slowed down in shallow water where subsurface water involved in the water motion is impeded by the bottom. That part of the wave which is moving in deeper water continues to travel at its original rate until it, too, reaches shallow water.

Because waves are not completely bent to be perpendicular to the shore, there is a component of motion in the water directed along the shore line. This establishes the *longshore current*. It is important in transporting sand and silt. Refraction is also of importance in that it focuses energy of the waves on the *headlands*, those parts of the shore that protrude into the ocean, rather than on bays or recessed parts of the shore. How this is accomplished is shown in Fig. 8–22. Energy of a wave is evenly distributed along the wave front while it is out at sea, but as it comes into shore and is refracted, that part of the wave's energy that enters a bay is spread out and distributed over a long shore line, and that part of its energy which is directed against the headlands is concentrated along a short portion of the shore (Fig. 8–23). For this reason headlands become eroded back by wave action much more rapidly than does the shore line as a whole.

Breakers

As A WAVE enters increasingly shallow water, subsurface movement begins to be inhibited by the sea bottom. The restriction of the wave

FIG. 8–24. / *Breaking wave. The water in the foreground is returning to the ocean under the breaking wave as an undertow. Such an undertow does not ordinarily create a strong current. (Photo by the author.)*

form causes the wave height to increase and the velocity of the wave to decrease. This change takes place rapidly and at a specific depth for waves of any given characteristics. The velocity of the top part of the wave begins to exceed the forward velocity of the wave as a whole; the top outruns the rest of the wave and spills over in front of it, forming a *breaker* (Fig. 8–24). The wave form is lost, and water is thrown onto shore, often with great force, as a rushing turbulent mass. Where waves break there is a great deal of movement of sediment on the sea bottom. Out beyond the zone of breakers there is little more than a slight shifting of sediment back and forth by wave movement, but within the zone of breakers sediment is churned up into the water. A slight depression, or trough, may form just within this zone. Sediment removed from the depression is piled up on the landward side to build a *bar* and eventually, in some instances, an *offshore beach*.

Rip Currents

ONCE A WAVE BREAKS, the water rushes onto the beach, stops, reverses its direction, and begins its return to the ocean. The belief that water from a dissipated wave slips under the incoming wave and goes back out to sea as an undertow is a popular misconception. Recent studies have revealed that undertow is not common; neither is it responsible for large-scale movement of water. Instead, water from a wave finds its way back to sea by moving along close to shore and almost parallel to the shore line as part of the longshore current, until it reaches a current moving rapidly out to sea. This outgoing current is called a *rip current* (also a *rip tide* or a *"sea puss"*). Rip currents are probably responsible for most drownings attributed to undertow. They are rapid and forceful movements of water certainly capable of knocking the unsuspecting wader off his feet. They are usually more or less confined to channels running out to sea perpendicular to the shore. The best way to escape one is to swim parallel to the shore across and out of the current, rather than to try to swim directly against it back to land. A rip current is fed almost continuously as each successive wave breaks, piling up more water along the shore.

Erosion by Wave Action

Coasts are undergoing an almost constant attack by waves. Small undersea volcanoes build cones several hundred feet above sea level, but when activity ceases the cone disappears sometimes almost overnight under the erosive power of waves.

Erosion by waves is accomplished mainly through the impact of sediment picked up and thrown against the shore as the wave breaks, and through the impact of the water itself as it is thrown forward in the breaking wave. Where erosion is active, waves are able to break down solid rocks. Armed with sand, pebbles, or larger pieces of rock, waves rapidly break down any exposed, loosely consolidated rock. The impact of boulders thrown by large waves is capable of breaking up the most resistant and massive rock units.

Erosion is most rapid when there is a ready supply of these "tools," but the force of the water alone is enough to be effective in dislodging fractured blocks. Water is forced into fractures and becomes highly compressed by the thrust of the water behind it. This pressure is greater than is generally recognized. A moderate-sized wave, 5 to 10 feet high, can exert pressures from 1,000 to 2,000 pounds per square foot against the rocks exposed at the point where it breaks. This is enough to extend or enlarge pre-existing fractures and to dislodge loose blocks.

Solution by sea water also has erosive capacity, but this is of minor importance even where relatively soluble rocks such as limestones are exposed along coasts.

Shallow Sea Transportation

An incoming wave is capable of moving sediment as soon as the depth of water is about half its wave length, but until the wave begins to break this capacity does not account for much erosion. The agitation and shifting associated with waves offshore does, however, sort sediments. Long-period sea swells can affect the bottom in this manner at depths of hundreds of feet.

Most movement of sediment is accomplished by breaking waves and longshore currents. Even after refraction, incoming waves hit the shore at a slight angle. In this water that is thrown on the beach obliquely, pebbles or grains of sand are rolled or tossed along. When the water returns, they are moved directly down the slope of the beach, perpendicular to the shore. Thus with each new wave there is a general tendency to move the sediment along the beach.

Water from waves is capable of moving the finer sizes of sediment in suspension, and they may be carried in the longshore current until the velocity of the current diminishes.

Deep-Sea Transportation

Surface currents moving across deep seas are too weak to transport sediment. Even in the rather extreme case of the Gulf Stream, which flows at certain points with a velocity as high as one or two miles per hour, only very small particles can be carried in suspension. Other oceanic currents are much too weak to move even the smallest sands and silts. Only clays can be carried in ocean currents, and most of these sink to the bottom soon after they enter salt water. Most of the load in the currents beyond the continental shelves is composed of floating and free-swimming marine plants and animals, and these are microscopic in size. Yet in spite of their size they make up a very large percentage of marine sediments on the deep-sea floors.

Landforms Shaped by Shallow Marine Erosion

Erosion is the dominant marine process along the coast of New England and the western United States. In these areas wave action is gradually gnawing away at the land, reducing it to the level of the seas. The rate of erosion is not always slow. The south shore of Nantucket Island retreats as much as five or six feet per year. Along the west coast in California and along the Chalk Cliffs of Dover in

FIG. 8–25. / Hurricane winds pile up waters of Biscayne Bay on Miami's North Bayshore retaining wall, September 21, 1948. (Miami Daily News photo, courtesy of U.S. Weather Bureau.)

England, wave action has undercut the sea cliffs, bringing about large landslides and slumps, products of which are broken up and graded by further wave action.

Cliffs and Terraces

WAVE-CUT CLIFFS AND TERRACES are two landforms often found where erosion is the dominant shore process. Sea cliffs are steep, and many are as much as several hundred feet high. At the foot of the cliff, below the level of the water, there is usually a sudden break in slope, and the sea floor either is nearly flat or slopes gently seaward. This platform or terrace is covered by rocks dislodged from the cliff, which contribute to further undercutting of the cliff as the water hurls them against it repeatedly. Sand can always be moved by the incoming

waves, and moderate waves are capable of picking up and hurling cobbles and pebbles. In times of storm (Fig. 8–25) even the largest boulders may be smashed against the base of the cliff. The effect of the breaking waves is negligible below the surface of the water, and the cliff stops abruptly just below the level of the water (Fig. 8–26). The width of the wave-cut terrace is limited by the fact that shallow water dissipates more and more of the wave energy before the wave reaches the base of the cliff, so that as the terrace becomes wider the capacity of the incoming waves to erode the cliff is reduced. If sea level rises steadily over a long period of time, the terrace will become very wide because that part formed early is increasingly submerged below the level of the wave action. With submergence the water depth is maintained, so waves break nearer shore.

syncline

FIG. 8–26. / *Shorelines along which structure of the rocks influences the shape of the shoreline. Broad, open folds control this Canadian shoreline (top, left). (Courtesy of the Royal Canadian Air Force.) Strata are nearly horizontal at the Chalk Cliffs (top, right). The wave-cut cliff and a broad terrace are prominent (middle, left). Strata are almost vertical, but they have been eroded to a nearly flat wave-cut terrace that is now high above sea level (bottom, right). Wave action has cut a nearly flat terrace across steeply dipping strata (bottom, left). (Photos Crown Copyright.)*

Guyots

GUYOTS are flat-topped seamounts found mainly in the Pacific Ocean. A large number of them have been discovered, and many are thought to be submerged volcanoes which were truncated by wave action. Most are covered by considerable depths of water, between 3,000 and 6,000 feet. The puzzling fact about guyots is the great depth at which they are submerged (Fig. 8–27). Sea level was undoubtedly lower during the ice ages, but it is unlikely that it was lowered as much as 3,000 feet. A second explanation is that there have been fluctuations in the level of the bottom of the ocean. Perhaps a combination of deformation of the sea floor and changes of sea level is responsible for these remarkable features.

Stacks, Arches, Sea Caves, Notches

As A SEA CLIFF is eroded irregularities develop in the coast. These may be due to differences in the concentration of wave energy or simply to differences in hardness or structure of the rocks. Retreat of the cliff may leave some columnar masses of rock standing isolated as islands just off the shore. Because these columns frequently resemble stacks sticking out of the water they are called *stacks* (Fig. 8–28). *Sea caves* and *arches* are likely to develop when the rocks exposed in the cliff are stratified sediments of varying hardness. The weaker units are undercut rapidly, sometimes leaving the resistant capping layers as a natural bridge or arch over them (Fig. 8–29). Such features, like the stacks, are transient. They will disappear due to erosion and perhaps be replaced by similar features farther inland. If the cliff is composed of a mass of a resistant rock, wave action may produce a *notch* near the base. Notches are the initial stages of undercutting, which will eventually lead to a large-scale movement as the cliff breaks away above the notch and falls into the sea.

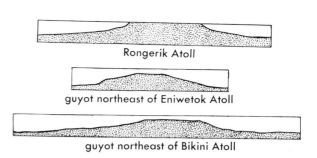

Rongerik Atoll

guyot northeast of Eniwetok Atoll

guyot northeast of Bikini Atoll

FIG. 8–27. / *Profile of a guyot.*

FIG. 8–28. / *Sea stacks.*

FIG. 8–29. / *Sea arch formed by wave erosion along the west coast. Note the smooth surface above the cave. This is a remnant of an elevated sea terrace. (Photo by the author.)*

Ocean Canyons

SUBMARINE CANYONS on the continental shelves would be quite impressive features if they were exposed where we could see them. Several are as deep as the canyon of the Yellowstone River, 1,100 feet. They are usually, although not always, located off the mouths of rivers and are characteristically V-shaped valleys with tributaries. They often wind in sinuous curves across the continental shelves. A large number of these submarine canyons are well known. One of the most prominent is the canyon of the Hudson River, which has been traced far out into the abyssal plain. Others have been mapped and studied along the coast of southern California. Among the California canyons are the La Jolla, Cape San Lucas, and Carmel-Monterey Bay canyons. Others have been found on the continental shelf off the mouth of the Congo, the Amazon, and many other rivers.

Some of these canyons undoubtedly were eroded during the ice ages by streams which flowed on the continental shelves. But then, as now, cutting of the canyons beyond the shelves was most likely the result of submarine debris-charged currents. It may be that the loads of streams are carried farther out into the oceans than we think, but it seems likely that much of the erosion of these canyons is accomplished when deposition of load by streams in canyons builds up steep piles of debris in conelike deposits. When these become too steep they are unstable. Slight earthquakes or the addition of more load may bring about a submarine landslide, which causes the debris to flow down very rapidly, eroding the canyon walls and floor (Fig. 8–30).

Evolution of Coastal Features

SEA LEVEL HAS PROVEN TO BE UNSTABLE in the past. It rises and falls in relation to the land as the crust is warped up or down, and in periods when glaciation traps large amounts of water in ice. This instability of the sea level is important in the evolution of features along shores. It means that over a long period of time the landforms that develop are not simply a result of continual wave action at a specific level, for wave action is intimately related to the relative rise or fall of the sea. Some of the earliest classifications of coasts were based on the distinction between coasts of emergence and those of submergence. Although it is highly desirable to classify coasts according to their modes of origin, this means of classification unfortunately fails because the same features may develop along shorelines of emergence and those of submergence at different stages in their evolution.

Forms that develop at the contact of sea and land are determined mainly by three factors:

Configuration of the land and sea floor,

Whether the shoreline is advancing across the land or receding from it, and

The nature of the processes of wave erosion.

The last of these is essentially the same throughout the world, but the first two are highly variable. Along the eastern coast of the United States there is a relatively broad, nearly flat continental shelf (Fig. 8–4). From Maine to New York the coast is irregular and characterized by sea stacks and wave-cut sea cliffs. As far south as the Chesapeake Bay rivers are partially drowned to form estuaries, arms of the sea extending up river valleys. The southeastern coast is marked by long, smooth offshore bars. From these bars the sea bottom gradually slopes out onto the continental shelf. This is also true of the Gulf coast of Florida and Texas. The continental shelf is narrow along the Gulf coast off Alabama, Mississippi, and Louisiana, and the outer part is highly irregular. The entire west coast of the United States is marked by sea cliffs, general irregularities, and narrow irregular shelves.

If sea level should drop throughout the world, the shoreline of the United States would be located out on the continental shelf. The entire eastern coast would then be a gently sloping surface. In the Gulf and along parts of the western coast, some of the present irregularities on the shelf would stand up as headlands. These irregular areas would resemble other areas where

FIG. 8–30. / "Sandfall." This "fall" was photographed in the Cape San Lucas submarine canyon, Baja California, by Conrad Limbaugh, a diving specialist at the University of California's Scripps Institution of Oceanography. The "fall" is about 30 feet high. Currents feed sand from the nearby beaches into the canyon. (Photo by courtesy of the University of California, La Jolla, Scripps Institution of Oceanography.)

sea level has risen in relation to the land, drowning river valleys and producing an irregular coast line with islands and headlands as dominant features.

The concept of evolution of coastal landforms is best illustrated by considering two fundamentally different examples:

Evolution along rugged coasts like those commonly formed when the coast has been submerged or has features of submergence, and

Evolution along low, smooth, gently sloping coasts such as recently-emerged parts of the continental shelf.

Evolution of Irregular Coasts (Classical Submerged Coasts)

IMAGINE THAT A HILLY or mountainous part of the country is lowered below sea level. Rivers will be drowned. The coastline will be highly irregular as valleys are filled with water. Offshore islands will appear. Hillsides will drop off sharply into the water. Initially, at least, no beaches, bars, or other marine deposits will be found along the coasts (Fig. 8–31). Because the water drops suddenly to a great depth, waves coming into shore will not break until they have almost reached land. As a result, a cliff will form rapidly. Debris from the cliff will consist in large part of blocks too large for longshore currents to move. These blocks will be rolled and gradually broken up, but most of the debris will rest on the bottom just offshore. Through this process a *wave-built terrace* will be formed. At the same time, continued wave action and mass wasting will cut the cliff back, giving rise to a *wave-cut terrace* at the foot of the sea cliff.

After some time a *profile of equilibrium* will have been established along most of the shoreline. A profile of equilibrium is obtained when the slope of the offshore sea floor is just sufficient to permit a seaward movement of material derived from the sea cliff to the edge of the wave-built terrace. The concentration of wave erosion on the headlands produces a shoreline with fewer irregularities. This is aided by the formation of bars along the shore. Some bars are built out from headlands into the bays. Others form at the heads of bays and along their sides. Eventually bars may entirely close off the bay, and the coast will become relatively smooth. Beaches that formed at headlands become essentially continuous with baymouth bars. Bays and lagoons left behind these bars are gradually filled in by sediments furnished from the land.

Of course, these processes take a great deal of time. Once the coast has attained the profile of equilibrium characteristics we have just described, it changes even more slowly. But it does not cease to change. Waves continue to break up rocks exposed in the sea cliff, and longshore currents continue to move material. The shoreline gradually retreats inland, and bars and beaches move with it. Eventually the shoreline lies along the heads of the drowned valleys. By this time, if there has been no fluctuation of sea level, there will be a broad wave-cut terrace, and the cycle of erosion will begin to approach what may be called *old age*. Actually, because of the relatively rapid fluctuations of sea level over geologic time, old age is seldom reached, if ever.

Evolution of Coasts with Gently Sloping Sea Floor (Emerged Shore Lines)

EMERGENCE OF OFFSHORE continental slopes would in most places bring to the surface an almost featureless plain sloping gently into deeper waters, since the slope of the typical continental shelf amounts to only a few degrees. A submerged bar would form on the landward side of the zone of breakers, and would be built up higher and higher until it emerged, extending parallel to the initially smooth shore. The almost continuous bars on the United States Atlantic coast from Cape Hatteras southward are of this origin. Once this bar has risen above the surface, a lagoon forms behind it. This lagoon will be a relatively still body of water; subsequently it may become a swamp and then later be filled with sediment. The only breaks through the offshore bar are *tidal inlets* and *outlets* for streams flowing from the continent.

The permanence of the bar will depend largely on the supply of sand and the nature of currents moving along the shore. If, over a long period, currents are capable of moving more of a load than they are being supplied, sand from the offshore bar will be removed, the bar will slowly disappear, and the shoreline will retreat toward the land. The lagoon will be drained and rapidly washed away, and wave action will be concentrated on the mainland. If the waves advance close to the shore before they break, they will cut a sea cliff and build a terrace, maintaining a profile of equilibrium. Once this stage has been reached, further modifications are identical with those of the shore of submergence.

FIG. 8–31. / *Evolution of shores, according to the idealized cycle of* W. M. Davis. *The early stage is at top in both of these sequences.*

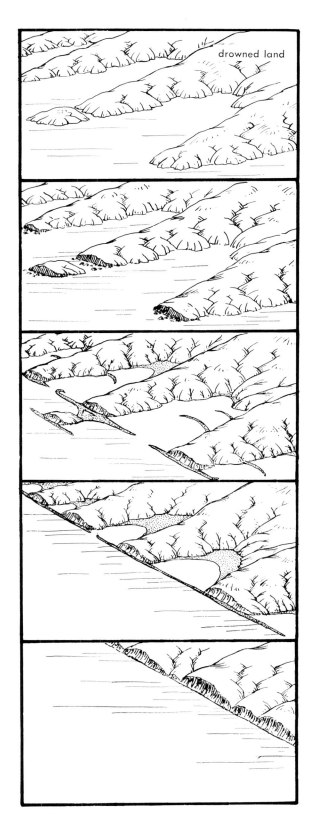

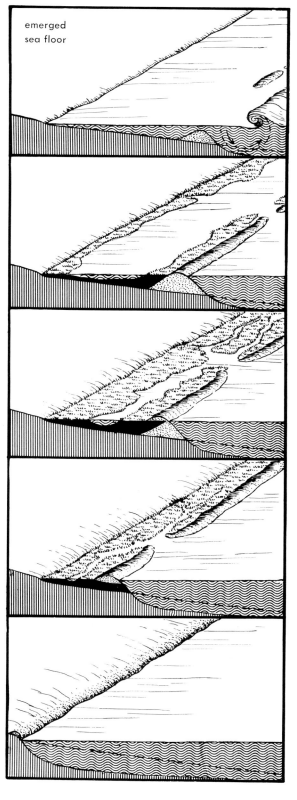

FIG. 9–1. / *Bay head beach. (Crown Copyright.)*

9 /

Modern Environments of Sedimentation at the Margin of the Ocean

MARINE ENVIRONMENTS ARE IMPORTANT NOT only because they are the principal sites of formation of modern sediments, but also because they have unique potential to reveal to us the geologic past. Many sedimentary rocks now exposed on continents were once deposited in oceans or in the zone of transition between oceans and continents. These sediments and sedimentary rocks have individual characteristics that reflect the influence of the environment in which they were deposited. Recognition that certain characteristics of a rock reflect some particular environment is one of the important keys to unraveling the history represented by the stratigraphic successions—the sequences of layers of rock deposited in ancient seas. Just as sediments deposited from air, water, or a glacier differ from one another in textural, compositional, and structural characteristics, so do other, more subtle environmental conditions leave their imprint on sediment. Fossil fauna found in a sediment provide valuable clues to such facts about the water in which it was deposited as temperature, depth, oxygen content, and penetration by light. Many sediments are composed largely of fossils or calcium carbonate secreted by animals. In other

sediments fossils are almost entirely absent, suggesting possible oxygen deficiency of the water in which deposition occurred. The nature of movements in the water is indicated by the presence or absence of certain structures. Consider the differences between deposition under the following types of circumstances—in a quiet lake, from a turbulent flow of sediment set off by a submarine landslide at the edge of a delta where a stream carrying large quantities of sediment in suspension loses its transporting power, on a rocky coast where wave action breaks up the sea cliff, and on a low shore where longshore currents sweep in sand and silt to be deposited on offshore bars. Other environmental factors governing deposition include the extent and configuration of the environment, the climate of the region, and finally the nature of the sediment supplied to the environment.

It is possible to group sedimentary environments which have essentially the same characteristics in a workable classification system. However, great variety exists within each of these. The truly marine environments are usually classified according to depth—*littoral* (tidal), *neritic* (shallow water), *bathyal* (intermediate depth), and *abyssal* (deep water). Lit-

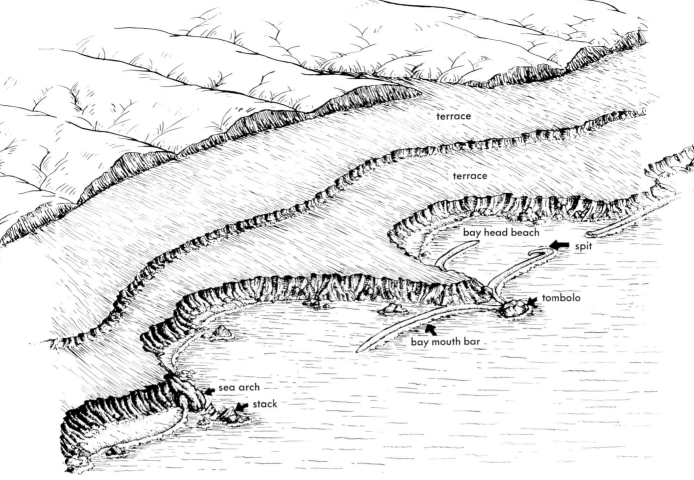

FIG. 9–2. / *Characteristic physiographic features found along a rugged coast.*

toral environments are well known and are readily subdivided. It is here that influences of both ocean and land are impressed on the sediment, for it marks the transition between the continental and marine environments. Within this transitional zone local features such as deltas, lagoons, beaches, and swamps provide specialized environmental conditions of importance.

Transitional Marine Environments

THE LITTORAL ZONE IS THAT PART OF THE shore between the highest flood tides and the lowest ebb tides. Among the most important factors that play a role in determining the nature of the deposits in the littoral zone are: the configuration of the shoreline, stability of the shore (whether it is stable, emerging, or submerging), quantity and type of sediment being brought to the shore.

There are three distinctly different types of littoral environments: those characterized by sea cliffs and wave-cut terraces; those located along low, open shores, similar to sections of the central Texas coast; and those with extensive, nearly level plains, known as *tidal flats*, submerged twice daily by tides.

Cliffed Shorelines

RUGGED SHORELINES have cliffs ranging in slope from 10 or 15 degrees to vertical. Usually there is a platform of more gentle slope at the base of the cliff, but some cliffs plunge into water of great depth, leaving no littoral zone at all. In other cases, particularly in bays, the platform is covered by a beach. More than any other environment, a cliffed shoreline is dominated by wave action and mechanical energy. The nature of the sediment supplied from the immediate vicinity depends to a large extent on the material making up the cliffs. If hard, crystalline igneous or metamorphic rocks, or compact sedimentary rocks are exposed, angular blocks and boulders will be found along the narrow littoral zone. If the cliff is composed of poorly consolidated sediment, masses which slump into the sea will tend to be broken up and carried off rapidly by current action.

Along irregular coastlines the most common site for a beach is at the head of a bay or an inlet (Fig. 9–1). Here the beach is protected from wave action and at least partially from longshore currents. Headlands projecting out on either side of the bay prevent rapid removal of beach materials by drifting. Headlands, as we have seen, are sites of the most intense wave erosion, but when the supply of sediment is very great, beaches may develop even at the foot of headland sea cliffs. These beaches are likely to be destroyed during storms, and they will reflect markedly any changes in supply of sand. Sands from headland beaches drift in the direction of longshore currents, and these sand beaches may even be built out across the mouth of the bay.

At first a submerged bar is built out from the tip of the headland beach. With the addition of more sand, this may emerge and form a projection out from the shore into the bay. Such a feature is called a *spit* (Fig. 9–2). The end of the spit is generally curved back into the bay, but with a sufficient supply of sediment it may continue to be built out even completely across the bay to form a *baymouth beach*. Such beaches are not likely to cross large bodies of water, because rivers empty into most such bodies, and the water must find an outlet into the sea. But the outlet may be no more than a narrow channel.

Tombolos (Fig. 9–2), are bars or beaches of sediment built between islands and the mainland. The islands are usually small patches of land, like sea stacks, left as a result of wave erosion. When the rate of wave erosion is reduced or when the supply of sand is increased, the small strait between such an island and the land slows the longshore drift of sand and a bar forms across the strait. As more sand is brought into the zone, the submerged bar rises above sea level. It is built up more during high

FIG. 9–3. / *Air photograph of coast in Lee County, Florida. Shore current deflects sediment brought into Gulf through inlet from Charlotte Harbor. (U.S. Dept. of Agriculture.)*

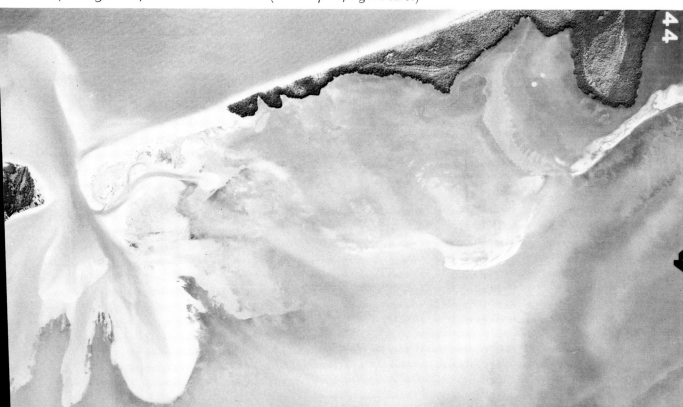

tides and even more during periods of higher waves, provided they are not so high that they destroy it.

Low Shorelines

LIKE THE CLIFFED shore, the low shore is dominated by wave action; however, most of the wave energy is spent before reaching the upper parts of the beach. Sand is by far the most common sediment along these shorelines, although cobbles, pebbles, silt, or even clay may be found. The type of sediment available, the distance of its source from the beach, and the strength of longshore currents govern which of these sediments will be found in any particular location. In seas containing a high concentration of calcium carbonate, sand may be composed of shell or reef fragments or even calcareous oölites (Fig. 9–18). Sands of this sort appear on shores of the Bahama platform and on some atolls. In some areas olivine or volcanic ash may make up the sand. Silts and clay may be components of sands in this environment, where rivers carrying them in suspension enter the sea.

Along most of the coast of the eastern United States from New Jersey to Florida, and along the Gulf Coast, long bars and beaches have been built up off the shore (Fig. 9–3). Generally a lagoon separates the offshore beach from the mainland, and there are occasional breaks through bars or beaches where streams enter the ocean or Gulf. Along coasts which have offshore beaches there is generally a submerged *offshore bar* beyond the beach. This bar is deposited in the same manner as the offshore beach. Where waves break, water is extremely turbulent, and the breakers are full of sand picked up from the bottom. This sand is rapidly dropped out as soon as the wave moves farther toward shore and the turbulence dies down. Therefore a shallow depression forms just within the zone of breakers and a bar forms on the landward side of it where the sand settles out. This bar may be built up by the addition of sediment carried along the shore inside the bar (Fig. 9–4). It is raised during periods of high waves, when sediment is brought in from great depths offshore (Fig. 9–5).

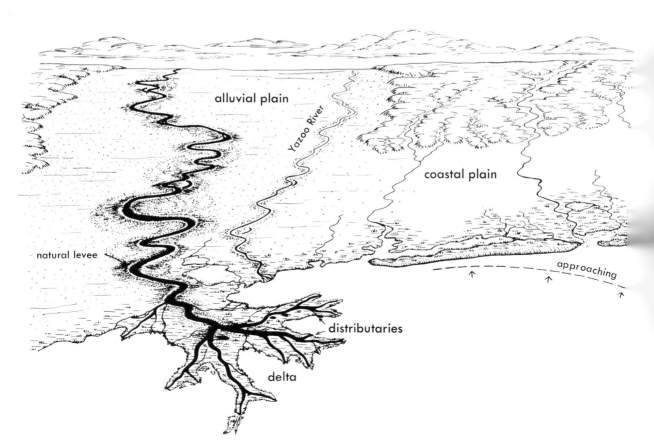

FIG. 9–4. / *Australian coastline. This is a shoreline of deposition. Note the spits, both modern and old, the marshes in which the river flows, the modern sand beaches, and the older beaches. The light color in the ocean water is caused by reflection of light from a shallow sandy sea bottom. (Photo by courtesy of the U.S. Air Force.)*

Marine Environments along the Central Texas Coast

THE CENTRAL TEXAS COAST is in many ways typical of low coastal areas throughout the world. Here are four principal types of environments—deltas, protected bays, barrier islands located offshore, and an open continental shelf (Fig. 9–7). Among the main factors influencing processes of sedimentation and types of sediments being formed are variations in wave and current action, in depth of water, in salinity, and in supply of sediments.

DELTAS: The deltaic environments are similar to those of the Mississippi River delta. Deposits are high in clay and organic content on the marsh top of the delta. Coarser sands and silts are found in channels of streams now flowing across the delta surface and also in abandoned channels. At the margin of the delta, silt containing wood fibers and calcareous aggregates are common.

BAYS: Shallow bays are protected from wave and current action by offshore barrier beaches. Water in these bays is calm, and generally is influenced by daily tides and, at several points, by freshwater

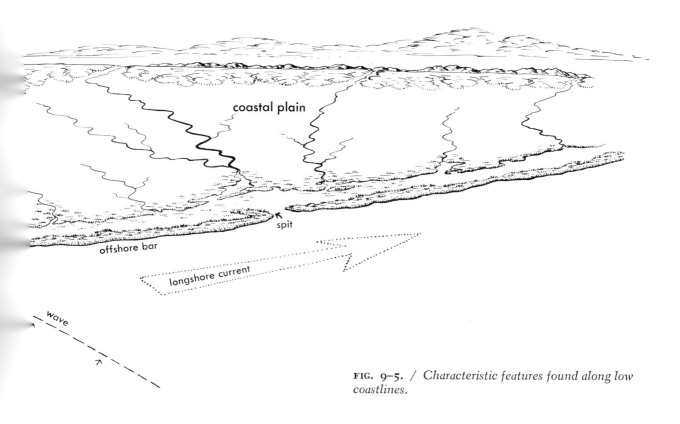

FIG. 9–5. / *Characteristic features found along low coastlines.*

streams. Like deltas, the bays are not uniform throughout. There are a number of subenvironments. These arise from slight differences between the conditions in the middle of the bays, where open water prevails, and around the margins, where the waters are influenced by sediments washed in around the edge. Other variations are found in the straits connecting bays and near the mouths of streams entering the bays.

BARRIER ISLANDS: The coastal bays and lagoons along the central Texas coast are separated from the open waters of the Gulf by a long, narrow belt of barrier islands and offshore bars. These bars are similar to others bordering most of the Gulf Coast and the eastern coast south of Cape Hatteras. In order to go from one of the bays out to a barrier island it is necessary to cross a low, swampy area. This is a shallow, partially submerged belt affected by tides. The floor of the swamp is covered by an intricate pattern of small channels carrying water from islands into the bays and ponds where circulation of water is restricted. In places, emerged parts of the swamp have narrow sand beaches around them, but elsewhere the swamp floor is covered by sand mixed with soft silt and clay. A large part of the coarser sediments in the swamp is made up of aggregates of clay and silt which harden together during low tides when the bottom sediments are exposed to sun and wind. At these times evaporation of the moisture in the sediment takes place, and as water in pore spaces near the surface evaporates more water is pulled upward by capillary action. This water contains calcium carbonate and salts. As water continues to evaporate, these salts crystallize or are precipitated and cement together the top layer of the sediment. In the swamp sediment there is also a large amount of organic matter, primarily wood fibers, decaying plant matter, shells of Foraminifera (microscopic marine animals), and the remains of echinoderms (starfish, sea urchins, etc.).

The barrier islands are largely covered by sand dunes. The sediment found in these is almost 100 per cent sand. The dunes are cross-bedded, and the sand is well sorted as a result of having been transported by the wind. Sand here is very much like that found on beaches on the Gulf side of the island. The source of supply for these sands is the beach. They are washed up by waves and then blown farther up on the island by winds. Most movement of the sand takes place during low tide, when there is time for the sand grains high up on the beach to become dry.

As long as they are being washed over by every incoming wave, water in pore spaces between grains of sand holds them together on the beach. Additional large quantities of sand are deposited above high tide level during storms. Beaches are composed of well-sorted sands which differ from dune sediment mainly in that they contain more shell fragments, particularly Foraminifera tests. Since these fragments are too large to be moved by wind, they are therefore almost absent from dunes.

CONTINENTAL SHELF. From the beaches the Gulf bottom slopes off irregularly for several hundred feet, into water that is about 20 feet deep. Irregularities in this zone are offshore bars and depressions apparently formed during storms. Essential differences between sands on the beach and those found in this near-shore belt are size and roundness of the grains. Near-shore sand is smaller and less perfectly rounded. Fauna are essentially the same as those on the beach. By far the most distinctive feature of these sediments is the presence of the mineral glauconite, an iron potassium silicate called green sand, in them.

FIG. 9–6. / Drainage pattern in the tidal mud flats at low tide, near Yarmouth, Nova Scotia. (Photo by courtesy of the Royal Canadian Air Force.)

Tidal Flats

TIDAL FLATS DEVELOP ON low-lying land which is near sea level yet protected from wave erosion and strong currents (Figs. 9–6 and 9–8). They are generally located near an abundant source of sediment, such as the mouth of a large river. Sediments on tidal flats consist of soft, water-soaked slime. There is a large amount of fine silt and clay and a little sand, all mixed with varying amounts of shell fragments, sea-urchin spines, fine plant detritus, and fragments of the shells of diatoms, Foraminifera, and ostracods. In some areas excrement of worms and other invertebrates makes up a significant part of the sediment. Many invertebrates inhabit the tidal-flat environment. These include gastropods, worms, and pelecypods.

Deposits on tidal flats—clays, sands, and silts—are stratified and cross-bedded, reflecting re-working of the sediment by shifting currents. The amount of sediment and rate of sedimentation on certain present-day tidal flats are surprising. As much as 7.3 meters of sediments were deposited within 3 years in the harbor entrance to Wilhelmshaven, Germany. The rate is sufficient to make continuous dredging necessary to keep the channel open for shipping.

Sources of muds vary from place to place. Some tidal flats are thought to originate almost entirely from deposition of suspended matter in streams, but others appear to be swamp or glacial deposits reworked by the forces acting in the tide zone. Animal excrement accounts for a large amount of sediment in some tidal flats and contributes to making a very rich soil. In Holland, when a tidal flat is built up close to sea level or slightly above it by storm waves, the Dutch construct dikes around a section of the flat, then drain it and use it for agricultural purposes.

Deltas

DELTAIC ENVIRONMENTS are composites of a number of different types of sedimentary conditions. No other type of environment contains

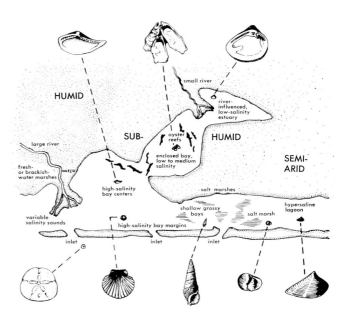

FIG. 9–7. / *Marine invertebrates. Schematic section showing some typical marine invertebrates found in each part of this marine environment. (After Robert H. Parker, Am. Assoc. Petroleum Geologists Bull. 43.)*

FIG. 9–8. / *Photo of tidal flats near Mont St. Michel. (Photo by French Cultural Services.)*

so many different physical, biological, and chemical conditions in such intimate association.

A delta forms when the amount of sediment being deposited by a stream exceeds the amount of erosion and removal accomplished by wave action and currents. If the stream supplies more than can be distributed, the delta grows. If a balance is reached, the delta becomes stabilized in size, and if the capacity of wave and current action exceeds deposition the delta will eventually disappear. Deltas are not confined to oceans and transitional environments. They form in lakes, and in streams where tributaries supply more debris than the main stream can transport.

Usually the stream enters and flows across

the delta on a low slope. Fresh water and sediment are carried out to the edge of the delta, where the stream enters a larger body of water. At this point the stream loses its transporting power. Coarse sand, silt, and other sediments are deposited. Clay materials, which are in suspension in fresh water, are deposited when the fresh water mixes with salt water and form an extensive layer of clay. Heavier substances are deposited on the slope of the delta front, and finer matter is carried farther out in suspension or solution before it settles to the bottom. Three sets of beds are formed almost simultaneously. The thickest are the layers of inclined sediment on the front slope of the delta; these units are called the *fore-set beds*. Beyond them finer sediments settle on a nearly flat bottom, creating the *bottom-set beds*. The third group, the *top-set beds*, is composed of flat-lying sediments deposited on top of the delta by streams flowing across the delta, marshes, or low areas on either side of the streams. These top-set beds are laid on truncated fore-set beds, forming cross-bedding, as the delta is built seaward (Fig. 9–9).

Mississippi Delta

ONE OF THE most intensively studied deltas in the world is that of the Mississippi River (Fig. 9–10). During the last 10,000 years the Mississippi River has carried more than 8,000 cubic miles of sediments into the Gulf of Mexico. Most of this has been deposited in the delta and near the coast. The weight of this mass has caused the continental shelf to be depressed by an estimated 300 to 500 feet under the delta.

The Mississippi River flows over an extremely low slope along its lower reaches. As it approaches the delta the river begins to break up into a number of smaller streams called *distributaries*. The pattern formed by these resembles that of a braided stream. These distributaries, carrying a heavy load of silt and dissolved material, flow outward across the delta into the Gulf. Seen from far above they resemble the veins of a leaf or the bones of a bird's foot. Between distributaries there are extensive marshes slightly above sea level. Streams are actually above the level of these marshes over a large part of the area, since seasonal floods build natural levees which confine the stream channels. As the distributaries reach the end

FIG. 9–9. / *Deltaic deposits. The foreset and bottomset beds of this small delta are clearly seen in the cliff face southwest of Clinton, Massachusetts. (Photo by W. C. Alden, courtesy of the U.S. Geological Survey.)*

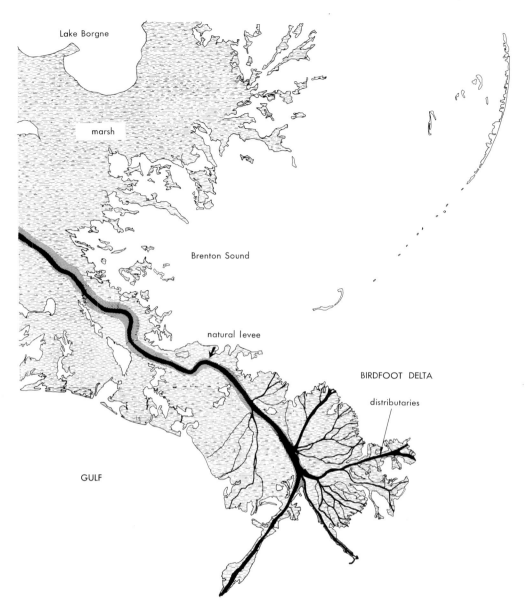

FIG. 9–10. / *Map view of the delta of the Mississippi River, the Birdfoot Delta. The various environments depicted are described in the text.*

of their channels, the stream loads are dropped as lobate deposits on the delta front. The streams have built these lobes out great distances, leaving bays and troughlike depressions between them. Farther out, the slope of the delta diminishes and grades onto the nearly flat bottom of the continental shelf.

Marine Swamp Environment

THE NAMES SWAMP, BOG, or MORASS are applied to low, spongy land generally saturated with moisture. This type of land is not confined to areas near sea level or even to flat land, although it is much more likely to form and less likely to be drained in one of these locations. Swamps cover large areas of continents. Some estimates put the amount of land covered by swamps of one sort or another at more than one million square miles. Not only are they important environments today, but there is a rich and extensive record of this type of environment in the geologic past. At various times swamps have covered much larger areas than they do today. Late in the Paleozoic Era swamps became

FIG. 9–11. / A restored Pennsylvanian coal swamp. It was from such forests as these that the coal fields of the continental interior of the United States originated. The ferns are similar to many living plants, but the lycopods, Sigillaria and Lepidodendron *are unlike any living trees. Notice also the small amphibian at the base of the largest trees. A large cockroach is in the foreground on a fallen lepidodendron. (Photo by courtesy of the Chicago Natural History Museum.)*

so extensive throughout the world that the periods are named for the carbonaceous rocks formed from the swamp deposits (Fig. 9–11).

Two general types of swamps are recognized —marine swamps, located along coasts where both brackish and fresh water are present, and fresh-water swamps (Fig. 9–12). Most fresh-water swamps are located in basins or on flat or gently sloping land that may be far removed from the sea. In general, however, the most favorable position for the location of a swamp is near sea level, thus explaining why this particular environment is so commonly preserved in the rock record; relatively slight elevations of sea level will cover them so that they are preserved under marine deposits. For this reason swamp deposits usually grade into marine sediments in stratigraphic sequences.

Abundant rainfall, or some other water supply, is necessary for the continuance of a swamp, which is generally characterized by slow circulation of water or by near stagnation. Biological factors dominate this environment. Swamps are especially favorable for the growth of plants, and remains of plants make up a large part of the sediment. The energy sources in this lush environment are largely chemical reactions and thermal energy supplied from the sun.

Marine Swamps

MARINE SWAMPS are not uncommon along coasts of the eastern and southern United States. Many of them have formed behind offshore bars that parallel the seashore. These were initially lagoons that have since been filled by sediment from the continent and by remains of plants. Other marine swamps originate when the sea floor is slightly elevated, exposing a broad, nearly flat plain during at least part of the day. Plant life is most abundant where there is little or no agitation of the water, thus the most favorable areas for swamp conditions are regions with a relatively small range between high and low tides. Quite a few swamps, however, are at least partially, and some completely, covered by sea water during high tide. Within a marine swamp different plants are favored by certain special

FIG. 9–12. / *Views of swamp in the Mississippi Valley. (Photos by the author.)*

conditions; in tropical climates, for example, marine swamps contain mangrove or cypress forests. However, a very large percentage of marine swamps are partially covered by moss, and most contain grasses and reeds in abundance. As plants die they fall into the water and begin to decay. If they can be buried rapidly enough by other plant remains or by marine sediments, there is a good chance that they will be preserved and may eventually be transformed into coal. If burial is not rapid, oxidation and bacterial action soon break them down. For this reason only thin accumulations of swamp deposits are found if the level of the swamp remains stable. Probably no more than a few yards of plant matter can accumulate, since water depth is seldom great. The thick sequences of swamp sediments so common in stratigraphic sequences of the Carboniferous Period must indicate changes in the position of sea level in relation to the swamp. A slowly subsiding area would obviously be the most favorable site for preservation of great thicknesses of such sediment.

Dismal Swamp

THE DISMAL SWAMP of Virginia and North Carolina is one of the largest marine swamps in the United States, and in many ways it is a typical example of this type of swamp environment. A thick, matlike body of plant matter and terrigenous sediment covers most of the swamp, which occupies a saucer-like depression on one of the terraces of the coastal plain. This depression is a recently emerged sea bottom which now stands a few feet above sea level. It is bordered by higher ground on the western side, but on the north, east, and south rims the surrounding land is not higher than the swamp itself.

In the swamp the mat of organic sediment, acting like a huge sponge, is able to soak up and hold water at a higher level. In the center of the swamp is a large body of water called Lake Drummond. The spongelike action of the swamp sediment keeps the surface level of this lake more than 20 feet above the elevation of the border of the swamp. There is doubt that the swamp will be able to continue building up a thicker accumulation of sediment. In all probability the mat is now drawing water to as great a height as it can maintain. Therefore, this is a good example of a swamp in which the accumulation of material has reached the maximum depth possible without subsidence of the area. If subsidence should occur, then the area would accumulate new sediment, and the mat would slowly build up until it had equaled its present height above sea level.

Below the level of the mat of organic debris, sediments of the Dismal Swamp are marine deposits of silt and sand interbedded with continental deposits. From this we conclude that the area has been alternately covered by and exposed above the sea. Terrigenous silts and clay are being brought into the swamp from the west today and are being interbedded with decaying remains of reeds, grasses, and other plants. A few small stream channels wind through parts of the swamp, and these are the only sites in the swamp that are covered by sand and silt.

Neritic Environments

THE OUTER MARGIN OF THE NERITIC ZONE corresponds roughly to the edge of the continental shelves; the inner margin is the position of the lowest tides. In this zone water depth varies from zero to about 100 fathoms. The neritic environment covers only about 10 per cent of the earth's surface, but it is by far the most important zone insofar as the formation of sedimentary rocks now exposed on the continents is concerned. The sediments of this environment are more diversified than are those of any other environment. Sediments are derived in part from continents and animals that are dependent on the shore and sea bottoms and in part from the pelagic communities. *Pelagic* communities are groups of marine organisms which live free from direct dependence on the bottom or shore. These communities are of two types—free-swimming forms, *nekton*, and floating forms, *plankton*. Because neritic environments are important and highly diversified, several noteworthy examples are considered, in addition to the general treatment of continental shelf deposits. These examples include an atoll and the Bahamian platforms.

General Features of the Continental Shelves

CONTINENTAL SHELVES are far from uniform in nature. Off the eastern and southeastern coasts of the United States a lowering of sea level to the edge of the shelf would reveal a wide, gently sloping land surface. Florida would be roughly twice its present width. Off the southern coast of California the shelf area is very irregular and includes deep basins and high mountain blocks situated between the coastline and the steep escarpment which borders the deep Pacific basin. The outer margin of the shelf off the Mississippi Delta is also very irregular. These irregularities are probably the results of subsidence and slumping of the edge of the shelf and may be related to a major fault zone bordering deep parts of the Gulf of Mexico.

The shape and extent of the shelf is determined by the nature of the continental margins. Along coasts characterized by young folded and faulted mountains the shelf is narrow. Wide shelves appear most often off coasts characterized by broad lowlands, off glaciated lands, and off many of the world's largest rivers. The largest shelf area is in the Arctic, where the width reaches 800 miles. Shelves are commonly between 10 and 20 miles wide.

The shelf environment is penetrated by sunlight. This tends to make it warmer and more suitable for a larger number of marine organisms than the deeper areas. The main forces of erosion and deposition in the environment are waves and current action and, to a smaller extent, chemical activity. Almost all the shelf is disturbed periodically by wave motion extending downward from the surface. Even the outer margins are affected by great waves associated with storms and tides, and longshore currents move continuously over the shelves. Temperature is an important environmental factor. It depends primarily on latitude and the temperatures of the water brought onto the shelves by oceanic currents.

Sediments on the shelves are dominated by terrestrial debris near shore, but at greater distances offshore biological factors become increasingly important. Several generalizations may be drawn regarding distribution of sediment.

1. Sediment textures do not vary systematically either along or perpendicular to shorelines. Many areas show a progressive decrease in size of sands or silts out from beaches for several thousand feet. But this often grades back into coarser sediments again. Several explanations have been offered to account for coarsening of sediment toward the continental shelf margins. One is that storm waves have carried both coarse and fine material out to that position, and that later the fine sediment has been sorted out and removed by weaker current and wave action. Along the edge of the shelf off the eastern coasts of the United States it may be that wave action has sorted the sediments and that the Gulf Stream has removed the finer sizes and carried them into deeper waters.

2. Not all shelves have coarse sediments at their outer margins. Some show a progressive decrease in the size of sediment from the shoreline out to the margin of the shelf.

3. Bottoms formed of bare rock are found on some shelves. They are more common on narrow shelves than on broader ones. Most are covered by a thin veneer of sediment that is in the process of being transported to deeper water. For many years it has been assumed that these were wave-cut and wave-built terraces. Photographs taken under water now show that the outer margins are not all wave-built terraces composed of deposits. Instead, rocky outcrops appear right at the edge of the shelf. The sediment that is deposited near the edge of these solid shelves periodically slumps off or slides downslope.

4. The character of sediments on shelves is closely related to the types of land that are located near them. Muddy sediments are generally found on shelves beyond the mouths of large rivers such as the Amazon, Mississippi, Elbe, Yangtze Kiang, and Indus. On shelves off regions recently covered by continental glaciers sediment is a mixture of rock fragments, sands, and mud like that produced by glacial erosion. This is typical of the Barents Sea north of Norway and Sweden, Baffin Bay between Greenland and Canada, Ross Sea in the Antarctic, and the Gulf of Maine. Where high mountains

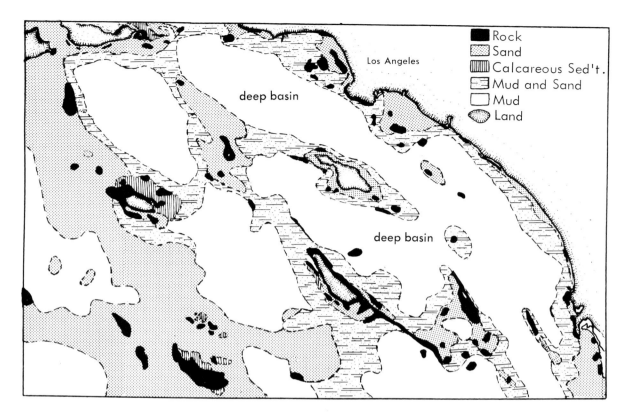

Rock
Sand
Calcareous Sed't.
Mud and Sand
Mud
Land

FIG. 9–13. / *Distribution of marine sediments off the coast of southern California. Compare the distribution of sediments here with those along the Texas coast and the northeastern coast of the United States. Here the shelf is very narrow and the region is characterized by deep basins separated by blocks which stand high and in a few cases appear as islands.* (Modified after Revelle and Shepard, Recent Marine Sediments, 1955.)

border the coast, an abundance of gravels, coarse sands, and other coarse sediments flood out onto the shelves. If lowlands or plains border the sea, sediments are usually fine and contain a large proportion of animal and plant remains.

Marine Environments off the Coast of Southern California

UNLIKE MOST DEEP SEAS, the submarine landscape off the coast of southern California is made up of a number of deep basins separated by higher blocks (Fig. 9–13). The basins are as deep as the abyssal zones in some parts of the area, and the blocks rise above sea level in a few places. Where these blocks have been elevated above sea level, they are bare of sediment, and shallow waters around them are typical of the neritic environments. This particular area is of special interest, because it is

an example of a region in which the topography has acted as a controlling factor in distribution of sediments.

Near the shoreline there is a narrow continental shelf often less than a mile wide. On this we find the sand and silty sediments carried into the sea by rivers. They are sorted by wave action and longshore currents before they are transported very far down the shore. In this zone near shore there is an almost perfect distribution of sediments according to size. Coarser materials are dropped nearest the shore, and these grade into progressively finer materials farther from shore. This progressive change does not, however, continue out to the edge of the shelf, where the sediment begins to get coarser, and even sand and gravels may be found. It is possible that storm waves creating movement down to the depth of the edge of the shelf cause shifting and consequent sorting of the sediments. In this way the finer sediments may be periodically removed to deeper water.

Submarine canyons cut across the shelf in a number of places. These are deep enough to be relatively free of any surface wave disturbances that might tend to sort the sediments. Sediments found in the canyons are generally fine silts and sands, but there are patches of coarser sediment where sides of the canyons have slumped into the gorge.

In the deep basins beyond the continental shelf sediments are not nearly as well sorted as those on the shelf. In the centers of the basins, which have relatively flat floors, mud is the most characteristic material. These muds are composed of fine matter carried out in suspension. Around the edges of the basins the muds appear mixed with sands and silts brought down from shallower water.

Barrier Reefs and Atolls

THE BATTLES in the South Pacific during World War II were largely fought on a number of small, isolated, volcanic islands surrounded by barrier reefs and others, called *atolls,* that were hardly more than ringlike reefs with beaches. Lack of understanding of the geology of the atolls and barrier reefs cost the lives of many American Marines during the early part of the war. Landing craft were halted a few hundred yards offshore by reefs that were only slightly submerged below water level. Such reefs caused some of the heaviest casualties of the battle of Tarawa. Aside from their strategic importance, atolls and other reef formations are famous for their beauty, and ancient reefs are among the most prolific oil-producing zones.

Although reefs are often called coral reefs, they are in fact usually composed of the remains of many types of organisms. Corals may not even make up the largest part of the reef. Colonial invertebrate animals such as bryozoans, marine bivalves, and plants are frequently as numerous in reefs as corals.

Barrier Reefs

THESE REEFS tend to encircle the island volcano, or groups of island volcanoes, with which they are associated. They vary in width and distance offshore, but many are 100 yards or more wide and are separated from the central island by a lagoon that may be several miles wide. On the oceanward side of the reef, debris broken off by storm waves lies at the base of the living reef. The reef itself is generally just about the level of the water and may be submerged during high tides and exposed at low tides. Fine sands and algal remains cover the bottom of the lagoon, which is relatively quiet water since the waves break at the reef. The central island may also be fringed by reefs similar to the barrier reef, but often they are not present.

Organisms that make up a reef are types that flourish in near-surface waters. Many, like corals, favor warm water that is relatively free of dirt. Corals are attached to the sea floor; they are not free to move about to gather food, so they live where food is brought to them. Clean, agitated waters near the surface are most favorable, and breaks in these reefs are found where muddy waters enter the ocean from streams flowing off the central islands.

The origin of barrier reefs was explained by Charles Darwin in 1839, and his explanation is still considered valid by most geologists. He held that for volcanic islands to have fringing reefs they must be situated in favorable climatic belts for corals and other shallow-water animals and plants and the position of sea level in relation to the islands must have fluctuated. During the ice ages up to 300 feet or more of water was removed from the sea and stored on land as ice. Warping of the sea floor can also cause sea-level fluctuations. Consider what happens when a volcanic island with a fringing reef begins to be submerged. If the volcano is extinct it does not grow upward, but the reef, composed of living organisms that live in certain depths of water, will be built upward and will maintain a position near sea level. Thus over a long period of time the original fringing reef becomes a barrier reef, and the island is separated from it by a lagoon. With still further submergence the volcano disappears completely, and what is left is an atoll.

One of the most extensive barrier reefs is the Great Barrier Reef along the northeastern coast of Australia (Fig. 9–14). It is separated

FIG. 9–14. / *View across the Great Barrier Reef, northeastern shore of Australia. (Courtesy of Qantas Empire Airways Ltd.)*

FIG. 9–15. / *Air view of an atoll, Cocos Island. Waves are seen breaking on the shallow portions of the reef. (Photo by courtesy of Qantas Empire Airways Ltd.)*

from the mainland by a lagoon that in places is narrow, but at other points is more than 200 miles wide. The reef is over 1,000 miles long.

Atolls

ONE POSSIBLE ORIGIN for the atolls (Fig. 9–15) has already been mentioned. Some almost certainly have been formed in this way. Others may be better explained by the theory put forth by R. A. Daly in 1910. He suggested that there does not necessarily have to be a relative movement between the sea and the islands other than that caused by glaciation. During the Pleistocene, when sea level was several hundred feet lower than it is now, waters of the ocean would have been cooler than at present and therefore less favorable for the growth of corals. As sea level dropped, volcanoes and their fringing reefs were exposed above sea level. Corals could not grow around the margins of the volcanoes fast enough to protect the islands from wave erosion. Thus the islands were beveled off to form platforms. When sea level began to rise from the melting glaciers and oceans began to warm up, new reefs formed near the margins of the platforms and maintained their positions during further rises in sea level, thus creating the atolls with their flat-bottomed lagoons.

Bikini Atoll

BIKINI ATOLL is an oval-shaped group of islands about 26 miles long and 15 miles wide (Fig. 9–16). Marginal reefs are almost continuous around the atoll. In places they are a mile wide. The central lagoon, which has an average depth of 26 fathoms (156 feet), covers approximately 250 square miles. Twenty-six islands surround the lagoon and stand at a maximum height of 25 feet above sea level. A number of passes a mile wide cut through the reef.

Reefs on the seaward side of the islands are abundant with life. There they are in direct contact with the open sea, which brings in a constant supply of water rich in food and nutrient salts. The nature of the marginal zone and of the assemblages of organisms that live there is determined by the slope on which the reef is located, the prevailing waves, the currents, and other ecological conditions. Reef rocks

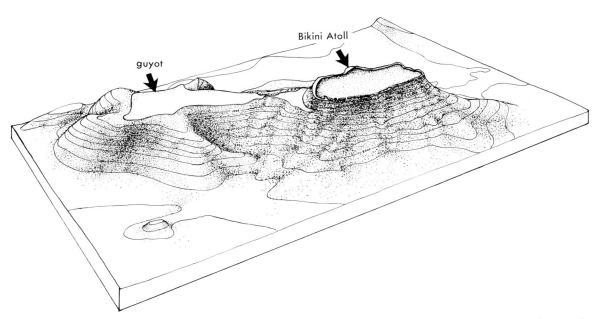

FIG. 9–16. / *Configuration of Bikini Atoll. The atoll is at the right. A similar flat-topped submerged mountain lies to the left of the atoll. (After Emery, Tracey, and Ladd, U.S. Geological Survey.)*

fall into two groups, algal or coral-algal reef limestone, and detrital-reef limestone. Coral-algal limestone is formed of organisms mostly in their original position of growth. Detrital limestone includes reef fragments mixed with finer fragments. The two types are mixed and grade into one another.

Where the reef is strongly grooved on the seaward side ridges between grooves are flattened and covered by massive coralline algae, which appear to be well adjusted to the strong, steady surf. Where marginal reefs are low, there is a rich growth of corals on the flat, inside portion of the reef. Where marginal reefs are high, two or three feet above the main reef flat, water circulation is restricted, and few living corals are found on the flat.

When grooves are weak or absent, no massive coralline algae are present. These smooth reefs are usually on the leeward side of the island. Some reefs of this type are smoothly scalloped. The seaward slope of the reef is steep, plunging into water about 200 feet deep. The marginal zone here contains coral and algae, but they rise only a few inches above the reef flat. On these smooth reefs, growth of the reefs exceeds the rate of erosion. Reefs of a slightly different nature are found where the most severe storms occur and erosion is more active. These storm waves break up the reef into large blocks which slump into deeper water but continue to be covered by a growth of new coral.

ISLANDS. The Bikini islands have formed where broken reef fragments have been piled up on reef platforms by waves, currents, and wind. Rocks on the islands include some consolidated gravels, conglomerates, and sandstones, but most of the islands are unconsolidated reef detritus made up of sand, gravel, and rubble. Some islands are bordered by beaches made of cobbles and boulders of reef debris. Sands are composed of Foraminifera shells, fragments of coral, algae, and mollusks, and some finer material.

LAGOON. A shallow terrace borders much of the central lagoon. The terrace is covered by 50 or 60 feet of water. It has a few enclosed depressions, suggesting that they are solution depressions, which would be an indication that the terrace stood above sea level at one time and was later drowned. The main basin of the lagoon is flat, except for coral knolls which are growths of isolated mounds of coral. The main sediments in the lagoon are tests of Foraminifera, a coral (*Halimeda*), and shells of mollusks.

OUTER SLOPES. Near the tops of the outer slopes numerous large blocks of reef broken off from the outer margin are mixed with sand and silt-sized detritus of Foraminifera and other organisms. Farther out, at depths of approximately 1,000 fathoms,

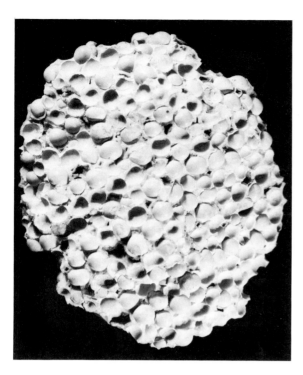

FIG. 9–17. / *Oölitic limestone from Carlsbad, Bohemia. (Photo by courtesy of the U.S. National Museum.)*

Globigerina ooze covers the botton. At still lower levels sediment of volcanic origin is found below the Globigerina ooze, which is a deposit formed of the skeletons of microscopic Foraminifera, mainly Globigerina, which live at the surface and only sink to the bottom after death.

Bahamian Platforms

THE BAHAMA BANKS, located south and east of Florida, cover more than 100,000 square miles of the Caribbean Sea (Fig. 9–18). They are most notable as an extraordinary example of a modern shallow-water area in which almost pure limestone is being formed. This condition is not new for the area. Calcium carbonate sediments have been forming there for approximately 130 million years, since the Early Cretaceous Period. Since that time virtually no sediment other than limestone has been deposited. These beds have an accumulated thickness of more than 14,000 feet, indicating a probably slow subsidence of

the platforms as limestone was deposited near the surface.

The banks are low-lying platforms covered for the most part by approximately 5 fathoms of water and separated by broad, flat-bottomed, deep channels. Around the banks coral reefs form rims which are islands separated by broad lagoons. Beyond the rims the water deepens rapidly toward the ocean basins. Only a small part of the exposed limestone is made up of reef debris. Most of it has been precipitated from solution. According to Newell the platforms developed from Early Cretaceous oceanic coral atolls which gradually became incorporated into the continent by the spread and coalescence of calcareous deposits.

The platforms may possibly be typical of shallow seas in which the calcium carbonate forming limestone accumulated in the geologic past. For this reason the environmental conditions that have led to the deposition of calcium carbonate here are especially important.

The region is free of terrigenous sediment and is usually covered by warm, dry air. This favors precipitation, since the rate of evaporation of water is accelerated. A solution is saturated when it contains all the dissolved chemical it can hold at that temperature; if the temperature is subsequently reduced or the solution is concentrated through evaporation, the solution will remain above saturation until conditions cause the dissolved material to be precipitated (to become a solid and settle). Average temperature in the Bahamas in winter is 70° F., and rainfall averages approximately 50 inches per year. The banks lie in the path of the easterly trade winds, which also accelerate evaporation. Surface waters of the Caribbean Sea are almost 40 per cent above saturation in calcium carbonate. As these waters are carried across the shallow banks there is naturally more surface evaporation, which further concentrates the calcium-carbonate solution, and agitation and heating cause a loss of the carbon dioxide essential in keeping $CaCO_3$ in solution. These conditions accelerate precipitation and a resulting accumulation of $CaCO_3$ over the shallow banks.

SEDIMENTS. The platforms may be subdivided into several sedimentary regions. Silt and sand composed of oölite grains and skeletal fragments of the reef faunas are found on the barrier rim. Sand is produced by wave action breaking up the shell and reef remains. Just behind the reef there are many lime-secreting organisms, which also account for a large part of the rim sediment. Over the platform as a whole much of the CaCO₃ is chemically precipitated ooze, oölite sand, and fecal pellets. Oölite sand is originating near the edge of the banks. Oölites, round balls named for their resemblance to fish eggs, tend to form in agitated supersaturated water where it first breaks and suddenly loses carbon dioxide. Oölites are made of concentric layers of calcium carbonate built around a central nucleus of aggregate grains of lime or fecal pellets (Fig. 9–17). The shelf lagoon is the site of accumulation of calcium-carbonate ooze, a mud which consists of microscopic crystals formed by direct precipitation.

FIG. 9–18. / *Bahama Banks. The banks are shown in black; the shallow water surrounding them is shaded. The shallow water surrounding Florida and Cuba is not shaded. The arrows indicate the direction of prevailing ocean surface currents. They bring warm waters rich in calcium carbonate up from the equator.*

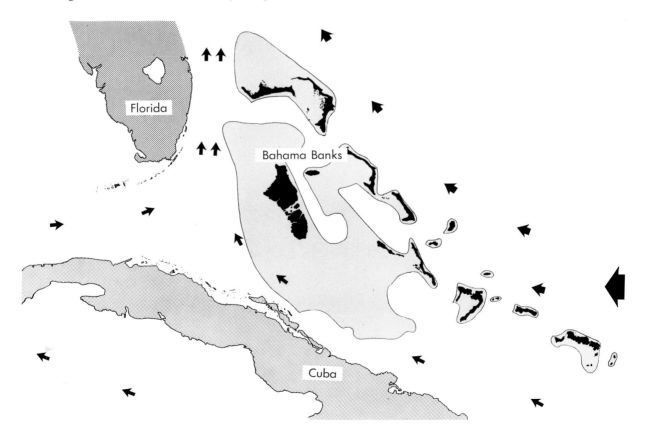

FIG. 10–1. / *Bathyscaph. The Trieste is one of the modern bathyscaphs which are capable of descending to the bottom of the ocean even at its deepest parts. The sphere beneath the vessel contains a window from which pictures can be taken and undersea life observed. In 1960 this vessel set a record when it descended 37,800 feet to the bottom of the Marianas Trench in the Pacific Ocean. (Official U.S. Navy Photo.)*

Gradation in the Deep Sea

BEFORE THE TWENTIETH CENTURY, MAN'S view of the deep seas was based almost entirely on speculation. There was little data on which to base any concrete understanding. The early geomorphologists, those who study the form of the earth, reasoned that running water, glaciation, wind, and ground water were effective agents of erosion only above base level, and that ultimate base level was sea level. At sea level glacial ice floats, and running water ceases to transport and erode. Samples of sea water were collected throughout the oceans and these samples were always free of suspended sediment when collected far from shore. It seemed logical to assume that the deep ocean basins were untroubled by currents and erosion and therefore subject to very little change. Such a view was expressed by Admiral M. F. Maury in 1855:

The geological clock may strike new periods; its hands may point to era after era; but, so long as the ocean remains in its basin—so long as its bottom is covered with blue water—so long must the deep furrows and strong contrasts in the solid crust below stand out bold, ragged, and grand. Nothing can fill up the hollows there; no agent now at work, that we know of, can descend into its depths, and level off the floors of the sea. . . .

Later, when it was recognized that surface waters of oceans contain vast quantities of small free-floating and swimming plants and animals, this view of the deep sea changed. Instead of bare exposed rock, the ocean floor was visualized as covered with a thick homogeneous blanket of sediment composed of remains of microscopic-sized marine plants and animals.

Deep-Sea Circulation

ALTHOUGH, AS WE HAVE SEEN, SCIENTISTS assumed until recently that there were no currents strong enough to move sediments on the ocean bottom, we know now that sediments on the floors of the oceans commonly contain current ripple marks (Fig. 10–3). Not only have the ripple marks been found in connection with turbidity currents, where they are readily explained by the rush of submarine land slides; they have also been found in places where no downslope movements could have contributed to their formation. Ripples have been photographed on almost all seamounts. This fact indicates that relatively strong deep-sea currents must exist. It has long been recognized that currents associated with the Gulf Stream extend down to depths of over 3,600 feet. Other forms of deep-sea circulation which may be strong enough to produce ripples are being studied.

Movement of water in the deep sea is controlled by:

temperature of the water,
amount of material in solution,
shape of the ocean bottom,
surficial currents, and
internal tides.

Water temperature, which affects relative density, is an important determinant of water movement. Water near the poles is cooled at the surface where it comes in contact with polar ice caps. Because it is more dense than warm water, cold water sinks, sliding downslope into the deep sea and forcing bottom water equatorward into equatorial latitudes, where it converges with warmer currents and rises to the surface. This is just one example of the power of a density differential to set deep waters in motion. Water motion is also caused by a variation of the amount of material carried in solution; an example is the sinking of water that has become heavily laden with salts produced by evaporation of surface waters in equatorial latitudes. Another determinant is the shape of the sea floor, which directs the path of sinking waters (Fig. 10–2).

Internal waves and *currents* are little-known characteristics of the oceans. The nature of internal waves can be seen by filling a container with two liquids of different density and color. The heavier liquid will sink to the bottom. If the container is slightly tilted back and forth waves will be set up in the liquids. They will be apparent not only at the surface but also at the boundary between the two liquids. Thus internal waves are set up within the liquids, and these ordinarily have greater amplitude than those at the surface. Recent studies led to the conclusion that *internal tides* are as common as surface tides, that the amplitude is much larger, and that they may establish internal currents sufficient to explain observed ripple and scour marks such as those seen around manganese oxide nodules in the deeps of the Pacific Ocean.

Deep-Sea Sedimentary Environments

THE BOUNDARY BETWEEN deep-sea and shallow water is 600 feet, 100 fathoms. This corresponds approximately to the edge of the continental shelves throughout most of the world. Water depths between 100 and 1,000 fathoms are called bathyal, and below 1,000 fathoms abyssal. Compared with other sedimentary environments, deep seas are little known to us, although they cover more than half the face of the earth.

From the point of view of sedimentary environments there is little reason to treat bathyal and abyssal zones separately. Other than the fact that the bathyal zone grades into the neritic zone, the two zones are similar. Both receive sediment from the following sources:

Finely suspended material in sea water,
Remains of the abundant floating and swimming life, mostly protozoans, in surface water,
Meteorites,
Debris which slumps and slides down in density currents from the edge of the continental shelf, and
Marine plants, especially diatoms.

Both zones are free of surface wave disturbance and current action (except for density or turbidity currents). Internal tidal currents may affect them, but very little is known about these. Neither zone receives light, nor do they contain nearly as abundant a *benthonic* (bottom-dwelling) population as shelf waters. Hydrostatic pressure is high, more than 2,000 pounds per square inch, and temperatures are low, close to freezing in the abyssal plains.

Deep-Sea Sediments

RED CLAY, found in the greatest depths, is the most extensive deep-sea deposit. Its actual color is brown to reddish. It contains films of manganese and manganese nodules. The origin of red clay is subject to considerable debate; it may be derived from the finest clay fractions taken into the oceans from land areas, but it

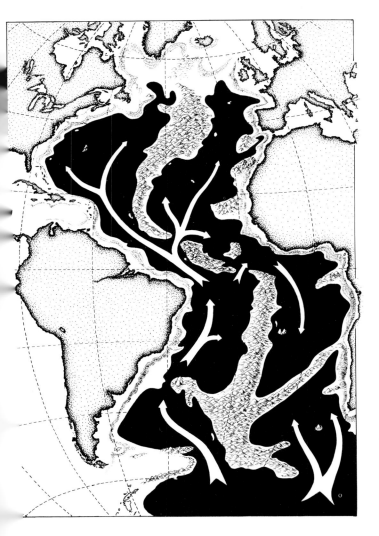

FIG. 10–2. / *Deep-sea circulation in the Atlantic. Shown is a schematic view of circulation at the level of approximately 12,000 feet depth. At this depth the Mid-Atlantic Ridge breaks up the flow of cold dense water from the Antarctic. (From Stommel, Scientific American, Jan. 1955.)*

FIG. 10–3. / *Deep-sea ripple marks. This picture was taken with a camera which was lowered to a depth of 700 fathoms in the North Atlantic Ocean. The presence of ripple marks there is a positive indication of current action. Likewise sandstones which contain ripple marks formed millions of years ago are indications of the currents which moved in ancient seas at the time of their formation. (Photo by courtesy of the Lamont Geological Observatory, Columbia University.)*

FIG. 10–4. / *Globigerina. This is one of the fora-minifers the remains of which make up a large part of the sediment on the ocean floors in the middle latitudes. (Photo by courtesy of the American Museum of Natural History.)*

FIG. 10–5. / *Foraminifer shells such as those found on the ocean floors. The protozoans shown here are about the size of a grain of wheat, but many are much smaller. (Photo by the author.)*

has also been attributed to submarine weathering of basic volcanic material and to accumulation of meteoric dust.

Globigerina ooze is the second most extensive deposit. It is a calcareous mud formed from the shells, called tests, of Globigerinas, protozoans of microscopic size which have a globular-shaped shell. The tests are made of calcium carbonate. There is almost no Globigerina ooze found below depths of 2,500 fathoms, because calcite is soluble under high pressure and at low temperature. Clays are usually mixed with Globigerina tests in these sediments and may make up more than 50 per cent of the deposit.

Diatom ooze is a deposit consisting of siliceous (silicon-containing) remains of the microscopic-sized plants known as diatoms (Fig. 10–6). Most of these are located between 40° S. and the Antarctic Circle. These beautiful but minute plants contain droplets of oil and may be the source of most petroleum.

Coral sand and mud is locally abundant in deep-sea areas around coral reefs, having been carried out and dropped by surface currents.

Less widely distributed sediments include muds which are named for their color (red, blue, green) and volcanic sand and mud. Red mud is confined to the coastal areas close to the mouths of the Amazon and Yangtze Kiang rivers. Blue and gray muds are of continental origin and occur in shallow to deep waters near land masses. Green muds probably get their color from the mineral glauconite or chlorite. Volcanic muds and sands are frequently mixed with other deep-sea sediments in volcanic belts throughout the world.

Deposits carried into the abyssal plains as turbulent high density flows exist in an abundance which is as yet undetermined. Some oceanographers suspect that these may account for a large part of the total volume of sediment of the ocean basins. There is little doubt that they are important. Activated through slumping along the edge of the continental shelf, sediments of the neritic zone move down into the deep water. That these sediments can move down low slopes for hundreds of miles has been definitely established. They account for the

FIG. 10–6. / *Diatoms. The siliceous remains of these microscopic-sized plants are important constituents of marine sediments. (Photo by courtesy of the General Biological Supply House, Chicago.)*

FIG. 10–7. / *Radiolarians. These are important constituents of marine sediments, particularly in very deep water and in high latitudes. (Photo copyright by General Biological Supply House, Inc., Chicago.)*

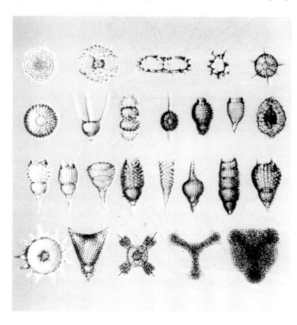

presence of neritic fossil fauna, ripple marks, and coarse sands in the abyssal environment. The distribution of deep-sea sediments must be viewed in terms of certain special conditions that are involved in their formation.

Sedimentary bodies deposited by density currents are lobate in form. The lobes originate from areas on the shelf which have slumped into the ocean deeps. Most of these slumped areas are slopes which have become over-steepened as a result of long-continued or rapid sedimentation. For this reason, density current deposits are most likely to occur off steep continental shelves, where sediment is carried out into the ocean by large rivers, and where there are no deep-sea trenches off the coast in which the deposits might be trapped.

Red clays are extremely widespread. They appear to be abundant where other types of sediment are lacking. It may be that the materials which make them up are deposited uniformly everywhere but are inconspicuous when mixed with large amounts of other sediment.

The chief source of other deep-sea sediments is marine animals and plants. Diatoms are most abundant near the surface in high latitudes where the ocean waters are upwelling and fertile. Of the single-celled animals radiolarians (Fig. 10–7) and Foraminifera are most abundant toward the equator; they are also more abundant near shore than away from it, since their food supply is most abundant in shallow waters. Although they are of little importance in shallow-water sediments, the skeletons of these tiny creatures are the main constituents of sediments of deeper waters. Most fragmental sediments are heavier and have dropped to the bottom long before they can be carried into areas of deep water. Protozoan remains make up a small fraction of sediments dominated by sand, silt, and limestone.

An important factor determining the dominance of siliceous sediment over calcareous sediment is the depth of the water. Calcium carbonate is much more highly soluble in deep, cold waters of the oceanic deeps. Thus siliceous remains of diatoms and radiolarians dominate these waters.

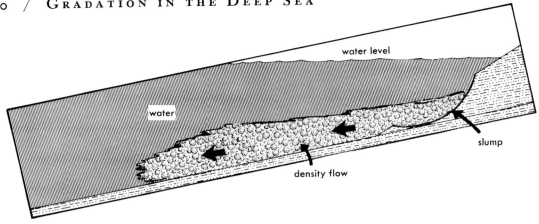

FIG. 10–10. / *Formation of a density or turbidity current by experiment. A layer of fine sediment was first placed in the tank. Then a pile of sediment was laid down at the right end of the tank to approximate the continental slope. As the tank is tilted the oversteepened slope slumps and a turbidity current is started.*

amounts of muddy water produced a slow current which flowed down the slope, but very little erosion or deposition accompanied the flow. With an increase in the amount of load in the current, however, velocity was greatly accelerated, and the stream of turbid flow eroded the sediment and carried it rapidly down into the lower end of the flume.

CABLE BREAKS. In November of 1929 a series of cable breaks occurred off the Grand Banks of Newfoundland. A full-scale investigation of the breaks was made in the early 1950's by the Lamont Geological Observatory. Bruce Heezen and Maurice Ewing advanced the hypothesis that the breaks were caused by a turbidity current initiated by a slump or landslide from the steep edge of the Grand Banks. Movement of unconsolidated sediments from the edge of the Grand Banks set sediment into suspension; like the muddy water in the flume, the resulting mixture of sediment and water moved down across the slopes as a density flow. The velocity of this current could be calculated from the times of the cable breaks, which indicated a movement of about 60 miles per hour. The turbid flow extended all the way down the slopes into the abyssal plains, 450 miles.

Deep-sea cores were taken throughout the area. It was found that a layer of graded silt almost four feet thick covered the normal deep-sea sediments, and that this layer contained neritic microfossils. It was possible to outline the lobate form of the turbidity current deposit through core samples from various locations. On tops of hills located near the foot of the continental slope no sign of turbidity current deposits could be found. Because of its high density, the flow moved along through low places in the submarine topography and did not go over hills. Photographs obtained by use of an underwater camera showed that silty sediment was covered by ripple marks—a definite sign that some relatively strong current must have been flowing over them (Fig. 10–3).

Further evidence has been obtained from a number of other sites. A notable case is that of the cable breaks in the Caribbean off the mouth of the Magdalena River of Colombia. These breaks occurred year after year at just about the same season. Invariably the breaks took place during the highest flood stages of the river. At these times the river carried large quantities of debris out from the continent, deposited it in the waters off the mouth of the river, and usually built up an alluvial cone of debris in the submarine canyon of the river. During the floods it was noted that the top of these deposits disappeared just before the cable broke. In 1935 when the cable was brought up from its position 12 miles off shore in nearly 5,000 feet of water, it had green grass wrapped around it—dramatic proof that the river debris had been carried down to the cable and almost certainly played a major role in its failure.

Form of Turbidity Current Deposits

SOUNDINGS OF THE DEEP-SEA trenches show that alluvial conelike deposits are accumulating around the flat bottoms of some of these trenches. It stands to reason that the trenches which almost completely encircle the Pacific Ocean are collecting most of the sediment which otherwise would be carried out into the Pacific Ocean by turbidity currents. This seems to be verified by the absence in the central Pacific of the type of deposits normally left by turbidity currents. Large areas of the Pacific Ocean bottom are covered by scattered nodules of manganese. The nodules are estimated to form at the rate of 1 mm. in 1,000 years. These nodules often contain shark teeth as nuclei. Thus it is possible to say that there has been either very little deposition or considerable movement of sediment in the time since the teeth were first deposited. If the trenches continue to receive turbidity current deposits, we may expect that they will become filled. And

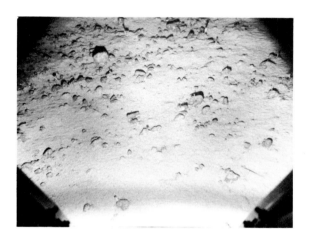

FIG. 10–11. / *Photographs of the sea floor in the North Atlantic Ocean. These photographs show some of the variety in the sediment types. At the top is a rough sea floor partially covered by sand. A number of large cup-shaped sponges are visible. The second photo from the top shows a rocky sea floor covered by volcanic debris. A little sand is visible. The third photo is a view of a sea floor which has a few rocks on a finer sediment. The bottom photo shows some very fine muds. Tracks of small animals are visible. (Photos by the author.)*

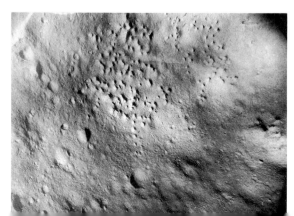

it is in this light that certain seismic observations of the Atlantic margins must be viewed. The seismic studies reveal great thicknesses of unconsolidated sediments in troughlike depressions beneath the continental slopes (Fig. 10–12). Could these have been old trenches that are now filled? The answer may very well be yes.

Once the trenches are filled, the next step would be for the turbidity currents to transport their loads into the deeper oceans. This is neither expected nor found in the Pacific. But in the Atlantic there are few trenches to intercept sediment at the present time, thus material carried into the Atlantic deeps by turbidity currents may well be the main factor in the formation of the abyssal plains. They may be plains of deposition by the combined processes of slow accumulation of shell fragments and extraterrestrial dust and rapid deposition of mud carried by turbidity currents.

This view helps to explain the fact that the midocean canyon in the Atlantic has sides slightly raised above the level of the ocean floor (Figs. 10–13 and 10–15). The canyon is physiographically very much like a natural river levee, and probably was formed in the same manner. Turbidity currents flowing down the canyon overflowed its sides, and the debris-laden water deposited sediment near the sides of the canyon in a wedge that thinned out away from the main path of flow.

FIG. 10–12. / *Sediment thickness off the eastern coast of the United States. The inner margin is the coastal plain. The black areas are those in which more than 15,000 feet of sediment and sedimentary rocks overlie the basaltic layer of the ocean floor. (Modified after C. L. Drake, Maurice Ewing, and G. H. Sutton, 1959. Reprinted with permission from* Physics and Chemistry of the Earth, *v. 3, 1959, Pergamon Press, Inc.)*

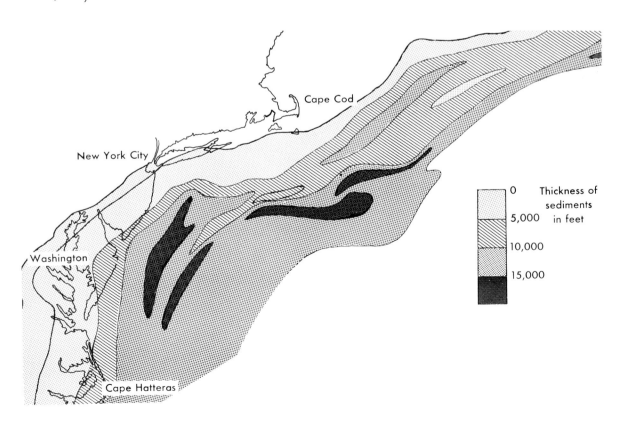

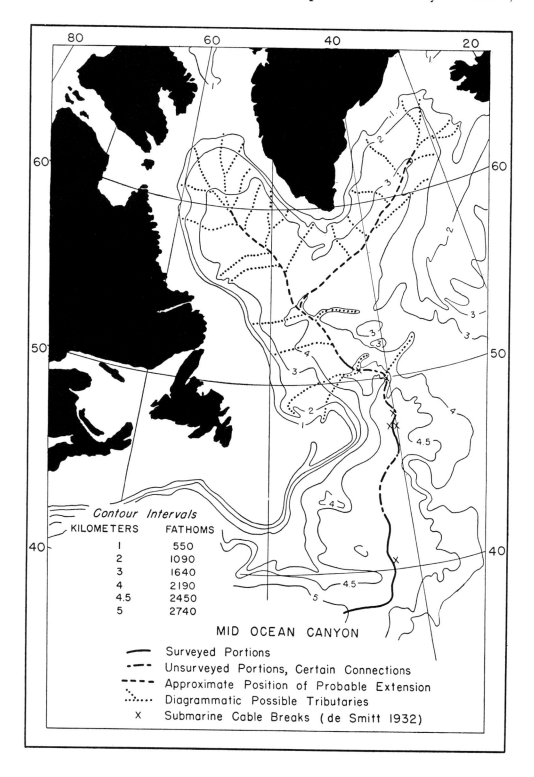

FIG. 10–13. / Map of the Mid-Ocean Canyon. (From Heezen, et al. G.S.A. Sp. Paper 65.)

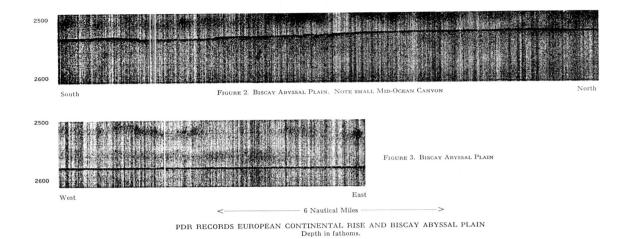

FIGURE 2. BISCAY ABYSSAL PLAIN. NOTE SMALL MID-OCEAN CANYON

FIGURE 3. BISCAY ABYSSAL PLAIN

6 Nautical Miles

PDR RECORDS EUROPEAN CONTINENTAL RISE AND BISCAY ABYSSAL PLAIN
Depth in fathoms.

FIG. 10–14. / *Echo-sounding profiles of the abyssal plains.* (*Courtesy of Lamont Geological Observatory.*)

FIG. 10–15. / *Profiles of the Mid-Ocean Canyon at Vema Gap.* (*From Heezen, et al.*)

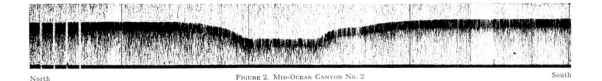

FIGURE 2. MID-OCEAN CANYON NO. 2

FIGURE 3. MID-OCEAN CANYONS IN HATTERAS ABYSSAL PLAIN, WEST OF VEMA GAP

PDR RECORDS OF MID-OCEAN CANYON NO. 2 AND CANYONS AT VEMA GAP
Depth in fathoms.

V/

MATTER, MINERALS, AND ROCKS

11 / Composition of the Earth

MATTER IS WHAT MAKES UP SOIL, ROCKS, MIN-erals, water, air, and indeed the sun and every other material body in the universe. What, then, is it? To answer this question is not easy, and we generally fall into the habitual practice of describing what matter is like, what it does under certain conditions—in short, its properties. This is excusable, since there is no simple definition of matter. Man's understanding of what makes up matter as well as how matter behaves has grown through the years. It is interesting to examine some of the views of the ancient Greeks on this subject.

Aristotle, Plato, and their followers subscribed to the idea that all material things are recognized by their properties. The four basic properties are heat, cold, dampness, and dryness. These occur in pairs: heat and dryness yield fire; heat and dampness make air; cold and dryness compose earth; and cold and dampness yield water. Fire, earth, air, and water are the four elements which Aristotle believed made up all matter. He held that all different types of matter contain varying proportions of these elements and that each of the elements can be derived from the other. For example, addition of fire to water yields air (steam). This view exercised a remarkable dominance of "natural philosophy" for many hundreds of years.

Views on matter of the Epicurean school were astonishingly similar to those of modern atomic physicists, but their lack of experimental equipment prevented them from advancing toward the sophisticated knowledge of today. The ideas underlying the atomistic theory were proposed and advanced by the Greek philosophers Leucippus (*ca.* 460–370 B.C.) and Democritus (*ca.* fifth century B.C.), and later by Epicurus (*ca.* 306 B.C.), but we owe the most vivid record of these ideas to the writings of the Roman poet, Lucretius (100–55 B.C.), in "The Nature of the Universe."

. . . there is an ultimate point in visible objects which represents the smallest thing that can be seen. So also there must be an ultimate point in objects that lie below the limit of perception by our senses. This point is without parts and is the smallest thing that can exist. It never has been and never will be able to exist by itself, but only as one primary part of something else. It is with a mass of such parts, solidly jammed together in order, that matter is filled up. Since they cannot exist by themselves, they must needs stick together in a mass from which they cannot by any means be pried loose. The atoms therefore are absolutely solid and unalloyed, consisting of a mass of least parts tightly packed together. They are not compounds formed by the coalescence of their parts, but bodies of absolute and everlasting solidity. . . .

Material objects are of two kinds, atoms and compounds of atoms.

A property is something that cannot be detached or separated from a thing without destroying it, as weight is a property of rocks, heat of fire, fluidity of water, tangibility of all bodies, intangibility of vacuum.

Unfortunately there followed a long delay through the Middle Ages before any really important advance in man's understanding of matter. During this period the Epicureans became much better known for their moral teachings than for their scientific ideas, and the atomistic theory did not win wide acceptance even at the time it was proposed.

Gases—Key to the Atomic Nature of Matter

THE ATOMIC THEORY WAS STILL SPECULATION when it was used by Francis Bacon, Newton, and others in the seventeenth century. Its greatest support during this period came from the experimental investigation of gases by Robert Boyle. Scientists had long recognized that matter is conveniently grouped into three states —solid, liquid, and gas. Now we know these are not as clear-cut divisions as we might like, but for everyday purposes they serve very well.

Boyle demonstrated in 1662 how the compression, or "spring," of the air could be explained by the atomistic view. It was known that a gas will expand to fill the volume of its container and that the same gas can be compressed into a smaller volume. Boyle showed that changes in volume are accompanied by changes in the pressure of the gas (PV equals a constant). This law was supplemented by the work of Jacques Charles and Joseph L. Gay-Lussac, who showed that the temperature of a gas is a function of the volume and that the two are inversely proportional (V/T equals a

constant). These two laws were then combined into the general gas law, which stated the interrelationship of pressure, volume, and temperature in a gas (PV/T equals a constant). Various models were constructed to explain these observed relations. The explanations proposed by Boyle were based on the atomistic theory; he suggested that if "atoms" or corpuscles of a gas do not touch all of the time, either they must be of variable size or they must move about rapidly, perhaps in some type of "subtle" fluid. The subtle fluid has never been found, although scientists looked for it for 250 years. The concept of atoms in motion was necessary to explain the volume-pressure relationship in gases and the fact that gases expand to fill the volume of any size container in which they are placed.

FIG. 11–1. / *Cerussite, a lead carbonate. (Photo by courtesy of the U.S. National Museum.)*

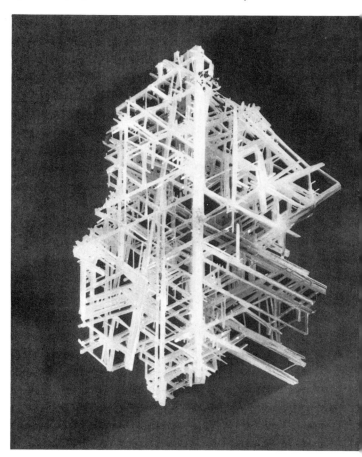

An alternative explanation was that gas is composed of corpuscles that are touching and act like little springs. This latter explanation posed the difficult problem of explaining how gases expand as they do.

Robert Boyle must be credited also with the concept of the chemical element. He proposed that the name *element* should be applied to those chemical substances that cannot be separated into different components by any chemical means.

Daniel Bernoulli (1700–1782) later offered a gas model that resolved the difficulties encountered by Boyle. He abandoned the "subtle fluid" speculation and suggested that the corpuscles are so small that they are almost infinite in number in any gas. They are visualized as being in rapid motion, striking against the sides of the container in which they are placed and thus exerting a pressure on the container. If the volume within which they are contained is gradually decreased, the number of impacts per unit of time increases and pressure goes up. He also explained the temperature relationship. If temperature is increased corpuscles of the gas move faster and collide more frequently with the walls of the container, increasing pressure. As is too often the case in science, these views of Bernoulli were overlooked for almost a century.

Dalton's Atomic Theory—Law of Definite Combining Proportions

THE GREAT EXPERIMENTAL CHEMIST JOHN Dalton (1766–1844) made vastly important steps toward the understanding of chemical reactions and behavior of gases. Dalton became interested in the surprising observation that the amounts of different elements in gases of the atmosphere seemed to appear always in the same relative proportions regardless of the altitude from which the sample had been collected. He tried in vain to explain this phenomenon. One particularly important aspect of his model was the proposition that "all gas particles of any particular chemical substance have the same

over-all diameter . . . but the particles of different gases have different over-all diameters." Although this proposition had to be abandoned as inaccurate, it led the way to Dalton's most important contributions to chemistry. In 1808 he published a treatise embodying the atomic theory of chemistry, which ultimately has proved to be the basis for modern chemistry. Principal points in Dalton's atomic theory were:

> Matter is made up of indivisible atoms.
>
> Atoms of an element are perfectly alike in weight and shape.
>
> Atoms are unchangeable [they were unchangeable by any means available at the time Dalton put forth this proposition].
>
> Different elements can combine to form a *compound*. Even the smallest part of the compound consists of a grouping of a definite number of atoms of each element. Today we call such a grouping a *molecule*.
>
> When a chemical reaction takes place, atoms are neither created nor destroyed, but only rearranged.

On the basis of this atomic theory Dalton was able to explain an earlier observation, called the *law of definite proportions*, that when two elements form a compound the ratio of the weight of one of the elements to the other is always the same. Dalton saw that this could be explained if the weight of single atoms of each of the elements were different. For example, it was known that when hydrogen and oxygen combine to form water the ratio of the weights of hydrogen to oxygen is 1:8. If the molecule of water consists of two atoms of hydrogen and one of oxygen, as we now know it does, then the ratio of the weights of the hydrogen to oxygen is 1:16; oxygen weighs 16 times as much as hydrogen. This constant relation ultimately provided the basis for our scale of atomic weights. One mass unit is equal to one-sixteenth of the weight of oxygen. The system used is arbitrary because absolute weight in terms of pounds, or grams, would be so extremely small all of the weights would be minute and awkward fractions.

The Italian physicist Amedeo Avogadro (1776–1856) devised a model of gases which has proved to be highly accurate. Of particular note is what is called *Avogadro's law:* under conditions of equal temperature and pressure, equal volumes of all gases contain equal numbers of particles regardless of whether the gases are elements, compounds, or mixtures. Now, examine how this law may be used to explain the observation that two volumes of hydrogen gas combine with one volume of oxygen gas to form two volumes of water vapor (the volumes of hydrogen and oxygen must be all of the same size and at the same temperature and pressure). Avogadro's explanation was that each of these volumes contains the same number of atoms, and that therefore the only way two volumes of water vapor can be produced is for one atom of oxygen to combine with two atoms of hydrogen to give one molecule of water vapor ($2H + 1O = H_2O$). Thus Avogadro's law combined with Dalton's theories to pave the way for determining the nature of combinations between elements and gave rise to the concept of compounds.

The work of Dalton and Avogadro provided a simple explanation for the law of definite proportions by finding that atoms of two elements combine in a definite ratio. It was soon realized that there was regularity in the way different elements combined, and that if the number of atoms in the molecules of several compounds were known, then predictions could be made regarding how many atoms of an element would combine with another element, even when no experimental evidence on the two was available. It was found, for example, that two atoms of hydrogen combine with one of oxygen to make H_2O, and that four atoms of hydrogen combine with one of carbon to make CH_4. From this last example we may predict that one atom of carbon will combine with two of oxygen to yield CO_2 (carbon dioxide). You might visualize this by imagining that each atom has a definite number of hooks on it (hydrogen with 1, oxygen 2, nitrogen 3, and carbon 4). The two hooks on each of two oxygen atoms are needed to take the four hooks of the carbon. In this simplified view the number of hooks is called the *valence* of each element.

Unfortunately time and space do not allow a full historical development of the work leading to the modern theory of the atomic structure of matter. We must pass over large parts of the important discoveries of Gilbert, Coulomb, Faraday, Joule, Maxwell, Clausius, Boltzmann, and others, but at least a few of the discoveries regarding the electrical nature of matter and the structure of atoms must be mentioned.

Electric Nature of Matter

THE CONCEPT OF ELECTRICITY CAN BE traced back to 600 B.C. One of the "seven wise men" of ancient Greece, Thales of Miletus, observed that amber will attract small fibrous materials when it has been rubbed with a piece of fur. Amber was called "electron" by the Greeks, and the name "electric" was applied to these effects by William Gilbert 2,100 years later. Gilbert discovered that many materials may be electrified by friction, and that both of the rubbed substances become electrified. If, for example, a rubber rod is rubbed by a piece of fur and then separated from it a short distance, the fur will be attracted to the rod. When two rods are rubbed by fur and then brought close together they repel one another. This led to the recognition of two types of electrical charges, called *positive* and *negative*. When two bodies with like charges are brought close together they repel one another, but when unlike charges are close they attract one another. Charles de Coulomb (1736–1806) demonstrated the relationship between such charges and the force of attraction or repulsion between them. Coulomb's law is very similar in form to the law of universal gravitational attraction. It states that the force of attraction or repulsion between two electrically charged bodies is directly proportional to the sum of the amounts of their charges and inversely proportional to the square of the distance between them.

If a copper or silver wire is used to connect two bodies that have different electric charges, then an electric current will flow until the two are equalized. The wire is said to conduct an electric charge. Charges will flow not only in metal wires but through some liquids. Distilled water is a poor conductor, but if a small amount of some salt or acid is dissolved in it water becomes conductive. Assume that some table salt, sodium chloride ($NaCl$), is dissolved in water and two electrodes, one positive and one negative, are placed in the water so that they do not touch, thus any electricity flowing between the electrodes must pass through the solution. After a period of time the negative electrode will be found to have a crust of sodium metal on it and bubbles of chlorine gas will be found to form and escape at the positive terminal. If instead of a salt a little acid is added to the water, the water molecules themselves break down and hydrogen collects at the negative terminal while oxygen collects at the positive terminal. These experiments provide proof that atoms exhibit an electrical character. Since opposite charges attract, we may think of the sodium, attracted to the negative terminal, as being positive. Thus hydrogen is also positive, while oxygen and chlorine are negative. When atoms of an element exhibit such an electrical character they are called *ions*. The process just described is known as *electrolysis*. Faraday carried the experiments further, concluding that ions carry electricity but that not all ions carry the same amount. This thought is expressed in the *second law of Faraday*—ions of elements which have chemical valences of two, three, or more with respect to hydrogen carry an electric charge greater than that of a hydrogen ion in exactly the same ratio as their valences. Thus it was shown that valences are closely associated with electrical phenomena.

Electricity and Chemical Bonds

THIS VIEW OF ATOMS behaving as charged particles provided a new way of looking at compounds. Charges can be viewed as a replacement for the hooks described earlier as holding atoms in a molecule. Atoms of some elements always

have positive ions or negative ions, while a few gases are inert and behave as if they are neutral all of the time.

Discovery of Electrons

J. J. THOMSON (1856–1940), a British physicist, studied the behavior of electricity in gases. The passage of electricity through a gas is well known, as in neon and fluorescent lights. Just as in the case of currents passing through liquids, electricity is moved by positive and negative ions going in opposite directions. In gases the difference between negative and positive ions is striking. The positive ions are essentially like those of the liquid, but negative particles, while of the same electrical charge as a single ion of chlorine (one negative unit), have vastly smaller masses than the mass of any atom. Thomson devised a device known as the cathode ray tube to study these phenomena (Fig. 11–2). This device is so designed that negative particles given off by the cathode (the negative pole) move along the tube missing the anode (the positive pole) and hitting a screen covered with a material that fluoresces when hit by highly charged particles. Thomson first placed a barrier in the tube and discovered that the negative particles traveled in straight lines, causing the barrier to cast a shadow on the fluorescent screen. In subsequent experiments he placed electric and magnetic fields across the tube and observed that the beam of particles was deflected in these fields. He derived the value for the ratio of the electric charge to the mass of these particles, which he named *electrons*. It remained for the American physicist Robert A. Millikan (1868–1953) to measure the charge on the electron. This made it possible to calculate the mass of the electron, which was set at 9.1×10^{-28} grams. So, for the first time, the Greek view of the indivisible atom was broken down. Electrons have less mass than an atom of any element. They are, instead, among the fundamental parts of all atoms. They possess a negative charge, and it is an excess or a deficiency of this negative charge that makes these atoms ions.

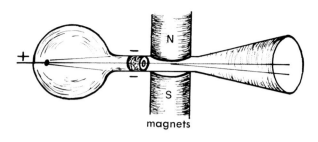

FIG. 11–2. / *Cathode ray tube schematic.*

Discovery of Radioactivity

THE DISCOVERY OF RADIOACTIVITY MUST be ranked among the most significant accidents of all time. The discovery was made in 1896 by A. H. Becquerel, who was studying fluorescence. He happened to place several boxes of unexposed photographic film in a drawer near a collection of minerals he was using in his studies. When the film was developed he found that all of it was badly fogged. He began to investigate the source of the fogging and finally traced it to the presence of the mineral pitchblende (one of the high-grade uranium ores). It was apparent that some type of strong radiation was associated with this mineral. X-rays had already been discovered, but they were produced only by special equipment that was driven by strong electric currents. When physicists found that this radioactive effect of fogging film was unaffected by water, chemical reactions, or the form of the compound, they concluded that the phenomenon of radioactivity was an intrinsic property of atoms of particular elements and that its source must be found in the structure of the atom.

Among the experiments conducted by Becquerel was one in which he placed a small amount of uranium in a deep hole in a lead block in order to allow only a thin beam of radiation to emerge. A magnet was placed over the block, and three different types of radiation were found to come out. There were rays that traveled in straight lines out of the hole and were unaffected by the magnetic field. These are similar to X-rays and are called *gamma rays*. Fast-moving negatively charged particles were deflected in one direction by the magnetic field while positively charged particles went in the other direction. The particles carrying a positive charge are called *alpha rays*, later shown to be the nuclei of helium atoms, and the negative particles, called *beta rays*, turned out to be electrons.

Marie Curie (1867–1934) was convinced that radioactivity of pitchblende was actually due to some impurity in the mineral and she began the task of trying to isolate that substance. After years of work and breaking down tons of pitchblende she isolated a few milligrams of a new element which she called *radium*. Radium, it happens, is much more radioactive than uranium, but the two differ primarily in degree, not type, as Madame Curie suspected. (The use of radioactive minerals in dating of rocks is discussed later, in chapter 27.)

Models of Atomic Structure

LORD RUTHERFORD (1871–1937) STUDIED atomic physics during the period shortly after the discovery of radioactivity and before its behavior was explained. The three types of radiation from radioactive elements, alpha, beta, and gamma rays, were known, but Rutherford was the first to realize that the phenomenon of radioactivity is caused by the spontaneous disintegration of heavy, unstable atoms. He recognized the potential usefulness of bombarding atoms of various elements with radiation from radioactive materials, particularly alpha (positive) rays. A beam of these rays was directed through a small slit and allowed to pass to a fluorescent screen, where tiny flashes would occur when they hit. The flashes were concentrated in a small point. When a piece of thin foil was placed in their path, the rays were scattered, hitting over all parts of the screen and even being deflected back toward the viewer. At this time the accepted model of the atom was one of negative

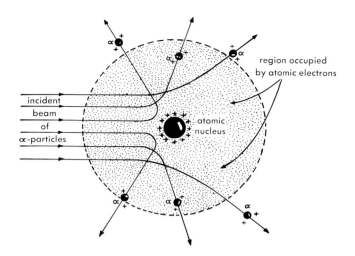

FIG. 11–3. / *The discovery of protons was made by directing a beam of alpha particles through a foil. Resulting scattering was explained by concentrations of positive charge in the nucleus.*

electrons floating in a positive electric fluid. Scattering of the sort observed would not be possible in such a fluid because negative electrons in the positive fluid would be so closely intermingled that large deflections of an alpha ray would not occur (Fig. 11–3). That large angles of deflection did occur led Rutherford to postulate that the atom has its positive charge concentrated at the center in a nucleus and that the electrons are far out from the nucleus. In order for them to stay out, they would have to be moving in orbits at great speed, as the planets of the Solar System revolve around the sun. Thus started the modern *planetary model* of the atom. Rutherford's model recognized electrons as carriers of negative charge, and postulated the existence of some other particle or particles in the nucleus as carriers of positive charge. The carriers of this positive charge were later recognized as *protons*, each of which carries a charge equal in magnitude to that of an electron.

Bohr Model of Atomic Structure

ONE OF THE GREATEST differences between the atom as visualized by Democritus and Lucretius and the atom as analyzed by modern atomic physicists lies in its internal structure. The Greek philosophers thought of atoms as indivisible particles, but they are now known to be composed of electrons, protons, neutrons, and several other smaller particles. Unlike the Greeks, we now know the size of atoms, and though they are too small to be seen in microscopes of the highest power, the mass, electrical charge, and other characteristics of atoms and their component parts have been successfully measured. To appreciate this, consider that if an atom were enlarged 100 million times it would be about the size of a pea, and that even at this size the electrons, protons, and neutrons still would not be visible with a high-powered microscope.

The *electron* is the smallest of the three fundamental particles. It has a mass of 0.00055 mass unit and it possesses one negative charge of electricity. The *proton* has a single positive

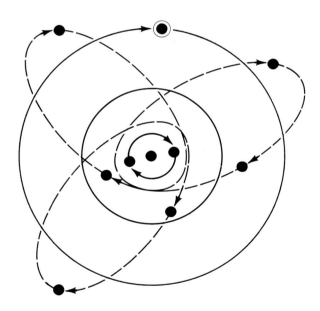

FIG. 11–4. / *Bohr's model of an atom. Compare this with the alternative representation, Fig. 11–5.*

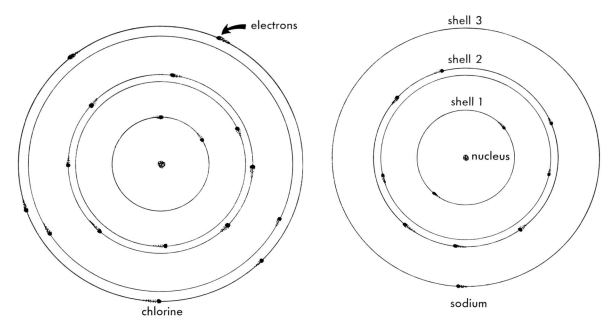

FIG. 11–5. / *Hypothetical model of the atomic structure of sodium and chlorine. This model shows the distribution of electrons in various shells.*

charge of electricity, but it is much more massive than the electron. It has a mass of 1.00758 mass units, which makes it about 1,800 times as massive as the electron. The *neutron* represents a compounding of a single electron and a single proton. It has no net resultant electrical charge. The mass is almost equivalent to the addition of one electron and one proton, or 1.00896 mass units.

Protons, electrons, and neutrons combine in various ways to form complex structures called *atoms.* Atoms formed by the various combinations are stable and cannot be broken down by ordinary chemical methods; these are *elements.* We know of 103 of these atomic configurations, which differ in the number of protons, electrons, and neutrons in each. The number of protons and electrons present range from 1 to 103 apiece. Each element possesses unique physical and chemical characteristics. An element's *atomic number* (chlorine, for example, is element No. 17) corresponds both to its total number of electrons and the number of protons in its nucleus.

The model of atomic structure which lends itself to easiest explanation and with a minimum loss of accuracy is that devised by the Danish physicist, Niels Bohr, who studied under Rutherford. His model is an extension of the model devised by Rutherford. Bohr was particularly concerned with understanding the motion of electrons about the nucleus. After much work he was forced to abandon some of the laws of classical mechanics in order to explain his observations. He concluded that in the case of motions of electrons in atoms the following rules hold:

Electrons are restricted to only a few circular and elliptical orbits around the nucleus, and selection of these orbits is carried out according to well-defined rules.

While an electron is moving in one of these orbits no electromagnetic waves (radiations) are given off.

Under certain conditions an electron may jump from one orbit to another. When it jumps from an outer orbit to one closer to the nucleus, it does so with the emission of radiant energy.

The validity of this theory was shown in part by the ease with which it could be used to explain the spectra of different elements.

According to the Bohr model, there is a concentration of positive charge in the nucleus, about which negative electrons move in circular and elliptical paths at relatively great distances from the nucleus (Fig. 11–4). Electrons occupy elliptical orbits only at certain specific distances from the nucleus. The number of electrons in each of these orbits is strictly limited. Two electrons, no more, may occupy the innermost orbit, which is called the *first shell*. In the case of atoms with more than two electrons, the additional electrons are located in other shells. The second shell may be viewed as having two subshells (Fig. 11–5). The inner subshell may contain up to two electrons, the outer subshell up to six, giving a total of eight electrons in the second shell. The element with eight electrons in its second shell is neon, one of the *inert gases*; neon has a total of 10 electrons, two in its first shell plus eight in the two subshells of its second shell. The third shell may have up to three subshells which are occupied by a maximum of 2, 6, and 10 electrons, respectively. The fourth shell may have up to four subshells occupied respectively by a maximum of 2, 6, 10, and 14 electrons.

Certain of the elements are remarkably stable. Until recently, no compounds of these elements were known. These are known as the *noble* or *inert gases*. They are helium, element No. 2; neon, No. 10; argon, No. 18; krypton, No. 36; xenon, No. 54; and radon, No. 86. Because these gases are inert, the grouping of the electrons in these elements must be very stable. The most stable electron configurations, except helium, which has two, contain eight electrons in the outermost orbit. Elements that have these configurations do not lose electrons from their outer orbits, but the other elements tend either to lose or gain electrons until there are eight electrons in the outer shell.

Ions

THE PRESENCE OF EIGHT ELECTRONS IN the outer shell, or orbit, of an atom makes it particularly stable. Atoms have a tendency to reach this stable form. Consider what happens if an atom does lose an electron. It will no longer have the same number of electrons in orbits around the nucleus as it has protons in the nucleus; therefore, having one more proton than electron, it will have a net positive charge. Likewise, if it should lose two electrons it will

have an excess of two positive charges. Charged atoms of this sort are called *ions*. Ions may be either positive or negative, depending on whether they gain or lose electrons. Which atoms are most likely to become positive ions and which negative ions is easily predicted. If a given atom has eight electrons in the next to the last shell and one in the last, outermost shell, then it is reasonable to expect that it will lose that one electron more readily than it will gain seven additional ones to achieve the stability of having eight in the outer shell. Likewise, an atom with two electrons in its outer shell is more likely to lose these than it is to gain six. On the other hand an atom with six or seven electrons in its outer orbit is more likely to gain one or two than it is to lose six or seven.

Compounds

COMPOUNDS ARE FORMED BY THE COMbination of elements through organic and inorganic processes. With the exception of some of the "native" metals, such as gold, silver, platinum, and copper, and a few other substances such as sulfur and pure carbon, we do not find many elements in pure, uncombined form. By far most of the minerals and rocks are compounds of two or more elements held together by electrical forces. Compounds have physical and chemical properties that differ from those of their component elements. The bonds holding elements together in the compounds are of three types—ionic bonds, covalent bonds, and metallic bonds.

Ionic Bonds

IONS FORM when an atom gains or loses one or more electrons to become charged. The amount of the net charge is dependent on the difference between the number of protons in the nucleus and the number of electrons in the orbits of the ion. Ions obey the laws of static electricity and are attracted to ions with an opposite charge and repelled by those of a like charge. If a large number of ions, some positive and some negative, are placed in solution in water or in some other medium through which they can move freely, they will tend to form an ionic compound. The negative ion will attract positive ions toward it, and they in turn will attract more negative ions. In this manner a large solid crystal may be built up. (See Table 4.)

Shape of the Crystal

THE PARTICULAR SHAPE that this crystal will assume is dependent on the size of the ions that make it up. Atoms and ions are visualized as spherical or nearly spherical, but they differ greatly in diameter. Ions with more shells or electrons may have diameters many times greater than those of the lower-numbered elements. The forces acting on the ions tend to pull them as close together as possible. How many positive ions can fit around one negative ion is dependent on the relative size of the two. Therefore, the most important factor in determining the shape of the configuration is the size of the ions involved.

NaCl

ONE OF THE MOST COMMON ionic compounds is sodium chloride, the mineral halite. It is a compound of sodium (Na) and chlorine (Cl). Sodium is element No. 11. We can predict that it will have two electrons in the first shell, eight in the second, and one in the third. Therefore, it will have a tendency to lose the single electron in the outer shell and become a sodium ion with a positive charge (Na^+). Chlorine is element No. 17. It has two electrons in its first shell, eight in its second, and seven in its third shell. It tends to gain one electron in the third shell to become a chlorine ion with a negative charge (Cl^-). The Na^+ ion and the Cl^- ion, having different charges, are attracted toward one another and pack as closely as possible. Their sizes are such that each negative ion has six positive ions adjacent to it in the configuration shown (Fig. 11–6). The resulting crystal is cubic in shape.

TABLE 4 / *In ionic bonding the radii of the ions is important in determining the way in which the ions will pack together. Given below are the ionic radii of several common ions and the predicted number of oxygen ions that can be packed around them (called the coordination number).*

ION	RADIUS	COORDINATION NUMBER
Si^{4+}	0.42 A°	4
Al^{3+}	0.51 A°	4 or 6
Mg^{2+}	0.66 A°	6
Ca^{2+}	0.99 A°	8

FIG. 11–6. / *Packing of sodium and chlorine ions in the ionic compound sodium chloride, NaCl, or common table salt.*

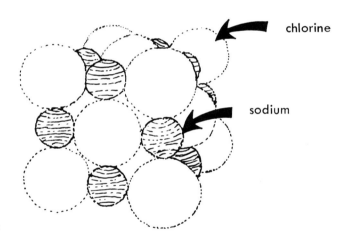

Covalent Bonds

A SECOND TYPE of bonding is formed when elements simply share electrons. It is possible for each of the atoms to achieve the stability of having eight electrons in its outer orbit by sharing those of one or more other atoms. An example of this type of bonding is methane, marsh gas, which is formed in swamps from the decay of organic matter. Methane is a compound of carbon and hydrogen. Hydrogen (H), element No. 1, has one electron in its orbit. Carbon (C) is element No. 6. It has two electrons in its first orbit and four in its outer orbit. A stable compound is formed when the carbon is able to share the electrons of four hydrogen atoms. Thus methane is expressed as CH_4.

$$H$$
$$|$$
$$H–C–H$$
$$|$$
$$H$$

Another common compound held together by covalent bonds is water, a compound of hydrogen and oxygen. Hydrogen has one electron, and oxygen, element No. 8, needs two electrons in its outer orbit to have eight. Thus one oxygen atom combines with two hydrogen atoms to form the compound H_2O.

Solution in Water

SOME COVALENT COMPOUNDS are made up of molecules that behave somewhat like small magnets. Water is one such molecule. Its magnetic qualities are caused by the way the two hydrogen atoms are attracted to the oxygen atom (Fig. 11–7). When the density of the electrons on one side of the molecule is increased, it acts as though one end is slightly positive and the other slightly negative. This *polar nature* of the water molecule is the reason it is such an effective solvent.

Consider a grain of salt or another ionic compound placed in water. Water molecules acting as small magnets become oriented with their positive ends toward negative ions in the solid and their negative ends toward positive ions. The effect of the attractions set up between water molecules and ions is to pull the ions out of the solid structure as soon as enough molecules are oriented to counterbalance the electrical forces within the crystal. There is a limit to the amount of solution that will take place, however, for when a large number of ions have gone into solution there will not be enough free water molecules left to attract ions of the solid effectively.

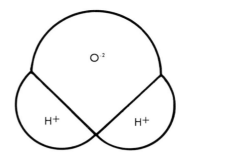
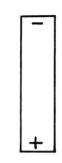

FIG. 11–7. / *Water molecule. Because the hydrogen atoms are close together the molecule acts somewhat like a small bar magnet. How this makes water a good solvent is explained in the text.*

Metallic Bonding

METALLIC BONDING, which is characteristic of pure metals, is different from ionic and covalent bonding in that electrons are shared throughout the crystal lattice. The atoms, all of which are the same size, are packed tightly together so that each has 12 others around it. Twelve spheres of a single size can always be packed around a thirteenth sphere of the same size regardless of what that size is. The electrons in this case move through the crystal lattice, making it possible for metals to conduct electricity.

Isotopes

NORMALLY EACH ELEMENT HAS A NUCLEUS composed of equal numbers of neutrons and protons; however, each element has alternate forms in which there are different numbers of neutrons in the nucleus. These forms have chemical and physical properties that are almost identical with those of the element. Such forms are called *isotopes* of the element. Some of these isotopes are unstable and break down spontaneously by the emission of radiant energy. Such isotopes are said to be *radioactive*. The energy they radiate is composed of protons and neutrons that make up the nucleus. Through the emission of these particles, the isotope disintegrates. The rate of this disintegration is constant for each isotope. Disintegration rates are such that a certain constant amount of time is required for one-half of the mass of the isotope to break down. This amount of time is called the *half life* of the isotope. As a result of the breakdown of an isotope new isotopes or elements may form. The new ones may also be radioactive and break down again, but eventually a stable isotope or element is formed. Because the half life of a radioactive isotope is a constant, and because a stable element is formed as an end product, it is possible to use radioactive isotopes as geologic clocks. This is possible only if the half life is known, if the steps in the radioactive breakdown and the half lives of each intermediate isotope are known, if decay is not complete, and if the stable end product is present. (See chapter 27 for a further discussion.)

Minerals

So far our discussion has been concerned with the elementary particles of matter and their arrangement in atomic structures. Geologists must normally deal with large quantities of elements or compounds in the form of minerals and rocks. A *mineral* is defined as a naturally occurring element or compound formed by inorganic natural processes and having a definite chemical composition and a certain characteristic atomic structure which is expressed in an external crystalline form and in other physical properties. Minerals are in turn components of rocks. Most *rocks* are aggregates of minerals. These are the raw materials with which we must become thoroughly acquainted if we seek a basic understanding of this and other planets.

Crystals

It is clear from the definition of a mineral above that not all matter is composed of minerals. Oil and gas, coal, water, and organic substances in general are excluded. Minerals are in a crystalline state. That means simply that atoms composing the mineral have an orderly internal arrangement like that described in de-

tail for NaCl. Because of this regularity the mineral has a geometrical framework built up of a vast number of unit cells or "building blocks." The unit cell for salt, a cube, is shown in Fig. 11–6. A single crystal of salt may be thought of as a large number of these units stacked together in an orderly fashion. Unit cells may have many shapes other than cubes. The shape depends on the size of the atoms involved, the elements present in the compound, and the way they are bound together.

These patterns may find outward expression in the shapes that crystals of that mineral assume. A *crystal* is a homogeneous body whose surfaces are smooth planes. As was previously discussed, one important factor determining the internal arrangement of atoms in a compound is the diameter of the elements making up the compound (Fig. 11–8). If a mineral in the process of growth or formation is restricted by the shape of the space in which it can grow,

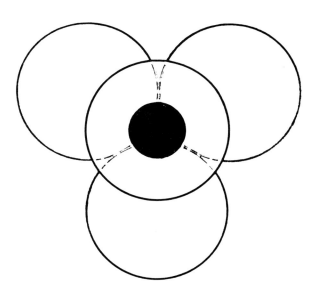

FIG. 11–8. / *The silicon-oxygen tetrahedron, seen from above. Four oxygen ions are packed around a single silicon ion. This structure is the chief building block in the most common rock-forming minerals.*

then it may not achieve the perfect shape of a crystal. Many minerals are formed from a molten mass of rock. As this melt cools, crystals form, but before solidification is complete there is competition for space, and many minerals are forced to crystallize in restricted spaces. Such a mineral still has an orderly internal atomic structure, and it is said to be crystalline although no crystal of that mineral may be seen.

X-Ray Method

ABOUT 1912 DR. MAX VON LAUE, A PHYSIcist, devised a method to test the hypothesis that crystals possess orderly internal arrangements of atoms. His experiments consisted of placing a crystal in the path of a beam of X-rays. The X-rays passed through the crystal and their paths were recorded on a photographic plate placed behind the crystal. When developed, the plate showed a dark spot in the center, where the X-rays had traveled directly through the crystal and a large number of small dark spots arranged around the center in a regular geometrical pattern. These small spots represent reflections of the X-rays from the systematically oriented planes of atoms within the crystal (Fig. 11–9). The symmetry of these patterns is an indication of the internal symmetry of the atomic arrangements.

Crystals can be classified and distinguished on the basis of their symmetry, which is an outward expression of the internal symmetry in the arrangement of their atoms. X-ray analysis can be used to determine the symmetry of a mineral even when the crystal form is not apparent. For this reason, X-ray analysis has been very important in identifying minerals, even in the forms of powders and clay. On the basis of symmetry crystalline substances are classified into six major systems, which are in turn subdivided into many smaller groups. The major systems are isometric, hexagonal, tetragonal, orthorhombic, monoclinic, and triclinic. Examples of some of the more common of these forms are illustrated in Fig. 11–10.

Mineral Groups

CLASSIFICATION OF MINERALS IS NECESSARY because several thousand different minerals have been identified. Minerals are classified on the basis of their chemical composition as well as of their crystal symmetry. In the chemical classification, a negative ion or group of ions are used to define the class to which the mineral belongs. The principal classes are:

Native elements: gold, silver, copper, platinum, arsenic, sulfur, diamonds.

Sulphides: sulphur compounds, i.e., galena (PbS), sphalerite (ZnS), pyrite (FeS_2).

Oxides: compounds of oxygen, i.e., ice (H_2O), hematite (Fe_2O_3), corundum (Al_2O_3), magnetite (Fe_3O_4).

Halides: compounds of chlorine or fluorine, i.e., halite ($NaCl$), fluorite (CaF_2).

Carbonates: compounds of carbonate (CO_3), i.e., calcite ($CaCO_3$), dolomite ($CaMg(CO_3)_2$).

Sulphates: compounds of sulphate (SO_4), i.e., gypsum ($CaSO_4 \cdot 2H_2O$).

Phosphates: compounds of phosphate (PO_4), i.e., apatite ($Ca_5(PO_4)_3(F)$).

Silicates: compounds of silicon and oxygen, i.e., quartz (SiO_2), feldspar $KAl_3Si_3O_8$, kaolinite $Al_2(Si_2O_5)(OH)_4$.

FIG. 11–9. / *X-ray diffraction diagrams showing the oriented molecular structure of a coal. (After Tyler, Bull. Geol. Soc. A., v. 69.)*

TABLE 5 / *Composition of the earth. Only the more abundant elements are listed. (From Mason, 1952.)*

Element	Symbol	Atomic Number	Percentage of Volume of Earth's Crust	Percentage of Weight of Earth's Crust
Oxygen	O	8	91.97	46.60
Silicon	Si	14	.80	27.72
Aluminum	Al	13	.77	8.13
Iron	Fe	26	.68	5.00
Magnesium	Mg	12	.56	2.09
Calcium	Ca	20	1.48	3.63
Sodium	Na	11	1.60	2.83
Potassium	K	19	2.14	2.59

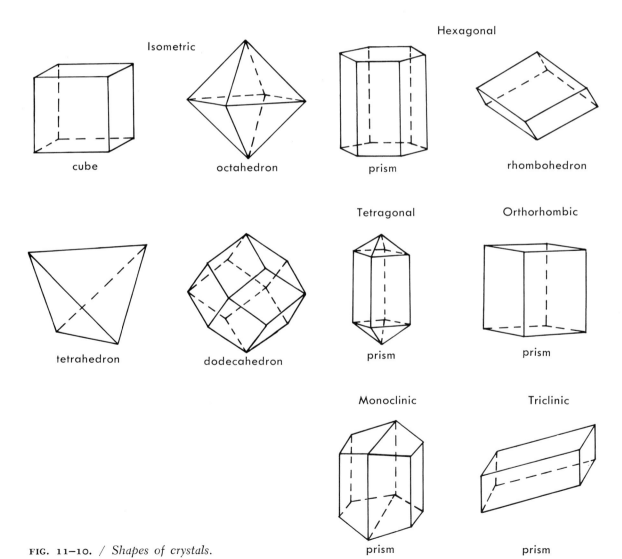

FIG. 11–10. / *Shapes of crystals.*

Of these groups the silicates are most important because they include most of the common rock-forming minerals—quartz, feldspar, mica, clay, amphibole, pyroxene, olivine, and garnet. The chief component of the structure of unit cells among silicates is the silicon-oxygen tetrahedron. These two elements are the most common elements in the earth's crust. The ion of silicon, element No. 14, has four positive charges, Si^{+4}. The oxygen ion has two negative charges. The ionic radii of these two elements are such that four oxygens fit around one silicon. The shape of the group is that of a tetrahedron, a four-sided pyramid, each of the four corners of the tetrahedron being occupied by one oxygen ion. This combination has a net electrical charge of minus four. Thus positive ions may be attached or two tetrahedra may share oxygen ions. When sharing oxygen ions the tetrahedra are joined together in various ways. In a double tetrahedral structure two tetrahedra share a single oxygen ion. Other combinations form rings, chains, sheets, and three-dimensional structures. In the more complex silicates there are a number of other ions present. Those may have positions in the mineral structure between sheets or chains of the tetrahedra.

Physical Properties of Minerals

Specific gravity. The density of a mineral is the ratio of its weight to that of an equal volume of water. Graphite is about twice as dense as water; that is, two cubic inches of water would weigh the same as one cubic inch of graphite. The specific gravity of graphite is therefore two. Some idea of the range of values found for the specific gravity of various minerals is gained from comparing graphite, 2, with hematite, the most commonly used ore of iron, 5.2, and gold, 19.

Cleavage. This is the property that some minerals exhibit of breaking along definite smooth planes. These planes are a simple indication of the difference in strength of bonds between atoms in the crystal. If bonds are strong

FIG. 11–11. / *Crystals of pyrite, "fool's gold."* (*U.S. National Museum*).

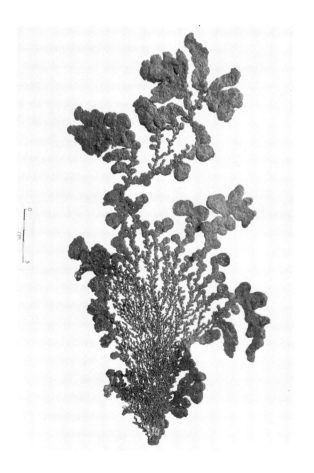

FIG. 11–12. / *Native copper from Bolivia.* (*U.S. National Museum*).

FIG. 11–13. / *Hematite, which occurs in banded, micaceous, and fossil forms also. (U.S. National Museum).*

FIG. 11–15. / *Malachite, copper carbonate. (U.S. National Museum.)*

FIG. 11–16. / *Cleavage specimens of calcite, left, and feldspar, right. (U.S. National Museum.)*

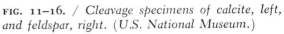

FIG. 11–14. / *Moss agate, a variety of quartz. (U.S. National Museum).*

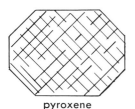 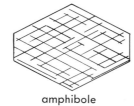

pyroxene   amphibole

FIG. 11–17. / *Cleavages of pyroxene and amphibole.*

FIG. 11–18. / *Natural asbestos, variety chrysotile.* (*U.S. National Museum.*)

FIG. 11–19. / *Quartz crystals.* (*U.S. National Museum.*)

between atoms in one plane and relatively weak between those in other planes, the mineral will break along the planes of weakness. In some minerals these differences are great; in others there is little difference in the strength of the bonds in different directions. Cleavages are very useful in identification of minerals. They differ in several ways in different minerals:

1. In number: there may be one or as many as six directions of cleavage.
2. In angles between them: two may be at right angles or oblique to one another; three may be mutually perpendicular, or all may intersect at acute angles.
3. In degree of development: some minerals break forming very smooth cleavage surfaces, in which case the cleavage is said to be perfect; others are not as easily broken—they have imperfect cleavage. Still others may break along cleavage only with difficulty.

Hardness. Hardness in the sense used here does not mean breaking strength, but the ability of one mineral to scratch another. A scale of 10 relatively common minerals is used as a basis for hardness comparisons. The scale is nonlinear (that is, No. 5 is not five times harder than No. 1; actually it is many times harder).

Hardness scale:
1. talc
2. gypsum
     (fingernail)
3. calcite
     (a copper penny)
4. fluorite
5. apatite
     (a steel knife)
     (plate glass)
6. feldspar
     (a file)
7. quartz
8. topaz
9. corundum
10. diamond

A mineral with a hardness of 6.5 will scratch feldspar, but it will not scratch quartz. Also it can be scratched by quartz, but not by the feldspar. The hardness of an unknown mineral may be found by scratching it with minerals or other materials of known hardness.

Fracture. It is sometimes helpful to note the way in which a mineral has fractured. Some break into splinters; others have smooth, even fractures. Some break in rough, irregular surfaces; and a few, such as quartz, break with a smooth, shell-shaped fracture known as a conchoidal fracture.

Luster. The luster of a mineral is the appearance of its surface in reflected light. Two large groups are recognized: metallic and nonmetallic lusters. Luster depends on the structure of the surface of the mineral, its transparency, and the way light is reflected or refracted from it. There is great variation in the nonmetallic lusters, and there is no substitute for personal observation in learning to identify these. The most common are:

    adamantine: brilliant luster of diamond
    vitreous: luster of glass
    resinous: luster of yellow resins
    greasy: luster of oily glass
    pearly: luster of pearl
    silky: like silk, usually resulting from fibrous
       structures.

Color. Of all physical properties color is frequently the most impressive and least definitive. Color in nonmetallic minerals is due to impurities. Very small quantities of some elements are sufficient to give large masses of other minerals bright colors. It is not uncommon for a single mineral to occur in as many as five or six different colors. Do not depend on color in identification of nonmetallic minerals.

Streak. The color of the powder of a mineral is called its streak. Although the mineral may occur in several different colors, the color of the powder will always be the same. Streak is tested by rubbing a piece of the mineral on an unglazed porcelain plate.

FIG. 11–20. / *Gypsum. The crystal variety on the left showing cleavages is called selenite; that on the right is satin spar. (Washington and Lee Univ. collection.)*

FIG. 11–21. / *Twinning striations in labradorite feldspar. (Washington and Lee Univ. collection.)*

Miscellaneous tests (special properties).

1. A few minerals may be identified by their taste.

2. Radioactivity may be tested by use of Geiger counters, scintillation meters, or similar instruments. All minerals containing uranium, vanadium, thorium, or other radioactive elements will register.

3. A few minerals are magnetic. One variety of magnetite, loadstone, will pick up bits of metal. Others will be attracted to a magnet.

4. Some minerals show a play of colors, the appearance of several colors in rapid succession, iridescence, when the mineral is turned. If a milky reflection is seen from the interior of the specimen it is said to display *opalescence*.

5. Fluorescence is the emission of light from within when the mineral is subjected to ultraviolet light. Colors produced may sometimes be useful in identification.

Twinning. Some common rock-forming minerals exhibit the property of having two or more crystals or parts of crystals grow together in such a way that the individual parts are related to their crystal structure. Some are simply two crystals growing side by side with a single plane between them; others appear to have grown so that one crystal penetrates the other. Twinning serves as a useful means of identifying certain minerals.

NATIVE ELEMENTS

COPPER (native) / 2½ [*copper red*]
Cu

It occurs in irregularly-shaped masses in pore spaces in lavas and gravels. It is ductile.

DIAMOND / 10 [*colorless*]
C

Hardness of diamond is its most distinguishing feature. Diamond crystals are most commonly octahedra, cubes, and slight modifications of these shapes, but they are often rounded and distorted. Diamond has octahedral cleavages which are perfect. In addition to the colorless varieties there are yellowish, red, green, blue, and black diamonds. The brilliance of diamond is due to its high dispersion of light.

GOLD (native) / 2½ [*gold*]
Au

It usually is found as rolled scales, grains, or nuggets. Its high specific gravity and color distinguish it from most other metals. It is malleable and ductile, has no cleavage.

GRAPHITE / 1 [*gray*]
C

Massive forms are most common. These are scaly, foliated, granular, or earthy. The color, dark gray, hardness of 1, and one perfect cleavage make it easy to identify. It feels greasy.

SULFUR / 2 [*yellow*]
S

Granular, fibrous, crusts, or compact forms are most common. Straw-yellow color is characteristic. There is no cleavage.

SULFIDES

BORNITE / 2½ [*bronze*]
Cu_5FeS_4

This important copper-bearing mineral occurs in massive forms that are usually granular or compact. It is opaque. The peacock-colored tarnish is most characteristic. It is found associated with chalcopyrite, malachite, and other copper-bearing minerals.

CHALCOPYRITE / 3 [*brass yellow*]
$CuFeS_2$

Crystals are usually tetrahedra, but it also occurs in compact and granular forms. It may be distinguished from pyrite by its deeper color and greater softness. Common associates are pyrite, bornite, galena, sphalerite, and chalcocite.

GALENA / 2½ [*gray*]
PbS

Cubic crystals and lead gray color combined with its high specific gravity make galena easy to identify. But it also occurs in granular aggregates. It has perfect cubic cleavage.

PYRITE / 6 [*brass yellow*]
FeS_2

Cubic crystals are commonly found. These crystals usually are striated. It. may also be found in massive granular forms. When weathered pyrite may turn into limonite.

SPHALERITE / 3½ [*brown yellow*]
ZnS

Resinous luster is one of the important characteristics. Yellowish colors are also typical. When in crystals they are tetrahedral. Cleavage is prominent in six directions.

CARBONATES

AZURITE / 3½ [*dark blue*]
$CuCo_3$

The azure-blue color is characteristic. It will effervesce in hydrochloric acid. It is a minor ore of copper, most commonly found with malachite.

CALCITE / 3 [*variable*]
$CaCO_3$

Crystals are found in many shapes. Crystals or granular aggregates are most common, but it is also found in stalactitic form in caves. Color is highly variable. In clear specimens double refraction of light may be observed—two images of objects below the calcite will be seen. There are three perfect cleavages not at right angles. Calcite will effervesce in dilute hydrochloric acid.

DOLOMITE / 3½ [*variable*] $(Ca, Mg)(CO_3)$	It is similar in appearance to calcite, but crystals of rhombohedral shape have curved faces. It also occurs in massive forms. It is distinguished from calcite by its failure to effervesce in weak hydrochloric acid.
MALACHITE / 4 [*green*] $CuCo_3$	Crystals are needle-like and form in groups. More commonly it is found in massive fibrous, stalactitic, kidney-shaped masses with internal banding, as velvety crusts or as earthy masses. The silky luster and bright green color are characteristic.

OXIDES

CASSITERITE / 6½ [*black*] SnO_2	It occurs as short prismatic crystals or in granular forms, sometimes with radial fibrous structures. Cleavage is indistinct, and the color is highly variable, but usually it is black.
CHROMITE / 5½ [*black*] $FeCr_2O_4$	It is usually found in granular masses. Grains are cubic. It is opaque, has a metallic luster, and is sometimes very slightly magnetic. It is an important ore mineral of chromium.
CORUNDUM / 9 [*variable*] Al_2O_3	It is frequently found in hexagonal and barrel-shaped prismatic crystals, but it also occurs in massive granular forms. Color is variable, but the most common colors are gray, green and blue. Hardness is the most distinguishing feature, but care must be exercised in determining the hardness because chlorite is often associated with corundum and makes it appear softer than it is.
HEMATITE / 6 [*red or black*] Fe_2O_3	There are several important varieties of hematite. *Specularite* is characterized by its metallic luster, steel-gray or iron-black color, and reddish streak. It occurs as crystals, in a micaceous form, and as granular masses. *Oölitic* or *fossil hematite* is characterized by very small egg-shaped bodies. Hematite may occur as a cement in sandstone, as oölites, or as a replacement of fossils. Compact hematite occurs as kidney-shaped masses that have fibrous radial internal structures. The luster is submetallic, and the color is iron black or brownish red. All hematite has a red streak.
LIMONITE / 5 [*rust*] $FeO(OH) \cdot H_2O$	It is usually in massive forms that are nodular, compact, earthy, or stalactitic. The rusty color is characteristic of the surface. The compact forms are fibrous, but earthy limonite is more common.

MAGNETITE / 6 [black]
Fe_3O_4

Crystals belong to the cubic system and are often octahedra. Magnetite also is found in compact, granular, and lamellar forms. Cleavage is indistinct. Unlike most other minerals it is strongly magnetic.

BAUXITE / [variable]
Al hydroxides

It is found in a massive, earthy or claylike form. Rounded pea-shaped concretions are characteristic. It is the main ore of aluminum. Hardness is variable.

SILICATES

AMPHIBOLE GROUP:

HORNBLENDE / 5½ [black]
$Ca_2(Mg, Fe)_5(OH)_2(Al, Si)_8O_{22}$

It occurs in long, prismatic crystals and in massive forms of small bladed, fibrous, granular, or compact grains. There are two good cleavages at angles of 56° and 124°.

CHLORITE / 2½ [greenish]
$Mg_5Al(OH)_8Al\ Si_3O_{10}$

Crystals are tabular, hexagonal, and often bent. It is micaceous in appearance in most occurrences. Colors are shades of green. One perfect cleavage is responsible for the micaceous appearance. It occurs in metamorphic rocks, and as a scaly coating on other minerals.

EPIDOTE / 6½ [green, brown, or yellow]
(Ca, Al, Fe, Al, Si, O)

It occurs as elongated prismatic crystals, but is more commonly found in massive forms that may be columnar, fibrous, or granular. The greenish brown, greenish yellow, and yellow colors are characteristic. Common associates are feldspars, amphiboles, and pyroxenes.

FELDSPAR GROUP:

MICROCLINE / 6 [green]
$KAlSi_3O_8$

ORTHOCLASE / 6 [pink, yellow, or brown]
$KAlSi_3O_8$

ALBITE / 6 [white or gray]
$NaAlSi_3O_8$

LABRADORITE / 6 [gray or green gray]
$(Na, Ca)\ (Al\ Si_3O_8)$

ANORTHITE / 6 [colorless or white]
$Ca\ Al\ Si_3O_8$

Both orthoclase and microcline contain potassium. They occur as thick tabular crystals and in massive forms that may be granular or cleavage masses. Common colors are white, gray, pink, and for microcline, green. They may be distinguished from other feldspars by rectangular cleavage, and by absence of fine striations on cleavage surfaces that are the result of twinning. Albite, labradorite, and anorthite are *plagioclase* feldspars. These contain various amounts of sodium and calcium. Albite is one end member of the group. It contains only sodium. Anorthite, the other end member, contains only calcium. Other members of the group contain varying amounts of sodium and calcium, and the physical properties vary with the relative amount of each of these constituents. The plagioclase feldspars are all twinned. There are fine striations on crystal and cleavage faces. Labradorite is the most easily identifiable member of the group because it is usually gray and has a play of colors as it is turned in light.

GARNET / 6½ [*variable*]
(Ca,Mg,Fe,Al)(SiO₄)

Crystals are common and are cubes or dodecahedra, but it occurs in massive granular forms also. Color is highly variable, but deep red colors are characteristic of some varieties. Cleavage is not distinct. Hardness is one of the best ways of distinguishing it from similar minerals.

KYANITE / 4–7 [*blue*]
Al₂SiO₅

Long, bladed crystals that are curved and radially grouped are characteristic of kyanite as are the bluish streaks or spots in it. The hardness varies with direction, being 4 in one direction and as much as 7 in the other. It occurs in metamorphic rocks.

MICA GROUP:

BIOTITE / 2½ [*black*]
K(Mg,Fe)₃(OH,F)₂Al Si₃O₁₀

LEPIDOLITE / 3 [*pink*]
K₂Li₃Al₃(F, OH)₄(AlSi₃O₁₀)₂

MUSCOVITE / 2½ [*white*]
KAl₂(OH,F)₂Al Si₃ O₁₀

Members of this group are hexagonal in shape. Scalelike sheets formed as a result of the one perfect cleavage are the most characteristic occurrence in rocks. Biotite is black, brownish, or blackish green. Muscovite is colorless, white, or yellowish. Lepidolite is pink or lavender. The colors are characteristic of these three.

OLIVINE / 6½ [*green*]
(Mg,Fe)₂SiO₄

It is usually found in granular masses. The green color is typical, and striations of the crystal faces may be apparent in larger crystals, but are difficult to see in granular aggregates.

PYROXENE GROUP:

AUGITE / 5½ [*black*]
Ca(Mg,Fe,Al)(Al, Si)₂O₆

Augite is the most common member of this group. It is most easily confused with hornblende, but the two can be distinguished by the angle between the cleavage faces. The acute angle between cleavages in augite is 87° compared with an angle of 56° in hornblende.

QUARTZ / 7 [*variable*]
SiO₂

Crystalline varieties are hexagonal prisms. Crystal faces are horizontally striated. This group includes rock crystal quartz and milky quartz. The conchoidal fracture, glassy luster, and hardness are characteristic. Cryptocrystalline varieties are also very common. In these the crystal structure is not apparent. They appear as massive forms which may be nodular, kidney-shaped, banded, concretionary, stalactitic, or compact masses. The luster of these forms is waxy or vitreous. *Chalcedony* has a waxy luster, hardness of 7, and conchoidal fracture. *Agate* is banded chalcedony. *Onyx* is agate in which the lines or bands are even and straight. *Jasper* is distinguished by its red color which is derived from specks of hematite in the quartz.

SERPENTINE / 2–5 [*green or black*]
Mg₆(OH)₈ Si₄O₁₀

It is found only in massive forms which may be compact, columnar, fibrous, or granular. The luster is greasy or waxy. It is often spotted, clouded, or multicolored. *Asbestos* is a variety.

SILLIMANITE / 6½ [*gray brown*] Al_2SiO_5	It occurs as long, thin needle-like forms or as radiating fibrous masses in metamorphic rocks. Silky luster is an important characteristic of most occurrences.
STAUROLITE / 7 [*gray, brown, or black*] $Fe(OH)_2 \cdot 2 Al_2O SiO_4$	Prismatic crystals are common. These are usually in a crosslike shape. It is found in metamorphic rocks.
TALC / 1 [*variable*] $Mg_3(OH)_2 Si_4O_{10}$	When in crystals it is thin and tabular. More common are the foliated massive forms or fibrous, granular, or compact masses. Luster is pearly, and it feels greasy.
TOURMALINE / 7½ [*black, pink, or brown*] A complex silicate of boron and aluminum	Crystals are common as long or short hexagonal prisms characterized by a triangular outline in cross section. Color is sometimes distributed zonally along the crystals, which may vary from transparent to nearly opaque.

OTHERS

APATITE / 5 [*highly variable*] $CaPO_4$	Crystals are hexagonal prisms. It also occurs in nodular or earthy massive form in crystalline limestone, ore deposits, and in igneous rocks. Color is highly variable. The single cleavage is imperfect.
CARNOTITE / − [*bright yellow*] (K, U, O, V, H_2O)	It occurs as a powdery incrustation in sand or sandstone. Canary-yellow color and radioactivity are the most distinctive characteristics.
FLUORITE / 4 [*variable*] CaF_2	It occurs in cubic crystals and in cleavage masses or in granular form. Color is variable, but purples and greens are most common. The cleavage is octahedral and is perfect. Fluorite is most often confused with calcite, but differs in that it has a hardness of 4.
GYPSUM / 2 [*white*] $CaSO_4 \cdot 2H_2O$	Crystals are tabular or prismatic. Massive forms may be laminated, granular, fibrous, or earthy. It is usually colorless, white or gray. Colorless transparent crystals or cleavage plates are called *Selenite*. Fibrous forms that have silky luster are called *satin spar*. Granular forms are called *alabaster*.
HALITE / 2½ [*colorless*] $NaCl$	Crystals are cubic in shape. Massive forms may be cleavable masses, granular, fibrous, stalactitic, or crusts. Colors are white, gray, or colorless. Because halite can absorb water it may feel damp and slick. The salty taste is characteristic, as is its perfect cubic cleavage. It is common table salt.

12 /

Formation of Igneous Rocks

THERE ARE TWO PRINCIPAL SCHOOLS OF thought regarding the origin of the earth. According to one view, not generally held today, the earth originated from the sun as a mass of fluids. These fluids cooled and became *magma*, and the minerals in this magma crystallized, forming rocks. The prevalent view today is that the earth was formed by the coalescence of a mass of small, cool particles, essentially meteorites. As these collected and were pulled together by gravitational forces, the interior of the earth became hot and eventually the entire earth was molten. In both theories the earth was molten in its early stages of development. Thus, all rocks have been derived ultimately from magmas. Such igneous and volcanic materials may be called primary rocks. The widespread existence of volcanism today is ample evidence that rock magmas continue to be generated.

Early students of volcanism thought that the earth's molten interior was covered by a thin crust through which fiery masses from below broke, causing volcanic eruptions. With the growth of seismology it has been recognized that the molten interior lies at a depth of about 1,800 miles. It is highly unlikely that magmas are coming from such depth. The modern view is that these magmas are generated within the crust or in the upper part of the mantle, at depths on the order of 5 to 50 miles. Once generated, magma moves in response to stresses and as a result of volume increases that accompany the melting process. The expanding volume of molten matter is forced upward along fractures and faults, if they are present, or it pushes the overlying strata upward into domes, through which it may eventually break along newly formed cracks. If magma finds its way to the surface a volcanic eruption takes place. If there are great quantities of gas held in under pressure, the eruption may be an explosion. If gases have been allowed to escape the eruption is usually quiet. When magma reaches the ground surface it is called *lava*. Lava, gases, and fragments of rocks through which the magma has moved are the principal products of volcanism. Magmas do not always break through to the surface. Many of them cool and crystallize beneath the ground surface, giving rise to many different types of *igneous rocks*. In the following discussions we will consider ways in which magma may be generated, the nature of magma, various types of volcanic eruptions and materials formed through them, how magmas crystallize, and some factors that give rise to the great variety of igneous rocks.

Products and Forms of Volcanic Materials

VOLCANOES DIFFER IN AMOUNT, SIZE, TYPE of materials ejected, and in the shape those materials take following eruptions. The materials include solids (called *pyroclastics*), lava, and gases composed largely of steam. Pyroclastics range in size from blocks weighing tons down to dust-sized particles. These fragments are broken from the vent during eruptions. Blocks weighing two tons have been thrown over two miles in some of the most violent eruptions. Smaller fragments such as bombs, lapilli, ash, and dust are more common (Figs. 12–1 and 12–2). *Bombs* and *lapilli* are formed from bits of lava blown into the air, where they cool and partially solidify before hitting the ground. They are often twisted in the air. An oval center with twisted ends is a common shape. When fragmental materials are the principal extrusives they form steep-sided cones (Fig. 12–3).

Lavas may accompany the eruption of pyroclastics, or lava and gas may be the main eruptives.[1] Not all lavas have the same composition or physical properties. Common types of lava are basalt and rhyolite. Normally basalts are more fluid and spread out rapidly from the vent or fissure through which they flow. Some flows are only a few feet thick, but cover large areas.

Lava and gases move to the surface through long, narrow fissures or pipelike feeders. *Central vent eruptions* give rise to *cinder cones* when pyroclastics dominate, or *composite cones* when lavas and pyroclastics are mixed (Fig. 12–4). Lava spreads the base of the cone while fragmental particles build up steep sides near the vent. Fissure eruptions build plateaus of broad volcanoes with shieldlike profiles (Fig. 12–5). Following eruptions, the central portion of a volcano may collapse as the ejected material subsides into the space left vacant below the surface. Such collapse features are called *calderas* (Fig. 12–6).

[1] See Paxton Springs Quadrangle, at end of book.

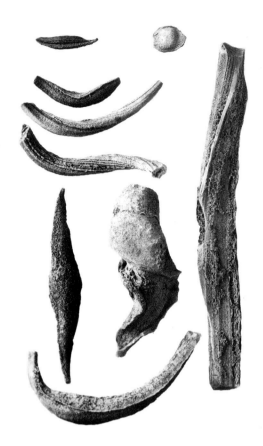

FIG. 12–1. / *Pyroclastics. Shown here are ribbon and spindle bombs from the Craters of the Moon National Monument, Idaho. (Photo by H. T. Stearns, courtesy of the U.S. Geological Survey.)*

FIG. 12–2. / *Lapilli cone south of Lava Butte, Deschutes County, Oregon. (Photo by I. C. Russell, courtesy of the U.S. Geological Survey.)*

FIG. 12–3. / *An extinct composite cone surrounded by its own erosion materials. This recently active volcano is located in Alaska. Note the steep slopes which are characteristic of cinder cones.*

Volcanism—Case Histories

ABOUT 500 VOLCANOES HAVE BEEN ACTIVE within recorded history, and the cones of many thousands of others show such slight evidence of erosion that they cannot be very old. The present and recent past may well be one of the periods of greatest volcanic activity. Volcanoes take many forms, and the activity that is associated with their eruption is highly varied. The activity of volcanoes differs in the amount

FIG. 12–4. / *Mt. Fuji, Japan, a composite cone. (Courtesy Japan Tourist Association.)*

FIG. 12–5. / *Crater of Mauna Loa in the Hawaiian Islands. This air view of the volcano crater shows a similarity to the craters of the moon. They may be features of similar origin. Volcanoes may be the ultimate source of the oceans and atmosphere.* (*United States Air Force Photo.*)

and type of material ejected. Sizes, temperature, and composition of material ejected determine the shape of the volcano or the form of the extrusion. Volcanoes also differ in the violence and the timing of successive eruptions.

Parícutin

ON FEBRUARY 20, 1943, a Mexican farmer was plowing his corn field when he noticed a thin cloud of steam rising from the ground. Within a day frequent small explosions were taking place in that part of the field; clouds of smoke and dust were boiling up from a small hole. Before the end of that week a volcano almost 140 meters high had been built of pyroclastics, and a flow of basalt lava had issued from a fissure located near the cone. Within the first year the cone rose to a height of 325 meters. Activity continued until 1952 when the volcano,

FIG. 12–6. / *Caldera.*

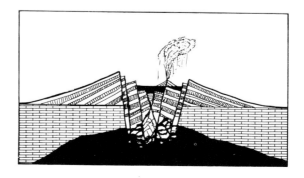

Parícutin, now 410 meters high, became one of many inactive volcanoes in the western part of Mexico.

Tamboro

THE MOST VIOLENT explosion of recorded history occurred on a small island in the East Indies in 1815 when the volcano Tamboro blew about 50 cubic miles of the crust into the air. The debris created by this tremendous explosion covered islands for hundreds of miles around. Explosions of this sort are relatively rare, and most of them occur in volcanoes that have been dormant for long periods of time. Explosion is a means of release of pressures built up beneath the volcano's vent in the *pipe*, the connection between the volcano and the magma, or within the magma itself. Magmas contain large quantities of gases. Gases are compressible and may continue to build up pressure until the pressure exceeds the strength of the plug of frozen lava in the pipe. If the gases can be released slowly, violent explosion is unlikely.

Krakatoa

ONE SUNDAY AFTERNOON in August of 1883 a few mild explosions rocked the island of Krakatoa, located in the Sunda Strait between Java and Sumatra. The next morning the cone of this volcano was ripped apart by an explosion that sent more than one cubic mile of rock into the air. A cloud of dust, gases, and debris rose nearly 17 miles into the atmosphere. Heavier debris fell back to earth, but smaller particles of dust were caught in upper air currents and were blown around the earth. For the next two years, before this great quantity of dust settled, it colored sunsets. Krakatoa and a neighboring island were literally blown to bits. A sounding was made over the original peak of the volcano, which had been 2,600 feet above sea level; the sounding was —1,000 feet. Few people lived on Krakatoa, but in the lowlands of the southwest Pacific islands thousands were killed by a *tsunamis*, or *seismic wave* (commonly and erroneously called a "tidal wave") created by the explosion.

The island of Krakatoa resembled numerous other volcanic islands in the Pacific. The majority of these have composite cones built up in the course of many eruptions. During some of these eruptions pyroclastic debris comes to the surface. Interbedded with these pyroclastic materials are layers of lava.

The site on which Krakatoa was built was one previously occupied by volcanoes. A fringe of islands marks the rim of a former volcano which collapsed or exploded before recorded history.

Mt. Pelée

MT. PELÉE, situated on the slopes above the city of St. Pierre on the island of Martinique in the West Indies, is famous for an eruption that took place in 1902. This eruption was so extraordinary and its effects so disastrous that the name "Pelean" is used to describe this particular type of violent eruption. Mt. Pelée stands over 4,400 feet above sea level. It was known to have been active, but eruptions were rare and never caused serious damage. In April of 1902 activity started. Fumaroles, holes from which gases and boiling water issue, formed in the upper valley of the volcano. A few weeks later ash began to be ejected and sulphur gases could be smelled. Late in April explosions began and increasing amounts of ash fell on St. Pierre. The population of the island became uneasy, but officials assured them there was no danger and troops were used to prevent people from leaving the city. By the morning of May 8 activity had subsided and only a thin cloud of smoke was rising from the crater when suddenly, at about 8:00 A.M., the volcano exploded in four great bursts. A huge black cloud spread out from the volcano and rolled down the slope, engulfing the city and port in two minutes. The cloud consisted of incandescent gases and dust. The population of the city, estimated to be about 30,000, was wiped out in a matter of minutes. The only survivors were on two of the eighteen ships in the harbor. Most people were killed by heat and poisonous gases; only a small percentage were buried under ash and lava.

Vesuvius

THE DESTRUCTION OF the city of Pompeii is one of the classic incidents in ancient Roman history. In 79 A.D. Pompeii was buried to a depth of 50 feet by a hot, thick mud of dust and ash mixed with steam.

Vesuvius now stands about 4,000 feet high in the center of the collapsed crater of an older and larger volcano, Mt. Somma. All that is left of Mt. Somma is a ridge that makes a half-circle around Vesuvius. Varied and periodic activity has been the character of Vesuvius' history in modern time. The volcano has been active frequently since the explosion which destroyed Pompeii. Activity seems to follow a pattern. After a period of violent eruption and explosion the remains of its composite cone begin to collapse where it is unstable or over-steepened. The crater catches much of this debris. Within a few years lava begins to flow into the crater and may eventually fill it. Weight of material in the crater allows pressure to build up within the pipe. Lava may break through the sides of the cone, and some may flow over the rim of the crater. Small craters form within the larger crater; these are accompanied by minor explosions. Eventually pressures within become too great to be contained, and a major eruption begins. This may take the form of a brilliant fireworks display with incandescent ash, bombs, and dust blown into the air, or activity may be in the form of a quiet extrusion of glowing rivers of red-hot lava. On steep slopes these flow rapidly downhill, carrying partially cooled blocks along with them. At the foot of the volcano, where the slopes break, the motion is slowed and the lava begins to consolidate. A crust forms over the top of the flow, but internal heat keeps the center fluid, and it flows, breaking and cracking the crust as it moves. The front margins of the flow look like a pile of smoldering broken blocks. The top blocks keep breaking off and falling in front as the margin gradually moves forward.

Katmai

LOCATED ON the Alaskan peninsula, Katmai has been a source of much information about volcanoes since its eruption in 1912. There was no previous record of activity at this deeply eroded and dormant volcano until it exploded, sending great quantities of dust and bits of *pumice* (a natural frothy glass) into the air. Fine dust was carried around the world while the larger particles were dropped out within a few hundred miles. So much material was ejected that parts of Kodiak Island, 60 miles away, were covered with several feet of dust. Robert Griggs described the activity at Katmai in his report of 1922:

Over an area of fifty square miles the ground is all broken open, and hot gases from the molten material below are even now everywhere pouring out, forming the several millions of fumaroles that constitute the Valley of Ten Thousand Smokes. . . . If such an eruption should occur on Manhattan Island, the column of steam would be conspicuous as far as Albany. The sounds of the explosions would be plainly audible in Chicago. The fumes would sweep over all the states east of the Rocky Mountains. . . . As far away as Toronto the acid raindrops would cause stinging burns wherever they fell on face or hands. . . . Ash would accumulate in Philadelphia a foot deep. . . . The whole of Manhattan Island, and an equal area besides, would open in great yawning chasms, and fiery fountains of molten lava would issue from every crack. In its deepest parts the near-molten sand would probably overtop the tallest skyscrapers, though the tip of the Woolworth tower might protrude. (From *The Valley of Ten Thousand Smokes* by Robert F. Griggs, National Geographic Society.)

Studies of the Valley of Ten Thousand Smokes have given us much information about volcanoes, their gaseous emanations, and their contents. One of the most interesting of the observations made there is that metallic minerals are dispersed in the porous *tuffs* (ash deposits) around fumaroles. Magnetite, specular hematite, molybdenite, pyrite, galena, sphalerite, covellite, and other metallic minerals are found. Thus it is demonstrated conclusively that gaseous emanations can collect, transport, and de-

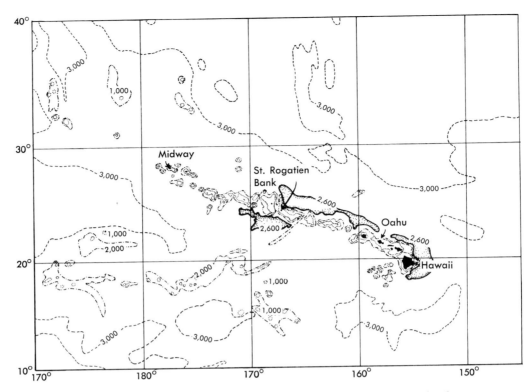

FIG. 12–7. / Map of Hawaiian Islands.

FIG. 12–8. / Schematic cross section of an idealized Hawaiian volcano. The magma source is from a depth of about 60 kilometers. The magma moves up through conduits to a shallow reservoir from which lava is erupted through dikes and sills. (After Eaton and Murata, Science, 1960.)

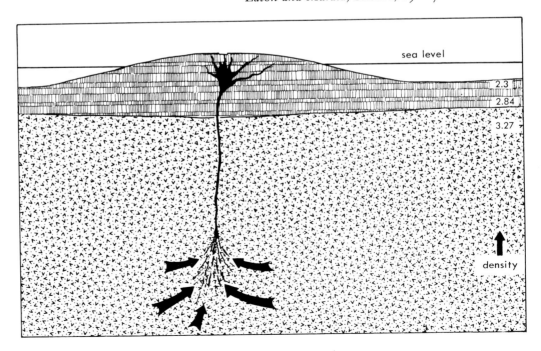

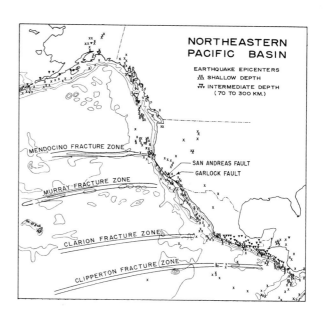

FIG. 12–9. / *Major rift zones in the floor of the Pacific Ocean. (After H. W. Menard.)*

posit metals, an important fact in the origin of ore deposits. It was also discovered that fumaroles around Katmai yielded approximately 1¼ million tons of hydrochloric acid and 200,000 tons of hydrofluoric acid each year. Such acids undoubtedly play an important role in the alteration of rocks near large intrusions.

FIG. 12–10. / *Geologic map of Hawaii. Located here are the main craters and some of the largest lava flows which make up these shield volcanoes. (After Gordon A. Macdonald, U.S. Geological Survey, Prof. Paper 214-D.)*

Volcanic Activity of the Hawaiian Islands

THE HAWAIIAN ISLANDS are one of the classic regions for study of volcanism. This chain of islands extending nearly 1,600 miles along a northwest-southeast line in the Mid-Pacific are formed entirely of volcanic rocks (Fig 12–7). The islands rise from the sea floor, nearly three miles deep, and reach peaks as high as Mauna Loa, which is 13,680 feet above sea level. This pile of lava and ash consists of many thousands of flows and extrusions which are being added to today in much the same way as they have for many thousands, perhaps millions of years. The lava flows are highly fluid and have resulted in formation of volcanoes which have the profile of a broad shield—hence the name *shield volcano*. Orientation of the islands along a nearly straight line supports the idea that they formed along one of the great fracture or rift zones of the crust (Fig. 12–9). This fracture zone undoubtedly provided lines of low resistance to the upward movement of magma generated below the crust. Movements of magma may be traced in the islands by sensitive seismographs which record earth tremors produced by faulting and by movement of magma in pipes. Magma starts from a depth of about 60 kilometers (Fig. 12–8). The magma has a lower density than the rocks that make up the oceanic crust, which creates an unstable situation facilitating upward movement of the magma when lines of movement are available. When magma reaches the surface it flows out without violent eruption through central vents and along fissures that open in the flanks of the volcanoes. The lava is basaltic in composition. (Basalt contains the minerals plagioclase, feldspar, olivine, augite, and hornblende.) While most of the basalts are similar in composition, there are variations that arise as a result of different minerals crystallizing at different temperatures and settling out of the melt. For this reason some magmas are much richer in olivine than others. This is one type of *magmatic differentiation*. The lava is over 1,000° C. as it flows to the surface.

One of the most notable eruptions in the islands took place in 1959–60 (Fig. 12–11). That eruption was described as follows by two members of the staff of the United States Geological Survey's Hawaiian Volcano Observatory.

The first suspicious sign appeared during September 1959, when a series of very shallow, tiny earthquakes began recording on the North Pit seismograph. . . . By the first of November, quakes of this swarm exceeded 1,000 per day. . . . A hurried remeasurement of tilting (tiltmeters are sensitive leveling devices used to detect changes in the slope of the volcano sides) at bases around the caldera . . . revealed that dramatic changes were in progress: the summit of Kilauea was swelling at least three times faster than during previous months. In mid-afternoon on 14 November earthquakes emanating from the caldera suddenly increased about tenfold in number and intensity. At frequent intervals during the next five hours the entire summit region shuddered as earthquakes marked the rending of the crust by the eruptive fissure splitting toward the surface. Then, at 8:08 P.M., the lava broke through in a half-mile-long fissure about halfway up the south wall of Kilauea Iki crater, just east of Kilauea caldera. Abruptly the swarm of earthquakes stopped, and seismographs around the caldera began to record the strong harmonic tremor characteristic of lava outpouring from Hawaiian volcanoes.

During the next 24 hours the erupting fissure gradually shortened until only one fountain remained active. But then the rate of lava outpouring, which had decreased as the erupting fissure shortened, began to increase again, and it continued to increase steadily until the fountain died out suddenly on 21 November. The 40 million cubic yards of lava poured into Kilauea Iki crater filled it to a depth of 335 feet, slightly above the level of the vent. . . .

During the following three weeks 14 more eruptive phases of shorter and shorter duration but with increasingly vigorous fountaining took place at the Kilauea Iki vent. The highest fountain was measured during the 15th phase, on 19 December, when a column of incandescent, gas-inflated lava jetted to 1,900 feet, by far the greatest fountain height yet measured in Hawaii. At its highest stand, at the end of the eighth phase, the lava pond was 414 feet deep and contained 58 million cubic yards of lava. At the end of each phase the fountain died abruptly, and from the 2nd to the 16th phase, a mighty river

FIG. 12–11. / *Kilauea flank eruption (eruption on rift zone) near the town of Kapoho in the Puna District, Hawaii, 1960. (Courtesy of Volcano Observatory, U.S. Geological Survey.)*

a. (top). Rift of fountains which have already built a spatter rampart along them but before the nearby trees were destroyed. Subsequently the fountains built a pumice and spatter cone over 300 ft. high.

b. (second from top). Steam cloud formed by pahoehoe lava entering the ocean. In less than two days after the eruption started the half mile wide lava front had flowed 2 miles from a 60-foot elevation to the ocean and had begun to extend the Hawaiian shoreline.

c. (third from top). Fountains about 200 feet high throwing new spatter onto the ramparts they are building around the erupting rift.

d. (bottom). Aa lava front creeping slowly into the ocean with its still hot fragments heating the near-shore water and killing the fish.

e. (top). A moving aa lava flow burning the Kapoho School building and covering the spot a few minutes later. The galvanized sheets of roofing mark the position of another school building site just covered.

f. and g. (second and third from top). Fountain of molten lava reaching over 1,000 feet above the previously flat sugar-cane fields on which it has built an extended cone over 300 feet high. High fountains produce a dark cloud of light-weight pumice fragments which are scattered over distances of several miles by the winds. Lava flows extend toward the observer and the cane and cane roads are covered with over 6 inches of pumice.

h. (bottom). Pahoehoe apron at the ocean front. One method by which lava flows extend the island boundaries is shown here as countless little tongues of pahoehoe lava form the patchwork apron. At the ocean front are several newly formed black sands areas formed by the molten lava being blown into glassy, sand-sized fragments by jets of steam produced at the littoral zone. Steam is seen to be rising from many places over the still hot lava field.

of lava surged back down the vent as soon as the fountaining stopped. . . .

Tiltmeters around Kilauea caldera showed that the volcano was swelling rapidly as phase after phase of the eruption delivered its lava to the surface and then swallowed it up again. When surface activity ceased at Kilauea Iki on 21 December, far more lava was stored in the shallow reservoir beneath the caldera than when the eruption began. It appeared that Kilauea was in an unstable state and that further activity was very likely.

During the last week of December a swarm of small earthquakes began to record on the seismographs at Pahoa. . . . The source of these earthquakes was soon traced to the east rift zone of Kilauea, about 25 miles east of the caldera. . . . The magma that inflated the summit region most probably exerted pressure on the plastic core of the rift zone, and earthquakes revealed where the rift zone yielded and where dikes began to extend toward the surface. . . .

On 13 January the village of Kapoho was rocked by frequent, very shallow earthquakes, and by nightfall a graben (a grave-like fault zone) 0.5 mile wide and 2 miles long that contained about half of the town had subsided several feet. At 7:30 P.M. the earthquake swarm gave way to harmonic tremor, and the flank eruption broke out along a fissure 0.75 mile long near the center of the subsiding graben, a few hundred yards north of Kapoho and nearly 30 miles east of the summit of Kilauea.

During the next five weeks nearly 160 million cubic yards of lava poured out of the vent north of Kapoho and reshaped the topography of the eastern tip of Hawaii . . . .

On 17 January, only four days after the flank eruption began, the summit of Kilauea began to subside precipitously as lava began to drain from beneath the caldera and to move through the rift zone toward the Kapoho vent.

Activity at Kilauea continued until April.[2]

Form of Igneous Intrusions

IT IS USUALLY EASY TO DISTINGUISH IGneous rocks that have crystallized at depth from volcanic materials extruded at the surface. The slower a magma cools the more likely the re-

[2] Eaton, J. P., and Murata, K. J., 1960, "How Volcanoes Grow," *Science*.

sulting rock is to be composed of large crystals. The two types of igneous rocks also differ in the form that the bodies of rock assume. Cinder cones, composite cones, shield volcanoes, lobate lava flows, and beds of volcanic ash (tuff) are indicative of extrusive activity. The form of intrusives below the surface is less clearly defined. As magma is forced upward under pressure it is natural for it to take the paths of least resistance. These paths in the earth are usually joints, faults, and planes between sedimentary strata or planes around different bodies of rock. Joints and faults are often nearly planar breaks that cut indiscriminately across rock types. When an intrusion follows one of these planes and assumes its shape it is called a *dike*. Dikes are tabular in shape and cut across the boundaries of rock bodies. They may be thin or thousands of feet thick. When the intrusion follows the plane of contact between rock bodies, such as planes between sedimentary layers, it is called a *sill* if the lateral extent is great. In a number of instances intrusions have spread out along bedding planes, but they have caused doming of the strata above, forming what is known as a *laccolith*. Dikes, sills, laccoliths, and a few less common intrusive forms are illustrated in Figs. 12–12 through 12–16.

The smaller intrusive bodies described above normally are associated with larger intrusions which lie at greater depth. These larger bodies which contain great quantities of igneous rocks are called *batholiths* and *stocks* (Fig. 12–16). Stocks are relatively small protrusions from batholiths (defined by size as those intrusive bodies with less than forty square miles of surface area). Batholiths have become exposed through weathering and erosion, which have removed the rocks which lay over them when the molten rock cooled. Thus it has been possible to study carefully the margins and internal structure of batholiths lying near the surface, but little is known about their shape at depth. The sides often dip out away from the center, suggesting that batholiths become larger at depth; there has been little drilling of deep wells in these rocks. They are no longer thought to extend downward into the subcrustal layers, but the

FIG. 12–12. / *Basaltic dike. (Crown Copyright.)*

FIG. 12–13. / *Felsic dike. (Crown Copyright.)*

way they taper off is left unanswered. At the margins the surrounding rocks have usually been highly altered by heat and chemical reactions with fluids of the magma. Often, important ore deposits are found in these zones of alteration. Blocks of the surrounding rock fall into the magma as it is intruded. These masses can be seen frozen into the igneous rock (Fig. 12–16). The gradual melting and loosening of blocks over the top of a magma may be important in the process of upward movement of the magma. *Flow structures* are sometimes preserved within the batholith, indicating the eddying and flowing motion which was taking place as the liquid slowly froze in place (Fig. 12–19). There are a number of large batholiths in the United States. The largest of these batholiths, located in the western United States, are illustrated in Fig. 12–18.

Generation of Magma

THERE IS NO WAY FOR US ACTUALLY TO observe the formation of magma within the earth. Thus we must rely on our knowledge of the materials involved and the processes acting in the earth. Two things influence melting—temperature and pressure. No mineral will remain solid after temperature reaches its *fusion point* under a given pressure. On the other hand, high pressure raises the fusion point. The temperature range for fusion of basalt (the most common rock formed from lava) under atmospheric pressure is 900°–1,100° C. This has been directly observed and also checked experimentally by melting rocks in the laboratory. Confining pressure on rocks within the earth is great. In order to generate magma, temperature must either be raised high enough to reach the fusion point of the rock under the great pressure, or pressure on already hot rocks must be reduced in some way in order to lower the fusion point.

Heat may be increased by disintegration of radioactive minerals, through friction along faults, or by heat coming from greater depth. Large quantities of radioactive minerals are known to exist in the earth's crust. If these are

FIG. 12–14. / *Cape Aiak sill, Unalaska Island, Aleutian Islands, Alaska. (Photo by G. L. Snyder, courtesy of U.S. Geological Survey.)*

more concentrated at depth than they are near the surface, temperatures generated by their decay and resultant release of energy might be sufficient to melt rocks locally.

The amount of frictional heat produced when two surfaces move over one another depends on the texture of those surfaces and on the force pushing them together. Surfaces in the earth along which such movement takes place are called *faults*. At depth these must be forced together by great pressures resulting from the weight of the overlying rocks. This seems to be a most likely possibility for generation of magma. It should not be difficult to test this hypothesis simply by determining if faults and magmas are commonly associated. Faults are often intruded by magma. There is also a frequent association of volcanic activity, earthquakes, and faulting in belts of mobility in the crust in which deformation is going on. The margins of the Pacific Ocean form such a belt. Here earthquakes and faulting movements in the crust frequently precede the eruption of volcanoes. These three phenomena—faulting, igneous activity, and earthquakes—are closely associated and most certainly are causally related, although it is not possible to say whether they result from a single or associated causes.

Upward movement of hot gases from the liquid interior of the earth might raise temperatures near the surface to the fusion point. There is no experimental or field evidence to substantiate this problematical view. A decrease in confining pressure could be effective in melting rock if temperatures were already above the fusion point for a lower pressure. Pressure within the earth may be reduced through arching of the crust. The site of most igneous activity is in the belts of mobility. These are places where extended mountain ranges stand high or are rising under pressures from within the earth. Two effects produced by this uplift are favorable to the release of pressures at depth under

FIG. 12–15. / *A cross section through Mount Hillers in the Henry Mountains of Utah. (After G. K. Gilbert.)*

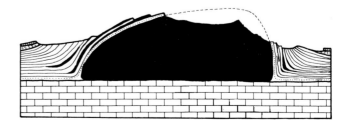

FIG. 12–16. / *Intrusions exposed in Canada. The large oval-shaped body is a stock. The region is cut by several dark-colored dikes and the light-colored rock has been intruded along fractures and as sills. (Photo by courtesy of Royal Canadian Air Force.)*

mountains. One is that, as mountains rise higher, forces of erosion cut into them at accelerated rates, removing great quantities of material from them and thereby reducing the weight they exert on underlying rock. Second, their uparching may act somewhat like any structural arch in a building, where part of the weight of the central portion is supported by the sides; this may be especially true as the weight of the central portion is reduced and the arch is able to bear a higher proportion of the total weight.

Nature of Magma

THERE ARE ESSENTIALLY TWO WAYS TO study magma. One is through lavas that flow from modern volcanoes; the other is by examining igneous rocks which have crystallized from rock melts. In neither case can we be entirely sure that our sample is truly representative of the magma as it existed at depth. Lavas that flow to the surface are extremely hot. All magmas have in common high temperature, some degree of fluidity, and a composition that is essentially that of a silicate melt containing large quantities of water and varying amounts of highly reactive fluids and gases held in solution. The specific temperature, exact chemical composition, degree of fluidity, and amount and kind of gases and solutions present are found to vary from one region of igneous activity to another. Variations also occur for a given volcano in different phases of an eruption. The degree of variation is shown by a comparison of chemical analyses of several widely different lavas from different parts of the world.

The range of variation in lavas may be illustrated by comparing two extremes in composition—basaltic and rhyolitic lavas. Compositions of typical basalt and rhyolite (lava of granite

FIG. 12–17. / *Xenoliths. This glacial boulder from North Sudbury contains basic xenoliths in a matrix of quartz. (Photo by W. R. Hansen, courtesy of U.S. Geological Survey.)*

TABLE 6 / *Chemical composition of the crust, and several types of magma (after Poldervaart, 1955).*

COMPOSITION (IN TERMS OF OXIDES)	PER CENT		
	Crust (as a whole)	Olivine Basalt	Granite (Rhyolite)
SiO_2	55.2	47.0	70.8
TiO_2	1.6	3.0	0.4
Al_2O_3	15.3	15.1	14.6
Fe_2O_3	2.8	3.7	1.6
FeO	5.8	8.1	1.8
MnO	0.2	0.2	0.1
MgO	5.2	7.9	0.9
CaO	8.8	10.9	2.0
Na_2O	2.9	2.7	3.5
K_2O	1.9	1.0	4.1
P_2O_5	0.3	0.3	0.2

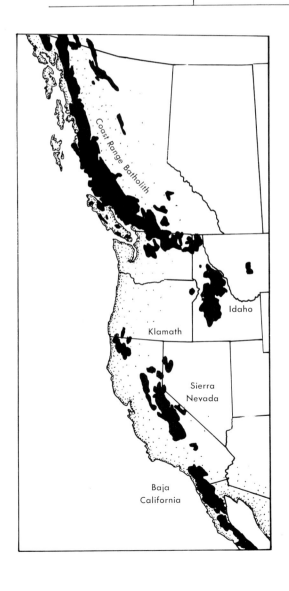

composition) are cited in Table 6 above. Both tend to be fine-grained and dense in appearance, but basalt is dark in color (black to greenish black) while rhyolites are generally light-colored (white or buff). The principal compositional difference lies in the amount of silicon dioxide present. Rhyolites are rich in quartz, crystalline SiO_2, but basalt has little if any quartz. The minerals of basalt are feldspar, hornblende, augite, and olivine.

Crystallization of Magma

FROM LABORATORY STUDIES WE KNOW AT what temperatures most minerals begin to crystallize. It is not a difficult matter to melt a mineral and then to cool it slowly and note the crystallization. It is not simple, however, to approximate the actual condition within magmas, because magmas are not simple melts containing only the necessary elements in the proper amounts to form a certain mineral. Magmas are much more complex. They were generated by the melting of a mass of rock that contained a number of minerals, each of which had certain

FIG. 12–18. / *A map of large batholiths located in the western part of North America. Most of these are of Jurassic age. Ancient batholiths are exposed in the Rocky Mountains and in the Canadian Shield.*

FIG. 12–19. / *Flow structure in granitic rock.* (*Photo by the author.*)

elements within it. Once melted, these elements lose all connection with the original minerals of which they were a part, and they are free to form new compounds with other elements. What new minerals result from crystallization will depend on:

compositon of the magma,

rate at which the magma is cooled,

impurities present,

presence of any solid nuclei (small fragments of minerals), and

events which bring about differentiation of the constituents during crystallization of the magma.

Rate of Crystallization; Texture

THE RATE AT WHICH A MAGMA COOLS IS particularly important in determining the texture of the rock. Texture refers to size, shape, and arrangement of minerals in the rock. Extreme variations in cooling rates are evident in comparing crystallization of a magma that is extruded from a volcano and flows rapidly into

the sea with one that is intruded 10 miles beneath the surface and cools, perhaps over a period of thousands of years (Fig. 12–20).

Mineral fragments act as seeds on which minerals grow. The most favorable nuclei are fragments of minerals that would ordinarily be crystallizing out of the melt. Nuclei will form spontaneously even from a pure melt, but the rate or the ability of certain minerals to form crystal "seed" differs. A crystal grows by having the necessary ions or elements come to its margin and become attached by one of the types of bonding. After a crystal begins to grow it almost immediately pulls to it from the immediate vicinity those ions or elements of the type required for its structure. This leaves around it atoms and ions that cannot fit into its crystal structure. Thus time is required for other necessary ions and atoms to be brought to the crystal. This can be accomplished by convection within the melt, or by movement of the crystal through the melt.

If a magma is cooling slowly and contains only a small number of nuclei, the rock that results eventually from crystallization will be one composed of few, but very large, crystals. As the rate of cooling and rate of nuclei production increase, many medium-sized crystals are formed. If the rate becomes very high the rock will become one with few crystals large enough to see. Finally, if the rate of cooling is extremely fast the rock, in effect, freezes. It cools so fast that only a very few or no crystals at all have time to form. Such a rock is a *glass*. It contains no ordered crystalline structure.

PORPHYRY. An igneous rock is called a porphyry when it is made up of large crystals, at least large enough to be seen by the naked eye, embedded in a groundmass of very small crystals or glass (Fig. 12–20). The origin of this texture is easily understood in the light of principles just outlined. Large crystals form while magma is cooling slowly at depth. The cooling rate is changed as the magma is forced upward toward the surface, where the cooling rate is much faster, and the remainder of the magma cools rapidly, giving rise to small crystals of glass.

FIG. 12–20. / *Textural variations in igneous rocks. Left, from top to bottom: Porphyry composed of fine groundmass and large crystals; a coarse-grained granite; a fine-grained felsite; a porous, vesicular rock called scoria. Right, top: graphic granite; bottom: obsidian, natural glass. (Photos by courtesy of the U.S. National Museum.)*

Magmatic Differentiation

THERE ARE MANY TYPES OF IGNEOUS ROCKS. They differ in composition as well as in texture. Such differences are frequently noted even within a single mass of igneous rock, all of which crystallized from a single magma. Some differences are of a gradational nature; composition of one rock being only slightly different from that of nearby ones. Others may be greatly different in composition. How do these variations come about? Although we are unable to observe processes within a real magma, it is possible to postulate some processes that certainly must play a part in bringing about differentiation within magma. These include gravity separation, filter pressing, mixing of magmas, liquid immiscibility, and assimilation.

If the first crystals to form in a magma are heavier or lighter than the melt, they will tend to sink or rise through the melt and become segregated either at the bottom or as a raft of floating minerals near the top of the magma chamber (Fig. 12–21). This may give the resulting igneous rocks a banded appearance near the top or bottom of the intrusion. Olivine, the

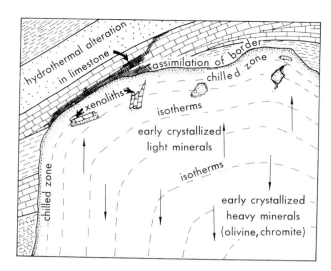

FIG. 12–21. / *Magmatic differentiation. Many different types of igneous rocks may originate from a single magma. The differences arise from rates of cooling, settling of early crystallized heavy minerals, contamination of the margins of the magma by the assimilation or melting of country rock, and other processes.*

first mineral to crystallize from a basaltic magma, is heavy and is frequently found concentrated near the bottom of basaltic intrusions. This process may also account for some ore bodies. Chromite is another early-forming high-density mineral, and it is known to occur in layers near the bottom of a number of large

FIG. 12–22. / *Classification of igneous rocks.*

		Oversaturated			Saturated			Undersaturated
		Quartz	Quartz and Feldspar		Feldspars			Mafic Minerals Predominate
			Orthoclase	Plagioclase	Orthoclase	Na rich Plagioclase	Ca rich Plagioclase	
Deep intrusions	coarse grained phaneritic	Vein Quartz	Granite		Syenite	Diorite	Gabbro	Peridotite
			Porphyry (mixed textures) →					
Extrusions and shallow intrusions	fine grained aphanitic		Rhyolite	Dacite		Andesite	Basalt	Olivine Basalt
	glass		Pumice			Scoria		
			Pitchstone					
			← Obsidian →					

LIGHT COLORS — DARK COLORS

intrusions. Examples are the Stillwater complex of Montana and the Bushveld complex of South Africa.

As crystallization proceeds the once-molten mass becomes a mesh of crystals loosely interlocked and connected. Surrounding these crystals and in pore spaces there are residual liquids. If the chamber becomes subjected to strong earth pressures, such as those that might have played a part in the generation of the magma, then the chamber could become deformed. Residual liquids are likely to be squeezed off from the solid crystal mesh and to become isolated. When this last remaining liquid solidifies it will be quite different in composition and possibly also in texture from the rocks formed earlier. This process of differentiation is called filter pressing.

One liquid is *immiscible* in another if it will not mix with it. Oil will not mix with water, and the two become separated by difference in their specific gravity. The same phenomenon may occur in a magma during the initial stages of cooling, with parts being immiscible, or at some later stage when the composition has been changed by the removal of certain constituents through crystallization.

Magmas are all very hot, but some are much hotter than others, and the difference may reach several hundred degrees. If two magmas, one 800° C. and one 1,200° C., were intruded into the same type of country rock (the name *country rock* may be applied to the surrounding rock regardless of its exact composition), effects at the margins might be very different. Any minerals in this particular country rock that melt at relatively low temperatures (quartz melts at 1700° C.) will melt around the margins of the magmas. But what will happen to the minerals that begin to melt at 800° C.? One magma would cause them to melt, the other would not. The very hot magma might cause pure melting of a thick zone surrounding the magma chamber. This new melt would mix with the magma and alter its composition, particularly around the margins. Even partial melting will cause a change in the composition of the magma. Thus the two magmas might result in

rocks of totally different types, even if their original composition before intrusion was the same.

Descriptions of Igneous Rocks

COARSE-GRAINED INTRUSIVE ROCKS

Granite. A coarse- to medium-grained equigranular rock composed of potassium feldspars (orthoclase and microcline) and quartz, with some biotite mica and hornblende, usually present in small amounts. Many other minerals may be present but in small amounts. These include black specks of magnetite, honey-yellow crystals of sphene, red grains of garnet, and other less common minerals.

Graphic granite. Rocks of granitic composition that have a texture consisting of an intergrowth of feldspar and quartz in such a way that the quartz has a geometrically regular pattern.

Granite pegmatite. A very coarse-grained granite. In some pegmatites crystals attain dimensions measured in feet rather than inches. A granite pegmatite is of the same composition as granite. It contains microcline feldspar, quartz, and mica (biotite or muscovite). A great variety of very rare minerals may be present.

Syenite. A coarse- to medium-grained equigranular rock composed primarily of orthoclase feldspar. It contains no quartz. There is usually some hornblende, biotite, and pyroxene present.

Diorite. A coarse- to medium-grained rock composed of plagioclase feldspar and biotite, hornblende, or pyroxene. Small quantities of quartz may be present. The amount of dark minerals ranges from an eighth to three-eighths of the total.

Gabbro. A rock composed of coarse- to medium-grained crystals mainly of pyroxene, hornblende, and biotite. The amount of these exceeds the amount of feldspar, all of which

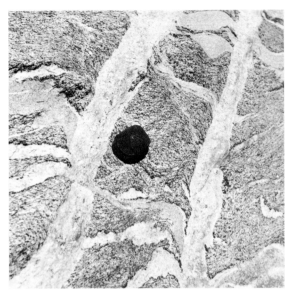

FIG. 12–23. / *Pegmatitic veins cross-cutting a foliated metamorphic rock. (Photo by the author.)*

FIG. 12–24. / *A single crystal of feldspar taken from a granitic pegmatite in the Virginia piedmont. (Washington & Lee Univ. collection.)*

FIG. 12–25. / *Shiprock, New Mexico. This is a volcanic plug that once occupied the pipe of a large volcano. Dikes radiate out from the plug. (Courtesy of the New Mexico Tourist Bureau.)*

FIG. 12–26. / *Basaltic lava flows in central New Mexico. (Courtesy of the New Mexico State Tourist Bureau.)*

FIG. 12–27. / *Basaltic porphyry dike from Wyoming. (Photo by the author.)*

FIG. 12–28. / *Polygonal jointing due to cooling and contraction in basalt. (Crown copyright.)*

is plagioclase. The mineral olivine is usually present, and quartz is absent. Most gabbros are dark because dark minerals predominate. They are equigranular. It is not uncommon to find gabbro pegmatites. Like the granite pegmatites, these are simply extremely coarse-grained equivalents of the gabbro.

Peridotite. A dark, coarse-grained, equigranular rock containing a large quantity of olivine and either pyroxene or hornblende, but no quartz and no feldspar.

Dunite. A rock composed completely of the mineral olivine.

Pyroxenite. A dark, coarsely crystalline rock composed mostly of pyroxenes.

Hornblendite. An igneous rock of coarse texture and nearly equigranular fabric composed mostly of hornblende.

FINE-GRAINED IGNEOUS ROCKS

Felsite. A general term applied to igneous rocks of fine-grained texture and light color indicating a granitic composition. If large crystals are present in a felsitic groundmass, it is called a felsite porphyry. Colors of felsites may range from white, gray, pink, yellow, brown, to purple and light green.

Basalt. A dark-colored, fine-grained rock. Basalts are dark because they contain large percentages of hornblende, pyroxene, biotite, olivine, or other dark minerals. Basalt is often an extrusive igneous rock and is frequently filled with cavities left by escaping bubbles of gas.

GLASSES

Obsidian. A glassy equivalent of granite or felsite; a solid, natural glass containing no

FIG. 12–29. / *An unusual variety of granite, orbicular granite, from Wyoming. (Photo by the author.)*

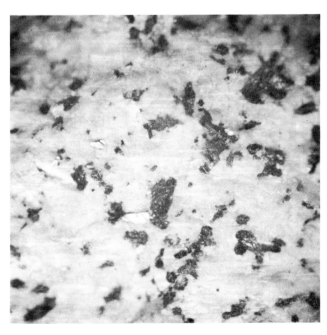

FIG. 12–30. / *Enlarged section of syenite composed mainly of hornblende and feldspar. (Washington and Lee Univ. collection.)*

crystals. Its appearance is in every way that of artificial glass. Most obsidian is black, but it also occurs in green and brown. It breaks with an unusual fracture, *conchoidal*, which is shaped like a shell. Natural glasses frequently contain round or spherical bodies composed of feldspar and silica of white, gray, or red color, and a radiating, fibrous internal structure. These bodies are called spherulites and form from the rapid crystallization of the glass. Also found in the natural glasses are the collapsed remains of glass bubbles (litho-physae). They form as gases escape from the glass. The bubbles break, and the hot glass flows back down but does not completely melt again.

Pitchstone. A variety of obsidian with a luster like that of a resin instead of glass. Pitchstone differs in composition from obsidian in that it contains five per cent or more of water. Obsidian contains less than one per cent. Colors include black, gray, red, brown, and green.

Pumice. An extremely vesicular glass, really a glassy froth. Colors include white, gray, yellowish, and brownish. Some varieties are almost fibrous in texture and luster. The cavities are very small and delicate. The light color is an indication of the siliceous composition.

Scoria. A dark-colored vesicular glass. The texture is much coarser than that of pumice. Cavities are formed by escaping gases. The dark color indicates that the composition of these glasses is much closer to that of the gabbros and diorites.

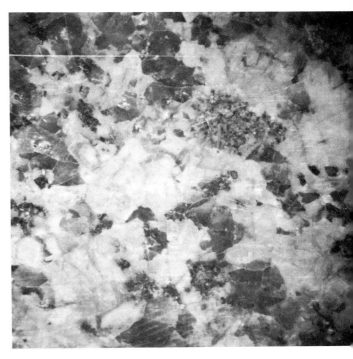

FIG. 12–31. / *Enlarged section of granite composed of quartz, feldspar, and mica. (Washington and Lee Univ. collection.)*

FIG. 12–32. / *Block of coarse-grained granite. (Washington and Lee Univ. collection.)*

FIG. 13–1. / *Deposition of sediments in stream valley near the the terminus of a glacier.* (*Royal Canadian Air Force.*)

13 / Sedimentary Rocks

SEDIMENTARY ROCKS COVER ABOUT THREE-QUARTERS of the land surface and are spread almost continuously across the ocean floors. The term *sediment* applies to anything that settles out of suspension in water, but it applies more generally to particles that settle out of water, wind, or ice as well. When these sediments become consolidated to form a hard solid rock, they are termed *sedimentary rocks*.

Sands and gravels found on the bottoms of streams; sands, silts, or cobbles that make up beaches; muds on lake bottoms; decaying plants and mud in swamps; salts in deserts; sands, dust, and ashes transported by the wind; debris that melts out of glaciers; and calcite deposited from water dripping in a cave; all are sediments (Figs. 13–1 through 13–6). If conditions prove to be favorable for their preservation they may become sedimentary rocks. But most sediments on land are not likely to be preserved for any extended periods of time. Forces of erosion continue to act upon them, and they are likely to be transported again toward the sea, where chances of burial and preservation are much greater.

FIG. 13–2. / *Boulders and cobbles of volcanic rocks in a stream on the flanks of Mount Hood. (Photo by the author.)*

Source of Sediments

THE PARTICLES OF SOIL, ROCKS, AND MINERALS that make up sediments are mostly derived from breakdown or decay of rocks. Some sediments are composed in part of meteoritic particles from outside the earth, other sediments are derived through volcanic action from sources deep in the earth, but the great majority of the sediments and sedimentary rocks that form the shallow veneer over the face of the earth simply represent a reworking of materials in the earth's crust by the hydrosphere, atmosphere, and biosphere, with which they are in contact.

Products of Decay

WHAT SORT OF PARTICLES are produced by decay and disintegration of the crust, and are therefore freed to become available to form sediments? Principal among these are clastic particles, ions, colloids, and organic matter.

CLASTIC PARTICLES. The term *clastic* means "broken off." Clastic particles are fragmental materials such as sand and gravel. These represent the mechanical disintegration of all types

FIG. 13–3. / *Tufa, hot spring deposits, being formed in Yellowstone Park.* (Union Pacific Railroad.)

of pre-existing rocks. A clastic sediment may consist of fragments of a sedimentary rock or any other type of rock. Fragmental sediments have not been completely broken down either mechanically or chemically in the process of their decay.

IONS. These charged particles are formed through solution of minerals in water. When many minerals dissolve they break down into their component ions. The process of solution may have been aided by the presence of acids or alkalies in the water. Solution is accelerated by mechanical breakdown of material that is being dissolved. Since solution takes place at the surface of a solid, the greater the exposed surface area the more rapidly solution can take place. Once a solid has gone into solution, either it is available for formation of a sediment by direct chemical precipitation or it may be removed from solution by animals or plants that use it to build their skeletons or shells. These in turn may become sediment after they die.

COLLOIDS. This term refers to a particular size of matter—anything in the range of 10^{-5} to 10^{-7} cm. (.00001 to .0000001 cm.) in diameter. Colloidal particles make up mud or clay. These particles are so small that we cannot distinguish them individually even with a high-powered microscope. If we stir clay in water until particles move through the solution in suspension, a separation of larger aggregates and particles from the colloids will take place. The heavier and larger aggregates will settle out, but colloids of clay will remain in suspension and move more or less at random through the solution. The dimensions of colloids approach atomic sizes, but they are about 10 times or more the size of an atom.

FIG. 13–4. / *Travertine deposits in Luray Caverns.* (Luray Caverns, Virginia.)

FIG. 13–5. / *Sand and silt in the river valley of Canadian River, Oklahoma. (U.S. Dept. of Agriculture.)*

ORGANIC MATTER. This term is used in a very general sense to include remains of plants, which may be converted into coal, excrement and other waste products of organisms, and solid parts of the animal itself, all of which may become part of the sediment. Some sediments are made almost wholly of such remains of plants and animals.

Lithification

MOST SEDIMENTS ORIGINATE AS UNCONSOLidated materials. All clastic sediments must first be laid down in unconsolidated form. When *chemical precipitation* occurs ions come together forming ionic compounds which either may settle as a mass of tiny particles, or, less commonly, may crystallize as a hard consolidated layer. Colloids often are deposited when fresh water carrying them becomes salty, which causes the colloids to settle in little lumps. At other times colloids coagulate, forming a *gel*. *Lithification* is the process or complex of processes by which these unconsolidated sediments become hard, consolidated rocks. Some sediments undergo internal reorganization of the material. In addition there can be reactions with water, and alterations due to solutions that may flow through the sediment.

One of the most universal processes affecting sediments is compaction. This is particularly important where sediments are deposited in an environment in which long-continued sedimentation is possible, as in the sea. Weight of the overlying sediment compresses the deeper sediment, forcing water out, eliminating void and open spaces, and pressing together any soft materials. Colloids (clays and clay mixtures) are particularly compressible. The volume of clay can be reduced by 40 per cent if it is subjected to a pressure equal to that found at a depth of several thousand feet. Sands and other clastic

FIG. 13–5. / *Sand and silt in the river valley of Canadian River, Oklahoma. (U.S. Dept. of Agriculture.)*

FIG. 13–6. / *Sediment being carried into the ocean. This vertical air photograph shows the sediment being carried to the left by longshore currents. (U.S. Dept. of Agriculture.)*

sediments are only slightly compressible. Pressure due to weight of overburden may facilitate recrystallization of some minerals. When this happens the compounds may dissolve at points of high pressure, where grains are in contact, and recrystallize in spaces of lower pressure, as in pore spaces.

Many sediments are mixtures of different sizes and types of minerals. When there is considerable mud it may act as a cementing material. When solutions passing through the sediment carry ions in solution these ions may precipitate in pore spaces and cement together the particles of sediment. The most common cementing materials are calcite, quartz, iron carbonate (siderite), and iron oxide (hematite). These may be derived from the sediment itself, or they may be introduced from outside by water flowing through the sediment. Cements are locally important economically. Iron oxide cement in the Clinton formation (Silurian

FIG. 13–8. / *Stratification in lake bed deposits, Bryce Canyon.* (*Union Pacific R.R.*)

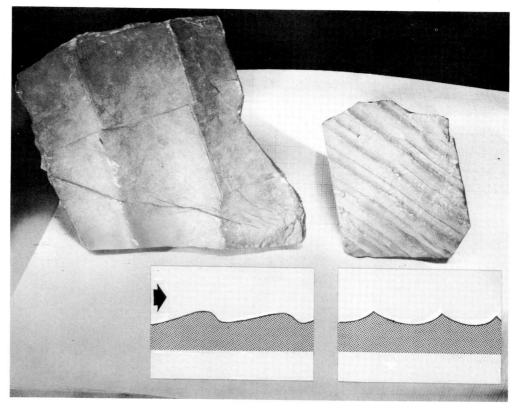

FIG. 13–9. / *Ripple marks. Current ripples are shown at left, oscillation ripples to the right. (Photo by the author.)*

FIG. 13–10. / *Cross bedding in ancient sand deposits. (Photo by the author.)*

FIG. 13–11. / *Cross bedding in Jurassic sandstones exposed in Zion National Park. (Photo by the author.)*

FIG. 13–12. / *Mud cracks in recent sediments. (Photo by the author.)*

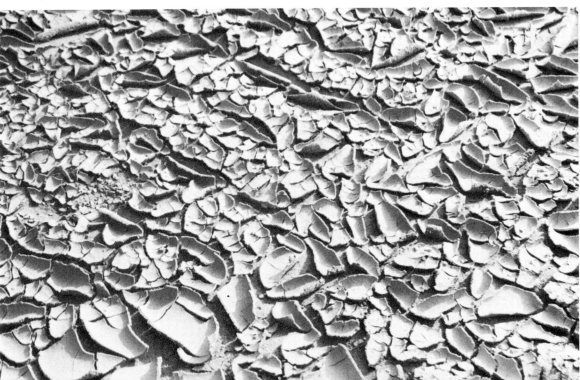

age) in the Appalachians is rich enough to make the sandstone an iron ore. It is the principal ore for the Alabama iron industry.

Processes of recrystallization and reactions between some minerals and sea water, which often saturates marine sediments even after they have been deeply buried, bring about further alteration of sediment. During lithification a number of unusual structures may develop in sedimentary rocks. These include nodular masses, concretionary structures, chert stringers, and radiating and fibrous textures.

Stratification

ONE OF THE MOST CHARACTERISTIC FEAtures of sedimentary rocks is the layering—stratification—that usually results from processes of sedimentation.[1] Consider a lake in which sediment is accumulating. If this lake is fed by streams, coarse sediments enter the lake at inlets. This sediment will fan out into the lake. The finest particles may be evenly distributed throughout the lake, but heavier particles are dropped near inlets. The fine sediments tend to form a thin layer over most of the lake bottom, but they are mixed with coarse sediment near the mouths of the streams. Any change in the type of material being brought into the lake by the streams tends to produce variations in the layers deposited, and this in turn causes stratification.

Stratification may be the result of variations in:
composition,
color of layers,
texture,
porosity, and
structure.

The layers are called *strata* or *beds* if they are thick, and *laminae* if they are very thin.

Not all sedimentary rock units are comparable to the lake deposits described above. How-

[1] Note the way stratification is reflected in the topography on the Maverick Spring Quadrangle, at end of book.

FIG. 13–13. / *Clay concretions.* (*U.S. National Museum.*)

FIG. 13–14. / *Ancient mud cracks in tightly cemented rock.* (*Columbia University collection.*)

ever, on continental shelves and in ocean basins, where most sediments are deposited, we find platelike sedimentary units which may cover thousands of square miles. Some of these units are very constant in thickness and composition. Others vary greatly both in composition and thickness, but stratification is almost invariably present (Fig. 13–15).

Environments of Deposition

ALTHOUGH MOST SEDIMENTS ARE ULTImately laid down in the ocean basins or around margins of oceans, there are many other places where sediments accumulate, and even within oceans there are many variations in environment. These environmental factors affect tex-

TABLE 7 / *Classification of sedimentary rocks*

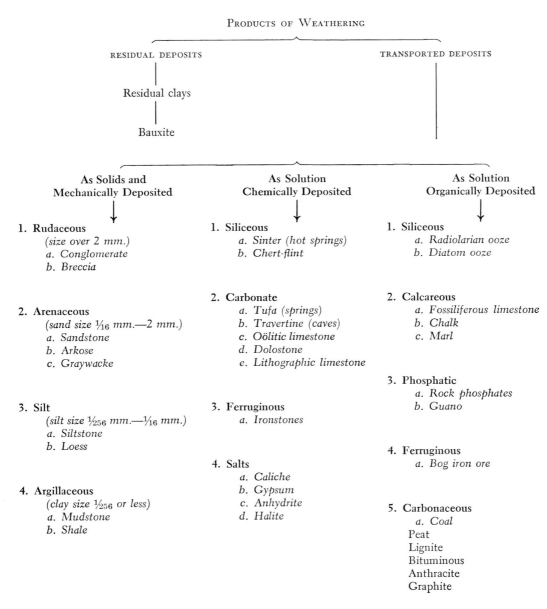

PRODUCTS OF WEATHERING

RESIDUAL DEPOSITS

Residual clays

Bauxite

TRANSPORTED DEPOSITS

As Solids and Mechanically Deposited

1. Rudaceous
   (size over 2 mm.)
   a. Conglomerate
   b. Breccia

2. Arenaceous
   (sand size $\frac{1}{16}$ mm.—2 mm.)
   a. Sandstone
   b. Arkose
   c. Graywacke

3. Silt
   (silt size $\frac{1}{256}$ mm.—$\frac{1}{16}$ mm.)
   a. Siltstone
   b. Loess

4. Argillaceous
   (clay size $\frac{1}{256}$ or less)
   a. Mudstone
   b. Shale

As Solution Chemically Deposited

1. Siliceous
   a. Sinter (hot springs)
   b. Chert-flint

2. Carbonate
   a. Tufa (springs)
   b. Travertine (caves)
   c. Oölitic limestone
   d. Dolostone
   e. Lithographic limestone

3. Ferruginous
   a. Ironstones

4. Salts
   a. Caliche
   b. Gypsum
   c. Anhydrite
   d. Halite

As Solution Organically Deposited

1. Siliceous
   a. Radiolarian ooze
   b. Diatom ooze

2. Calcareous
   a. Fossiliferous limestone
   b. Chalk
   c. Marl

3. Phosphatic
   a. Rock phosphates
   b. Guano

4. Ferruginous
   a. Bog iron ore

5. Carbonaceous
   a. Coal
   Peat
   Lignite
   Bituminous
   Anthracite
   Graphite

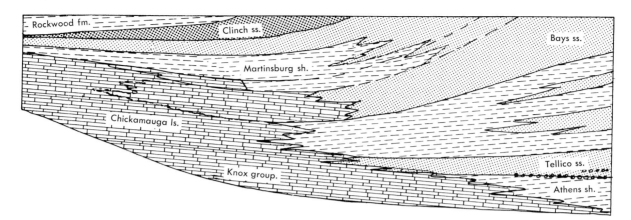

FIG. 13–15. / *Cross section across eastern Tennessee. The coarser sediments of the east grade westward into finer sediments. Limestones were laid down across the entire section early in the Middle Ordovician, Knox, but by the end of the period coarse sediments were laid almost to the westernmost end. The section is a little over thirty miles long. (After P. B. King.)*

ture, composition, or structure of sediments that form. Some hard consolidated sedimentary rocks now exposed on the flanks of mountain ranges hundreds of miles inland originated in the ocean. It is sometimes even possible to tell how deep the water was, and the approximate temperature of the water.

There are three major groups of sedimentary environments—marine, transitional, and continental. Some of the important subdivisions of each are:

MARINE ENVIRONMENT (See chapters 9 and 10)
 shallow water (neritic)
 intermediate-depth water (bathyal)
 deep water (abyssal)
TRANSITIONAL ENVIRONMENTS (See chapter 9)
 deltas
 lagoons
 beaches
CONTINENTAL ENVIRONMENTS
 deserts
 glacial environments.
 streams
 lakes
 swamps
 caves

Characteristics of deposits formed in each of these environments will be discussed as we consider the natural processes acting in each.

Classification of Sedimentary Rocks

BECAUSE OF THE DIVERSITY OF THEIR ORIgins, textures, compositions, and occurrences, sediments may be classified in many ways. One problem almost always incurred in attempting to make exact classifications of sedimentary rocks is that many of them are mixtures of two or more sediments. By far the most common sedimentary rocks are sandstone, made of sand; limestone, composed of calcite in various forms; and shale, consolidated mud. Completely pure limestones, sandstones, and shales are rare. Most limestones have a small amount of sand or mud in them, most sandstones contain either calcite or mud impurities, and most shales are partially limestone or sand, or both.

The classification shown in Table 7 recognizes that most sediments ultimately are derived from weathering or decay of the crust. Decayed material either remains in place as a residue where it originated, or it is transported to another locality by water, wind, ice, or downslope mass movement. Material that is moved is carried either as a solid or in solution. Its deposition is eventually brought about through some mechanical process, such as settling from suspension, if it is carried as a solid. Those materials transported in solution as ions are either deposited chemically, as by precipitation, or organically. Organisms may either cause them to be deposited directly or use the material for their own structures, in which case they are deposited as a part of the organism when it dies. It is most satisfactory to classify sediments carried as solids according to their size (their most obvious and easily measured characteristic). Sediments that originate from chemical deposition and from organisms are conveniently classified, first, according to their chemical compositions, and, second, according to special features of either textural or genetic significance.

Clastic Textures

CLASTIC ROCKS are fragmental. The size of fragments is the most apparent and easily applied method of identifying them. There is no natural grouping of sizes in nature. Everything from colloids up to boulders hundreds of feet across can be found, and every intermediate size is known. The difference in size between the smallest and largest fragments is extreme. To make analysis of sediments relatively easy, a system of sizes has been arbitrarily selected. This scale, known as the *Wentworth classification*, defines the limits of each type of clastic particles.

boulder	anything above 256 mm. in diameter
cobble	64 mm.–256 mm.
pebble	4 mm.–64 mm.
granule	2 mm.–4 mm.
sand	1/16 mm.–2 mm.
silt	1/256 mm.–1/16 mm.
clay	1/256 mm. or less

Nonclastic Sedimentary Textures

NONCLASTIC TEXTURES form as a result of deposition through chemical reactions. Crystalline texture is one of interlocking aggregates of crystals. Crystals may be small, medium, or large, or they may even exhibit a mixture of sizes. Crystals may exhibit certain definite shapes (i.e., equidimensional, fibrous, or scaly). It is not ordinarily possible to distinguish those

formed by inorganic chemical reactions from those deposited through reactions caused by organisms.

Formation of Crystalline Textures

MOST OF THE CRYSTALLINE TEXTURES ARE formed by direct precipitation from a saturated solution. Crystals grow from many centers and spread until they form an interlocking crystal framework or mosaic. Commonly, centers of crystals are small clastic particles of irregular shape and size. Crystalline textures are also formed through recrystallization. In the process of recrystallization new crystals grow and replace the original crystals. The new crystals may be simply larger crystals of the same mineral that originally was present, but often elements from several minerals combine to form new minerals that were not originally present. Usually part of the rock is slightly dissolved by solutions moving along boundaries of individual crystals. The dissolved substance is carried along, and it may eventually crystallize as part of another crystal. In the process many small particles or masses of a mineral are dissolved, and a few larger crystals grow.

When colloids coagulate they may form a gelatin-like mass, a *gel*. This mass may lose water and harden to form an *amorphous* (lacking crystalline structure) solid. This amorphous substance is not stable, and it may be changed into a crystalline mass. When and if crystallization of a hardened mass of colloids does take place, the mass tends to have a fibrous structure first, but it may later become granular by recrystallization. Some of the textures of common colloidal deposits are nodular, oölitic, and spherulitic (Figs. 13–16 through 13–29). *Oölites* are small, nearly spherical bodies between 1/4 and 2 mm. in diameter. Oölites are made up of a series of concentric shells, which have either a fibrous radial or a finely laminated structure. *Spherulitic* texture is characterized by small spherical bodies with radial structures originating at the center and extending out to the margins. *Nod-*

FIG. 13–16. / *Coarse conglomerate from the Belt of Montana. (Photo by the author.)*

ules are of nearly oval or spherical shapes without internal radiating or concentric structures.

Descriptions of Sedimentary Rocks

Mechanically Deposited Sedimentary Rocks

RUDACEOUS (*coarse-grained fragmental or clastic rocks*)

Conglomerate. The name is applied to a consolidated gravel commonly mixed with varying amounts of sand, silt, and mud. Fragments that make up conglomerate may be composed of any other rock. An appropriate prefix may be added to indicate the size of the major constituents of the rock, i.e., as pebble conglomerate or boulder conglomerate. Fragments in a conglomerate are rounded, usually as a result of rolling in a stream or from repeated tossing and impacts in waves.

Breccia. The fragments are angular instead of rounded. In other respects it is like conglomerate except for its origin. A breccia might form anywhere a rock is broken up but not rounded. Breccias occur in volcanic vents where sides of the vent or pipe are broken by explosions. They might form in the collapse of the roof of a cave, or from fragments of rock where brittle rock units are folded and broken up, or when a fault causes mechanical breakdown.

ARENACEOUS (*sand-dominated rocks*)

Sandstone. A sandstone is any rock composed of fragments of the size range $\frac{1}{16}$ to 2 mm. regardless of composition. Most sandstone is

FIG. 13–17. / *Pebble conglomerate from the Unicoi formation of Virginia. (Photo by the author.)*

FIG. 13–18. / *Shale outcrop in the Athens (Edinburg) formation of Virginia. (Photo by the author.)*

FIG. 13–19. / *Well developed cleavages in shaly limestone, Edinburg formation. (Photo by the author.)*

largely composed of quartz fragments. But many other minerals may dominate sands. In the Antarctic there are sand dunes composed of fragments of ice, in Italy some beaches are made up of sand composed of olivine derived from volcanic rocks, and in the White Sands National Monument, sand dunes are composed of gypsum.

Arkose. This arenaceous rock is made up largely of a mixture of quartz sand and feldspar fragments. It may contain small angular rock and mineral fragments. Arkose looks something like a granite and is ordinarily thought to be derived from decomposition of granite. Frequently arkose is red or pink, colors derived from oxidation of ironbearing minerals.

Graywacke. In general it applies to impure sandstones and is made up of quartz and feldspar fragments, and small fragments of igneous, metamorphic, and sedimentary rocks. One common association is ash and volcanic dust with quartz and feldspar fragments. The color is most commonly gray, which comes from a slatelike matrix. This matrix is composed of a mixture of mica, chlorite, and quartz. The importance of graywackes comes from their widespread occurrence in mobile belts. They make up a large percentage of the total volume of sediments.

SILTY ROCKS

Siltstone. This is a consolidated rock composed of clastic particles in the size range of $\frac{1}{16}$ to $\frac{1}{256}$ mm. in diameter. Rocks composed of a large amount of silt are much less common than are sandstones or shales. Much of the silt is probably mixed in shales, which may contain up to 50 per cent silt. Layers of

FIG. 13–20. / *Fossils etched out on the surface of a fossiliferous limestone. (Photo by the author.)*

FIG. 13–21. / *Finely stratified limestone. (Photo by the author.)*

FIG. 13–22. / *Crinoidal limestone.* (*Washington and Lee Univ. collection.*)

siltstone are generally thin and hard. Unlike sand, a silt particle is usually angular, and most siltstones contain a large amount of platy minerals such as micas, but a microscope is needed to see most of the constituent minerals.

Loess. This is a light-buff unconsolidated silt. It is unstratified, composed of angular particles, and can stand in very steep cliff faces. When cut along roads, as in the Mississippi Valley, it is stable in vertical cliffs. The particles of loess are very well sorted; they are almost all the same size, averaging from .01 mm. to .05 mm. It is fine enough to be a wind-blown deposit in many places. It may have come from lakes formed at the margins of the continental ice sheets that have covered parts of North America in the last 100,-000 years.

ARGILLACEOUS (*A term applied to all rocks composed of clay or having a high percentage of clay in them. The term is used as an adjective modifying other rock names when they have some clay in them.*)

Shale. Shale is consolidated mud and clay. It often contains sand (arenaceous shale) or lime (calcareous shale) in large amounts. Shale has an earthy odor when breathed upon. The manner in which a shale breaks is characteristic. It is fissile—that is, it breaks or splits easily along nearly parallel planes. Other important properties are its slight permeability and porosity, the particle size, less than $\frac{1}{256}$ mm in diameter, and its composition. Shales are composed of clay minerals, quartz, sericite, chlorite, feldspar, calcite, and small quantities of many other minerals.

FIG. 13–23. / *Calcareous tufa, stream deposit.*

FIG. 13–24. / *Enlarged view of grains of sand.* (*Bausch and Lomb Co.*)

FIG. 13–25. / *Conglomerate.* (*U.S. National Museum.*)

FIG. 13–26. / *Conglomerate of shells, coquina.* (*U.S. National Museum.*)

Chemically Deposited Sedimentary Rocks

SILICEOUS DEPOSITS (*containing silica*)

Many of the siliceous sediments are colloidal deposits; others are formed through chemical processes. Some of the siliceous deposits are laid down directly from water, while others are formed through processes of recrystallization in sediments during consolidation. There are few reliable criteria by which these two modes of origin can be positively identified. The most common occurrences for siliceous deposits are as nodules or concretions in layers of limestone. Many of these nodules of siliceous material contain fossils at their centers showing that they are of a secondary origin.

Chert (flint). The most common of the siliceous sedimentary rocks is a dense, hard rock. Its colors range from white through gray to black. Chert is a form of quartz, SiO_2. It has the same hardness, seven, a conchoidal fracture, and semivitreous luster. Chert occurs in other sediments as pebbles.

Siliceous sinter. This is a chemical sediment formed at mineral springs. It consists of silica, is white or light-colored, and is porous. That formed around the vents of geysers is known as geyserite.

CALCAREOUS DEPOSITS (*largely composed of calcium carbonate, calcite*)

It must be noted that many of the calcareous sedimentary rocks are or may be classed as organic rocks. The calcareous rocks include all limestones. Calcium and carbonate ions are both present in large quantity in sea water; under the proper conditions the water becomes saturated with these ions and limestone is deposited as a precipitate. Favorable conditions include:

1. Warm water, which can hold large quantities of ions in solution.
2. High rate of evaporation, as at the equator, where the ions become concentrated near the surface as the amount of water decreases; and

3. Agitated water in which precipitation is encouraged.

Except for particular structures that characterize various forms of limestone, all limestones are similar. All contain calcite as the dominant mineral constituent. Siliceous limestones, arenaceous limestones, and argillaceous limestones are all known and are common. Limestones tend to have many of the physical properties of their main constituent, calcite. They have a hardness of about three, and they effervesce in hydrochloric acid.

Travertine or **tufa.** These are limestones formed by evaporation of spring and stream waters containing calcium carbonate in solution. Tufa, a surficial spring deposit, forms in

FIG. 13–27. / *Diatoms of the type that make up large areas of sediment on the sea floor. (U.S. National Museum.)*

hot and cool springs and in running water. It is a spongy, porous, fragile rock with an earthy texture. The deposits frequently contain branches, twigs, and other debris that fall into the water.

Travertine is formed in caverns by evaporation of waters that percolate through rocks above and emerge in the cave along fractures, or as springs. It is a dense, banded deposit.

Caliche. This limy deposit forms in the soils of semiarid regions underlain by rocks composed of calcium carbonate. Capillary action draws ground waters, in which calcium carbonate is in solution, to the surface, where they evaporate, leaving the deposit as a cement in the soil or as thin layers.

Dolomite (dolostone). A sugary-textured dense-gray rock which does not effervesce in dilute acid, dolomite is a calcium magnesium carbonate $(Ca,Mg)CO_3$. Most dolomites are probably formed during recrystallization of calcareous sediments. Calcium and magnesium ions are nearly the same size so that it is possible for magnesium to replace calcium in the calcite structure. Dolomitized fossils have been found, but no animal is known to construct its shell of dolomite. Dolomite occurs irregularly as patches through limestones, and dolomitized oölites have been found. The only dolomite found in present-day sediments occurs near the Bahamas.

FERRUGINOUS DEPOSITS (*iron-bearing sediments*)

Bedded siderites. These rocks, which are mined as iron ore in the Gogebic range in Michigan, contain an association of siderite $(FeCO_3)$ and chert. In this area both siderite and chert are thought to be direct chemical precipitates.

Iron-silicate sediments. Chamosite and glauconite are two silicate minerals that contain iron. Chamosite occurs in mudstones and limestones. Its origin is still in question. Glauconite (iron-potassium silicate) is forming on the sea floor today. It is commonly known as greensand and looks very much like other sands except for its color. Glauconite is a colloidal deposit laid down where streams carrying colloids, formed through weathering of iron minerals exposed on the continents, enter the sea. Sea water is an electrolyte and neutralizes charges on the colloids, making it possible for them to settle through the sea water to the bottom where they form aggregates or granular masses.

Sedimentary hematites. Many of these are oölitic hematites, and some provide important iron ores, such as the Clinton iron ores mined and used at Birmingham, Alabama. Some of these are composed of fossil fragments that have been replaced by hematite. In others the oölitic ores have cores of quartz grains around which layers of hematite were deposited.

SALTS (*deposits formed from concentrated solutions of brines*)

Three salts are of particular importance. These are halite (common table salt, sodium chloride), and gypsum and anhydrite, which are calcium sulfates. These, along with some less common salts, are precipitated in a sequence from sea waters that become saturated. Such saturation of sea water with salts may occur when a portion of the sea becomes cut off, leaving an isolated body of water which slowly evaporates. Similar conditions hold for inland bodies of water such as Great Salt Lake.

Organically Formed Deposits

SILICEOUS DEPOSITS (*those composed of large amounts of silica*)

Radiolarian oozes. Radiolarians are a group of single-celled animals, which construct skeletons of silica. They float in upper parts of the ocean. When they die, their remains sink to the bottom. These accumulate in large quantities and may form a large part of the sediment in areas where rates of sedimentation are slow, and particularly where water is deep. Calcareous shells tend to dissolve in cool temperatures and high hydrostatic pressures found in the deep seas, but silica is stable.

Diatoms. These are siliceous plants, also of microscopic size. They have many different shapes, from rodlike to spherical and circular. These plants inhabit the oceans in tremendous numbers. They float in the surface waters and may become concentrated in large quantities. Each diatom contains a droplet of oil, which may be the principal source of most petroleum. The rock formed from remains of these plants has an earthy appearance and texture. It is a loose, fine, white, powdery rock, resembling chalk.

CALCAREOUS DEPOSITS (*containing calcite or calcium carbonate*)

Fossiliferous limestone. Most limestones are of organic origin. We include here primarily those limestones formed from the shells of marine animals. These shells are composed of the mineral calcite, which the animal is able to take from sea water and build into structures that house soft parts of the animal. You can see the cleavages of calcite in the broken fragments of many shells. Shells accumulate in quantity in shallow seas and eventually become cemented by calcite, silica, or some other material being precipitated in the water.

Chalk. This is a fossiliferous limestone composed of the shells of protozoans and particularly one which has a globular-shaped shell, called *Globigerina.* Chalk is white, light weight, and has the property of being so soft that it will easily mark most things it is rubbed on.

Marl. This name applies to mixtures of shells and shell fragments with muds and sand. It is an impure limestone usually found in a semiconsolidated state, held loosely together.

Coquina. This is the name given to those sediments composed of a loose aggregation of shell fragments.

PHOSPHATIC DEPOSITS

Two organic sources for phosphate are bones and bird excrement. Neither is common. Deposits of bird excrement, guano, are confined to a few islands where birds have lived in large numbers for long periods of time. Bones are the remains of land animals and are rarely found in large enough quantities to be called rocks.

FIG. 13–28. / *Petrified wood formed through action of ground water.* (*U.S. National Museum.*)

FERRUGINOUS DEPOSITS

Deposition of ferric oxide and ferrous sulfide may be brought about by certain bacteria and perhaps by algae. The iron bacteria can extract iron from solution and deposit it around their cells. Others may perform the function of gathering the materials, which are then directly precipitated. Accumulation of bacteria casts and precipitated granules forms a rock called bog iron. As the name suggests, it is deposited in bogs, swamps, or marshes.

CARBONACEOUS DEPOSITS (*containing large amounts of carbon*)

The important rocks of carbonaceous composition and of organic origin are the coal formations. Coal does not have a definite mineral composition and should not be classified as a rock unless we accept the idea that any naturally occurring solid that makes up a large part of the earth's crust is a rock.

FIG. 13–29. / *Cavity fillings, called geodes, banded quartz, agate.* (*U.S. National Museum.*)

14 /

Metamorphic Rocks

Rocks formed at the surface of the earth in streams, lakes, and in oceans are subjected to a remarkable change in environment if they become buried to depths of thousands of feet. They were formed under temperatures of about 50° C. and in pressures of only a few atmospheres (one atmosphere is the normal pressure at sea level—about 14.7 lbs/in²). But at a depth of several thousand feet they are subjected to temperatures in the range of 100° C. to 600° C., and pressures of several thousand atmospheres. Certain of their component minerals are unstable at these temperatures and pressures and tend to react with other minerals present to form new stable minerals. These adjustments of the rock to a new environment are called *metamorphic* changes. They are changes from less stable to more stable compositions and forms. Such changes may take place in igneous and sedimentary rocks, in unconsolidated sediments, or in previously metamorphosed rocks.

FIG. 14–1. / *Folded vein of quartz and feldspar in gneiss. Folds of this character are called ptygmatic. (Photo by the author.)*

Nature of Metamorphic Changes

Metamorphic changes take place in solid rocks. If temperatures become high enough to melt the rocks and a silicate melt evolves, then the newly formed rocks are igneous, not metamorphic. Thus there is a fine line of distinction between igneous activity and metamorphism. The two phenomena grade imperceptibly into one another.

Through metamorphism rock is transformed into an entirely different metamorphic rock. The new rock usually contains different minerals, but the bulk chemical composition of the metamorphic rock is the same as that of the rocks from which it was formed. Most metamorphic changes take place without addition or removal of elements. What does happen is that new minerals form, old ones are recrystallized, new textures develop, and the internal structure and fabric of the rock change. These changes are influenced by a number of factors.

Factors in Metamorphic Changes

TEMPERATURE. Elevated temperatures accelerate most chemical reactions. This is an important factor in any metamorphic changes taking place in the presence of heat. It is particularly important near the contacts of igneous intrusions, where temperature may become the dominating factor. The country rock may be baked without melting. This type of alteration is found at the contacts of sills, dikes, batholiths, and in fragments of country rock which may become broken off the sides or top of an intrusion and fall into the magma.

ROCK PRESSURE. This form of pressure is almost exactly like hydrostatic pressure. The amount of pressure is dependent primarily on depth. Pressures increase rapidly with depth, but few of the rocks exposed at the surface have ever been at depths of much more than 10 miles. These few are exposed at the surface in regions where uplift and folding have forced them up as mountains.

DIRECTED PRESSURE (STRESS). If pressure is exerted on a rock or mineral so that the rock or mineral tends to move, or so as to change the shape of the material, it is a directed stress. Such stress is an important factor in bringing about textural recrystallization changes. Solubility increases under pressure. A weighted wire will cut through ice and eventually fall out at the bottom of the block, but the ice will still be a solid mass. The points of greatest stress under the wire will have been the sites of solution. Solutions will have moved around the wire, and water will have recrystallized above the wire in a position of less stress. The same can happen in rocks. Granular rocks have points of greatest stress where grains touch one another. Points of less stress are pore spaces around grains. Under stress grains may go into solution at the points of contact, and the material moves into the pores where it recrystallizes. In stratified rocks lines of easiest movement are parallel to beds, not across them. When a stratum is metamorphosed under pressure, there is a tendency for elongated bands of new minerals to form parallel to old bedding surfaces.

Directed pressure may cause rocks to shear if the magnitude of the stress is great enough to overcome the strength of the rock. Such shearing will break the rock or bring about slippage parallel to the direction of the shearing (Fig. 14-2).

CHEMICALLY ACTIVE FLUIDS. Fluids may be extremely important in initiating chemical reactions and in providing a means by which products of these reactions may be moved. Fluids that move through solid rocks and cause recrystallization must move along grain or crystal boundaries and through interconnected pores. Chemically active fluids may be introduced, as in the case of magmatic activity when gases and fluids produced in the rock melt escape into the surrounding country rock. In effect, this changes the net chemical composition of the surrounding rock and increases the chances of formation of new minerals.

Water in rocks, either introduced or *connate water* (trapped in the rock during its formation), has an important influence on what chemical reactions take place, the rate at which they take place, the movement of materials through the solid rocks undergoing change, and, therefore, the nature of new minerals that form. Early in the 1950's a series of experiments were run at the Geophysical Laboratory in Washington, D.C. Metamorphic rocks were reproduced experimentally by varying the temperatures and pressures applied to certain sedimentary rock minerals. The results of these studies showed that it is possible to produce different metamorphic rocks by varying the amount of water present even if temperature and pressure are held constant.

GRAIN SIZE. Since chemical reactions take place on the surfaces of fragments or crystals, the amount of surface area exposed partially determines the time needed for completion of the reaction. A given volume of rock is increased in surface area as it is broken into smaller and smaller pieces. For this reason fine-grained sediments such as clay or shale are sensitive to many slight metamorphic changes that might not affect coarser rocks.

FIG. 14–2. / *Sheared metamorphic rock. Porthluney Cove, Cornwall. (Crown Copyright.)*

ORIGINAL COMPOSITION. The original composition of a rock places certain limitations on possible metamorphic reactions. Under different metamorphic processes and conditions rocks of any given composition can form only a limited number of different metamorphic rocks.

Processes of Metamorphism

FOUR PROCESSES TAKING PLACE DURING metamorphism are responsible for most of the observed features of metamorphic rock textures, composition, and structure:

    rock flowage,
    granulation,
    recrystallization, and
    recombination.

The specific geologic circumstances causing and the particular group of factors controlling metamorphism determine which of the four processes will be most effective.

ROCK FLOWAGE. Things we are accustomed to thinking of as solids are often pseudosolids or viscous materials. Old glass window panes are thicker at the bottom than at the top. Although they look solid, and even behave as brittle materials, they will flow over a long period of time. At higher temperatures flowage is increased. Likewise most rocks will deform slowly without the development of fractures or breaks. Rock flowage accompanying metamorphism is accelerated by movement of solutions and migration of elements toward points of less stress.

GRANULATION. When directed stress on a rock becomes great enough to fracture or break it down, granulation may result. Usually this takes place under such great pressure that visible open fractures do not occur, but mineral grains become flattened or smeared. Grains may eventually form a powdery substance resembling mortar. Granulation is favored by intense directed stress, high rock pressures, and the presence of brittle, hard, insoluble minerals that do not have a tendency to flow or recrystallize.

RECRYSTALLIZATION AND RECOMBINATION. Consider the changes that may take place in a rock subjected to high temperatures and pressure, in the presence of water, but from which nothing is removed and nothing is added to the total composition. A complete reorganization of elements of the original compounds may take place. Unstable minerals break down into their constituent parts, which recombine to form new minerals that are stable under the prevailing conditions. A reaction of this sort might be diagrammatically represented as $AB + CD \rightarrow A^+$, B^-, C^+, and D^- ions which recombine to form $AD + BC$. Compounds AB and CD were unstable, while AD and BC are stable under metamorphic conditions. An alternative change may be that the original minerals recrystallize into larger crystals or slightly different forms of the same minerals.

Types of Metamorphism

SPECIAL GEOLOGICAL CIRCUMSTANCES BRING about metamorphic changes. There are three such conditions:

Metamorphism at the contact of an igneous body.

Regional metamorphism.

Dynamic metamorphism resulting from deformation.

Contact Metamorphism

METAMORPHISM OCCURS near contacts of a magma. Gases and liquids from magma may not be introduced into the country rock; but, if these are present and if the country rock is susceptible to them, they may play an all-important role in the contact phenomena. Among the principal considerations must be:

How hot the magma is.

What liquids and gases are present.

What the country rock is.

Other factors, such as size of the intrusion, rate of cooling, and composition of the magma, may also prove important. Rocks are not good conductors of heat; therefore, it is to be expected that contact effects will be fairly localized near boundaries of the magma. If the country rock is porous or fractured near the contact and the magma contains gas, effects may be extended far beyond the margins. Since temperature is greatest at the marginal contact and decreases outward, zones of different metamorphic effects are established.

Regional Metamorphism

THIS IS THE CHEMICAL ADJUSTMENT of rocks to temperatures and pressures imposed on them by depth of burial. Certain parts of the earth's crust are more stable than others. Some have had a tendency over long eras of geologic time to move up and down. These areas are mobile belts ranging up to thousands of miles in length and hundreds of miles in width. Within these belts great thicknesses of sediments have accumulated—in some instances as much as 50,000 feet. From near-surface observations we would conclude that as you descend into the earth temperatures increase at the rate of 1° C. per 100 feet. If this rate continues to a depth of 50,000 feet, rocks buried to that depth are subjected to temperatures of at least 500° C., certainly enough to bring about drastic reorganization of the unstable constituents. In addition, pressures increase with depth at a very rapid rate.

Dynamic Metamorphism

DYNAMIC METAMORPHISM is due to high directed stresses like those that cause faulting and folding. Thus products of dynamic metamorphism are most likely to occur in the folded mountain belts, especially in their central portions, where deformation is most intense and higher temperatures and confining pressures are contributing factors in altering the rocks. Slate, formed from shales (consolidated sediments rich in clay), is one of the rocks created through high directed stress. Colloids are very sensitive to stress and become reoriented perpendicular to the applied stress. When metamorphism occurs, recrystallization of clay minerals takes place and new platy minerals are formed. These also become highly oriented, inducing in the rock a tendency to break in closely spaced *cleavage planes*, the planes along which a rock tends naturally to break, or "cleave." This rock cleavage cuts across stratification, which is often hardly visible in slates. The cleavage is usually parallel to a plane approximately bisecting the fold (Fig. 14–3).

Many other metamorphic rocks show signs of the effects of directed stresses. They may have the mortar-like texture of fine granulation, or they may be sheared in such a way that individual minerals are drawn out in stringers.

TEXTURES OF METAMORPHIC ROCKS. Most metamorphic rocks may be classed as *foliated* or *unfoliated* (Figs. 14–4 through 14–7). "Foliation" and "schistosity" are terms designating any parallel or nearly parallel structure or mineral fabric that induces a tendency in the rock to break easily along those planes. A number of structures may be responsible for this tendency, including: the parallel orientation of masses of tabular, platy, or prismatic minerals such as micas, chlorite, and sericite; finely spaced planes of slippage or fracture; and bands or layers of different minerals, causing a laminated structure.

Both foliated and unfoliated metamorphic rocks are crystalline. Unlike a magma, in which the early crystals grow in a liquid melt, metamorphic crystals must compete for space in an already solid rock. Nevertheless, many of the metamorphic rocks contain large, perfectly shaped crystals (Fig. 14–8).

Description of the Common Metamorphic Rocks

FOLIATED METAMORPHIC ROCKS

Slates. These are the most perfectly foliated metamorphic rocks. Common blackboard slates have been split from large blocks. Slaty cleavages are so closely spaced that a single piece of slate may be split into remarkably thin sheets. The foliations are caused by de-

FIG. 14–3. / *Axial plane cleavage.* (*Crown Copyright.*)

FIG. 14–4. / *Deformed banded gneiss. Original layers are shown displaced and rotated.* (*Photo by the author.*)

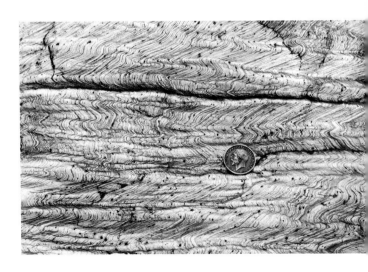

FIG. 14–5. / *Small folds developed in metamorphic rocks. Note the cleavage.* (*Crown Copyright.*)

FIG. 14–6. / *Banded gneisses. Light layers are granitic in composition. Dark layers are rich in hornblende. (Photo by the author.)*

FIG. 14–7. / *Small isoclinal folds developed in gneisses. (Photo by the author.)*

formation of shales, which alters clay minerals to micaceous minerals aligned parallel to one another. These mineral constituents are so small that they cannot ordinarily be identified megascopically.

Schists. Schists are strongly foliated rocks of medium to coarse crystalline texture. Most of the mineral constituents are easily identified without the use of a microscope. Foliation, or schistosity, is caused by parallel or nearly parallel alignment of micaceous minerals. The most common minerals are quartz, feldspars, and micas. Usually the name of one or more of the principal constituents of the schist is attached to the name as a modifier: garnetiferous mica schist, quartz schist, hornblende schist, or chlorite schist. Most schists are products of regional metamorphism.

Gneisses. These are the most abundant of all metamorphic rocks. Their characteristic feature is layering. Certain of the minerals are concentrated in bands, probably as a result of segregation during metamorphism, although many are thought to reflect the original stratification of sedimentary rocks. Some gneisses are formed by metamorphism of igneous rocks, others from sediments. Quartz and feldspar are the most common minerals, giving gneisses a composition very close to that of granite.

Phyllites. Phyllites are fine-grained schistose rocks that are less common than slates, schists, or gneisses. They are identified by the lustrous sheen which characterizes light reflected from chlorite and muscovite micas of which they are composed. They are usually greenish or red.

NONFOLIATED METAMORPHIC ROCKS

Marble. This is the metamorphic equivalent of calcite, limestone, or dolomite. Some marbles appear to be foliated, particularly if they contain large amounts of impurities that are micaceous, but most are unfoliated. The

FIG. 14–8. / *Garnetiferous mica schist. The large crystals of garnet grew to their present form during metamorphism through recrystallization. (Photo by courtesy of the U.S. National Museum.)*

texture is usually that of a large interlocking mosaic growth of calcite or dolomite crystals. Marbles of each locality tend to be slightly different either in color or in structures and patterns. Some are much more highly prized for their textures than others, although all are essentially similar in mode of origin.

Quartzite. Quartzite is the metamorphic equivalent of quartz sandstone. Sometimes the boundaries of the original grains of sand are visible, but they have become firmly cemented together. The cementing material is silica, and the bonds are so strong that when quartzite is broken fractures will cut indiscriminately across sand grains and cement. In contrast, when a sandstone is fractured, the fracture cuts through the cement and around the grains of sand.

Hornfels. These are nonfoliated, dense, usually dark-colored metamorphic rocks formed near the contacts of igneous intrusions. They are much less common than marble or quartzite. The term does not apply to any particular compositional type of rock.

Amphibolites. As the name suggests, these rocks are composed of large amounts of the minerals that belong to the amphibole group, usually hornblende. They also contain plagioclase feldspars and biotite. These are sometimes foliated when the hornblende and biotite are aligned.

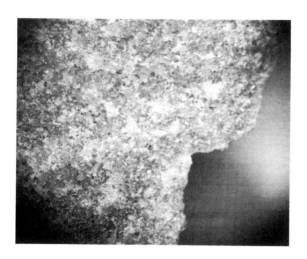

FIG. 14-9. / *Comparison of quartzite and marble. At the top is a large block of quartzite with some mica. In the middle is a greatly enlarged view of the edge of a piece of quartzite. Fractures go through the sand grains. At the bottom is a greatly enlarged view of marble showing the recrystallized calcite. (Photos from Washington and Lee Univ. collection.)*

VI /

SURFACE FEATURES

OF THE EARTH

15 / Gradation of the Crust

MOST SCULPTURE OF THE CRUST TAKES PLACE through processes acting so gradually that man rarely thinks of them as significant. It is the slow downhill movement of soil, the downslope scattering of bits of dislodged rock, slow solution of limestone by rainwater percolating through it, the constant movement of grains of sand by the wind, that over long periods of time account for removal of most material. We are conscious of the muddy water in streams after heavy rainfalls. We take note of the shifts in sand bars along coasts. We see glaciers covered by rock fragments slowly pushing their way down mountain valleys. But we do not always perceive that these are parts of a large-scale pattern by which landforms so familiar to us were brought into existence, and by which they will one day vanish from the face of the earth.

The pattern is one of degradation of the surface of the earth, the shifting of materials and their redeposition elsewhere. Movement is accomplished by wind, water, glacial ice, and downslope movement of surficial materials. It is always directed from higher elevations to lower elevations. Thus the long-range tendency of these processes is toward leveling of the face of the earth. The rate of removal of materials from continents today is estimated to be such that about 21 million years would be required to level the continents. The earth is more than 3 billion years old. Enough time has elapsed for the surface to have become flat many times over. Thus it is obvious that some forces are tending to combat the tendency toward degradation. The constructive forces are diastrophism and igneous activity, including vulcanism. These forces move material from lower to higher positions. Thus the particular configuration of the surface of the crust at any given time—the present, for instance—represents a sort of balance between forces of upheaval in the crust and forces of erosion and degradation. Throughout most of geologic time forces of upheaval have slightly more than counterbalanced the forces of degradation. Shapes and sizes of continents have varied, but the rock record indicates that continents have persisted above sea level.

Gradation Is a Three-Fold Process

FIRST THE SURFACE IS DECAYED AND eroded, then products of this decay and erosion are transported, and finally they are deposited.

Erosion is facilitated by chemical and mechanical disintegration of rocks where they are brought into contact with the atmosphere, waters of the surface, and plant and animal life. Once rocks are decomposed or have partially disintegrated they are easily moved. If they are on sloping surfaces, they tend to move down those slopes under the constant pull of gravity. Eventually they may come in contact with running water or with a moving body of ice, and are carried along until the ice melts or the velocity of the water becomes too low to move them. Then they drop out and may become consolidated into sedimentary rocks.

Geomorphic Agents

CERTAIN AGENTS FUNCTION TO BRING about gradation and the resulting changes in landforms. These may be called *geomorphic agents*. They are:

On land:
mass movement—driven by gravity
running water—driven by gravity
ground water—driven by gravity
glaciers—driven by gravity
wind—driven by rotation of the earth and thermal activity within the atmosphere.

In oceans:
mass movements—driven by gravity
waves—driven by rotation of the earth and wind
currents—driven by rotation of the earth and temperature and density distribution
tides—driven by gravitational attraction of the moon and sun
tsunamis (seismic waves)—caused underwater by earthquakes and volcanic explosions

Base Level

IF THE SURFACE OF THE EARTH WERE NOT affected by diastrophism and volcanism, it would be slowly reduced to a uniform level known as *ultimate base level*. Most processes tending to lower continents cease to be effective when the area approaches the level of the oceans, so sea level may be taken as the ultimate base level. If reduction of the entire earth to sea level did occur, sea level would be substantially above its present position.

The term *"temporary base level"* is used to describe a transient condition for a region or small area. It is a level below which the dominant forces of erosion will not reduce the area. If a region is being eroded mainly by running water, it will not reduce the level of the region below the level of a lake into which the water drains as long as the lake exists. The lake acts for the local area just as the ocean does for the earth.

Geomorphic Processes Leave Their Imprint upon Landforms

EACH OF THE GEOMORPHIC AGENTS functions in a way peculiar to itself, and produces characteristic erosional and depositional landforms. It is possible to recognize the origin of landforms although the processes by which they were formed may have ceased to operate.[1]

Structure of the Crust and the Development of Landforms

FOLDS, FAULTS, UNCONFORMITIES, DIFFERences in the hardness and susceptibility to decomposition of rock units, and disintegration provide a framework within which geomorphic agents function. Physiographic forms are almost always influenced by the structure of the underlying rock.[2] Thus the erosion of a particular geologic structure primarily by one geomorphic agent will result in a predictable landform.

[1] Compare the topography as shaped by running water (Portage Quadrangle), glaciers (Holden Quadrangle), and ground water (Mammoth Cave Quadrangle), at end of book.

[2] As shown on the Maverick Spring Quadrangle, at end of book.

Evolution of Landforms

IF A PARTICULAR STRUCTURE IS SUBJECTED to the effects of certain geomorphic agents, acting over a long period of time, a particular sequence of landforms will develop. The landforms will slowly undergo systematic change, or evolution, unless some external conditions bring about a change in the dominant structure or geomorphic agents.

FIG. 16–1. / *Weathered granite in the Black Hills of South Dakota. The rounded pinnacles are characteristic of the weathering of this massive rock. (Photo by courtesy of the South Dakota Highway Comm.)*

Weathering Processes
and Development of Soil

IN THE SIXTEENTH CENTURY MANY PHILOSO-phers thought that rocks and minerals were living substances—that they were simply lower forms of life than plants and much lower than animals. This belief was founded mainly on the observation that rocks appear to be in various stages of life—youth, maturity, and old age. The same rock seen in one outcrop to be a solid, strong, fresh, and youthful substance might be recognized elsewhere as a decaying mass obviously dead and starting to disintegrate. The philosophers were observing what we would today call effects of weathering. *Weathering* changes occur where rocks and minerals come in contact with the atmosphere, surficial waters, and organic life under conditions normal to the surface of the earth. Mechanical breakdown and alteration by chemical changes are producing new minerals which are stable at the surface of the earth from minerals formed under other conditions not normal to the surface.

The surface of the earth continually under-goes gradation, accomplished by the shifting of material. Weathering of rocks is not directly a process of gradation, but is related to it in that weathering brings about decay and disintegra-tion of rocks and facilitates their removal by geomorphic agents. It is usually a very impor-tant, but not always necessary, initial step in degradation.

Evidences of weathering are all about us. Sidewalks and concrete highways are built in separated sections to prevent them from crack-ing when temperatures fall and concrete con-tracts. Houses in moist climates must be painted frequently to prevent decay and disintegration of wood. A knife left outside in the rain will be acted on by oxygen and water to form rust. The surface of the crust is constantly exposed to attack by these and other weathering agents. The effects are not confined to the surface; they penetrate into the crust along fractures and faults, between crystals, and along grain bound-aries within rocks. Gradually they bring about loosening, decay, and disintegration of even the hardest and most resistant rocks (Fig. 16–1). One of the most important results of weather-ing is production of soils. Because soils form slowly, they are a valuable natural resource which must be conserved.

Processes of Weathering

BREAKDOWN AND DECOMPOSITION OF SOLID rock into soil is a slow process. The speed and nature of the process varies from one climatic region to another and depends on the composition of the rock itself (Fig. 16–2). Aside from climate and rock composition, it is possible to isolate a number of naturally occurring processes that bring about weathering. They may be grouped into mechanical processes which result in disintegration and chemical processes which cause chemical decomposition. Important among mechanical processes are freezing of water, frost action, unloading, crystal growth in soil, daily temperature variations, and organic activity. Chemical processes include oxidation, carbonation, and hydration.

Mechanical Weathering

FREEZING. Freezing water is effective in breaking down rocks because water expands when it crystallizes. In this respect it is different from most other liquids. Normally liquids contract when they crystallize, but water increases in volume by nearly nine per cent when frozen. As expansion takes place high pressures are exerted on all sides of the space confining the water. Experiments have shown that when water is frozen in an enclosed vessel, pressures up to $2,100 \text{ kg/cm}^2$ (about $29,500 \text{ lb/in}^2$) are developed at temperatures of $-22°$ C. Such pressures far exceed the strength of even the hardest and most durable rocks. In nature this fact is of great significance, because rainwater seeps into fractures in rock both where it is exposed and beneath the soil cover. If freezing takes place while water is in a fracture, the fracture may be spread apart and extended in depth, or new fractures may be formed. The process is most effective where daily temperatures are above freezing and nightly temperatures below freezing. Once fractures have been opened, new surfaces become available for other types of mechanical and chemical weathering.

FROST ACTION. Frost action and frost heaving result from formation of layers of ice in soil (Figs. 16–3 and 16–4). Even when frost heaving occurs only rarely, or is restricted in degree or amount of area involved, it loosens soil and allows air to pass into it. This process may be healthful for the soil; on the other hand, it may be destructive through heaving up building foundations or through loosening soil on steep slopes where it can creep downhill or be washed away by rain. Normally layers of ice form in soils where differences of composition or texture occur. Once ice starts to crystallize, water is pulled into the surface of the layer by *capillary action*. This is possible because intergranular spaces in soil or rock act as capillary tubes. When crystallization takes place a slight amount of heat is liberated, and this keeps on the layer of ice a film of water which is connected to water in pore spaces; so the process continues—water freezes on the ice surface, the ice slowly expands, more water is drawn in to freeze—and layers of considerable thickness are built. In the process the overlying soil is forced upward. At high elevation and in high latitudes rock fragments may even be forced up through the soil by this process.

CRYSTAL GROWTH. After a light rain in the plains or on a desert, water rapidly soaks into the ground. This water may dissolve limestone or other soluble constituents of the rocks or soils directly beneath the surface. When the sun comes out and evaporation begins, water present near the surface may be drawn back up to the surface as though it were in a *capillary tube*. Connected pore spaces in the soil are about the same size as capillary tubes and act in the same way. At the surface water evaporates, and whatever material is in solution is precipitated to form crystals or crystalline aggregates in the soil. As crystals grow they can exert large expansive stresses, breaking up soil and even some rocks. This is the mode of formation of layers of calcium carbonate, *caliche*, which is a commonly found layer or nodular mass in soils underlain by limestone in semiarid plains or deserts. Other

FIG. 16–2. / *Bryce Canyon, Utah. Differential weathering is responsible for the unusual shape of these pinnacles. Some of the units of rock are more resistant to the weathering processes acting in this region than others are. (Photo by courtesy of the Union Pacific Railroad.)*

crystals that grow in this manner include sulfates, phosphates, nitrates, gypsum, calcite, alum, epsom salts, and saltpeter.

UNLOADING. In quarrying granite for building stones it is sometimes possible to take advantage of natural forces to split the granite. A set of joints or fractures, called *sheeting*, may develop parallel to the surface of the ground (Fig. 16–5). Sheeting represents a response of the rock to the release of confining pressure when the weight of overlying rock is removed. The process is not limited to quarries but may occur wherever erosion is removing material from underlying rocks.

FIG. 16–3. / *Ice vein in muck, Seward, Alaska. (Photo by S. Taber, courtesy of U.S. Geological Survey.)*

FIG. 16–4. / *Effects frost action. Frost boil near the Bering Sea, Alaska. (Photo by H. B. Allen, courtesy of U.S. Geological Survey.)*

FIG. 16–5. / *Sheeting in granite at the Mt. Airy Quarry, North Carolina. (Photo by the author.)*

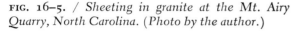

INSOLATION. Daily variation in temperature is among the most universal processes bringing about mechanical breakdown of rocks, but its importance is still not clearly evaluated. Variations of 60 or more degrees may take place in desert regions where exceedingly high temperatures reached in the day are followed by rapid cooling at night. When solids are heated they expand; when they cool they contract. However, the amount of expansion and contraction is small. The question is whether or not repeated expansion and contraction will, over a long period of time, lead to mechanical breakdown of a rock. Experiments with repeatedly heating and cooling rocks through wide ranges of temperature have failed to produce mechanical disintegration. But there is a time factor in nature which cannot readily be duplicated by short-term experiments. Possibly very slight fractures are formed. Differential expansion of different minerals in the rock would allow gradual breakdown between the grains. Once grains are loosened, solutions could get into them and bring about chemical decomposition. The development of scalelike sheets on exposed rocks is a phenomenon often thought to be due to insolation. Such scaling is called *exfoliation* (Fig. 16–6). Scales form on massive granites and other igneous rocks. Because they only form parallel to the surface of the exposed portion, they are thought to be due to some surficial weathering process. Many have thought exfoliation is related to insolation, but it has also been found on the surfaces of rocks imbedded in jungle soil where insolation could not be very effective. It appears likely that either the feature has multiple explanations or results from a combination of mechanical and chemical processes.

Chemical Weathering

THE ATMOSPHERE CONTAINS a number of constituents that can react with minerals. Most important of these are water, carbon dioxide, and oxygen. Effectiveness of these chemical agents depends on the composition of the rocks and the size of their constituent particles. Quartz, for example, is a very stable substance; it is almost insoluble in rainwater and is unaffected by carbon dioxide and other constituents of the atmosphere. Thus rocks composed primarily of quartz decompose very slowly. Other minerals are highly susceptible to water and show marked signs of reaction within a few months of exposure to the atmosphere. Three processes are notably responsible for chemical weathering. They are oxidation, hydration, and carbonation.

OXIDATION. *Oxidation* is the process by which oxygen combines with elements or compounds. The combination is aided by the presence of water and high temperatures. Oxygen has a particular affinity for iron compounds, and these are among the most commonly oxidized materials. Pyroxenes, hornblende, and olivine all contain iron. As minerals are broken down they become oxidized, and iron is converted to ferric

oxide (hematite) or hydroxide (limonite). These processes are accompanied by color changes in the minerals and in the soils. Green and black soils are changed to red, yellow, or brown colors as limonite is formed. Soils of these colors are most common in warm, moist climates. Reduction, the process by which oxygen is freed from its compounds, is not common in weathering.

HYDRATION. *Hydration* refers to absorption and combination of water with other compounds. *Hydrolysis* is a reaction between water and another compound. These processes, especially when combined with carbonation, are extremely effective in weathering of common rocks and minerals.

CARBONATION. This is the process by which carbon dioxide is added to oxides of calcium, mag-

FIG. 16–6. / *Half Dome in Yosemite National Park, California. Note the disintegration of the rock. Exfoliation and frost action are the dominant processes promoting the disintegration.* (*Photo by courtesy of the U.S. Geological Survey.*)

nesium, sodium, and potassium to form carbonates of these metals. Carbon dioxide is a gas and is a common constituent of the earth's atmosphere. It combines with water to form a weak acid, called *carbonic acid* (H_2CO_3). Thus rainwater, which contains minute quantities of carbon dioxide removed from the atmosphere, is a weak acid and is the most common solvent acting on the crust. Its action is commonly evident in the formation of green copper carbonate on exposed copper roofs.

Susceptibility of Rocks to Weathering

BOTH TEXTURE AND COMPOSITION OF rocks make them of varying susceptibility to weathering. Because chemical reactions take place on surfaces, fine-grained rocks open to solutions are more easily broken down than those that are coarse-grained and impervious. Fractures, bedding planes, and pore spaces all provide lines along which solutions can move. In addition, between crystals there are sometimes fine openings of capillary size along which solutions can be drawn.

Composition is of particular importance in chemical weathering. Some minerals will not react with solutions and gases normally found in the atmosphere and in the ground; others break down in their presence. The most common rock-forming minerals include quartz, the feldspar group, micas, pyroxene, amphibole, and calcite. Of these, quartz is virtually unaffected by chemical weathering. Calcite can be dissolved, and the others undergo complex chemical reactions. All but quartz are affected by carbonated water (rainwater). Feldspars react with carbonic acid and water to form clay, potassium carbonate (in solution), and silica (in solution). When biotite reacts with water, oxygen, and carbonic acid it forms limonite, clay, silica, and potassium and magnesium bicarbonate. Calcite, which is normally very slightly soluble in pure water, can be dissolved more readily in carbonic acid (rainwater).

Whether or not a rock of a given composition actually undergoes chemical decomposition depends largely on the climate. The amount of rainfall, its distribution through the year, the average temperature, and the temperature range all are important factors in determining rate and extent of chemical decomposition even of susceptible minerals and rocks.

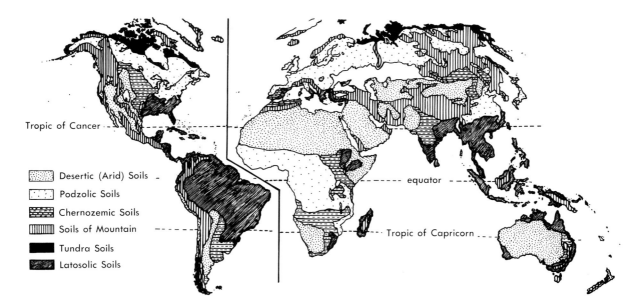

Tropic of Cancer

equator

Tropic of Capricorn

Desertic (Arid) Soils
Podzolic Soils
Chernozemic Soils
Soils of Mountain
Tundra Soils
Latosolic Soils

FIG. 16–7. / *Generalized map showing soil types.* (From Soil, *U.S. Dept. of Agriculture.*)

TABLE 8 / *Chemical weathering of feldspar and biotite.*

$$2KAlSi_3O_8 + H_2CO_3 + H_2O \rightarrow \quad K_2CO_3 + Al_2(OH)_2 Si_4O_{10} + 2SiO_2$$

feldspar   carbonic   water   potassium   clay   silica
                acid   carbonate   (in solution)

$$2KMg_2Fe(OH)_2AlSi_3O_{10} + O + \quad 10H_2CO_3 + H_2O \rightarrow \quad 2KHCO_3 + 4Mg(HCO_3)_2 + Fe_2O_3 \cdot H_2O +$$

biotite   oxygen   carbonic acid   water   potassium   magnesium   limonite
                                                    bicarbonate   bicarbonate

$$Al_2(OH)_2Si_4O_{10} + 2SiO_2 + H_2O$$

clay   silica   water
(in solution)

Soil

MOST OF THE LAND SURFACE OF THE EARTH is covered with soil (Fig. 16–7). Where it has been carefully studied and the processes governing its fertility, formation, destruction and value are understood, it has been conserved and continues to provide the riches of agricultural production. Where study of soil has not been given careful attention, it has generally been depleted, eroded, and gradually abandoned as a consumed natural resource. At a time when overpopulation and starvation are among the most significant problems facing mankind, a thorough understanding of the soil is most important. Soil science has expanded and now is a field apart from geology in much the same way as meteorology.

Because soil is the decay product of rock, it is apparent that the type of rock from which a given soil is derived will be an important factor in its formation and in determining its qualities. In the light of the preceding discussion of weathering processes, it is also obvious that more than one type of soil may be derived from a given rock type, depending on weathering processes. Among the most important factors governing soil formation are:

1. Rock from which the soil was derived.
2. Climate (particularly temperature, precipitation, and distribution of these).

3. Shape of the surface on which soil develops (i.e., slope, relief).
4. Biological factors (amount and types of plants).
5. The length of time in which these factors have been acting.

The great number of combinations of different parent materials, climates, and other factors is reflected in the variety of soil types. Soil scientists recognize forty major types of soil, and for purposes of agricultural research these forty are subdivided into hundreds of subtypes. In this discussion we will consider the gross characteristics of only the largest categories of soil types.

Where a cut is made through soil to underlying rock it is usually possible to see well-defined zones called A, B, and C *horizons* (Fig. 16–8). Below the C horizon lies unweathered parent material such as solid rock, or sediment. The *C horizon* contains weathered parent material, loose and partly decayed rock. It is from this material that the overlying soil is derived. Soils sometimes develop on material that is no longer located in its place of origin; thus rock in the C horizon may have been transported and the overlying soil may not be related to the bedrock below.

The B horizon is called the *subsoil*. It normally contains fewer organisms than the overlying layers, but more than the C horizon. Weathering has reduced all rock to loosely consolidated material in the B horizon. It often contains more clay than either the A or C layers, and consequently it is harder when dry and stickier when wet than either of the others. Iron and aluminum oxide tend to be concentrated. Essentially, the B layer is the site of accumulation of suspended materials from the overlying soil. Clayey material often has a blocky or prismatic structure.

The top layer of soil, *A horizon*, is the site of maximum organic activity. Processes of removal of soluble constituents in water are most active here. From the top down, through an idealized A horizon there would be leaves and loose organic debris that is largely undecomposed, matted and partially decomposed organic material, a mixture of organic and mineral matter, a transition into clayey subsoil (Fig. 16–8).

The variability of soil has been emphasized. This applies also to the degree of development and presence of the three horizons. Some soils show no zones at all, others have a zone missing, and many have more than the general zonal character outlined above. Texture and structure of soil are also highly variable. Soil constituents can be divided into sand, silt, and clay sizes, and these occur in all degrees of mixture. Structure as it is used in soil science refers to the way the soil particles stick together. Four kinds of structure are recognized. These are *granular, blocky, columnar* (also prismatic), and *platy.* Of these, granular and blocky soils have the best structure for most plants. Through proper soil management it is possible to influence structure.

Chemical decomposition of a rock's constituent minerals is of particular importance in soils. The common igneous and metamorphic rocks (granite, gneiss, schists, and basalt) are made up primarily of a relatively few minerals (notably quartz, feldspar, micas, hornblende, augite, and olivine). Of these, quartz does not decompose. The others break down into clay minerals, iron compounds, silicon dioxide, and other compounds in solution (Table 8). Thus of the over one hundred elements only a relatively small number are common in soils, but many more may be present in trace amounts.

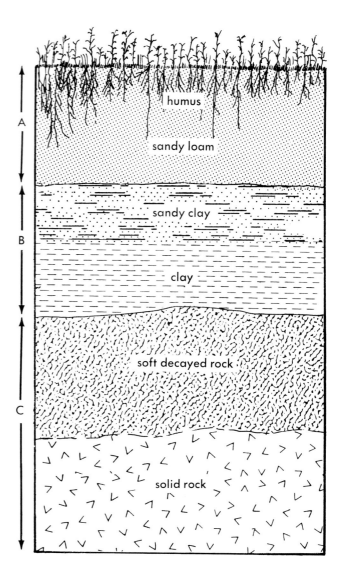

FIG. 16–8. / *A soil profile of residual soil. The A horizon is characterized by decayed organic matter and sandy loam. The B horizon contains clay, and the C horizon is composed of the rock from which B and A are derived.*

Sediments and sedimentary rocks are products of breakdown and sedimentation of igneous and metamorphic rock constituents. Sedimentary rocks form the underlying rock beneath soil over nearly three-quarters of the earth's land surface. Common sediments are sand (particularly quartz sand), limestone, mud, and mixtures of these found in varying degrees of consolidation.

Of the various minerals present clay minerals are of particular significance because they contain such an extensive variety of elements and also because they are so small that they are more readily involved in chemical reactions in soil. For this reason, clay plays a particularly significant role in chemical reactions taking place in soil. Clay, at least in small quantities, is present in most sediments and sedimentary rocks, and clay is also one of the most common weathering products of igneous and metamorphic rocks (Fig. 16–10).

Typical soil contains clay colloids, fine mineral fragments, organic matter, and some moisture. Mineral fragments undergo chemical decomposition very slowly. The effect of the process is to dissolve the minerals or break them down into their ionic constituents. These

go into solution in soil moisture. Some of the ions stay in solution, but because clay colloids are negatively charged they can hold some of the positive ions on their surface. This is particularly true of hydrogen, calcium, and sodium. In addition smaller quantities of aluminum, magnesium, and potassium are held in this way. Concentration of hydrogen ions in a solution determines the acidity of the soil. Acidity is expressed as pH. A neutral solution has a pH of 7. Acid solutions range from zero to 6 pH; alkaline solutions from 8 to 14 pH. The pH range for soils is between 4 and 10. The most common ions in acid soils are hydrogen and aluminum, calcium and magnesium are com-

FIG. 16–9. / *Humus-rich top layer in soil developed on Coastal Plain sediments, Mississippi.* (*Photo by the author.*)

mon in neutral soils, and sodium is most common in alkaline soils. Most plants grow best in soils of a particular acidity.

The chemistry of soils and soil solutions is complex, but it may be viewed simply in terms of a sort of equilibrium condition. Positive ions (such as H^+, Ca^+, and Na^+) may be exchanged between the solid and liquid phases of soil, tending to establish an equilibrium condition in which the concentration of ions is maintained at the same level as ions removed from the soil by plants for use as food are replaced by ions liberated from minerals and organic matter and from clay colloid surfaces. It is the tendency to maintain this balance that accounts for the continued application of lime necessary to keep many acid soils neutral. This is desirable because most plants thrive in soils with a pH of 6 or 7. When hydrogen ions in an acid soil solution are neutralized by lime, more hydrogen ions are released (or exchanged for calcium ions) from the surfaces of the colloids. The properties of soils which control their ability to exchange ions and maintain a supply of needed ions determine their desirability as a medium in which plants may grow. Some sixteen elements are necessary for plant growth—carbon, hydrogen, oxygen, nitrogen, phosphorous, sulphur, potassium, calcium, magnesium, iron, manganese, zinc, copper, molybdenum, boron, and chlorine.

In most soils the total supply of plant nutrients is high compared with the need of plants supported by it. When the plant dies in uncultivated areas most of the ions are returned to the soil as decaying organic matter. If the plants are crops the soil loses these constituents as the crops are removed. The same thing happens when plants are burned off, and to a greater extent if the ashes are washed away.

Major Soil Types

Desert Soil

"A ZONAL GROUP that have light-colored surface soils and usually are underlain by calcareous material and frequently by hard layers. They are developed under extremely scanty scrub vegetation in warm to cool arid climates" (*Soil*, U. S. Dept. of Agriculture yearbook).

Large portions of some deserts do not have soil covers at all. Chemical weathering is particularly important in causing soil to form. Where there is little or no free moisture, bare rock, sand, and desert pavement are likely to predominate. *Desert pavement* is the name applied to boulders, cobbles, or pebbles left as a residual cover on deserts when finer sediment is blown away. When soil is present it is likely to be thin, loose, and friable. The low rainfall prevents leaching of soil and favors accumulation of salts. Salt content is exceedingly high in low portions of desert basins. Soil here often has salt crystals growing near the surface as a result of evaporation of water which has dissolved the salts from deeper in the soil. A hard layer containing calcium carbonate or silica is sometimes found in the soil. This layer is referred to as *hard pan*.

Tundra Soil

TUNDRA SOIL MAY BE FOUND on high mountains at low latitudes, but the vast expanse of it is within the Arctic Circle. It forms where there is very cold weather most of the year. Over large areas in the Arctic there is permanently frozen ground at a depth of a foot or more. The upper foot of soil freezes in the winter. As freezing takes place water crystallizes out in layers of irregular size. The soil is forced up and disrupted, forming small mounds. These mounds are usually covered by a dense growth of moss, sedges, and flowering plants. Over much of the Arctic the land is low and poorly drained, giving rise to swamps and ponds. This poorly developed drainage is due to low slopes, permafrost, and the sheet of glacial deposits dropped there as continental ice sheets melted away. The soil is poorly drained in summer when ice in upper portions of the soil melts. Though there is abundant moisture, the rate of evaporation is low and there is little rainfall because of low temperatures. Low temperatures tend to slow down chemical reactions and inhibit growth of most plants, so the soils tend to be very thin.

Podzol Soil

"A ZONAL GROUP having surface organic mats and thin, organic mineral horizons above gray leached horizons that rest upon illuvial [formed of colloids and soluble salts from above] dark-brown horizons developed under coniferous or mixed forests or under heath vegetation in a cool-temperate, moist climate" (from *Soil*).

Podzolic soils have been the traditional agricultural soils in Europe and North America. They are widely developed in the central and eastern United States, which has a humid climate and large areas of hardwood forest cover. One common variety of podzolic soil has a gray-brown color and is crumbly and composed of silty loam. These loams are composed of a mixture of clay, silt, sand, and organic matter. In wooded areas it has a matted layer of decaying leaves near the surface. The A horizon supports abundant plant growth and animal activity. Often there is a lower layer that has a light gray color and is partially leached. This layer tends to crumble readily and it is a silty loam also. The B horizon is richer in clay, coarser in texture, and darker in color than the A layer. The two, A and B, normally have an aggregate thickness of three feet. The C horizon is composed of blocky clay. The soil profile is very similar although it develops on rocks as different as limestone, shale, and glacial deposits. The soil is acidic and requires liming, but it supports a wide variety of plants, including cereals, legumes, root crops, vegetables, and fruits. Outstanding crop production can be expected when adequate care is taken to fertilize the soil, but even where this is not done the soil will produce for many years.

Chernozem Soil

"A zonal group having deep, dark to nearly black surface horizons and rich in organic matter, which grades into lighter colored soil below. At 1.5 to 4 feet, these soils have layers of accumulated calcium carbonate. They develop under tall and mixed grasses in a temperate to cool subhumid (semiarid) climate" (*Soil*).

These soils develop in climates where moisture is not abundant or consistent. Most years tend to have above or below normal precipitation. A large expanse of this soil group is found in central western North America. The soil is very dark in color, almost black, but it does not support a wide variety of crops. Cereals are best adapted to it, and this region is the great wheat producing area of North America. The low rainfall does not favor removal of ions from soil water by leaching. For this reason there is little need for fertilizer. Where calcium carbonate is dissolved near surface and moved down, the soil often has accumulated a layer of lime in the subsoil, but not to any great depth.

Tropical Soil (Latosolic)

There are possibly more different soil types in tropical and subtropical climates than in all other climates combined. This is due in part to the great variety of combinations of high temperature, variable amounts and distribution of rainfall, and topography. Tropical climates generally have heavy rainfall, but it is evenly distributed throughout the year in some areas while there are hot, humid periods of high rainfall separated by warm dry spells in others. Portions of the tropics have up to 400 inches of rainfall per year.

Soils in this climatic belt are almost always very thick. Conditions are ideal for chemical weathering. Plant matter tends to be abundant, and it usually quickly decomposes into soil. Plant nutrients are liberated rapidly from decomposing minerals, but the high rainfall soon washes these out of the soil. For this reason the soils become exhausted in a period of a few years if the forest cover is stripped and crops are cultivated. The usual farming practice is to cut a strip out of the forest, cultivate it for four or five years, then let it grow up in forest cover again and cut another strip. It takes about fifteen years for soil to become fertile again after farming is stopped. Because leaching is so extensive soils are richest where they are continually rejuvenated by addition of new mineral supplies. These can come from volcanic ash, from stream deposits, or from the erosion of soil parent material at a slow but continuous rate. Because fires are so common during dry seasons, minerals from plants are often lost before they are returned to the soil.

Laterite is a special type of clay-rich soil which has a tendency to harden into a bricklike solid. It is found where the rainfall is highly variable, causing a large range of fluctuation in the level of the water table from within a foot or two of the ground surface to depths of tens of feet. Silica is extensively leached from such soil and there is a concentration of hydrous aluminum oxides. In many instances these soils contain so much aluminum that they are potentially valuable sources of the metal. It is thought that further alteration of some laterites leads to the formation of *bauxite*, the principal ore of aluminum (Fig. 16–10).

Alluvial Soil

MATERIAL TRANSPORTED by streams and deposited in stream valleys is called *alluvium*. Large streams flowing on low slopes usually have wide valleys, and during flood stages waters cover valley floors extensively. Soils developed on this transported alluvium are often rich and provide valuable farm land. Where soils are formed along modern rivers the soil is young and original materials have not been modified very much by soil-forming processes.

Mountain Soil

ALL OF THE OTHER types of soil can be found in mountains, and often several types occur close together, for climatic conditions on a mountain depend greatly on elevation. Usually mountain soils contain fragments of broken rock in slow transport down the mountainsides.

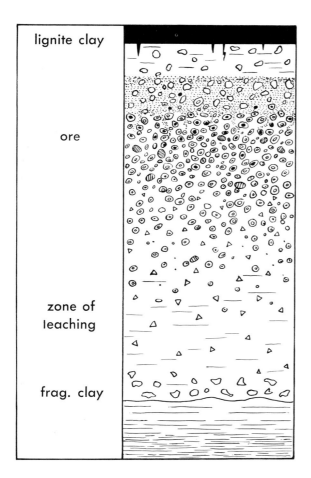

FIG. 16–10. / *Arkansas bauxite region. The bauxite in Arkansas is formed from the leaching of aluminum-rich clays. The clays are weathering products of syenite. The association of the bauxite with lignite coal suggests the types of climatic conditions which prevailed when the bauxite was formed. (After Gordon, Tracey, and Ellis, U.S.G.S. Prof. Paper 299.)*

17/

Mass Movement

Downhill movement of rock and soil due to the force of gravity is the most universal of all processes of erosion. Such mass wasting mechanisms as landslides, slump, earth flows, soil creep, and subsidence in combination with transportation by running water, glaciers, wave action, and sea currents are responsible for almost all erosion. No matter where you are, you do not have to look far to find evidence of mass movement. Principles governing it are simple, but the variety of combinations of types of movement, of materials moved, and of physiographic forms assumed by these masses is great.

The driving force behind all mass movement is the force of gravity. This force is directed toward the center of the earth, but components of it act along any inclined plane. The steeper the inclination the greater will be the component of force acting down the slope. This force will be most effective in moving materials that are unstable in their existing position, such as loose or water-saturated soil, or masses of rock and soil resting on surfaces (fracture surfaces or bedding planes, for example) over which they might slide.

In referring to materials moved by mass wasting the terms rock, earth, soil, debris, and mud are commonly used.

Rock is applied to solid rocks and consolidated fragmental rocks.

Earth is a general term used to describe disintegrated rocks and loosely consolidated sediments.

Soil is the product of rock disintegration and decomposition by weathering.

Debris is a general term applied to mixtures of rock, soil, plant matter, or mud.

Mud is a mixture of water and the finer particles of earth and soil.

When movements occur they normally take place through sliding along some surface, or by an internal rotation of constituent particles, resulting in general flowage of the entire mass. Sliding is promoted by the existence of faults, fractures, or bedding planes. When these are inclined downslope the material above can move along them. Flowage is a much more com-

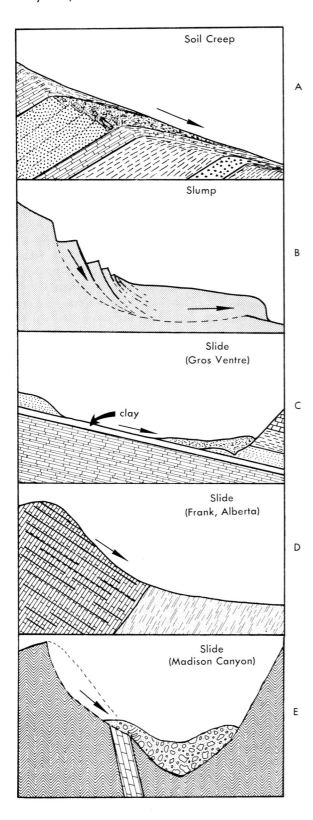

Soil Creep

Slump

Slide
(Gros Ventre)

clay

Slide
(Frank, Alberta)

Slide
(Madison Canyon)

FIG. 17–1. / *Types of mass movement. A: the effects of soil creep where rock units outcropping at the surface have become partially disintegrated and decomposed by weathering processes. B: in a slump the steepened slope breaks away at the top where a prominent fracture or break in the ground surface appears. The slump mass rotates with the toe rising and moving forward. C: the conditions that existed at the site of the Gros Ventre slide. The sandstone slid down the wet clay units, filling the valley below. D: the approximate conditions at the Turtle Mountain slide in Alberta. The limestone is jointed. Note the orientation of the joints so that slippage along them was possible. E: hypothetical section through the Madison Canyon, Montana, showing the location of the dolostone strata and the attitude of the foliation in the schists.*

plicated process, but it can occur in all types of material. Flowage involves rotation, slippage, and sliding of the materials inside the moving mass. Flowage of masses may take place slowly in nearly imperceptible movements called *creep* or at velocities of up to sixty miles an hour, as in debris avalanches. Flowage is possible in dry masses, but high water or ice content have pronounced effects on the nature and velocity of the flow. On the basis of the type of material moved, and the rate and type of movement, the following classification may be compiled:

> *Slow flowage*
>> Rock creep
>> Talus creep
>> Soil creep
>> Rock-glacier creep
>> Solifluction
> *Rapid flowage*
>> Earth flow
>> Mud flow
>> Debris avalanche
> *Sliding*
>> Slump
>> Debris slide
>> Debris fall
>> Rock slide
>> Rock fall
> *Subsidence* (the sinking in of the ground over underground caverns).

Streams, glaciers, and mass movements are all driven by gravity. While one might reasonably expect to have little difficulty in distinguishing a stream from a glacier, and either of them from a mass movement, the distinction is not so clear-cut. Glaciers carry heavy loads of rock, soil, and debris; so do streams; and mass movements usually contain some proportion of water or ice. The three types of movement are represented in Fig. 17–2 by a triangular diagram which is indicative of the gradational character of each. In some of the following descriptions of rock glaciers and mudflows the truly transitional character of downslope movements of all types will become more evident.

A great variety of forms of mass movement is evident in high mountains. The following examples serve to illustrate some of the more common types.

Stone Polygons

To those unfamiliar with such areas it is usually surprising to discover that the summits of many ranges are not peaks at all but broad plateau surfaces. If there is a sufficient amount of precipitation these surfaces will be covered with thick grass through which irregular blocks of rock protrude. Quite common among the strange assortment of rock shapes are the elongate masses standing on end, giving the appearance of having been picked up and stuck into the ground on a pointed end. In some regions these are so numerous that they almost completely cover the plateaus; in others they form polygonal-shaped rings, called *stone polygons*. Both situations are the result of frost heaving. As water in the soil freezes and expands, the rocks are forced upward. Then, as thawing begins, soil slumps down into the spaces under and around the lifted blocks before they can move back into their former positions. As this process continues, with every freezing the rocks are pushed up farther and farther out of the soil. Similar stone polygons are common features in the high latitudes where the ground is permanently frozen.

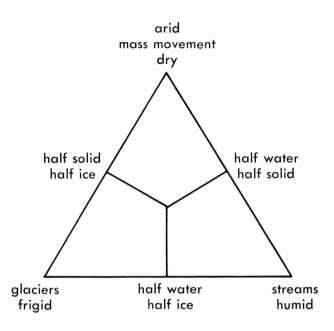

FIG. 17–2 / *Process of degradation. Degradation is accomplished through breakdown and transportation of the crust. These decay products move downhill under the pull of gravity. They are transported dry, in water, in ice, and in combinations of these three.*

FIG. 17–3. / *The mechanics of downslope movement through swelling or frost heaving. The rock is uplifted perpendicular to the ground surface; then it is pulled straight down by the force of gravity and gradually moves downslope when disturbed.*

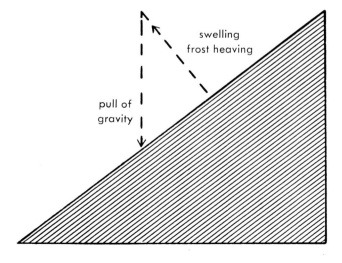

When frost heaving moves soil on a slope it is usually pushing the soil or rocks straight out, perpendicular to the ground surface. When thawing occurs, the material settles back, but not along the same path. It is pulled down by the force of gravity toward the center of the earth, as indicated in Fig. 17-3. Thus, there is a component of downslope movement with each cycle. This same principle may be applied to any mechanism which tends to lift material up from the ground surface and then allows it to fall back freely.

Talus

DROPPING DOWN FROM plateau surfaces and high peaks of the mountains are broad, deep, amphitheater-shaped bowls, called *cirques*, which once formed at the heads of glaciers. Their walls are nearly vertical and in places as high as 1,000 feet. Huge blocks of rock break loose from these oversteepened sides. As they bounce and hit the wall they dislodge other rocks, sometimes starting landslides and leaving a cloud of dust along their path. As this rock debris, called *talus*, hits the bottom of the cirque, it generally piles up to form what is known as a *talus cone* (Fig. 17-4). This in turn becomes a *talus sheet* as it spreads out with the continual addition of broken blocks. The talus cones or sheets are naturally composed of whatever rocks make up the face of the source cliffs. They may be of any rock type. Mechanical weathering on such steep slopes, particularly freezing and thawing, is so much more rapid than chemical decay that the talus rocks on top of the piles usually appear freshly broken. These broken blocks are of all sizes, but seldom have dimensions smaller than several inches. In the example given here talus in a glacial valley is described. Similar cones and sheets of talus are found in unglaciated mountains also. Talus may form anywhere rock outcrops are subjected to weathering and erosion over long periods of time.

Rock Glaciers

ON THE FLOORS of mountain valleys, talus may lie where it falls, moving at very slow rates and then only because it is disturbed by freezing and thawing, by animals, or by impact of new rocks falling on it. But if the valley floor, whether covered with ice or dry, is inclined, converging piles of talus form a tongue-shaped projection down the valley. These lobes of talus move so slowly that their motion can be detected only by checking the position of the end of the lobe over a period of years. Such is the movement of the rock glacier (Fig. 17-5). As a rock glacier advances it assumes garland-shaped loops, giving the appearance of being a very viscous liquid. Some of these sheets have considerable amounts of ice mixed with rock, making the movement of the glacier more rapid than completely dry sheets at lower elevations and lower latitudes.

Creep

BESIDES MASS MOVEMENT on steep slopes there are many other forms of a still slower nature. These become apparent on close inspection of almost every hillside. Soil is being gradually pulled downslope. In some places clay remnants of rocks and boulders are drawn out into long, lens-shaped masses. Small, parallel rows circling many hillsides, originally paths used by grazing animals, show signs of this creeping downslope movement. Fences and telephone poles set on slopes may give an indication of these surface movements as they slowly become inclined downhill.

Mass wasting takes still other forms than those already described. The following examples illustrate the variety of forms and the effects produced. Although the slower types of mass wasting, which usually pass unnoticed, have the most important effects because of their widespread occurrence, there are other movements which are occasionally quite spectacular and often disastrous.

FIG. 17–4. / *Talus cones. These cones line the side of this high mountain cliff in the Madison Mountains of Montana. (Photo by the author.)*

FIG. 17–5. / *A rock glacier seen from the trail pass near the head of Horseshoe Basin, Silverton quadrangle, Colorado. (Photo by courtesy of the U.S. Geological Survey.)*

Madison Canyon Landslide

ABOUT MIDNIGHT on August 17, 1959, a severe earthquake shook the region west of Yellowstone Park. Surface waves in the crust rocked water in nearby lakes, threw the soil up in waves, and cracked the highways and ground surface over a large area. The movement was caused by a displacement along a fault. This fault extends near a narrow and very steep canyon 1,300 feet deep (Fig. 17–6).

The earthquake triggered a movement in decayed soils and rock debris on the side of the canyon, and in the chaos that followed about 35 million cubic yards of rock, soil, and trees slid off into the canyon, leaving a scar from the top of the mountains almost to the river. The debris engulfed the valley, a campground, and the highway, burying about 135 acres of land with an average thickness of 150 feet of rock. The movement was extremely fast—perhaps as high as 60 miles per hour. The mass forced air in the valley aside, setting up a wind of gale force. When the slide hit the river, water was splashed out leaving mud splashes in trees high up on the sides of the valley. Material broken loose moved with such impetus that it continued up the opposite valley wall 400 feet. As the slide filled the valley, a wave of water was forced up the river for almost a mile. Material in the slide ranged in size from blocks 30 feet across to fine soil particles.

The potential for mass movement had been there for many years. Slopes had been oversteepened to angles of 40 to 60 degrees, and deeply weathered Precambrian gneisses and schists (more than 600 million years old) were exposed on them. These deep soils were held on the slope by the presence near the bottom of the valley of a massive layer of dolostone, which is resistant in such semiarid climates.

The gneiss, schists, and dolostone are inclined toward the river on the south side of the valley, and are fractured. Thus there were many potential planes of slippage. When earthquake movements began, blocks of the dolostone dislodged and released the main mass movement.

Solifluction

THIS TERM, WHICH LITERALLY MEANS soil flowage, is applied to downslope movement of soils, rock debris, and other fragments in climates where the ground is solidly frozen in the winter and only partially thaws in the summer months. When thawing occurs, upper layers of the soil, which have been forced up and deranged by frost heaving, are bathed in meltwater. Lower layers of the soil remain frozen. This facilitates flowage and slow movement of the upper layers over the lower frozen layers, even on very low slopes. The moving mass of soil and debris takes sheet, lobate, or tongue-like forms as it moves. Where valleys are present, it will move into and down them. The nature of the debris depends on the composition of the soil. On Bear Island of the North Atlantic the surface is covered with a thick flowing mud in the warm months, while in places on the Falkland Islands the debris is made up of quartzite fragments.

Mudflow

ONE OF THE MOST spectacular mudflows occurred on the steep slopes of the San Gabriel Range of southern California. A few years before the flow there was an extensive forest fire which destroyed the vegetative cover. The flow started on a warm day when the heat caused melting of the snow cover in the high mountains. Meltwaters percolated into the thick,

FIG. 17–6. / *Madison River Canyon slide. This giant slide filled the Madison River Canyon to a depth of 200 feet with weathered rock debris from the valley side. This slide is more than 400 feet high on the right-hand side of the valley. A lake is seen as it began to form on the upstream side of the natural dam. This landslide was triggered by an earthquake. The dark covering on the slide is a mass of uprooted trees. (Photo by courtesy of the Montana Highway Commission.)*

weathered cover of decaying schists. When the weathered material became saturated it broke loose, leaving a scar extending 1,000 feet up the mountainside with cliffs 150 feet high around the edge. The mudflow continued for five days, and at its height splashed mud 20 feet into the air, leaving a mud coating on treetops. The mixture was about 25 per cent water.

Mudflows occur commonly in deserts. Here fine weathering products are dry most of the year. When rain does fall it comes in large quantities, perhaps with a large part or all of the annual rainfall coming in a single rain. Water seeps into the weathering products, and the mixture moves rapidly down steep slopes, more slowly on lower slopes. Flows slip into channels and gullies. They are not dry, but the mass does not contain much free water. Sometimes even large boulders will float in the mud. Mudflows are favored by intermediate water supply, little vegetation, and unconsolidated rock debris.

Gros Ventre Slide (Earthflow)

WHERE THE GROS VENTRE RIVER cuts through the mountains east of Kelly, Wyoming (just east of the Teton Mountains), earth flowed slowly from one side of the river valley into the valley during 1909–11. Movements there were facilitated by the structure of the sedimentary strata exposed on the mountainside. The strata exposed there are clays and shales interbedded with thin sandstones and dip at about 20 degrees toward the river. The stream cut through the sandstones overlying the muds and shales, then slow flowage and slipping began in layers of plastic clay. Flowage was most rapid after spring thaws, when meltwater from ice and snow seeped into the top of the flow scars and saturated underlying clays. Sliding occurred on this slippery clay base. The mass left a large scar extending up the mountain, and a lobelike mass of earth filled the river valley and moved up the opposite side of the valley during the most rapid movements. It formed a dam across

the river and backed up a large lake (Figs. 17–7 and 17–8). The river topped the dam, and in 1925 it rapidly cut through the weak clays and sand of the dam, causing a flood which destroyed most of the town of Kelly.

Panama Canal—Slides, Slumps, and Plastic Flowage

CONSTRUCTION OF THE Panama Canal was plagued by many costly earth movements. At times they were so bad that some question arose as to the feasibility of completing the canal. Slumping of the sides of the canal became worse where the canal was cut through the Cucaracha formation. This unit is partially composed of a highly plastic clay. At first slides were a result of cutting the sides of the canal too steeply—material slid because the slope exceeded the angle of repose for the material. Conditions were aggravated when the sides were cut down to lower slopes because the material removed was dumped just above the top of the cut. The weight of debris piled up in that position led to the development of slumps. A *slump* is bounded beneath by a curved fissure along which movement occurs (Fig. 17–9). As the top cracks and moves down, the toe or bottom moves up and out. The first sign is development of a crack at the top of the slumping mass. After the crack forms, the slumping mass may move rapidly, on a steep slope, or creep slowly downward.

Other mass movements plagued construction. In places plastic clays underlie the bottom of the canal. When the canals were dredged to deepen the channel, the mixture of water and clay was pumped up on the sides. The weight of this mass further compressed the layers of clay, and the plastic clay was squeezed along within the clay zone until it came to a point where the pressure was less—this point, of course, was where the canal had been cut. So lumps of clay continued to rise in the canal. This process continued until the clay layer was squeezed off, and the canal became stabilized.

FIG. 17–7. / *This view of the Slumgullion mudflow shows its source. The flow is seen here to extend to Lake San Cristobal. (Photo by courtesy of the U.S. Geological Survey.)*

FIG. 17–8. / *The Gros Ventre slide, Wyoming. (Photo by the author.)*

FIG. 17–9. / Topographic forms due to landslides in Dolores County, Colorado. (Photo by courtesy of the U.S. Geological Survey.)

1964 Alaskan Earthquake

As in the Madison Canyon slide, an earthquake of high intensity initiated extensive mass movements in southcentral Alaska on Good Friday, March 27, 1964, which were responsible for the loss of over a hundred lives and property damage of hundreds of millions of dollars. The earthquake resulted from movement on a major fault which is known to extend over five hundred miles along a south-southwest trend from the point on the ground surface over the focus of the earthquake, located about halfway between Anchorage and Cordova, Alaska. As a result of the faulting, blocks of the earth's crust were displaced. At Cordova the area was uplifted nearly seven feet, at Anchorage the region was depressed relatively about three feet, and at Kodiak, nearly five hundred miles south, the relative depression amounted to nearly six feet.

The secondary mass movements at Anchorage were described as follows by Oakeshott (1964):

The city [Anchorage] lies on a glacial outwash plain which slopes from the base of the high and rugged Chugach Mountains down to the sea, where it drops off abruptly along a series of bluffs or seacliffs about 30 to 50 feet above sea level. Under the entire city is the flat-lying formation called by geologists the Bootlegger Cove clay. The Bootlegger Cove clay is gray clay, silt, and mud deposited from melting glaciers in lagoons during the Pleistocene Epoch; it ranges in thickness from about 100 to 250 feet and lies only a few feet below the land surface under most of Anchorage. When water-saturated, as it is in the Anchorage area, this material completely lacks structural strength. When the tremendous shaking of the earthquake occurred, the Bootlegger Cove clay failed, partly by sliding out toward the waters of Cook Inlet on slip-surfaces of especial weakness, and probably also partly by "liquefying" to flow at low angles toward the waterfront. . . . Great landslide cracks opened back of the bluff; some of the houses were carried toward the sea as far as 500 feet. About 200 acres of the terrace surface broke into a series of blocks each a few feet across, tilted at various weird angles to form a chaos of blocks of the bluish-gray Bootlegger Cove silt and clay, brownish peat and muskeg, black soil, and road pavement.

. . . In front of some of the advancing blocks compressional "pressure ridges" were formed. Most of the damage in Anchorage was of this type; that is, due to direct landsliding and to landslide fractures, cracks, and in some cases to the pressure ridges built up along the fronts of the slides. . . .

Seismic sea waves, or "tidal waves," generated by the large displacement of the surface of the earth under Prince William Sound affected various coastal towns selectively, depending on the configuration of the coastline, the depth of water, the configuration of the sea bottom, proximity to the movement of the surface of the earth in the Sound below sea level, and probably other factors. The little town of Kodiak on Kodiak Island, besides being dropped about six feet in the western block, was hit by tidal waves up to 30 feet high.

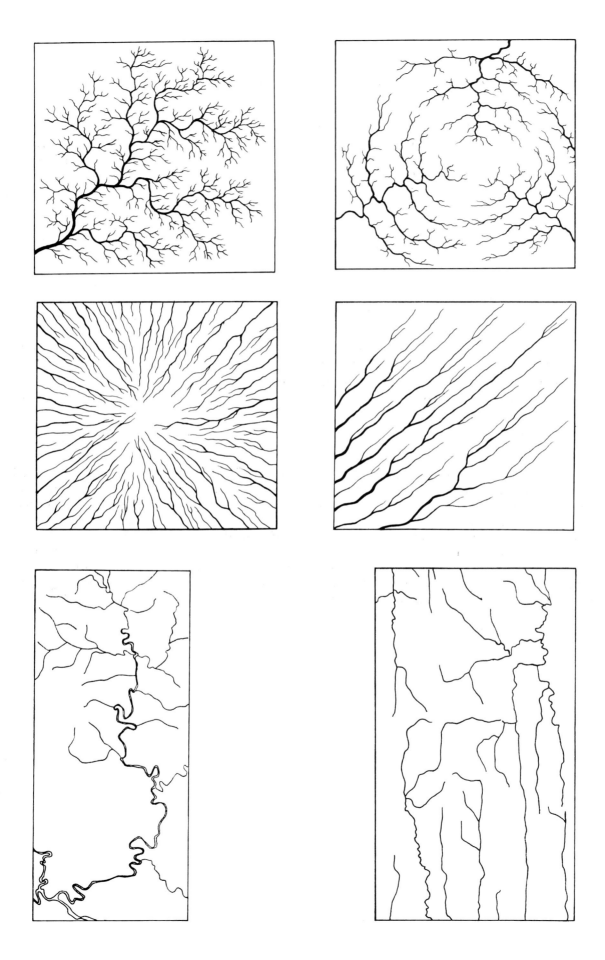

18 / Rivers

Patterns of Surface Runoff

THE DIVERSITY AND INTRICACY OF STREAM patterns hint at the complex factors governing the flow of precipitation that runs off on the ground surface. The nature and pattern of the flow is determined by such varied factors as amount, distribution, and intensity of rainfall, quantity of water in streams, structure of rock units over which the stream flows, dominant weathering and erosion processes, and age and history of the stream.

The surface of the continents can be divided into a mosaic pattern of interlocking drainage basins. A *drainage basin* is the area drained by any given stream and its tributaries.[1] The drainage basin of a river like the Mississippi includes several large basins, those of the Arkansas, Ohio, and Missouri rivers, and each of these may be subdivided into basins of its tributaries.

If a stream's path is governed primarily by the slope of the ground surface the stream is called a *consequent* stream, since its path is a consequence of the slope. Three patterns are commonly developed where this is the case—straight streams flowing down steep slopes, *dendritic* (treelike) patterns formed by a main stream with branching tributaries, and *radial* patterns developed on domed surfaces such as volcanoes and structural domes (Fig. 18–1).[2] If a stream's course has become adjusted to the structure of the underlying rocks and follows a path determined by structure rather than by the original slope of the land, it is called a *subsequent* stream. Common patterns formed in this manner are *rectangular* or *trellis* patterns. These form where rock units of varying resistance are aligned in parallel ridges. If the underlying rock strata are folded or domed so that weaker units outcrop in circular or arcuate patterns, the stream patterns developed here will reflect those patterns.

[1] Most of the drainage of a small stream is shown on the Portage Quadrangle at end of book.

[2] See Maverick Spring Quadrangle at end of book.

FIG. 18–1. / *Drainage patterns. The patterns shown are (top left) dendritic; (top right) annular; (middle left) radial; (middle right) linear or straight; (bottom left) meandering; and (bottom right) modified rectangular or trellis pattern.*

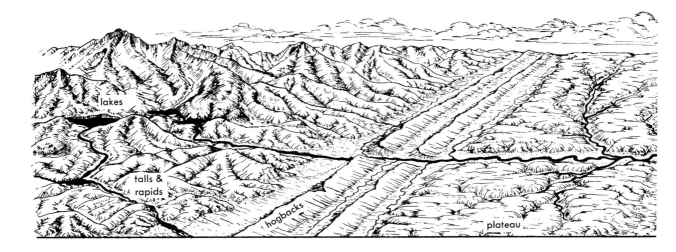

FIG. 18–2. / *Profile of a long river. Note the variations in the stream pattern from the mountains through the rolling countryside and the flat coastal plain to the coast. The greatest part of the load carried by the stream is obtained in the mountains where the slopes are very steep. Once out of the high country the stream follows a sinuous course across rolling countryside. In the flat coastal plain the stream begins to meander across its valley, and when the steam reaches the ocean the load it carries along is dropped to form a delta.*

Nature of Stream Flow

IT IS THE PULL OF GRAVITY ON SURFACE waters that causes them to run down slopes, forming streams, and to continue toward sea level. Although the pull of gravity is a constant, the nature of the flow undergoes many changes in the course of the journey. It may start in mountains where the water is confined to narrow channels filled with boulders and rock debris and literally jumps, boils, and foams as it rushes down steep slopes. At the foot of the mountains the stream is more likely to follow a sinuous course through rolling landscapes (Fig. 18–2). The water is quieter, except for occasional floods and rapids, as it moves toward lower elevations. Finally, as the stream approaches sea level it may follow a broad meandering path across a flat countryside. The water flows gently with only mild surficial disturbances.

Along the course of almost any river obvious changes in the nature of the movement of the waters can be seen. These range from the extreme turbulence of water where it cascades down a rough stream channel or drops to the foot of a waterfall, to the very smooth, even flow at the lip of a waterfall or wherever the slope of a smooth stream channel suddenly steepens. Turbulence is brought about by obstructions, which deflect the water from a straight path, disrupting smooth flow patterns and setting up eddy currents, whirlpools, and boiling movements. Flow in most streams on medium to low slopes is slightly turbulent and is called *streaming flow*. The surface of the water is smooth in some places, slightly undulating in others. A mild, slow eddying and boiling may be visible. Turbulence in streaming flow arises from irregularities in the bottom and sides of the stream channel and at the surface. At these places there is frictional drag on the water. Even air offers some frictional drag.

At the opposite extreme of complete turbulence is *laminar flow*. In laminar flow water moves as though it is made up of very fine layers that are free to slip over one another. The path of a particle in any one layer is smooth or streamlined. Laminar flow is most closely approached when water is moving very slowly through a channel with smooth sides, or when velocity increases rapidly at the top of a waterfall. A lip forms where the water, dropping over the suddenly steepened slope, runs ahead of that upstream. The surface of the water drops and becomes smooth.

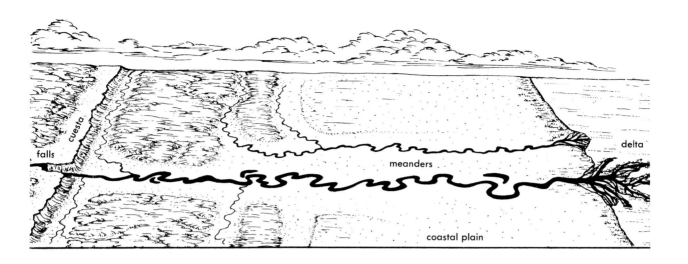

falls | cuesta | meanders | coastal plain | delta

Transportation by Running Water

SUSPENSION. Muddy waters characterize streams of all sizes after a heavy rainfall, when increased surface runoff sweeps large quantities of dirt and weathering products into them. Water appears muddy because part of its load is being transported in suspension. The lightest particles may float, as everything is buoyed up by a force equal to the weight of water displaced. Suspended load is usually made up largely of silt and clay sizes. Larger particles may be suspended if the water is turbulent.

SOLUTION. Some weathering products are carried in solution in most streams. A large part of the soluble load in streams in humid climates comes from ground water that finds its way into surface streams. Streams flowing out of deserts where large quantities of soluble minerals may exist at the surface of the ground also have large loads in solution. In most streams the load in solution is a small part of the total load; slow, sluggish streams are an exception. Limestone, dolostone, and salts are notably soluble. An estimated 270 million tons are removed from the United States in solution each year.

TRACTION. The remainder of the stream load is carried along the bottom in traction. Sand, pebbles, and small cobbles may bounce along the bottom, hitting irregularities and traveling as suspended material for a short distance until the pull of gravity brings them back to the bottom again. Larger cobbles and boulders are rolled along the bottom or slip and slide downstream. Experimental evidence indicates that the largest size that will roll along a gently sloping stream bottom varies as the sixth power of the velocity of the water. Thus a slight increase in velocity will bring about a great increase in the sizes that the stream can move in traction.

Part of the load of most streams is carried by each of the above means, but most of the load may be moved in any one of the three ways, depending on conditions at a particular time. Along the lower Mississippi River most of the load is carried in suspension and solution, and only a small part in traction. The load of the Arkansas River in the Rockies is largely carried along the stream bed in traction. The amount of load in transport is also dependent in part on the availability of debris. Streams do not always have enough debris coming into them to fill them to *capacity*, which is the total amount that could be transported under the conditions existing at any given time. Similarly, a stream is not filled to capacity if it cannot pick up the sizes available. This applies both to boulders which are not moved because of their mass, and to clay which is held together so tightly by cohesive bonds that it is not readily dislodged. In both cases the stream may have unused capacity in one of the three methods of transport. Fine sand and coarse silt are the most easily moved sizes.

Sources of Load

PRODUCTS OF rock distintegration are moved downhill by mass wasting. Downslope movement is accelerated and facilitated by surface wash, often the chief source of a stream's load. After a heavy rain, ground on steep slopes is covered by small rills or trickles of water carrying dirt and soil. Second in importance as a source is the channel. Ordinarily a stream channel is partially filled with bed load which cannot be transported. This condition does not prevail during periods of unusually high water. Even rock or sediment below this channel fill may become a source during floods. Banks of streams and sides of channels are also sources. The stream may slightly undercut banks on curves, bringing about slumping or sliding of the sides into the river. Melting glaciers, windblown materials, and volcanic dust are important sources of stream loads in some localities.

Distribution of Velocity and Turbulence

TURBULENCE IS GREATEST WHERE IRREGUlarities are present in a stream, that is, near the outside perimeter, the water–channel contact. The net effective forward velocity of a stream is reduced by turbulence and frictional drag along the bottom. In a straight channel the greatest velocity is usually found in the deepest part of the stream channel, about one-third of the way down from the surface. If a stream channel is symmetrical, the greatest velocity is usually toward the middle, but if the channel is asymmetric, as in a curve, the greatest velocity is shifted toward deeper water. The deepest part of the channel is generally on the outside of a curve. Maximum turbulence lies just beneath and to either side of the maximum velocity.

Hydraulic Factors

HYDRAULIC FACTORS ARE THOSE THAT INfluence behavior of fluids in motion. They are an interrelated group that determine the nature of running water. *Discharge* is the amount of water passing through a given cross section of the stream at any given time. Quantity of the discharge may be calculated by multiplying the area of the cross section by the velocity of the water measured in volume, as cubic feet per second. *Load* is the total amount of material being transported in solution, traction, and suspension. *Gradient* is the slope of the bottom of the stream channel between two specified points. The gradient along a stream is variable. *Channel roughness* is determined by the irregularity of bottom and sides. Width, depth, and shape of channel, size of sediment in transport, and velocity of the stream are all important hydraulic factors.

Discharge and load are determined by the geology and physiography of the drainage basin. They are independent factors. Discharge is controlled by the amount of rainfall, the amount of surface runoff, and the size and shape of the drainage basin. Similarly, load supplied is a function of the nature of the load sources and how readily it can get into the stream.

Gradient is dependent on many other factors. Adjustments of the slope of the bottom of a stream channel occur constantly. If the amount of load being brought into one part of the stream is more than the stream can carry, then some is left in the channel, and the downstream slope is increased. Processes acting within the stream tend to adjust the slope of the stream so it can carry its load.

The roughness, width, and depth of the channel, size of material in transport, and stream velocity are partially dependent on processes acting within the stream. They are complexly interrelated or interdependent. The complexity of these interrelations is much greater than was originally recognized. In recent years much more attention has been directed toward understanding these interrelationships as in-

FIG. 18–3. / *Pot holes formed in a limestone rock.*

FIG. 18–4. / *A V-shaped valley. (Crown Copyright.)*

creased efforts are made to control flooding and make the best possible use of our natural water resources. Results of scale-model experiments have been closely related to actual observations along streams. Measuring stations have been set up at thousands of points along rivers and smaller streams to obtain data necessary for the work. Results show that:

1. Width, depth, velocity, and suspended sediment load are all functions of the amount of water discharged.
2. Shape of a river cross section and its roughness determine distribution of velocity in the cross section.
3. Shape of the channel is at least partially determined by erodibility of the beds and banks.
4. For a given width and discharge, the total load depends on velocity. Any change in velocity will be accompanied by a change in depth.
5. Slope tends to become adjusted to provide the velocity–depth relation necessary to carry the load. Steeper slopes cause higher velocity and greater transporting power.

Stream Erosion

STREAMS ARE USUALLY CONSIDERED THE most important geomorphic agents bringing about degradation of the land surface. Certainly streams are responsible for moving more material than any other agents, but they are effective in accomplishing erosion primarily because mass wasting keeps a constant supply of material moving toward them. Sheet wash plays an important role in this movement. Stream channels and banks are eroded through processes of abrasion, solution, and impact.

Potholes (Fig. 18–3) are striking evidence of the work of solution and abrasion. These smooth rounded holes found in the bottoms of many streams where solid rock is exposed are formed by continued circular motion of eddy currents carrying sand, silt, and gravel. The surface of the hole is repeatedly abraded, and dissolved and suspended products are washed up and out of the hole. Most potholes are relatively small, only one or two feet across, but they occasionally become 20 feet or more deep.

Erosion is concentrated on the bottom of the channel in streams flowing rapidly on steep gradients. Debris transported is constantly moved by turbulence, but its motion is usually directed toward the bottom because of the downward pull of gravity. Streams of this sort tend to concentrate erosion straight down (Fig. 18–4). The Bighorn River in Wyoming flows through a canyon that is more than 200 feet deep and not much wider at the top than at the bottom. At the Royal Gorge in Colorado the Arkansas River has cut a narrow gorge more than 1,000 feet deep. The Black Canyon of the Gunnison River in western Colorado has a similar feature. In these places lateral erosion is negligible.

Lateral cutting does take place in streams flowing on low slopes. The channel usually follows a sinuous course. At each turn water is shifted toward the outside of the turn, and consequently more turbulence and erosion will occur there. The channel is deepened and the bank steepened on the outside of the curve. This makes the outside unstable, and it slumps into the stream. In this fashion the stream brings about lateral erosion of its valley.[3] Impact of larger materials being transported against sides and bottom of the channel is also an effective means of stream erosion. Heavier materials dislodge loose debris or crack even the hardest and most solid rock.

Stream Piracy

THIS IS THE PROCESS by which a stream diverts drainage from streams of one drainage basin into streams of another basin. Consider the following simple case. There are two parallel valleys separated by a ridge composed of tilted rock strata. Channels of the main stream in each of these valleys are at the same level, or one may be slightly lower than the other. Somewhere along the valley a small tributary

[3] See terraces on Voltaire Quadrangle at end of book.

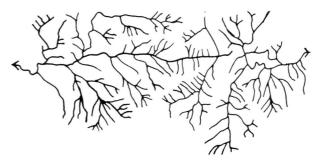

FIG. 18–5. / *Stream capture near Asheville, North Carolina. The stream flowing toward the right has captured the upper tributaries of the westward-flowing river.*

flows from the steeper side of the ridge into the lower valley. Because this face of the ridge is steeper, it will be cut back more rapidly than the other side and its steeper gradient will contribute to the more rapid erosion of the valley below. As this tributary stream cuts headwardly into the ridge, the crest of the ridge is breached and a notch is formed. As this notch is worn lower by headward erosion of the stream, the divide shifts toward the center of the second valley. Eventually, through continued headward erosion and lowering of the stream channel, the head of this tributary intersects the main channel of the stream in the upper valley. Now the path of movement of water from the head of the stream in the upper valley shifts, flows through the gap, called a *water gap* (Fig. 18–6), and into the main trunk of the lower stream valley. The process of piracy is complete. The tributary of the lower stream is called the *pirate stream*. The stream it has diverted or captured is said to be *beheaded* (Fig. 18–5).

The process of stream piracy does not necessarily require that the slopes of the separating ridge be different. Essentially the same steps will take place if streams on opposite sides of the ridge have different gradients. The stream flowing on the steeper gradient will lower its channel more rapidly.

Deposition

LIKE MARK TWAIN, EVERYONE WHO MUST pilot a boat through rivers learns to predict where shifting sand bars are likely to be found.

Higher velocity is shifted toward the outside of the curve. Increased turbulence picks up debris from the bottom on that side of the channel until it becomes deeper. If the amount of water in the river hasn't changed, the inside of the curve must be shallow. Where water is shallow there is more frictional drag, which slows it down, and deposits of sand accumulate.

The most important factor in bringing about deposition is a decrease in velocity. Decreases in velocity occur where:

1. The slope of the stream channel is reduced.

2. There is either a loss or a spreading-out of water. Streams in arid climates lose their water by evaporation. When the water table is lowered below the level of a stream bed, water moves out of the stream toward the water table. Spreading of the water may occur where the shape of the channel has altered or where the channel splits into several distributaries, as it does near the mouth of the Mississippi River.

3. Streams encounter obstructions in their paths. These obstructions include natural dams, timber rafts, or fans of debris piled into a stream by one of its tributaries.

4. Local stagnant pools form or the stream enters a standing body of water, such as a lake or the ocean. Flow may stop altogether. A similar condition exists where a stream enters the standing backwaters of a flooded area.

Streams also deposit part of their load if there is more load than the stream is capable of transporting. This condition may be caused by excessive loads produced by rapid weathering and surface wash. Surface wash may be enormously and suddenly increased by loss of soil cover such as forests. Man is sometimes a major factor in the creation of these conditions. We carelessly burn forests or allow soil to be removed without thought of the added erosive effects which may be the consequences of these actions. Thus we pay for our carelessness by loss of valuable topsoil and increased flood hazards.

Concept of the Graded Stream

"A GRADED STREAM IS ONE IN WHICH, OVER a period of years, slope is delicately adjusted to provide, with available discharge and with prevailing channel characteristics, just the velocity required for the transportation of the load supplied from the drainage basin. It is a stream in equilibrium; its diagnostic characteristic is that any change in any of the controlling fac-

FIG. 18–6. / *Vertical view of a water gap cut through a cuesta. (Courtesy of U.S. Air Force.)*

tors will cause a displacement of the equilibrium in a direction that will tend to absorb the effect of the change" (J. H. Mackin). The graded stream is not a perfectly stable stream, but one in which the various hydraulic factors are constantly changing, shifting, and compensating to maintain a state of equilibrium. Grade is reached when the stream is just able to remove all the debris supplied to it from its drainage basin.

Features of Streams on Low and Moderate Slopes

STREAMS FORM MANY TYPES OF PATTERNS and flow in a great variety of valleys, but it is possible to select four examples to represent those most commonly found. These are streams with a braided stream pattern, those that follow sinuous courses, those flowing in broadly meandering patterns, and those confined to nearly straight channels. Each of these is characterized by features which are peculiar to it. Other features may be found in valleys occupied by any of them. Three features which may be found in any of the valleys are floodplains, deltas, and alluvial fans.

ALLUVIAL FANS. Alluvial fans are formed where streams flow out of an area of high relief into one of low relief—that is, where a stream passes from a steep to a low gradient. At such a place velocity is reduced and deposition takes place. The stream flowing from a mountainous region may carry great quantities of material which is too coarse to be transported across lower surfaces without large increases in velocity. The result is formation of a broad, low, cone-shaped deposit called an *alluvial fan*.[4] Such fans are composed of poorly sorted, stratified stream deposits. Usually streams on them are not confined to particular channels very long. The stream shifts position back and forth across the cone, or it may form distributaries that spread the debris evenly across the fan's surface. Fans

are best developed in semiarid and arid climates where the process is accelerated by lack of abundant rainfall, which creates an even greater imbalance in the amount of water in relation to load. The high stream velocity and the force of gravity on the steep mountain slopes are both suddenly reduced at the head of the fan and no longer compensate for the small volume of the flow.

DELTAS. Deltas are submerged equivalents of alluvial fans. A delta is built where the amount of load entering a body of water is in excess of that which can be moved. Counterparts of the famous deltas of the Nile and the Mississippi may be found in many small lakes and streams. Deltas may be built into a large stream where a heavily loaded tributary flows into it. In the Mississippi River's delta a huge area has been flooded with debris eroded off half the surface area of the United States. The debris is spread out across marshes of the lower Mississippi Valley through a system of distributaries (Fig. 9–10). When the load is dropped at the edge of the water the coarsest material settles out first, and finer silts are carried out into deeper water.

FLOOD PLAINS. Flood plains are broad, nearly flat areas near the level of the streams (Fig. 18–7).[5] They occur where stream channels on low and moderate slopes are not confined in location and change position by lateral erosion. When the channel shifts it leaves behind a channel filled with transported load. Shifts of this sort become increasingly common in regions of low relief and where unconsolidated sediments underlie the channel. Similar plains are formed where tributaries come into the main stream. Eroded surfaces on either side of the stream are approximately at the same elevation as the main stream, and they are periodically flooded when the water rises. Sometimes the flood plain may actually be lower than the river surface, if the stream has built high natural levees.

[4] See Antelope Peak Quadrangle at end of book.

[5] See Voltaire Quadrangle at end of book.

FIG. 18–7. / *Lateral erosion by this braided stream is apparent. The stream is confined on either side by cliffs. The streams have shifted back and forth across the alluvial plain, undercutting and defining the valley. Arrow indicates edge of alluvial plain. (Photo by courtesy of the Royal Canadian Air Force.)*

Meandering-Stream Patterns

THE MISSISSIPPI RIVER and its valley below Cairo, Illinois, are a classic example of a meandering stream and features associated with it. The Mississippi's floodplain is as much as 20 miles wide in places. If there were no artificial levees, waters would cover large parts of this plain, spreading over it a thin veneer of material carried by the river. This still happens during unusually high floods. Floodplain sediments are thickest near the stream channel, where velocity is high and where most of the load is carried just before and after flooding starts. Once waters spread beyond the main channel they become shallow, frictional drag is great, and the heaviest material is deposited. As they begin to recede, velocity decreases and more deposition occurs. A wedge-shaped layer of sediment is thus deposited. The thickest part of the wedge is on either side of the channel,

where the decrease in volume is greatest. Thus the river builds *natural levees* by the flooding process itself. Effects of this process are most interesting along the Mississippi south of Baton Rouge, where the river flows down a narrow ridge built up above the delta surface by floodplain deposits.

Meanders are looplike channel patterns. Some of these almost double back on themselves. They are common where the gradient of a stream becomes extremely low. The lower Mississippi is flowing down a slope that is approaching the horizontal—two feet per mile. Because velocity is greatest on the outside of a curve, it is possible for a stream to move laterally by undercutting banks or by bringing about collapse through sliding and slumping of the outside banks of bends. Since the process is largely one of slumping, it is very slow when the river flows against resistant soil or rock. This may cause the direction of lateral movement

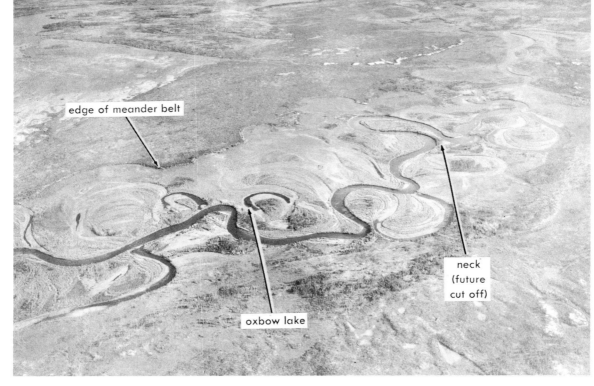

FIG. 18–8. / *Features of the meandering stream and its valley. The edge of the floodplain is marked by a cliff. Oxbow lakes, meanders, meander scars, and a neck are clearly shown. The natural levee is not obvious. (Photo by courtesy of the Royal Canadian Air Force.)*

FIG. 18–9. / *Vertical photograph of the braids in the Tanana River, Alaska. Braided streams are characterized by shallow channels and great width, and they are most common where debris is supplied in great quantity such as near the margin of a melting glacier. Most braided streams are found on very low slopes. (Photo by courtesy of the U.S. Air Force.)*

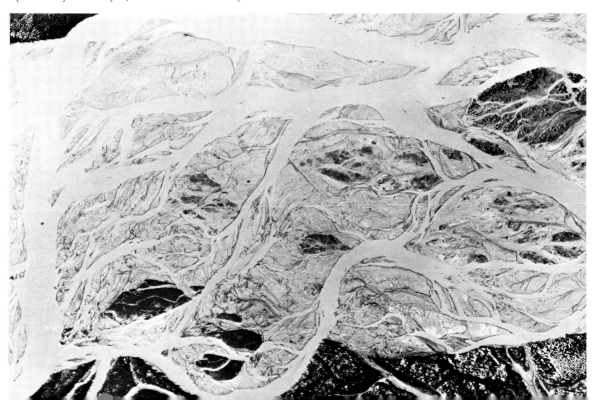

to be stopped or reversed. The presence of other loops on either side tends to limit the extent to which a meander may grow. If the loops begin to get too large they cut into each other and a cutoff occurs, the river channel straightens out its path for a short distance, and a meander loop is left isolated from the main stream (Fig. 18–8). These loops become detached from the stream when clay and silt are deposited by the main stream in the quiet waters at the entrance to the loop. Thus a loop-shaped lake, called an *oxbow lake*, is formed.

Some of the sediment removed from the outside of the curves migrates downstream and stops in the quiet waters of the inside of the next meander. Thus curved bars of sand are formed on the inside of the curves. That part of the river may be diverted and return more or less to an older path of flow inside these bar deposits. Such a course is called a *chute*.

Braided Streams

THESE ARE STREAMS that flow in two or more channels which interfinger or form interwoven patterns giving the appearance of a braid (Fig. 18–9). Coarser fractions of the load form islands in the center of the stream, which breaks up into paths around them. These streams almost always are broad and shallow. In many instances the amount of load held in the stream channel is no more than might be found in the bottom of the channel of a meandering or sinuous stream, but the channel is not cut deeply below the surface of the stream, so the load is spread out. In this respect many braided streams are no more heavily loaded than other types.

Evolution of Landscape

THE LANDSCAPE, WHICH APPEARS TO BE so permanent, is actually in constant change. Changes are slow but relentlessly brought about by weathering, mass movement, and erosion by streams, glaciers, wind, and ground water. While we cannot readily perceive the magni-

tude of changes that take place over periods of millions of years, we can recognize that landforms around us were shaped by particular agents of erosion. Moreover, in different places on earth we can recognize that these same agents have produced landforms that, when compared, appear to fall into a sequence. This concept that landforms follow a sequential development is what is meant by "evolution of the landscape." In its simplest form, we might envision the evolution if a section of the continental shelf were suddenly uplifted to an elevation of thousands of feet and subjected to erosion by weathering, mass wasting, and running water. Gradually the land would be eroded away. As long as any appreciable surface relief lasted erosion would continue to shape and reduce it. Ultimately an erosion surface should result that would be so low that erosion would be essentially stopped. We see then that throughout its history a given region will undergo gradual changes. If the structure, composition, climate, and other variables were known, these changes could be predicted. Nature is rarely so simple. Uplift of sediments deposited in ancient seas has taken place, but usually very slowly, and often at inconsistent rates. Uplift may cease altogether and then recur, interrupting the sequential development of topography. The climate of a region may undergo changes that alter the dominant processes acting to shape the land. In ice ages glaciation supplements running water as a prominent shaper of the land. Similarly, changes from arid to humid climates bring about shifts in the relative importance of different agents of erosion and deposition.

Geologists agree that the landscape does undergo change under the influence of the geomorphic agents, but there is widespread disagreement on the question of exactly how these changes come about and what landforms will result from long continued dominance of a particular set of geomorphic agents. According to the long established theory of William M. Davis, an uplifted land area will undergo a series of alterations which will produce a distinctly different set of landforms during each of several stages (known as youth, maturity, and old age) in a cycle. In other words the form of the landscape is to a large extent time-dependent. Many of those who disagree with this view subscribe to the idea that at any given time the landforms represent a result of a condition of dynamic equilibrium in which "every slope and every channel in an erosional system is adjusted to every other. When the topography is in equilibrium and erosional energy remains the same all elements of the topography are downwasting at the same rate. Differences in relief and form may be explained in terms of spatial relations rather than in terms of an evolutionary development through time. It is recognized, however, that erosional energy changes in space as well as time, and that topographic forms evolve as energy changes" (Hack, 1960).

Certain geomorphic agents dominate erosion of the surface in any particular area, but they must function within an imposed framework.

BASE LEVEL. Base level is the ultimate or temporary level toward which the land surface may be reduced, and below which the land surface cannot be reduced by subaerial agents of erosion. With this as the lower limit of effective degradation, we can deduce that the ultimate or last stage in the evolution of landforms, regardless of what combination of agents act, will be the production of a broad, low erosion surface. Further evolution of a region which has been reduced to such a surface must await uplift or igneous activity to build the area up again.

DEFORMATION. Uplift or igneous intrusions and extrusions initially bring land above sea level, where erosion may commence to sculpture and reduce it. These movements may be very slow, and they may continue over a great part of the erosional history of a region.

INTERRUPTIONS. Of particular importance is the fact that because of deformation the sequence of development of landforms may be interrupted. This interruption may be a slow or rapid upward or downward warping, or may involve folding and faulting.

STRUCTURE. The nature of the rocks exposed at the surface, their hardness, resistance to weathering and erosive processes, and their shape and distribution play an important role in determining what landforms are possible. The surface of any uplifted part of the crust has certain unique physiographic forms before the new cycle begins. Consider, for example, the initial differences in the surficial features of the continental shelf, folded mountain structures, volcanoes and lava plateaus, glaciated plains, lake beds, and deserts. Each of these will undergo at least initial differences in sequential development of landforms.

TIME. According to the theory of Davis, each stage in the evolution of the land is characterized by a particular group of landforms in harmony with the stage's place in the cycle of erosion within the limitations of structure, deformation, and base level. In the alternative view of Hack, evolution takes place mainly through changes in the erosional energy available, and this may or may not change in time, but it is not time-dependent.

Landforms in Arid and Semiarid Climates

THE NATURE AND EVOLUTION OF LANDforms in arid and semiarid climates are considered before those of humid climates for two reasons. Arid and semiarid regions cover more surface area and have far simpler landforms than do regions with humid climates. Although the origin and evolution of landforms in different climates have long been a subject of controversy, there has been general agreement by most geomorphologists that differences between landforms of humid-temperate, semiarid, and arid environments are differences primarily in degree, not in kind. This being the case, it is much easier to proceed from the simpler forms of arid climates to the more complex forms of humid environments.

Deserts

EFFECTS OF WIND EROSION are most obvious in deserts, but more important is the fact that most physiographic features of deserts are the result of mass wasting and running water—not wind erosion.

What exactly is a desert? Common fallacies are that deserts have no vegetation, that they consist mainly of drifting sand dunes, that they are always hot, and that wind is responsible for most desert landforms. Arid regions make up more than 30 per cent of the land surface of the world. They are regions characterized by scarcity of rainfall and consequently relatively thin vegetative cover. Rainfall in deserts is typically torrential; that is, it comes down rapidly in a short period of time. The entire year's rainfall may be concentrated in no more than three or four rains, but several inches of rain may fall during each of these. Long dry periods between rains exclude most common plants of humid regions, but others adapted to the small supply of rain flourish. Tropical deserts may be hot or at least warm throughout the year, but those in the middle latitudes undergo seasonal temperature changes that are very much like those of the humid regions, and are frequently more extreme. In high latitudes deserts may be cool or cold most of the year. Even in tropical deserts there is a high daily variation in temperature. Because there are fewer leafy plants, less moisture, and few clouds, heat is lost rapidly from the desert at night.

Many deserts are characterized by *internal drainage*. That is, the amount of rainfall is so small and the rate of evaporation is so great that a well-developed drainage pattern is lacking and no water flows out of the desert area. Some deserts are drained by large streams such as the Nile and the Colorado rivers, but there are few tributaries within deserts even in these instances and the rivers hardly do more than pass through, eroding as they pass. Particularly in the southwestern United States the deserts are basins that are almost entirely enclosed by mountain ranges. The result of weathering processes in deserts is production of great quantities of broken rock debris which the available water and wind are incapable of moving.

Weathered debris on the ground surface in deserts is moved by wind, mass movement, and by rain wash. Wind selects only the finest materials, mass movement is most effective where relief is great, and erosion by water is accomplished mainly through sheet floods or sheet wash. During a typical desert cloudburst, rills and sheets of water containing a very heavy load form immediately. Most of the streams flow for a brief time following a rain, but disappear soon afterward as water evaporates or soaks into the ground. Channels formed during these rains are called *washes* or *wadies*.[6]

Desert Landforms

THE MOST PROMINENT LANDFORM in deserts is plains. These are formed in a variety of ways. In the Southwest there are prominent structural plains, flat surfaces of structural origin, such as uplifted sea floors. In addition there are plains formed through erosion and deposition—playas, bajadas, pediments, and stream floodplains.[6]

PLAYAS. In deserts consisting of basins enclosed by mountain ranges, drainage is toward the center of the basin from all margins. Where these drainage lines converge we expect to find a lake. In general there is a nearly level plain that has been built up by gradual influx of sediment from the basin sides. When there is sufficient water this plain is covered by a broad shallow lake called a *playa* (Fig. 18–10). Playas usually contain water only a short time after a rainfall. Water is lost through evaporation or by being soaked into the ground. The lake becomes the site of deposition of salts precipitated from lake waters. Such salt-covered plains are called *alkali flats* or *salinas* if there is a high concentration of salts.

BAJADAS. Playas occupy positions that have been built up through successive deposition of alluvial

6 See dry stream valleys on Antelope Quadrangle at end of book.

FIG. 18–10. / *Playa lake. This view is southeastward across Harney Lake playa, Oregon. (Photo by A. M. Piper, courtesy of U.S. Geological Survey.)*

FIG. 18–11. / *The gently sloping surface in the foreground is called a bajada when it is due to deposition of sediment. Closer to the mountains, bedrock is close to the surface of the ground and the name pediment is applied. (Photo by the author.)*

material washed into the basin by sheet flooding and surface runoff. These are often deposits of coalescing alluvial fans. Surfaces of these deposits slope upward from a flat plain at the center of the basin to the surrounding mountains. These low alluvial deposits at the base of the mountains and near the center of the basin are called *bajadas* (Figs. 18–11).

PEDIMENT. Closer to the mountain the gently inclined plain that slopes up to the base of the mountains is often an erosional rather than a depositional feature. As the mountain front has retreated away from the center of the basin, solid rock that lies close to the surface has been eroded, forming a pediment (Fig. 18–12). The pediment surface may be covered by a thin veneer of debris, but this is not a permanent deposit. It is material in the process of moving from the high slopes toward the center of the basin.

Evolution of landforms in deserts is primarily related to formation and extension of pediments. A number of different processes play a part. These include lateral erosion by streams and unconcentrated sheet wash. The net effect of all of these is to bring about retreat of mountain slopes. Fault scarps are prominent along edges of some mountains in the Basin and Range province of Nevada and portions of the surrounding states. Sharp folds and downcutting of streams through rock units of varying resistance also give rise to cliffs and steep slopes. Such steep slopes may retreat parallel to the original slope. Hillsides or mountain slopes may be divided into four elements. At the top there is a broad, nearly flat, somewhat rounded surface. This passes into a cliff that has been washed clear of soil and debris. At the foot of this cliff talus slopes form. In hard, resistant rock there is a pronounced break from this rather steep slope to the low slope of the pediment, but in weak rocks there is a gradual lowering of the slope onto the pediment surface. Usually the most active of these slopes are the cliff and the talus slope. Mass wasting is most effective on them, and surface wash is most capable of moving debris across steep surfaces. Material from these steep slopes is washed out across the pediment. In arid climates movement of debris is most active from the start of rain to shortly after rain stops. Since the pediment is a smooth landform, it permits sheet wash over large parts of its area. The amount of water moving on the pediment increases downslope. Water becomes deeper, turbulent, and highly erosive. Wadies form, and gullies are cut into the pediment. Moving water is the dominant process responsible for transportation of material across the pediment.

If the steep slope becomes covered with vegetation or stops actively retreating for any other reason, then the slope above it will become smoothed off and will gradually develop a convex form where it breaks away into the steep slope. This rounded form may become so pronounced that the cliff and the talus slope appear convexly rounded at the top.

Evolution of the physiography in an arid region, once pediments are formed, consists essentially of parallel retreat of the steep face above the pediment. The slope of the pediment is maintained. If pediments occur on both sides of a mountain range they gradually converge. Eventually the range is reduced to a broad dome with slope equal to that of the pediment on either side of a crest that consists of a narrow ridge of small scattered domes. These residual hills are known as *bornhardts* (Fig. 18–13). Once bornhardts are removed from the landscape further reduction of the land is negligible.

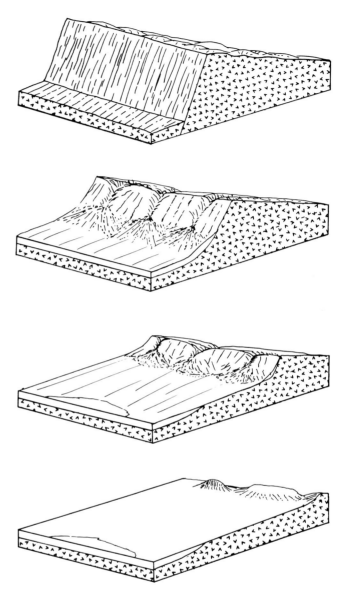

FIG. 18–12. / *This illustration depicts the evolution of an uplifted block-faulted mountain according to the concept of slope retreat.*

Evolution of Landforms in Humid Climates

THE IDEA OF LANDFORM EVOLUTION WAS first conceived by Major J. W. Powell, a one-armed Civil War veteran who headed the United States Geological Survey, studied the arid Southwest, and made the first trip through the Grand Canyon on the Colorado River. It was William Morris Davis who developed the idea. A student of his, Douglas Johnson, applied and elaborated the application of the concept to the landforms of the world. Both Davis and Johnson concentrated on the application of the concept to landforms in humid temperate climates. Other regions and different landforms were treated as deviations from the cycle of evolution in humid regions, or as climatic accidents. They visualized landscapes as passing through stages in development somewhat comparable to the stages of life—youth, maturity, and old age. Youth is a period following uplift, when erosion is active on land which has just experienced a lowering of base level. Maturity is reached as processes of erosion and deposition begin to become adjusted to the topography. Old age is reached when the topography, after millions of years of gradual reduction, begins to approach a level, nearly featureless surface. Davis and Johnson recognized that there would be interruptions in the cycle if uplift of the land lowered the regional base level at any time during the cycle. But if the cycle goes to com-

pletion—old age—then in the ideal case the cycle might be started once again by uplift, and the sequence of development would be essentially the same as in the previous cycle.

Davis' Ideal Fluvial Cycle

THE EROSION CYCLE projected by Davis commences with rather rapid uplift. Consider a cycle in which there is a minimum of complication. Let us assume at first that the following conditions are met:

The rock units are sedimentary rocks composed of sandstones, limestones, and shales that are warped up above sea level from the sea floor.

There are no complex structures such as faults, folds, or prominent angular unconformities.

There are no interruptions in the cycle.

FIG. 18–13. / *Erosional remnants in an Australian desert. These isolated masses of rock are all that remains of a formerly higher and more rugged topography. Note that the units of rock are stratified and that these strata are turned up on the end, indicating that strong deformation once affected the area.* (*Photo by courtesy of Qantas Empire Airways Ltd.*)

It is further assumed that the landscape evolves in a temperate humid climate in which erosion is accomplished mainly by running water, weathering, and mass wasting.

A number of deeply incised, narrow valleys will be formed at first. These will be widely separated and will have narrow floodplains, many rapids, and waterfalls. When streams become graded, lateral erosion begins to be more important. When a graded condition is reached, most irregularities, such as waterfalls and cascades, will have been removed from the river

FIG. 18–14. / *Stages in the erosion cycle. These photographs show areas that are in various stages of erosion. The drainage pattern in loosely consolidated sedimentary rocks in China (top) is in youth. The high mountains in China have a well developed drainage system in late youth or early maturity. The low rolling topography shown (left) is typical of late maturity; however, in this case glaciation as well as running water has contributed to the pattern. At bottom is a view of a meandering stream and features associated with old age. (Photos courtesy of the U.S. Air Force.)*

channel. Valleys are broader, there are floodplains, the drainage pattern is complex, broad upland tracks near divides are gone, and streams follow sinuous courses. At this time the landscape has become mature. Streams cut their channels lower only at a very slow rate after they become graded. Valley sides are then reduced by weathering, mass movements, particularly surface creep and wash, and lateral erosion. Gradually valley sides are reduced to lower and lower slopes. Divides between drainage basins are likewise lowered until they are almost

completely flattened. According to Davis, a low-land of faint relief remains at this time. This landform, which is the ultimate in the erosion cycle and can be worn down no farther by erosion, is called a *peneplain* ("nearly a plain") (Fig. 18–14).

Effect of Interruptions in the Cycle

As WE SAW, one of the three assumptions made in treating the idealized cycle was that there would be no interruptions in the cycle. Actually, however, interruptions do occur. It seems probable that compound or multicyclic evolution is more common than single cycles. We can recognize such a change where the topography, which is generally characterized by features of old age or maturity, contains elements of youthful landscape. This process by which the landscape begins to revert to youthful characteristics is called *rejuvenation*. It may occur in a number of ways:

Uplift: Old or mature topography may be uplifted as the crust is raised in relation to sea level.

Lowering of sea level: This changes the relative position of the base level just as effectively as lifting the land surface. Stream profiles are steepened, especially at the mouth, and channels are cut down toward the new level.

Changes in hydraulic factors: If load supplied to a stream decreases, or if discharge increases, the channel may be cut deeper.

Landforms Resulting from Rejuvenation

TWO LANDFORMS in particular are characteristic of rejuvenated landscapes. These are entrenched stream channels[7] and river terraces.[8] Entrenched meandering streams are commonly found in the Appalachian Mountains. In this region the streams follow broad meandering

patterns which in some places almost form cutoffs, but there are no floodplains. Valley sides rise steeply from banks on one or both sides of the stream. It appears that these streams were once meandering on a broad, flat floodplain and that this was interrupted by a regional uplift with consequent downcutting of the stream. Once downcutting started, lateral erosion became minor, and the stream was unable to straighten out its path before it became entrenched.

TERRACES. A common characteristic of topography in regions of geologically recent uplift is stream terraces (Fig. 18–16).[9] Such terraces may be clearly demarked in the topography or they may be so obscure that detailed profiles across the valley are needed to reveal their presence. Such terraces commonly appear on both sides of the river valley and at the same level. These are *paired terraces,* and are simply explained as resulting from entrenchment of a stream into its own floodplain. Multiple paired terraces signify repeated periods of entrenchment separated by periods of stability during which the stream eroded laterally. When terraces do not occur at the same level on opposite sides of the river, it appears most likely that entrenchment was a more or less continuous process. *Unpaired terraces* result if a river continues to cut downward as well as laterally as it migrates from one side of its floodplain to the other.

Effects of Deformed Strata: Shifting Divides

CONSIDER NOW WHAT HAPPENS if there is a sequence of folded and faulted sedimentary rocks of varying hardness buried beneath flat-lying sediments. If this segment of the crust is uplifted, water initially flows from it as a consequence of the slopes. Deep V-shaped valleys are cut (Fig. 18–4). Divides are broad and flat, and at first drainage is poorly developed. But as the streams cut down into the sediment they begin to encounter the deformed rocks with their different resistances to erosion. The sedi-

[7] See entrenched stream on Mammoth Cave Quadrangle at end of book.
[8] See Voltaire Quadrangle at end of book.

[9] See Voltaire Quadrangle.

FIG. 18–15. / *Water gap of San Rafael River on east side of the San Rafael swell, Emery County, Utah. (Photo by courtesy of U.S. Dept. of Agriculture.)*

FIG. 18–16. / *Succession of alluvial terraces of the River Findhorn cut out of glacial deposits, marking stages in the lowering of the Findhorn Valley. (Crown Copyright.)*

FIG. 18–17. / *Schematic cross section of an anticlinal valley.*

FIG. 18–18. / *Schematic cross section of a synclinal mountain.*

ment veneer is soon stripped from the surface because it is easily eroded. Positions of main stream channels remain fixed if they have established channels in consolidated rocks before the surface covering of sediment is removed. If this has happened, they will cut their channels across rocks of varying resistance. Thus they may flow across structures of the deformed rocks.

Tributaries to the main streams tend to assume positions on less resistant rocks, along fault zones or other lines of weakness. Weathering is most effective on less resistant units, and these are lowered much more rapidly than harder units. Streams may be established in weaker units regardless of their position on the structures. If weak rock units are exposed along the crest of an anticline (Fig. 18–17), the crest will be lowered, and an *anticlinal valley* will be formed. If the resistant units are exposed in the center of a syncline, a *synclinal mountain* may form (Fig. 18–18).

LAW OF EQUAL SLOPES. Further development depends largely on angles of slope of the ridges and valleys and on the gradient of the stream. Where a resistant rock unit is exposed there is generally a difference in slope of the two sides. The steeper slope will be cut back more rapidly than the low slope, and the divide between the drainage on the two sides of the ridge will shift in the direction of the lower slope. This is the *law of unequal slopes*.[10]

Classical Fluvial Cycle Applied to the Appalachians

THE FLUVIAL CYCLE WAS FORMULATED largely as a result of studies in the humid regions

[10] See Maverick Spring Quadrangle at end of book.

of the eastern United States and especially to account for the landforms of the Appalachian Mountains. In this region a distinctive topography exists. Particulary in the central Appalachians (Pennsylvania–northern Virginia) there is a general concordance of the elevations of the crests of the Blue Ridge and the ridges of the Allegheny Mountains to the west. So striking is this concordance that it appears likely to many students of geomorphology that this region was once a vast, nearly flat surface, a surface known as the Schooley Peneplain. If it was a peneplain, it should have formed near the ultimate base level, sea level, according to Davis. To explain the present elevation and the formation of the valleys between the ridges it is necessary to postulate regional uplift. As a result of this uplift the streams cut down (into the less resistant rock units) creating a second partial peneplain known as the Harrisburg Peneplain. A second uplift in the region caused a repetition of this, and a third partial peneplain, the Somerville Peneplain, was formed. Before this surface could be much enlarged another uplift occurred, and the present streams are entrenched and downcutting. Thus repeated uplifts were needed to explain the various concordant levels recognized in the topography. To explain the fact that the Schooley surface is not flat over the region as a whole, unevenness in amount of uplift is postulated. Thus the region of the Smoky Mountains was uplifted higher than the region to the north. Some isolated peaks are described as being remnants that stood above the peneplain even when it was near base level.

Most of the streams in the Appalachians are subsequent and follow courses parallel to the folded ridges, which are usually capped by sandstone and quartzite, but the major streams north of the James River in central Virginia flow perpendicular to the ridges through water gaps in the ridges to the Atlantic. To explain this anomaly it has been postulated that the sea advanced across the Schooley Peneplain and a blanket-like deposit was laid down over the region. When uplift first took place the streams were consequent and flowed approximately in the direction of the modern major streams. It is further postulated that the tributaries to these became subsequent as downcutting into a folded sequence of rocks of variable resistance took place.

This theory also offered a ready explanation for the modern entrenched streams, some of which flow in meandering patterns. They were streams that were flowing on a partial peneplain before the last regional uplift. The value of a theory is based on its usefulness in explaining a complex of interrelated observations; and this theory of Davis's is a good theory according to this criterion. Yet alternatives to the theory are being proposed and a growing number of geologists are giving up this theory in favor of a more modern approach. Before turning to the modern theory of dynamic equilibrium let us examine some of the weaknesses of Davis's theory.

Objections to the Humid Cycle Evolutionary Concept

THE CONCEPT OF THE PENEPLAIN IS THE most frequently challenged idea involved in the evolutionary concept. (Hack, 1960.) The Schooley Peneplain in the Appalachians bears no remnants of the sediment that was postulated as having covered that peneplain, although sediments of this age lie in the Coastal Plain area. Thus there is no proof that this surface has ever been nearer to sea level than it is now since the mountains were initially uplifted.

A second major argument is based on estimates of the current rate of degradation of the continents which indicates that only 10 to 20 million years would be required to level the con-

tinents. (Over 200 million years have elapsed since the Appalachian Mountains were folded into a high mountain system.) In view of this estimated time it is reasonable to ask why there are no modern peneplains—nearly flat surfaces near sea level where streams meander across rocks of complex structure. Many of the areas which have topographic features of old age are depositional surfaces which have never had high relief, as in the case of the Mississippi River on the Coastal Plain between Cairo, Illinois, and New Orleans.

A third argument involves the concept of the graded stream. According to Davis, streams become graded just at the start of maturity. At this point the streams cease to cut down and begin lateral planation. Opponents of the erosion cycle question whether streams begin lateral planation at any particular stage or as a result of reduction in slope of the channel. It may even be that streams increase in capacity to remove material from their drainage basin as gradation proceeds. Still another argument is found in studies of the hydraulic factors along modern streams. These studies reveal that the interrelationships between these factors and sediment load are just as consistent in graded as ungraded streams. It is also found that, contrary to Davis's theory, the capacity of a large stream on a low slope may be greater than the same streams' upper tributaries where they flow on steep slopes.

Concept of Dynamic Equilibrium in Landscape Development

"AN ALTERNATIVE APPROACH TO LANDSCAPE interpretation is through the application of the principle of dynamic equilibrium to spatial relations within the drainage system. It is assumed that within a single erosional system all elements of the topography are mutually adjusted so that they are downwasting at the same rate. The forms and processes are in a steady state of balance and may be considered as time independent." According to this theory (see John

Hack, 1960, Am. Jour. Sci., v. 258-A), streams achieve a graded condition almost immediately and maintain a graded condition during the period of degradation, or until some change in the drainage system occurs. The particular landforms found in a drainage system are related primarily to the geology of the basin—such features as structure and variable rock resistance to erosion being particularly important. In the Appalachians, for example, the ridges that make up the Schooley surface are almost all of similar composition and structure. Many of the water gaps are located at structural zones of weakness in the ridges, places where headward erosion through the ridge would be facilitated, allowing stream capture of drainage in the Valley and Ridge Province.

On the basis of the dynamic equilibrium theory, waterfalls or rapids would be characteristics resulting from the resistance of the underlying rock to erosion while streams on weak rocks might have low slopes. One of the particular advantages of this theory is that it offers an explanation for the observed unusual mixtures of topographic features which would belong to different stages of Davis's erosional cycle, thus avoiding the need for periodic uplifts necessary to explain the various levels or peneplains found in mountain systems.

The dynamic equilibrium theory does not abandon the idea of evolution in landscape development entirely. There would be rapid evolution following certain types of changes, such as diastrophism or changes due to nature and quantity of stream load such as might be brought about by change in climate or through exposure of a weak rock unit as a result of removal of an overlying resistant unit.

As an example of an erosionally graded or equilibrium topography Hack uses several features of the Appalachian region as follows:

. . . in a landscape like that of the Appalachian region in which large areas are mutually adjusted, the diversity of form is largely the result of differential erosion of rocks that yield to weathering in different ways. Such topography may be referred to as erosionally graded.

Many of the erosionally graded landscapes in humid temperate regions belong to the almost ubiquitous type that is commonly known as the "maturely dissected peneplain." Preferring a term that has no genetic connotation, a more descriptive one such as "ridge and ravine topography" is suggested. This term refers to the monotonous network of branching valleys and intervening low ridges that make up the landscape of large areas. This topography may be concisely explained in terms of dynamic equilibrium. . . . The important elements of the topography could be divided into two domains. The first [is] a domain of stream sculpture represented by channels in which the slopes are concave upward, because the transporting power of a stream per unit of volume increases with the volume; the transporting power also increases with the slope; and a stream automatically adjusts slope to volume in such a way as to equalize its work of transportation in different parts. The other domain is that of creep, represented by the slopes between the channels. In this domain slopes are mostly convex.

The forms of well-graded ridge and ravine landscapes vary within wide limits. The regularity of the landscape and the rather uniform height of the hills owe their origin to the regularity of the drainage pattern that has developed over long periods, by the erosion of rocks of uniform texture and structure.

Differences in form from one area to another, including the relief, form of the stream profile, valley cross sections, width of floodplain, shape of hilltops, and other form elements are explainable in terms of differences in the bedrock and the manner in which it breaks up into different components as it is handled on the slopes and in the streams.

FIG. 18–19. / Evolution of an uplifted block-faulted mountain according to the concept of slope reduction as visualized by Johnson. (After H. M. Davis.)

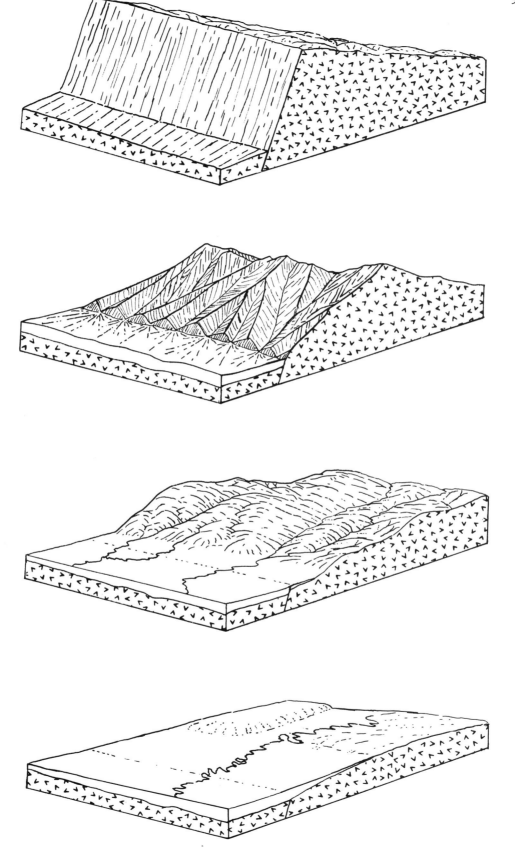

19 /

Glaciation

THE PRESENT IS AN AGE OF GLACIATION. GLA-ciers occupy valleys of many mountains in all parts of the world. A thick sheet of ice almost covers one entire continent, Antarctica, and others cover a large part of Greenland, Iceland, and islands in the Arctic Ocean (Fig. 19–1). If we could not actually walk across these glaciers, watch them in action, and see deposits forming at their margins, it is doubtful that we would ever believe that the semiconsolidated sand, silt, and morainal deposits that cover the northern United States and northern Europe had been left there by an advancing sheet of ice. We probably would not consider accumulation of such large bodies of ice a condition that might normally be expected on the face of the earth. For many years glacial deposits that are so prominent in northern Europe were thought to be debris dropped during the Flood in the time of Noah.

Glaciation has not played a very important role in formation of deposits or in shaping the face of the continents of past ages. Only four periods of glaciation are known. Thus the present is an unusual time in this respect. Although glaciers have not always been prominent factors in shaping the landscapes in the past, they have been extremely important in producing the present configuration. In fact, most of the present topography of the world has formed within the past few million years, and for the past million years ice has been present in large quantities at the poles and in mountains all over the world.

Formation of Glaciers

WITHIN THE LAST MILLION YEARS A SHEET of ice covered most of Canada. It extended southward into the United States, where its terminus is marked by ridges of debris called *moraines*. These moraines form a ridge on Long Island, cross Staten Island into New Jersey, and can be traced across Pennsylvania to the Ohio River. The southern margin of the ice cap is marked approximately by the position of the Ohio and Missouri rivers. Today there is no sign of an ice cap in Canada. This causes us to wonder in what way conditions differed when ice did cover such extensive areas, and if there is any chance that glaciers might return. We do not have a definite answer to the second question, but it appears that the only condition

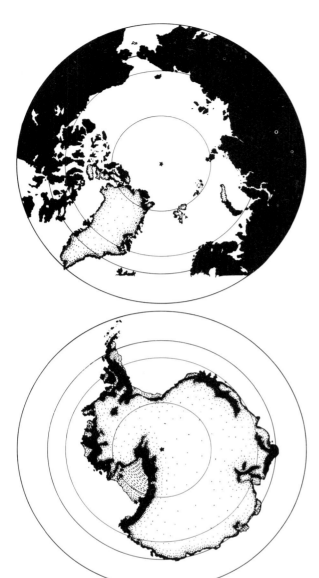

FIG. 19–1. / *The North and South Polar regions, sites of modern ice sheets of continental extent.*

necessary for the growth and expansion of glaciation is that the amount of accumulation of snow and ice must exceed the amount of ice wastage through melting and sublimation for an extended period of time. Growth of glaciers is accelerated by increased precipitation in the form of snow and sleet, and temperature low enough for the ice to be preserved throughout the year. Extreme temperatures of the Antarctic, which average —60° Fahrenheit, are certainly not necessary for formation and growth of continental glaciers. In fact, glaciers are most likely to grow when temperatures are only slightly below freezing, because the air at that temperature can hold much more moisture than can air at extremely low temperatures. If the average annual temperatures over the face of the earth dropped 5° to 10° F., it would almost certainly bring about formation of large masses of ice on the continents. These would form first in high mountains, where temperatures are now nearly low enough to promote large-scale mountain glaciation. Accumulation occurs where snow is permanent throughout the year. The lower limit of this area of perennial snow is called the *snow line.*

Snow is the crystalline form of water and consequently is a mineral. Snowflakes display an almost infinite variety of delicate and beautiful hexagonal patterns (Fig. 19–2). If the temperatures remain below freezing after the snowfall, individual flakes recrystallize. The extremities of the delicate patterns dissolve and the water moves toward the centers of the flakes until all the ice is crystallized in small balls called *firn* or *névé.* Newly formed firn is usually covered by more snows. As more snow is added, pressure of the overlying snow and firn compacts the ice grains together at depth. If the snow is lying on an uneven surface, and this is usually the case in mountains, the rounded grains of firn will rotate and move downslope under the weight of the overlying firn and snow. Once the thickness

FIG. 19–2. / *Enlargement of a snowflake. (Courtesy of U.S. Weather Bureau.)*

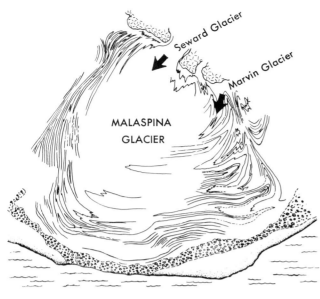

of overlying snow and firn reaches about 200 feet, the weight is so great that the firn compacts into a solid mass of ice. Grains become part of this mass of ice when they are so oriented that one grain fuses into another, becoming a single crystalline mass. In this fashion large crystals grow. Movements of the ice layers are largely accomplished by slippage between layers of atoms making up the ice. Zones of shearing within ice are sometimes visible as blue streaks. The net effect of these small slippages is like plastic flowage (Fig. 19–3).

Types of Glaciers

GLACIERS MAY BE DIVIDED INTO TWO MAIN groups: *valley glaciers* and *continental glaciers* (Figs. 19–4 and 19–5). The main difference between them is that valley glaciers are confined to mountains, and continental glaciers spread out over continents, burying whole mountain ranges. *Ice caps* are glaciers flowing in all directions from a center; although they are one type of continental glacier, they are not usually called continental glaciers unless they cover great areas. The prime mover in all glaciation is the force of gravity. Like valley glaciers, con-

FIG. 19–3a. / *Malaspina Glacier, Alaska. The map view shows folds which have developed in the ice as it flowed. Note the position of Seward and Marvin Glaciers which feed into Malaspina Glacier. (After a diagram by R. P. Sharp, G.S.A. Bull., v. 69, No. 6, 1958.)*

FIG. 19–4. / *Sketch of some of the important features, such as moraines, kettles, outwashes, and eskers, formed by erosion and deposition by continental glaciers.*

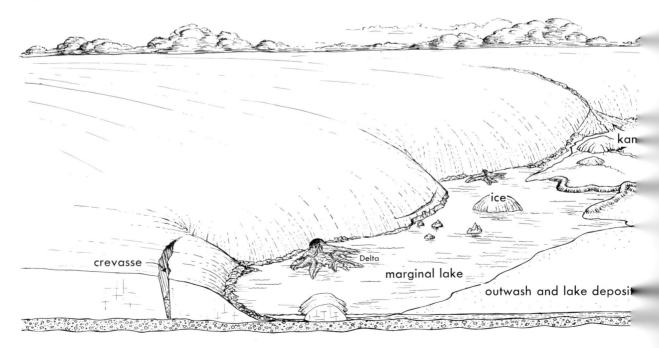

crevasse

Delta

marginal lake

outwash and lake deposit

ice

kam

tinental ice sheets move downslope, but if their volume is sufficient they also flow over extensive flat regions and even over high irregularities in the same way as a stream flows over boulders. In part this is accomplished through the push exerted on the front of the lobe of ice by ice moving downslope behind it, but for a sheet covering an area the size of Canada this is hardly a sufficient explanation. A plastic will deform continuously once a certain threshold value of stress is applied to it. The ice sheets that covered Canada accumulated to a very great thickness, probably comparable to that in the Antarctic, 10,000 feet in places (Fig. 19–6). Once the thickness became great enough, pressure on lower layers from the weight of the overlying mass caused plastic flowage near the bottom of the ice sheet. Thus the sheets slowly spread out over irregularities.

FIG. 19–3b. / Air view of Malaspina Glacier. The dark streaks are debris covering the ice and enfolded in it. (Photo by courtesy of the U.S. Air Force.)

Rate of Movement

MANY EXISTING VALLEY GLACIERS ARE moving at slow but measurable rates. The motion of a large number of glaciers has been studied. One early technique was to drive a series of stakes across the surface of the valley

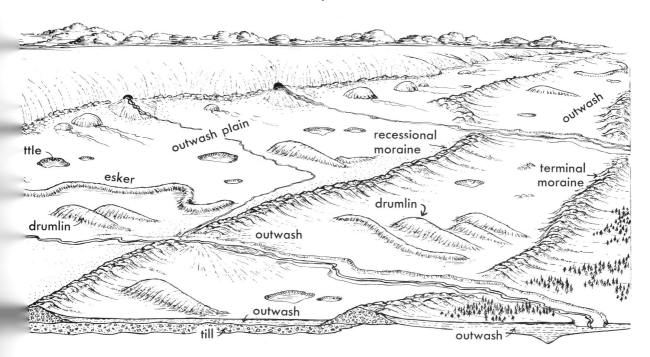

ttle

esker

drumlin

outwash plain

outwash

outwash

till

recessional moraine

drumlin

outwash

terminal moraine

outwash

outwash

FIG. 19–6. / *Equal-area polar projection, showing regions of continental glaciation during the late Pleistocene. (From Donn, Farrand, and Ewing, 1961.)*

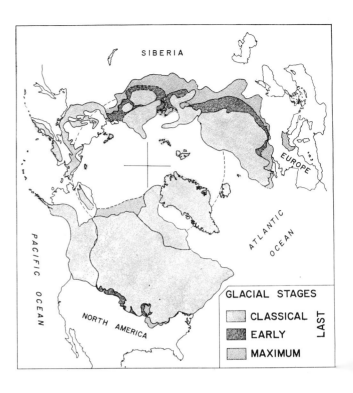

glacier in a straight line and come back periodically to observe the position of these stakes. The distribution of movement is similar to that in a stream. Frictional drag along the contact between ice and the earth at the sides and the bottom retards movement there. The center moves along much more rapidly. Probably the maximum velocity of a glacier is near the surface instead of a third of the way down, as in streams, because frictional drag of air on ice is negligible, whereas that on water is significant. Some glaciers move so slowly that trees and other plants grow in the debris on top of them; others move at rates as high as tens of feet or, in exceptional cases, 100 feet per day. That the margins of continental glaciers are in motion

is shown by the continual spalling off of masses of ice where the sheet extends into the seas. This process is called *calving*. The big blocks of ice broken off in this way form *icebergs* (Fig. 19–7).

Erosion by Glaciers

THE NATURES OF EROSION BY CONTINENTAL ice sheets and by valley glaciers are similar, but the two types of erosion are not equally effective. The glaciers differ greatly in thickness and extent.

SCRAPING AND PUSHING. The front edges of glaciers function somewhat like a bulldozer, pushing and scraping the ground in front of them. This is particularly effective in removing soil and semiconsolidated sediments. It is a truly abrasive action. The term *rasping* is often used to describe the scraping or abrasion on the sides and valley floor accomplished by rocks frozen in the bottom of the ice sheet. The results are much like that produced by a rasp—bare rock surfaces are scraped and scoured, leaving long grooves, striations, and polished surfaces as evidence of the abrasion.

MASS WASTING. Mass wasting plays an important role in glacial erosion. Along the margins of a valley glacier the valley sides are scraped and blocks broken off are frozen into the ice and carried away. This leads to undercutting of the sides of the valley. Once a side is undercut the probability of mass wasting is greatly increased. Slumping, sliding, and debris avalanches bring great quantities of debris onto the top surface of the glacier.

FIG. 19–5. / *Sketch of some of the important physiographic features which result from erosion and deposition.*

PLUCKING (QUARRYING). During summer months the surface of a glacier may partially melt, or rain may occasionally fall on the glacier. Meltwater or rain seeps down along the sides of the ice mass into cracks and fractures in rocks along edges and at the head of the glacier. When temperatures drop this water freezes and breaks up the rock by frost action. Broken blocks may be gradually forced out from the walls as successive wedges of ice form behind them, or ice in cracks may become frozen to the glacier. When the glacier moves these blocks are pulled along and frozen in suspension in the ice. Open cracks do not usually form in the sides of a glacier, but at the head, where it breaks away from the snow field, a large crack is frequently formed, refilled with ice and snow, and then pulled open again. This break is called the *bergschrund*. It forms between the glacier and the valley walls at its head. It is within the bergschrund that plucking of rocks from the walls goes on most rapidly. Through this plucking process glaciers erode in a headward direction toward the divide (Fig. 19–8).

Methods of Transportation

A LARGE PART of the load of valley glaciers is carried on the surface, where it is dumped by mass wasting stepped up by the increased frost action during glaciation. Large quantities of talus fall on the margins of the valley glaciers. Much of this load is carried frozen within the ice. Some of the debris may remain in the ice all the way from the cirque to the terminus of the glacier, where it melts out. Larger blocks slowly work their way down into the ice toward the bottom. Eventually this leads to accumulation of a heavy load near the bottom of the ice mass. This part of the load is responsible for the rasping and abrasive action of the glacier.

The remainder of the load is pushed along in front of the ice mass or retained in the body of the glacier.

Continental glaciers carry very little surface load because once the sheet has become thick enough to flow over flat areas its top surface is usually above all but the highest mountain peaks, so mass wasting is not responsible for supplying much debris to it. For this reason valley glaciers carry a much greater load per unit volume of ice than do ice caps or sheets, since almost all their load is carried frozen into the bottom of the sheet or pushed along in front.

Features Produced by Erosion

MANY SMALL-SCALE erosional features are common to continental and valley glaciers. Striations, grooves, and polished surfaces are found both on the bare rock over which the ice moved and on the rocks carried in the bottom of the ice. They are known as *scour features*.

Large-scale erosional features produced by continental glaciers are not nearly as distinctive as those produced by valley glaciers. In general the continental ice sheet tends to streamline pre-existing topography, removing irregularities like peaks and sharp ridges (Fig. 19–9). The effect is to repress any landforms that might stand out (Fig. 19–10). One of the streamlined features shaped by continental sheets is the *drumlin* (Fig. 19–11). Drumlins are streamlined hills shaped somewhat like the back of a whale, with the steeper slope facing the direction from which the ice moved. They are composed of glacial till—unconsolidated earth materials in a great variety of sizes and compositions, which has been shaped by movement of the glacier over the till. They are products of combined erosion and deposition.

FIG. 19–8. / *High oblique view of the Beartooth Mountains, Montana. Note the plateau surface, 11,000 feet high. This ancient, nearly flat erosion surface has been dissected by glaciers, but now mass movement is one of the main processes tending to change its appearance. High piles of talus may be seen on the sides of the valleys. These converge at the bottom of the valleys to form rock glaciers which slowly move downhill under the pull of gravity. The tops of the plateaus are strewn with frost-heaved boulders. (Photo by courtesy of the U.S. Air Force.)*

FIG. 19–7. / *Icebergs calving from the margin of a continental glacier. Notice how these are breaking out along a set of perpendicular fractures. This is in the Antarctic. (Photo by courtesy of the U.S. Navy.)*

FIG. 19–9. / Rock basin formed by glacier action. Note the streamlined suppressed topography. (Crown Copyright.)

FIG. 19–10. / Air photograph showing a surface of Precambrian crystalline rocks eroded by continental glaciation in Canada. (Courtesy of the Royal Canadian Air Force.)

FIG. 19–11. / The island in the foreground is a drumlin. (Courtesy of the Royal Canadian Air Force.)

Erosional Features of Valley Glaciers[1]

CIRQUES. The heads of most glaciers occupy hollowed out amphitheater-shaped features called cirques (Fig. 19–5). The cirque is the site of glacial quarrying, or plucking, where the bergschrund is formed as the glacier pulls away to start its movement down the valley. Walls of cirques produced by this quarrying action become precipitous and may drop almost vertically as much as 1,000 feet before they curve out into the floor of the valley. Cirques usually form at the head of the glacier near former

drainage divides of streams that predated the glaciers, but they can develop on the valley sides where no stream valleys preceded them. The bottom of the cirque is often so gouged out that it is lower than the bottom of the valley. After the glacier melts, a small lake, called a *tarn*, usually occupies this depression (Fig. 19–12).

The natural course for a glacier to follow is the old drainage pattern through the mountains. Thus glaciers begin by following the line of

[1] Many of the following features are shown on the Holden Quadrangle at end of book.

least resistance, but the flow and erosion methods of streams and glaciers are so different that stream valleys are not suited for optimum movement of glaciers. Where ice is forced around sharp curves, mountain spurs that extend out toward the major valley between stream tributaries are rapidly cut back. These features are called *truncated spurs*. Ice streamlines the valley, cutting off or smoothing out curves and removing obstacles. It cuts out a U-shaped valley instead of the V-shaped valley characteristic of mountain streams (Fig. 19–13).

Valleys of tributary streams also become sites of glaciers, but like the streams which preceded them these tributary valley glaciers are smaller than the major glacier, accomplish erosion at a slower rate, and do not cut their valleys as deeply as that of the glacier to which they are tributaries. If the glaciers recede, valleys of the tributary glaciers are exposed. They open into the larger valley high up on its sides and are called *hanging valleys* (Fig. 19–14). Waterfalls or cataracts develop where renewed streams flow out of the hanging valley into the larger valley.

FJORDS. These features, which characterize the coast of Norway, are formed where a glacier flows from the mountains into the sea (Fig. 19–15). The glacier ice is able to carve its valley below sea level before the ice is melted in the sea water or breaks away to form icebergs. Thus the U-shaped valley may continue right out into the sea. Today these large valleys are partially filled with sea water. This is partly due to rises in sea level since the last major glacial advance.

ARÊTES. Arêtes are sharp ridges produced by glacial erosion (Fig. 19–5). Rugged ridges form along the crest of a mountain range, between two mountains, and between mountain spurs that separate cirques. Plucking, quarrying, and rasping cause the cirques to cut into the walls behind them. Eventually they may come so close together that an arête is produced.

COLS. A col is a pass formed where two cirques converge, cutting into the same wall and thus lowering it below the level of the remainder of the summit area (Fig. 19–5).

HORNS. Horns are sharp peaks formed by glacial erosion (Fig. 19–16). The Matterhorn is a classic example. Horns are formed during a late stage in glaciation after the summit of the preglacial mountains has been reduced to a few isolated peaks. If there is more than one they are often aligned, since they are remnants of a long arête.

Deposition[2]

GLACIERS CARRY AS GREAT AN ASSORTMENT of rock types as streams. Deposition takes place when the ice melts. Thus deposition from ice occurs most rapidly at its terminus, where meltwater carries the smaller particles of the load out beyond the ice. The terminus may slowly move forward as melting occurs. It may remain in one position with the amount of melting and sublimation just equal to the amount of ice moving to the end of the glacier, or melting may exceed the rate of movement, in which case the terminus of the glacier recedes. Glacial deposits are of two types, stratified drift and till.

Till

UNSTRATIFIED, UNSORTED glacial debris, dropped more or less in a random fashion, is called *till*, a term also applied to moraines pushed up in front of the ice and to those left on the ground after the glacier melts. Till is characterized by its variability. It is probably more variable than any other sediment or rock known by a single name. Its constituents range in size from clay particles to boulders. It may be compact, loose, or firmly cemented into a hard rock. It rarely has any apparent fabric or orienta-

[2] Glacial deposits over a portion of the central United States are shown in the map at end of book.

tion of particles, although careful study may reveal alignment of elongated cobbles. Larger fragments of till are often striated or polished.

Glaciofluvial Deposits (Stratified Drift)

THESE ARE DEPOSITS laid down under and beyond the glacier by meltwaters. *Stratified drift* and till both differ from other sediments in that particles of which they are composed are fresh; that is, they consist of fragments and particles of rock that have been broken down by disintegration, not decomposition. Such minerals

as hornblende, feldspar, and other easily decomposed minerals are present. Except for their composition, glaciofluvial deposits have the same characteristics as other water-deposited sediments. They are stratified, sorted, and may have cross-bedding or other primary sedimentary structures. A milky-colored water often issues from streams flowing out of glaciers. The material in this water, a product of abrasion, is called *"rock flour"* and is deposited beyond the end of the glacier. This may be the source of surficial windblown deposits, called *loess*, that cover the central part of the Mississippi Valley (Fig. 21–5).

FIG. 19–12. / *Glacial lakes formed in a valley cut in the high plateau of the Beartooth Mountains, Montana. (Photo by the author.)*

Landforms of Glacial Deposits

TERMINAL MORAINES.[3] Terminal moraines are formed along the line of a glacier's furthest advance by debris pushed ahead of it, supplemented by debris continually melting out of the glacier while it remains in one location. Meltwaters flow over the terminal moraine while the glacier is close to it, but when the glacier begins to retreat the great quantity of meltwater usually forms a lake, tops the dam made by the moraine, and drains out, carrying finer debris which is laid down in glaciofluvial deposits out beyond the terminus.

[3] A portion of the moraine of the last continental ice sheet in the U. S. is shown on the Kingston Quadrangle at end of book.

RECESSIONAL MORAINES. As the margins of glaciers retreat load is dropped. If the end margin remains in one position for any period of time, a ridgelike mass of till accumulates from the debris dropped by the glacier. The formation of these ridges is similar to that of the terminal moraine—they differ only in position. Moraines may be destroyed if the glacier readvances, in which case they are simply redeposited in a new position or on the terminal moraine.

GROUND MORAINES. This name is applied to the material carried at the base of a glacier and later deposited. These moraines have low relief and consist of till.

FIG. 19–13. / *The Sierra Nevada Mountains, California. The large valley in the center is a glaciated valley. (Photo by U.S. Geological Survey.)*

FIG. 19–14. / *Hanging valley, Glen Lyon, Perthshire. (Crown Copyright.)*

FIG. 19–15. / *Tongues of ice descending from an ice-cap into a large U-shaped valley at the head of a fiord. (Courtesy of the U.S. Air Force.)*

LATERAL MORAINES. In valley glaciers a large amount of the load may be carried along the margins on the surface of the glacier. This debris sometimes forms very noticeable ridges on the surface of the ice. When the ice melts it is laid down along the edge of the valley in ridgelike lateral moraines. Like other moraines, these are composed of till.

MEDIAL MORAINES. Where a tributary glacier enters a larger glacier, ice from the tributary is squeezed in downslope along the side on which it enters. If the tributary has debris piled on top of the ice near the sides (such as that forming lateral moraines), after confluence the large glacier has two ridges of debris from the tributary glacier. As the glacier flows these two loads are brought together and deflected toward the center of the glacier. A glacier may have many tributaries and many medial ridges. Once the glacier melts, these may appear as long ridges of till more or less paralleling the lateral moraines, but in the middle of the valley.

ESKERS. Both continental and valley glaciers may partially melt during summer. Water flows on the surface of the ice or seeps down along the margins or even moves through holes in the ice. Some of it accumulates beneath the glacier and forms a stream beneath the ice. This stream may be quite different from ordinary streams, however, in that its banks are composed of ice. All types of material in the transported load of the glacier may get into the stream. The small fractions of the load are carried easily downstream, but the coarser boulders and blocks are not. After the glacier melts a sinuous ridge of this debris may remain, marking the former stream channel; this ridge is called an esker. Eskers also form where the stream cuts into weak rock beneath the glacier and leaves deposits of the coarser part of its load. After the glacier melts the weak rock on either side of the stream deposits may be eroded more easily than the material of the esker, leaving the esker etched out (Fig. 19–17).

KAMES. Glaciofluvial deposits formed by sediments washed into depressions on the top surface of a glacier by surficial meltwaters are known as kames. As the ice melts, the material that formerly filled depressions on top of the glacier is dropped and makes small hills. Streams also flow along margins of valley glaciers or along troughlike depressions in continental ice sheets, and meltwaters also concentrate debris in these channels. If the water cannot carry the entire load, part is dropped. Terraces, called *kame terraces,* are built in this way along the sides of the valley.

OUTWASH PLAINS. When a glacier first begins to melt there is a great deal more debris to be carried than the meltwater is capable of transporting. This is deposited as broad flat alluvial fans or, in the case of continental ice sheets, as a series of coalescing alluvial fans called the *outwash plain* (Fig. 19–18). Here rock flour is dropped along with most of the silt, sand, and clay carried from the glacier. Because the streams are overloaded, and because they are shifted by often-changing conditions, braided stream patterns characterize the outwash plain streams. Later, if the rate of melting begins to increase, the streams may establish more permanent channels through which large amounts of the debris are moved on beyond the immediate region of the glacier.

ERRATICS. The name *erratic* is applied to any rock that is carried by a glacier and laid down on a different type of rock. The size of some of these is astonishing. One that rests on the north shore of Long Island is as large as a one-story house.

FIG. 19–16. / *The Matterhorn, the classic example of a horn. Isolated peaks such as this give us an idea of how high the surrounding country was before erosion cut it down. (Photo by courtesy of Trans World Airlines, Inc.)*

FIG. 19–17. / *An esker in northern Canada. (Courtesy of Royal Canadian Air Force.)*

FIG. 19–18. / *Pitted outwash plain. The depressions are kettles. (Photo by courtesy of the Royal Canadian Air Force.)*

Ground Water

THOSE OF US WHO HAVE SPENT MOST OF our lives in areas of abundant rainfall rarely think of fresh water as a valuable natural resource. At a time when industrial demands for water are so great, when populations are increasing, and when there is more pollution of fresh water than ever before, we should be more aware of the value of this resource, take steps to determine the extent of our holdings, and make careful plans for its future use and conservation. A few cities in the United States have already experienced periods of short water supply, and we may expect more widespread shortages in the future.

That water is stored in the soil and rocks of the outer crust of the earth is apparent from springs that issue from valley sides, from geysers, and from wells that produce most of our drinking water. So common is the experience of seeing water come out of the ground that we are lulled into a feeling that water supplies are inexhaustible. However, this feeling is not shared by informed people in regions of perennial overdraft.

Origin of Ground Water

THE WATER CONTAINED IN THE GROUND, which man uses for drinking, for irrigation, and for industrial purposes, entered the earth from one of three sources.

Rainwater (*meteoric water*) includes rain, sleet, snow, hail, and other forms of precipitation. A total of about 26,000 cubic miles of water falls on the continents each year, fills the soil and rocks, and provides most surface runoff. It is the most important source of water used by man.

Connate water is marine or fresh water trapped in sediments when they are deposited on lake or sea bottoms. Since most sediments originate in marine water, connate water is usually salty. This is the source of much water found deeper in sedimentary units in the crust. Connate water is often in rock units with oil. Oil floats on it and rises upward until it is trapped.

Juvenile water (*magmatic water*) is water produced by volcanoes and magmatic activity. It is hard to determine how much of this water is coming to the surface of the earth at present. Many volcanoes are located under water, and

FIG. 20–1. / *Highly magnified view of sandstone showing intergranular pore spaces. Sandstone such as this might have a porosity of 15–20 per cent. (Washington & Lee Univ. collection.)*

many more are found around the margins of the oceans. More than 90 per cent of all material coming out of volcanoes is steam, but we do not know how much of this is water that has been supplied to the volcano from the surface. It may be that a large part of the water gets into volcanic vents from the ground or oceans.

Water Storage Underground

WATER GETTING INTO THE CRUST MAY BE stored in a variety of ways. Many people think that in order to strike underground water you must find a buried river or lake. There are some underground streams, but they are small in size and few in number. Most water is stored in intergranular pore spaces (Fig. 20–1), solution pores and cavities (Fig. 20–2), and fractures and faults.

The volume of pore spaces in a rock is called the *porosity* of the rock, usually expressed as a percentage of the total volume. Some pore spaces are formed at the time of deposition, particularly in sedimentary rocks. Others are induced at a later date by weathering or deformation. How much porosity a granular rock has depends on shape, packing, size, and degree of sorting of its components.

Sorting and size. It might seem likely that a boulder conglomerate would be more porous than a sandstone, but the reverse is usually true. Large particles are likely to have smaller sediments mixed in, filling up spaces between larger sizes. Thus a great assortment of sizes in the sediment is unfavorable for the development of maximum porosity.

Shape and packing. A mass of cubes may have almost no porosity if the cubes are stacked

FIG. 20–2. / *Solution cavities in limestone. The dark areas are cavities. (Washington and Lee Univ. collection.)*

FIG. 20–3. / *Variations in porosity. Water is stored in intergranular pore spaces, in fractures, and in cavities of all sorts in the earth. How much water may be stored and how readily the water may move depends on the nature of the rock in which it is stored. This illustration points out some of the variations in porosity which result from differences in size, shape, and packing of a clastic sediment.*

together in an orderly fashion, but it will be very porous if they are jumbled together. Likewise, rounded particles can differ in porosity according to the way they are packed. If each sphere is directly above the center of another, maximum porosity results (Fig. 20–3); minimum porosity occurs when the spheres are offset. If the particles in a rock are elongate minerals, the porosity of one rock in which the particles are all aligned in one direction will be very different from that of one where they are oriented at random (Fig. 20–3).

Storage in solution cavities is much more irregular than that in intergranular pore spaces. Caverns provide some lakes and channels which may be filled with water, but more commonly solution pores are small. They may be solution cavities located along fractures or where disseminated soluble minerals have been etched out.

Fractures are common in all types of rocks. Sometimes they are open, and almost always there is enough space for water to seep down along the fracture surface. Fractures provide adequate storage for water, and are the main source in some areas.

Destruction of Porosity

PORE SPACES may be closed or filled in by natural processes. Ground water usually carries elements in solution, and these may be deposited, cementing cavities, pores, or fractures, and thereby preventing future storage of water. Man may also destroy porosity of some water-bearing sedimentary units by drawing water out of them too fast or too completely. If water is removed, some sediments will become more consolidated and compacted, for water in a sediment tends to buoy up part of the weight of the individual grains. Removal of this buoyancy allows them to become more compact and less porous.

Water in clay behaves quite differently from that in silt or sand. Clay colloids absorb water; therefore clay has a very high porosity, up to 50 per cent, but water is held to the colloids and does not readily drain out. Because clay is so impervious it does not yield much of its water content. Water in granular sediments and fractures is held mainly by surface tension. *Specific yield* is the percentage of the porosity that can be freely drained. The specific yield of clay is low compared with other mixtures and sizes of material.

Geology of Ground Water Occurrence

IN LOOKING FOR GROUND WATER THE FIRST consideration is surface and subsurface geologic conditions. Primary among these are the types of rock units present. Most important of the rock units which now provide sources of water are unconsolidated sediments such as sand, gravel, and mixtures. These occur primarily as river alluvium along modern water courses, as abandoned or buried river valleys, in plains where sediments have been eroded from adjacent mountains, in intermontane valleys where alluvial fans are deposited on flanks of mountains, in glacial deposits, and in blanket-like marine deposits from which the original salt water has been naturally flushed. Some water is obtained from nearly all other rock types. Limestones are highly variable as water sources, the amount of porosity depending on the extent of solution. When there has been little solution they may contain little or no water. That water which is found is usually "hard," that is, it has a high content of ions. Because movement is governed by solution cavities, limestone regions often have large springs. Volcanic rocks also are sites of large springs. These rocks have high porosity, but the pores are not always interconnected. Water occurs in shrinkage joints formed when the lava cooled, in fractures caused by deformation, in brecciated zones of block lava, in lava tubes, and between successive flows. Crystalline igneous and metamorphic rocks have the lowest porosity. Most water held in them comes from fracture systems. Clays and clay mixtures contain large amounts of water, but it is not readily obtained.

The United States can be broken up into a number of ground-water provinces on the basis of types of underlying bedrock (Fig. 20–4). Among the important provinces are:

1. Glacial deposits found near the surface in the northern states.
2. Large regions of intrusive igneous and metamorphic rocks such as the Piedmont, New England, and Wisconsin highlands, and most of the central portions of mountains in the west.
3. Paleozoic sedimentary sequences, including limestones, shales, and sandstones; found in the Appalachians, in the central and eastern interior regions, and at depth in the Great Plains.
4. Mesozoic and Cenozoic sheetlike deposits of alluvial materials deposited in the Great Plains and in the basins of the Rocky Mountain region.
5. Cenozoic marine sedimentary deposits of the Atlantic and Gulf Coastal Plain.
6. Recent Cenozoic alluvial fan deposits in the basins of the Basin and Range region of the west.
7. Volcanic eruptives which cover extensive areas of the northwestern states.

Movement of Ground Water

A ROCK CAN BE VERY POROUS AND STILL not allow fluids to move through it. *Permeability* is a measure of the ability of a stratum or rock unit to transmit fluids. For movement of water, pores must be interconnected. Most well-sorted granular rocks have high porosity and high permeability. Partially cemented rocks, those composed of clay particles, and massive igneous and metamorphic rocks tend to be less permeable unless they are fractured.

Most ground water in the upper parts of the crust comes from precipitation. This water must find its way from the surface of the ground

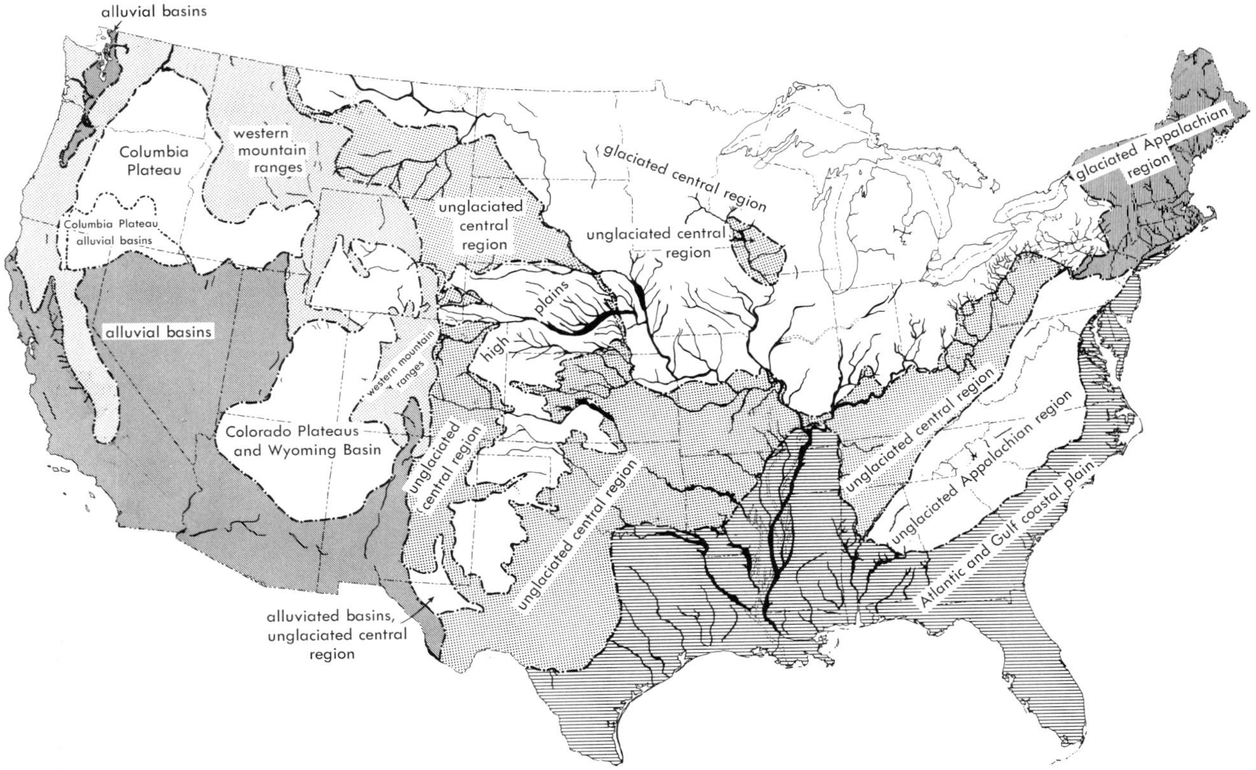

FIG. 20–4. / *American ground water provinces. The heavy black lines mark important watercourses where ground water is replenished by perennial streams. Other important provinces are alluvial basins as marked and glacial deposits. In the Atlantic and Gulf Coastal Plain water is produced from sedimentary units, sands and silts, of Cenozoic age. In the unglaciated Appalachian region water is held primarily in fractures in metamorphic rocks. In the Central region bedrock is composed of late Paleozoic and Cenozoic sedimentary units. The Columbia Plateau is largely underlain by lava flows. In the western mountains most water supplies come from surface streams. The Colorado Plateau and Wyoming basin are underlain by Cenozoic and Mesozoic sedimentary units. (Provinces after H. E. Thomas from U.S. Geological Survey Water Supply Paper 1800.)*

down into the permeable rocks below. The exact way in which this movement occurs is as varied as the soils are. The water is pulled downward by the force of gravity; it is pushed down by the weight of water above it; and it is retarded by surface tension of the water as it clings to the particles of soil through which it must pass. Gradually it seeps into and through the soil. In this zone it is mixed with air, and together they bring about decay of the soil and its rock fragments. After passing through the soil the water strikes the contact between soil and unaltered rock. If the rock is porous and permeable, water will continue into the rock; if the rock is im-

permeable, water will either accumulate or will tend to move laterally downslope along this contact. If the rock is of homogeneous, porous, and granular material, water moves through it until it reaches a depth below which the rock is saturated with water. The contact between the zone in which air and water are moving rapidly downward, called the *zone of aeration*, and the *zone of saturation* is called the *water table*. The term may be somewhat misleading because the water table is not flat, nor does it maintain the same level or configuration all the time. Immediately above the water table there is a thin zone in which very thin tubelets of water extend up into

FIG. 20–5. / *Experimental set-up to test the validity of Darcy's Law. The law states that the velocity of the flow of water through a unit is proportional to the permeability of the rock, K, and the hydraulic head, h, and inversely proportional to the length of the path of the flow. This law enables us to predict the amount of water which may be pumped from aquifers.*

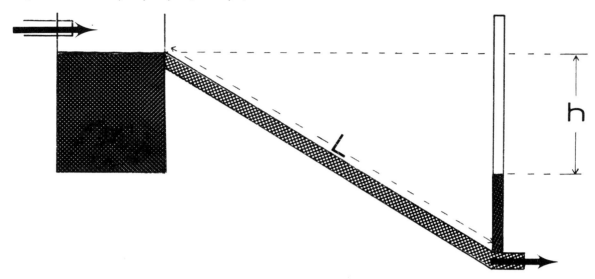

the overlying rock. These behave as capillary tubes, and the zone is called the *capillary fringe.*

Movement of ground water has been the subject of many experiments whose theoretical results can be applied with success to natural conditions. Of notable importance is the work of Henry Darcy. He proved that the velocity of movement of water between two points on the top of the water table is equal to the product of the rock permeability and the slope of the water table. In the case of confined water such as that confined in an aquifer between impervious strata the velocity is the product of the permeability and the hydraulic gradient, in this case a pressure gradient, which is equal to the difference in hydraulic head between two points divided by the length of the path of flow (Fig. 20–5). In applying this to ordinary groundwater problems it is possible to measure the length of the path and hydrostatic head, and to determine permeability by making tests on the rock types through which the water passes. Thus the velocity of movements along particular paths may be calculated by *Darcy's equation* (Fig. 20–5).

Rates of water movement beneath the water table are very slow. They vary considerably from one place to another according to the permeability and structure of the rocks. A typical value for the rate of movement is 50 feet per year, but it may be as great as several hundred feet per day under exceptional circumstances.

Configuration of the Water Table

THE CONFIGURATION OF THE WATER TABLE and changes that take place in it depend on the shape of the ground surface, permeability of rocks below, and the supply of water.

GRANULAR PERVIOUS MATERIAL. This represents the most general case, since most of the continents are underlain by sedimentary rocks and these are in large part granular pervious units. As a generalization we may say that the water table conforms to the shape of the land surface. It is depressed most under hills, and comes closest to the surface at lakes and along streams. If, as a result of long periods of drought or any other condition causing a lack of water, the table becomes deeply depressed, then lakes and streams tend to lose water because it migrates downward through the earth toward the water table. A stream that loses its water in this manner is said to be in an *influent condition* (Fig. 20–6). The normal condition is the *affluent condition*, when water moves down into lakes and streams from the water table.

PERCHED WATER TABLES. If water is moving down on an impervious layer faster than it is being transmitted laterally and faster than it is passing through the layer, then a localized water table develops above that unit. When the level of the regional water table is below this impervious unit a *perched water table* is said to exist above it (Fig. 20–7).

Quality of Ground Water

How PURE WATER MUST BE DEPENDS ON the purpose for which it is to be used. To determine its quality, water must be analyzed. A chemical analysis is made to determine the kinds and quantities of ions present in solution. Concentrations of ions are often expressed as parts per million, *ppm*. One ppm is one part by weight of the ion to a million parts by weight of water. When there is no need to determine what different types of ions are present, the total amount of dissolved solids can be quickly estimated by a test measuring the electrical conductivity of water, which is, in turn, a function of the salt content. Bacteriological analysis is made, particularly on drinking water, to ensure that there has been no contamination from sewage. Other tests may be made to determine temperature, color, odor, and taste.

The United States Public Health Service sets standards for most drinking water supplies. Mandatory maximum limits are set for ppm of lead (0.1), fluorides (1.5), arsenic (0.05), selenium (0.05), and chromium (0.05), and a maximum total solids concentration of 1,000 ppm. Desirable limits for many less dangerous elements are also provided, along with standards for physical characteristics and bacterial quality. One of the common expressions of quality of water is its *hardness*. This usually refers particularly to

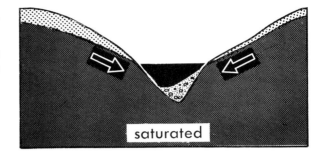

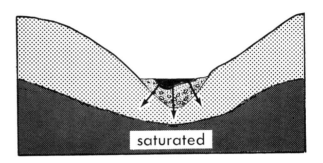

FIG. 20–6. / *Cross section of an effluent stream (top) and an influent stream (bottom). The black parts of the sections indicate portions of the ground which are saturated with water. Arrows indicate the general directions of water movement.*

the amount of calcium carbonate and magnesium carbonate in solution, rather than to the quantity of all ions present.

Many industries must have extremely pure water or water containing low concentrations of certain particular ions, but these standards vary greatly from one industry to another.

Even waters used for agricultural purposes must meet certain standards. Some plants are very sensitive to concentrations of certain salts. For example, apples, pears, oranges, plums, peaches, and strawberry plants all have low salt tolerances, as do green beans, celery, and radishes. Date palms, spinach, asparagus, sugar beets, and barley can stand concentrations of three or four times the tolerable limits for the plants previously listed. This problem becomes particularly important where irrigation is most desirable, because water found in such regions is likely to have high salt content. There is also the possibility that pumping water to the surface for irrigation will have the effect of in-

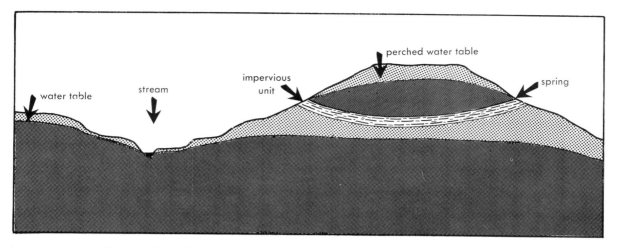

FIG. 20–7. / *Cross section of a region showing one condition which might give rise to a perched water table. The shale unit in the mountain is impervious and prevents the flow of water to the lower regional water table.*

creasing the salt content of all the water in the vicinity. In returning to the water table the water may dissolve salts from the soil and carry the added salt load to depth, contaminating other water supplies. If the same water is pumped up again its content of salts is again increased as it carries more salts downward, until eventually it may not be suitable for irrigation.

A great many other conditions may cause ground water quality to be lowered. These include inadequate treatment of sewage before water is returned to the ground, dumping of sewage into streams, and dumping of wastes such as food products, oil, chemicals, and tailings from mines and mineral processing plants. Water can be contaminated by natural causes as well. Magmatic waters often contain high concentrations of salts. In addition, water may deteriorate from the way it is brought to the surface. Excessive pumping may cause intrusion of salt water near the coasts, or water of lower quality may be drawn from one ground-water basin into another.

Development of Ground Water Supplies

INCREASING ATTENTION IS BEING GIVEN TO the most effective ways of developing ground water supplies. This is particularly true in areas where annual precipitation does not equal the rate at which ground water is withdrawn. Such areas in the United States are located primarily in the arid and semiarid portions of the southwest. Study of water in such areas has been most successfully approached on the basis of comprehensive analysis of natural basins. A *ground water basin* may be thought of as an area bounded by natural geologic conditions which cause ground water within it to be more or less separated from adjacent basins. These conditions are met particularly in the western states, where many structural basins exist. For example, in the southwestern states there are numerous more or less isolated basins in which great thicknesses of sedimentary rocks have accumulated. These basins are sometimes nearly completely enclosed by high mountains of impervious crystalline rocks which essentially separate one basin from those around it (Fig. 20–8).

The amount of water which can be withdrawn from a basin without producing undesired results is called the *safe yield* for that basin. In the broadest meaning of the term, undesired results include not only results which may be harmful to the ground water supply, but those damaging to the economics of the area as well. Within this framework it is necessary to consider the water supply in terms of the economics of industries and agriculture dependent on water, quality of water, and legal rights to water. It is apparent that undesirable effects include long-term overdrafts which lower the water table, cause sea water intrusions, or bring about contamination of ground water. It is as undesirable to lower water quality through irrigation or industrial contamination as to allow industries or agriculture to fail economically through inadequate water supply.

In more and more areas of the world people must face the fact that there is not an unlimited supply of water underground. For any given area a certain amount of water is held in the ground, and a certain amount is annually recharged into the ground by natural means. To remove more water from the ground for drinking, agriculture, or industrial use than is normally recharged is to *mine* the water. When water is "mined" it may eventually be exhausted, just like any other mineral resource. Thus the amount of water in the ground, the rate at which it is naturally recharged, and the ability of man to recharge the water supply by bringing water into the area create a limit to the potential development of that area.

Understanding the geology of ground water can provide us with the necessary information to make intelligent use of water resources. When there is sufficient information available a basin can be analyzed in terms of the *equation of hydrologic equilibrium*. An equilibrium condition is said to exist when the total amount of water coming into a basin just equals the amount taken out. Factors in hydrologic equilibrium include the amount of water in surface and subsurface storage; the quantity brought into and taken from the area by streams, underground movement, man-made devices, and precipitation and evaporation; and the volume consumed. The equation of hydrologic equilibrium may be stated as:

> surface inflow through streams + subsurface inflow + precipitation + importation by pipes and canals — decrease in surface storage in reservoirs — decrease in ground-water storage (lowering of water table) =
>
> increase in surface storage + increase in subsurface storage — surface outflow — subsurface outflow — consumptive use — exported outflow.

Long-range planning for any area should be based on the proposition that an equilibrium condition must be maintained. One of the most frequently suggested remedies for water shortages is importation of water. It is now economically feasible to recover fresh water from sea water along coasts in arid areas, and this will undoubtedly be part of the solution to future water needs in the coastal areas of the world, but the cost of transporting water inland over mountains and long distances make it much more logical and imperative for us first to develop existing ground-water supplies as completely as possible.

FIG. 20–8. / *Cross section of a typical basin and range within the Basin and Range province.* (Modified after P. B. King.)

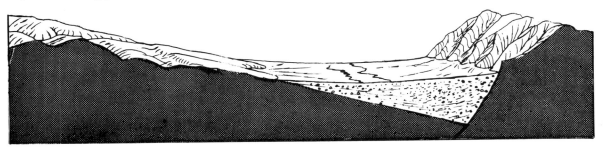

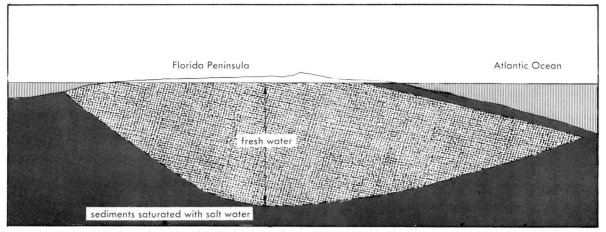

Florida Peninsula   Atlantic Ocean

fresh water

sediments saturated with salt water

FIG. 20–9. / *Storage of water in sediments in contact with the ocean. The fresh water tends to float on the more dense salt water. For every foot of elevation of the water table above sea level there are 38 feet of fresh water beneath.*

Water Tables in Contact with Salt Water

ALONG COASTS WHERE SEDIMENTS ARE largely sandstones it is normal to find fresh water bounded below by a contact with salt water. Because of its lower density, fresh water floats on salt water. Consequently a salt-water wedge extends from the ocean under the edge of the fresh water. Along this wedge there will be some salt-water contamination of the fresh water, making it unsuitable for drinking purposes. The density differential between salt and fresh water is such that a balance is reached when there is about 38 feet of fresh water below sea level for every foot of elevation of the water table above sea level. This condition prevails in Florida, where fresh water is stored in porous limestones and sands that underlie the peninsula (Fig. 20–9). The fresh water supply is a large dome-shaped mass. Problems arise when the rate at which water is pumped from the ground greatly exceeds the rate at which water is moving toward the area pumped. Excessive pumping brings the salt-water wedge closer to the surface and therefore endangers the supply of fresh water.

Geysers

SINCE ITS DISCOVERY IN 1870, OLD FAITH-ful geyser in Yellowstone National Park (Fig. 20–10) has regularly spurted forth 10,000 to 12,000 gallons of steam and water to an average height of 130 feet about once every hour. Very few geysers are this regular, but many others are known, and the nature of their activity is similar. Outside of Yellowstone Park other areas of geyser activity are found in New Zealand and Iceland. Geysers follow a regular cycle of activity:

1. Immediately following an eruption water goes back into the ground at the vent or through nearby holes. A small part runs off in small streams flowing away from the cone.

2. This is followed by a period of quiet during which only a few whiffs of steam rise from the vent.

3. After about 30 or 40 minutes more steam starts to rise from the vent, and a little water appears at the surface.

4. Water and steam rise and flow out of the vent in a series of small outpourings. Some of this water runs off, but most goes back into the vent.

5. Several small eruptions occur, throwing bubbling water out of the vent to a height

of several feet above the ground. This continues for several minutes.

6. The main eruption starts, and a column of water and steam spurts forth, occasionally as high as 250 feet. The eruption lasts several minutes, then dies down, and the cycle is repeated.

Heat from a mass of very hot rock rises to the surface, heating the ground water. Water coming from Old Faithful and other geysers is mostly rainwater. It contains only very small quantities of common volcanic gases and solutions. Surface waters flow into the fractured and porous igneous and volcanic rocks that underlie Yellowstone Park. Beneath the surface the vent of the geysers is connected to an irregularly shaped network of fractures and cavities dissolved by the hot waters. It is from these cavity networks that the ejected water comes. After eruption, time is required for water to percolate back into the channels and refill them. The water, which has just been cooled by its ascent into the air, is warmed immediately. Since the heat in the rocks increases with depth, the water in the lower parts of the network becomes hot more rapidly than that higher up. Water boils when it reaches 100° C. at the surface, but water at the bottom of the system is under the pressure exerted by the weight of the column of water above it, so it must be heated much more before it will begin to boil. Eventually the boiling point is reached at some point in the network, and steam forms. The expansion of water into steam exerts sufficient pressure to force overlying water out at the top of the vent. Just a little is forced out at first, then more, finally enough is removed to lower the pressure on the network and permit large quantities of water to convert suddenly into steam. The main part of the eruption starts when this explosive generation of steam occurs at depth.

A large amount of silica dissolved from the underground cavities is carried in solution by the hot waters. It is precipitated at the surface when the waters cool. Usually a colloidal gel is formed. This consolidates to an amorphous form of silica and leaves a deposit known as *geyserite*.

FIG. 20–10. / *Old Faithful in eruption, Yellowstone Park. (Photo by courtesy of the Union Pacific Railroad.)*

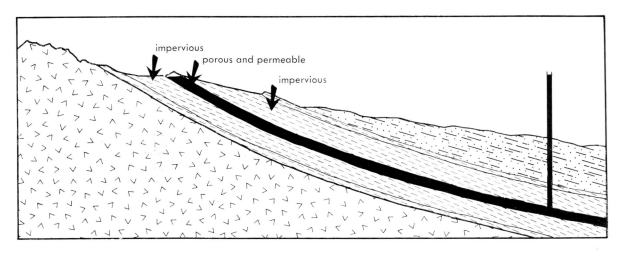

FIG. 20–11. / *Artesian conditions. Water percolates into the aquifer at the mountain front. When a well is drilled in the plains, water flows to the surface and almost up to the level of saturation in the aquifer.*

Artesian Conditions

UNDER ARTESIAN CONDITIONS WATER WILL rise to the ground surface from depth and flow out under pressure (Figs. 20–11 and 20–12). *Artesian conditions* arise from hydrostatic pressure of water trapped or confined within a porous and permeable unit that is both overlain and underlain by impervious units of rock. Water comes into such a unit where it is exposed at the ground surface or overlain by other permeable rocks. The water moves down into the *aquifer*, as the layer is called, gradually fills it, and thereby builds up hydrostatic pressure. If the aquifer is tapped at some elevation lower than its intake area, water will flow from it under the pressure of the hydrostatic head above that point. Under natural conditions an artesian spring may originate where a fault cuts the unit; a well drilled into the aquifer is called an *artesian well*. Artesian conditions may arise in ex-

tensive rock units or in smaller bodies of rock, such as lenticular sand bodies surrounded by clay and silt sometimes found in old river channels and in alluvial fans.

Caverns

CAVES MAY FORM THROUGH LONG-CONTINued solution by water moving downward along fractures toward the water table, or by waters moving near the water table. The process is somewhat analogous to the solution of a cube of sugar by dropping drops of water on it. Lime is slowly etched away along fractures until blocks are freed. They fall or shift, and solution continues. Eventually solution removes enough material to cause a subsidence in the level of the ground surface. This may create an enclosed depression, called a *sink hole*, which forms a small drainage basin, catching all rain

FIG. 20–12. / *This section drawn from the Black Hills shows the Dakota sandstone, one of the important aquifers in the Great Plains. Note the piezometric surface, shown by a dashed line, slopes away from the Black Hills. (After Darton.)*

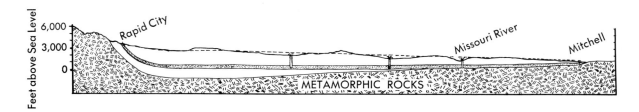

that falls into it and a large part of that coming downslope and draining into the cave. Once this process starts, the cave is supplied with large quantities of water and solution is accelerated. If the cavity extends far into the ground, a path is available for the movement of large quantities of water. If enough water flows into the cave a stream is formed underground. Then the cave is enlarged by processes very much like the erosion by surface streams, a much faster process than solution by ground water. A great many caves have streams flowing through them, and most of them show signs of stream erosion throughout.

In an active cavern, moisture drips from the ceiling and sides of the cave and forms pools and streams on the floor. This is ground water seeping into the cavern. The cavern is in the zone of aeration (it would be filled with water if it were below the water table). Here a mixture of water and air is percolating through the rock, which is most often a limestone. Many caves are formed along fracture zones which have become channels for underground streams. Points at which water drips from the ceiling become sites of calcite deposits which at first take the shape of thin straws. They are called *stalactites* and may be seen in various stages of development. As a drop of water hangs from the ceiling some of the water within the drop evaporates, leaving a thin ring of calcite. After a long period of time this ring is lengthened by

FIG. 20–13. / *Formation of cave deposits. The photograph shows stalactites, stalagmites, and columns of various stages of formation. The sequence of events in the formation of a column like that at the left is described in the text. (Photo by courtesy of James F. Quinlan, Jr., Mineral Industries Journal.)*

more deposits until it becomes a long straw. Finally the inside of the straw becomes so filled with calcite that drops can no longer flow through it. Water then moves as a thin film over the surface of the straw and slowly builds up layer on layer of calcite until a large tapering cone is formed. Water that drops from the end of a stalactite falls to the floor, where it evaporates further and precipitates more calcite. Slowly a stump-shaped deposit rises from the floor. These new formations are *stalagmites* (Fig. 20–13). Usually they have a small saucer-shaped top into which drops of water fall from the ceiling. Overflow from this saucer goes down the sides of the stalagmite, building it out. Eventually stalactites and stalagmites may grow together to form *columns*. Other formations may grow from the sides of a cavern. There droplets of water evaporate leaving small, rounded, knoblike projections of calcite on the walls.

Calcite being deposited in these cave formations comes from dissolved limestone through which the ground water moved. The ground water was originally rainwater containing enough carbon dioxide to form weak carbonic acid, which dissolved the limestone. Precipitation of calcite as cave deposits comes from loss of carbon dioxide and reduction in the water content when it reaches the cave. The remaining water is saturated with calcium and carbonate ions. The rate at which cave formations are built is highly variable. In active caves supplied with large quantities of water the rate is high —as much as a centimeter a year—but where the supply of water is limited the rate is slow, or formation may have ceased altogether. Calcareous cave deposits are known as *travertine*.

Springs

SPRINGS FORM WHERE THE WATER TABLE intersects the land surface or where water under artesian conditions finds its way to the surface. The most common places at which springs occur are illustrated (Fig. 20–15). Spring deposits, usually composed of calcium carbonate, are called *tufa*. Springs are commonly surrounded by plants and trees. Organic matter from these may be covered by the calcium carbonate deposits and become incorporated into the tufa, making it very porous. Tufa is often poorly consolidated material. Where it has been firmly cemented it may be cut and used as a building stone. The porous, rough texture makes it uniquely valuable for soundproofing.

Karst Geomorphic Cycle

SUBSURFACE MOVEMENT OF WATER MAY become a dominant process in causing alteration of the landscape, but it is never the sole factor. Wherever there is enough water for formation of caverns there will be surface drainage as well, and mass wasting invariably plays a part in degradation. *Karst topography* is a feature most likely to develop in humid climates where limestones or other soluble rocks are exposed or are near the surface of the ground. How these become exposed is important in determining the initial forms. The Ocala limestone of the Florida peninsula is broadly exposed over a large region after its uplift from the sea floor, but in the karst topography around the Mammoth Cave in Kentucky[1] a resistant

[1] See map at end of book.

FIG. 20–14. / *The Big Room of Carlsbad Caverns, New Mexico. This photo shows evidence of two stages in the history of the cave. First the cavern was formed through solution of the limestone by underground waters. Then began deposition of massive columns and pointed stalactites of calcium carbonate. (Photo by courtesy of the New Mexico State Tourist Bureau.)*

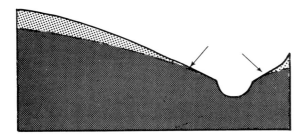

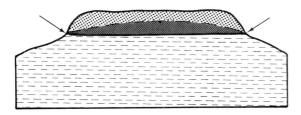

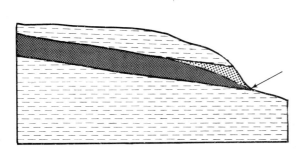

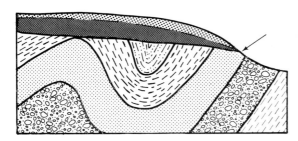

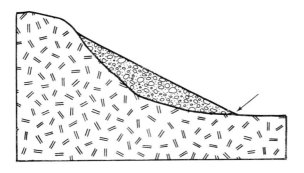

FIG. 20–15. / *Cross sections showing conditions in which springs may form. These are but a few representative situations which give rise to the formation of springs.*

sandstone unit covers the soluble limestone. This resistant cover must be at least partially removed before karst topography can develop. In such areas, where the units are flat or tilted, the limestone is first exposed along valleys, then exposure spreads as the overlying units are eroded away (Fig. 20–16).

The erosion cycle commences with surface drainage on a limestone that is above the base level of the region. In many karst regions the cycle appears to have started with uplift that initiated downcutting of the surface streams and finally caused them to become entrenched in their present courses. At first a large part of the precipitation runs off on the surface of the ground, and a small part infiltrates into the ground, bringing about solution along fractures, faults, bedding planes, and any other zones of weakness. Underground drainage passages begin to develop. At the same time slow percolation and solution result in solution sinks in the ground surface. Where solution beneath the surface leaves sizable cavities, collapse or subsidence forms sink holes. There are few and isolated sink holes at first, but through the years more and more of these enclosed depressions form. One of the important consequences of formation of more sinks is that a larger amount of surface drainage is trapped before it reaches main trunk streams. Small tributary streams gradually become less prominent as water originally carried by them is diverted to underground passages. This water eventually finds its way to the main streams. The water table ordinarily outcrops along the channels of these streams.

After subsurface drainage becomes well developed there are many large and small caverns. Sink holes become so numerous that the sides begin to touch one another. Surface drainage becomes limited to short *sinking creeks*, those

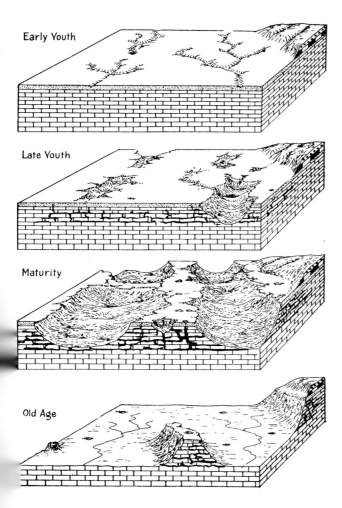

Early Youth

Late Youth

Maturity

Old Age

FIG. 20–16. / *Stages in the erosion of a terrace in which solution is an important process in shaping the landforms. (Armin K. Lobeck, 1929, The geology and physiography of the Mammoth Cave National Park: Kentucky Geological Survey, ser. VI, v. 31, pt. 5, pp. 327–399.)*

that disappear into the ground. Along some such streams you can see the vortexes where water swirls into openings leading into caverns. Such holes are called *swallow holes*. So-called *blind valleys* form. These are valleys that lead into a hillside or gradually lose the characteristics of a valley as water from their streams is lost to subsurface channels.

Subsurface drainage channels and solution cavities etch out more of the limestone and a full-scale karst topography develops. Collapse features begin to dominate the surface of the ground. *Karst windows* form where collapse of the surface over an underground stream exposes the channel. These karst windows gradually expand with the collapse of their margins and mass wasting of their sides. Eventually the depression becomes much larger, exposing the stream or caverns over a greater area. At this stage streams flow for long distances through karst tunnels and there are *natural bridges* where tunnels have partially collapsed (Fig. 20–17). Mass wasting gradually causes overhanging or steep cliffs, formed where collapse has occurred, to retreat away from streams.

As the cycle nears its completion, drainage returns to the surface of the ground. The tunnels, natural bridges, and sink holes disappear. All that remains are a few more or less isolated rounded hills of limestone in which caves initially formed. These hills stand out above a relatively flat surface into which stream channels are cut. This surface may be flat if it is near regional base level, or it may be that a very resistant insoluble unit is exposed beneath the limestone. There may be more limestone, even part of the same stratigraphic rock unit, below the level of this surface on which the streams flow. In this case further reduction has been stopped by the position of the base level, and uplift would be necessary to start the cycle over again.

FIG. 20–17. / *Natural Bridge, Virginia. The natural bridge may have once been a long tunnel. The stream, which once flowed as an underground river, is again flowing on the ground surface as a result of the collapse of the roof.* (*Photo by courtesy of the Natural Bridge Company, Virginia.*)

21/

Wind Action

Turbulent flow of air occurs near the surface of the earth where obstructions set up eddies, whirlwinds, updrafts, and downdrafts. Movements observed in dust and smoke coming out of a smokestack are a fair representation of movements in convection currents in air. Natural convection comes from heating of the surface of the ground. Where the ground absorbs heat from solar radiation it heats the air directly above it. This hot air expands, becomes lighter, and rises. This expansion and rising is itself a form of turbulent motion. Turbulence extends hundreds of feet above the ground, but at high altitudes wind moves in steady currents without much turbulence. This type of steady flow is called *laminar flow*. The effective forward velocity of wind is greatly reduced near the ground by turbulence set up by movement of the wind around irregularities. Higher, the velocity becomes steady and the wind moves in a smooth, directed stream, except near the jet stream and in storm areas.

Transportation

A strong wind can move sand. If the velocity is fairly constant the sand is confined below a certain level above the ground. This zone is usually a few inches high, and only during storms does it reach more than 18 inches. Below this level the sand is actively blown, but above it the air is almost completely free of sand. Sand grains roll along the ground rapidly. These hit other sand grains and bounce into the air. Once in the air, they are carried forward, and their velocity is increased. The pull of gravity on a grain will overcome the upward thrust from the wind, and the grain will follow a slanted path back to the ground. The increased velocity will give it more momentum. When it hits the surface again the impact dislodges other sand grains which start rolling or bounce into the air. Soon a chain reaction has been established, and transportation is under way through a series of bounces. The process is called *saltation*. Most of the material transported in this way is sand and silt, ranging in size from about 2 mm. down to $\frac{1}{256}$ mm. As sand is moved it tends to become rounded and sorted, and small pits, like those found on a sand-blasted piece of glass, form on windblown grains. Larger sizes may be lifted from the ground during unusually intense windstorms. Tornadoes are known to pick up roofs from houses, toss cars into trees, overturn railroad cars, and blow down trees along their paths, but tornadoes are not common enough to be an important agent of gradation. Hurricanes and typhoons also have localized effects, although in the long run the effect may be comparable to other forms of wind action.

Pebbles may be rolled along the ground during normal high winds, but they are rarely lifted from the surface. Larger boulders may be moved by a combination of wind and mass movement. The wind blows the finer supporting material from beneath the boulder, which then moves in the direction in which support was lost. Boulders on slopes may thus be freed to roll down.

Finer sediment sizes are the main load of the wind. Wind carries sand and silt in saltation, but the finest particles—dust, cloud particles, smoke, and haze—are moved in a different way. These particles are so light that the force of gravity exerts only a slight pull on them, but they are large in relation to their weight. Dust is often composed of flat, tabular particles with large surface area. This makes it possible for the force of upward motions of wind currents to more than counterbalance the downward pull of gravity (Fig. 21–1). Dust settles slowly and is easily wafted back up higher in the air by slight updrafts. Large quantities of volcanic dust carried aloft during explosions of Krakatoa and Katmai stayed up for several years and were carried around the earth in upper layers of the atmosphere.

These smaller particles are blown directly into the air by impact of the wind against their surfaces, or are lifted up by the pressure created by velocity differentials. To illustrate this effect, take a piece of paper and fold about an inch of the two ends toward each other. With the two ends at right angles to the rest of the paper, place the folded paper upon a flat surface so it forms an open-ended box. Then blow under the paper. If properly done, the paper will not be blown away, but the top will be pulled down toward the surface. The velocity of the air under the paper was greater than that above it. This created a difference in pressure on the opposite sides of the paper. The pressure dropped where the wind velocity was greatest, and the force of the pressure above pushed the top of the paper down. The same thing can take place in any fluid medium. It happens in the wind and in running water. When wind velocity causes a decrease in downward pressure, upward pressure may be enough to lift dust-sized materials into the air.

Sources of Windblown Material

POTENTIAL SOURCES OF WINDBLOWN MATERIALS are found anywhere small particles come to the surface and are not held down. Plant and vegetative cover tend to prevent removal of material by wind, as does soil moisture, which acts as an adhesive. Once either of these is lost the particles may be carried away. Sources include:

Any place where loosely consolidated sandstone, siltstone, or shale are exposed at the surface. Also floodplain sediments, deposits washed out of glaciers, beach sands, and dried lake sediments.

Volcanic explosions. Unlike material from other sources, large quantities of dust are placed directly in the air. Old deposits of volcanic ash are also potential sources of windblown material.

Man has often played an important role in making available to the wind material that would not otherwise have been exposed. This has come mainly through poor conservation practices in farming and forestry. Plowing during years of drought exposes what moisture there is in the soil to more rapid evaporation. Moisture is lost, soil is loosened, plants die, and material small enough to be transported by the wind is blown away. The results have been disastrous in some places, where fertile farms have been converted into deserts of windblown sand and dust. Similar effects may be produced by removal of forest cover from semiarid lands, thus exposing the soil to wind erosion.

FIG. 21–1. / *Heavy black clouds of dust and sand rising over the Texas "Panhandle." (Courtesy of U.S. Weather Bureau.)*

FIG. 21–2. / *Dust storm in New Mexico. "The day had been relatively calm with light wind from the southeast. The dust storm rolled in on a very light wind, but about 15 minutes later a regular hurricane struck which lasted about 30 minutes. Visibility was zero, and tightly closed rooms were filled with fine choking dust." (Photo by courtesy of the U.S. Soil Conservation Service.)*

FIG. 21–3. / *"Camel Rock." This oddly-shaped formation is located a few miles north of Sante Fe, New Mexico. It is one of the land forms typical of wind erosion processes. The impact of wind-transported sand has undercut the rock. (Photo by courtesy of the New Mexico State Tourist Bureau.)*

Erosion by Wind

THE WIND ACCOMPLISHES EROSION BY DE-flation (blowing away of materials), corrosion and abrasion, and impact. *Deflation* includes removal of dust and smaller particles, and the transportation of sand and silt by saltation. Sand, silt, and dust are wind tools; they bring about scraping or abrasion as they move over surfaces. In wind erosion impact is more important than abrasion. Impact occurs when a sand grain is blown into or against a rock surface or into the soil. The momentum is used in dislodging other granular material. Impact may break the cement of a rock, freeing other sand grains. The effect of impact can be seen in any sand-blasting operation. Old paint or stone is chipped away, exposing a new surface. The same method is used to frost glass and to cut letters in polished stones. Even granites may be cut by sand-blasting. Evidence of impact can be seen in most samples of windblown sand. The surfaces of grains are pitted or frosted as a result of repeated impact. Where sand has been blown over rocks for a long time, the rocks become worn from repeated abrasion, and smooth, polished surfaces result. Such stones are called *ventifacts*.

Landforms of Wind Erosion

THERE IS SOME QUESTION as to just how important wind erosion is. It is most effective in shifting about debris that has been weathered from solid rocks. It keeps the land swept clear of this debris in places and shifts it and piles it up elsewhere as sand dunes, or distributes it widely as sheets. Some landforms are due primarily to wind erosion. These include:

Broad shallow depressions in deserts where soil has been blown out by repeated movement of currents in one direction.

Broad shallow caves in the sides of hills where the impact and abrasion of sand have sculptured the lower slopes of the hill.

Mushroom, table, and pedestal rocks (Fig. 21–3). These are isolated rocks from which the base has been partially cut by undercutting by windblown sand. Some of these

forms are quite spectacular, such as the balanced rocks. Often the top of the form is a different rock unit from the bottom, which has been cut away because it is more susceptible to wind erosion.

Sorting

WIND IS AN EXCELLENT agent for *sorting*, separation of particles according to size, shape, or weight. Wind velocity determines just what maximum size of material it can transport by rolling, by saltation, and in suspension. Thus a very distinct separation is accomplished. Smaller sizes are suspended and carried away, heavier particles lag behind on the ground, and sand and silt bounce along. Loads in suspension and saltation are further separated. Of that in suspension only the lightest can be carried and maintained at extreme heights. Of the saltation load some will be moved more rapidly than

FIG. 21–4. / *Distribution of glacial deposits in the United States. The areas covered by ice sheets and regions which are overlain by loess deposits are indicated. Most of the loess deposits are thought to be windblown deposits, but some are most likely stream deposits.*

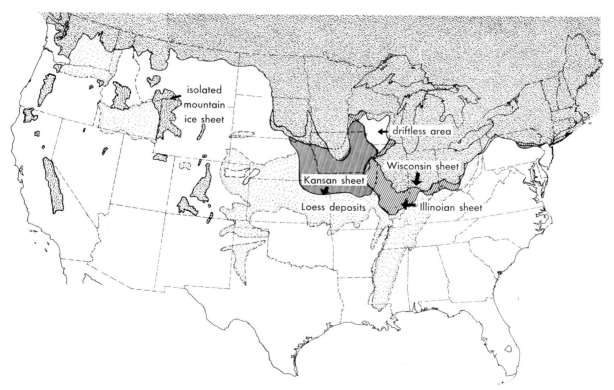

others. Thus the wind's load becomes initially sorted while it is in transport.

When the wind begins to die down and its velocity drops, the *critical velocity*—the minimum wind velocity required to move a particle—will be reached for each size, and that size will settle. The result is a well-sorted sediment.

Deposition

WIND DEPOSITS TAKE TWO GENERAL FORMS —dunes and sheets. Sheets are dust deposits laid down over large areas. Within sheets, thickness varies, generally thinning out farther away from the source. Two excellent examples of the sheet-like nature of some windblown deposits are the deposits of volcanic dust from the eruption of Katmai and the layer of loess that covers much of the central United States (Figs. 21–4 and 21–5). These sheetlike deposits cover much greater areas than do sand dunes.

Loess deposits are well exposed in vertical road cuts through the Mississippi Valley region. Loess is composed of small, angular particles derived from a variety of rock types. The angularity of its particles makes loess cliffs stable, and road cuts in it often have vertical sides. Loess is semiconsolidated. Since it contains small snail shells of a type that lives on land, loess has most likely been deposited by wind. This conclusion is supported by the presence of small tubes of calcite that apparently fill holes left after the decay of tall grasses. Windblown silt and dust sifted down over fields of grass so slowly that the blades of grass were not forced down. As the dust fell it buried the snails. Composition of loess found in the United States is the same as that which would be produced by grinding up rocks now exposed in the northern part of the country and in Canada. Glaciers over that part of North America in the Pleistocene probably ground these rocks into the material found in the loess. Finely-ground particles were likely carried out to areas in front of the ice sheet by meltwater and deposited in the outwash plain, where winds sweeping from the ice sheet dried the loess and picked it up, carried it southward, and deposited it along the Mississippi Valley.

Sand Dunes

SAND DUNES ARE relatively rare features even in deserts, and they are by no means confined to deserts. Some of the most extensive accumulations of sand in North America are found along the eastern coast and around the Great Lakes. Sand dunes may be formed wherever there are strong, constant, or intermittent winds, a source of sand, and obstacles that can initiate dune formation.

Sand sources are highly varied. Along coast lines the most common sand is quartz sand, in Italy it is olivine derived from volcanic rocks, and in the Azores it is volcanic ash. In the Arctic and Antarctic there are large quantities of ice sand which form dunes, and in the White Sands National Monument in New Mexico sand is composed of gypsum.

Dune Formation

SAND ACCUMULATIONS may start wherever there is an obstruction in the path of the sand movement. Sand moving by saltation hits the obstacle or falls behind it when the wind velocity is suddenly decreased. A streamlined pile of sand forms (Fig. 21–6). On the windward side a low slope forms up which sand moves in saltation. Just beyond the crest, wind velocity is reduced. A back slope forms from slumping and sliding of sand and assumes the characteristic angle of repose of loose sand, about 35 degrees. This surface is barely stable and any addition of sand at the top causes small slides on the back slope. Sand on the windward side is steadily blown over to the back slope, which is over-steepened and slumps and slides to correct its angle of repose. Thus sand dunes move, some as much as 100 feet each year.

FIG. 21–5. / *Exposure of loess, wind-deposited dust, and silt, near Vicksburg, Mississippi. (Photo by the author.)*

FIG. 21–6. / *View of the slip face of a large dune. The wind blows from the right to the left. This dune is located on the Oregon coast. (Photo by courtesy of the Oregon State Highway Department.)*

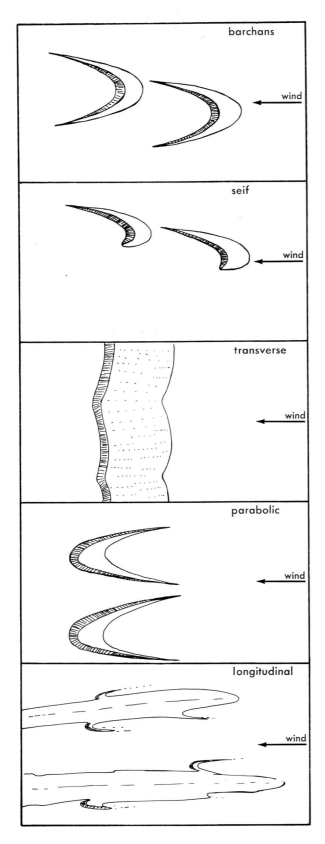

barchans

wind

seif

wind

transverse

wind

parabolic

wind

longitudinal

wind

FIG. 21–7. / *Five common types of sand dunes. The steep (slip) faces are indicated by the closely spaced lines. Wind direction is from the right.*

Dune Forms

THE SHAPE of any given sand dune is determined by how much sand is supplied to the dune, wind velocity, constancy of the wind direction, rate at which the sand is supplied, and amount and distribution of vegetative cover (Fig. 21–7). Dunes with regular shapes are not always formed. Isolated dunes may be scarce where there is a great deal of sand and dunes coalesce, losing their individual characteristics (Figs. 21–8 and 21–9).

BARCHAN DUNES. Barchan dunes are crescent-shaped with points or wings directed downwind. They are common where the wind direction is constant and moderate, and where there is little irregularity in the surface over which the sand is moving. The steady wind sweeps the ends of the dune ahead, forming the crescent points.

SEIFS. Seif dunes are similar to barchans, except that one wing is missing. This is caused by occasional shifts in wind direction with no shift in the direction from which the sand is being supplied. Seifs may form large ridges as much as 700 feet high and many miles in length.

LONGITUDINAL DUNES. Longitudinal dunes form where sand is in short supply and the direction of the wind is constant. Characteristically they are linear, have nearly symmetrical cross sections, and extend parallel to the dominant winds.

TRANSVERSE DUNES. Transverse dunes are aligned perpendicular to wind direction. They are likely to originate when the wind direction is at right angles to an elongate source of sand. This condition is found along coasts and lake shores. These may be very long, but they rarely attain heights of more than 15 feet.

FIG. 21–8. / *Sand dunes in Death Valley. (Photo by courtesy of Santa Fe Railway.)*

PARABOLIC DUNES. Parabolic dunes develop where vegetation is thick and at least partially covers the sand. In spots where the vegetation is missing a "blowout" will occur. In such instances there is more sand exposed and consequently removed from the center of the spot. Sand movement at either side is inhibited by the vegetation. A parabolic dune with wings pointed upwind results.

FIG. 21–9. / *A complex of prominent longitudinal dunes. In the foreground barchans stand out. Note the long ridges of dune sand in the background. (Photo by courtesy of the U.S. Air Force.)*

VII/

STRUCTURE AND
INTERIOR OF THE EARTH

22 /

Interior of the Earth

THE INTERIOR OF THE EARTH POSES MANY PROB-lems for those who would try to unfold its secrets. A knowledge of it is fundamental to an understanding of the origin of the earth, causes of mountain formation, development of deep trenches in the ocean basins, and the probable nature of other planets. Processes in the earth's interior have controlled, directly or indirectly, de-velopment of most of the features within the crust and on the surface. Yet there are few opportunities to make direct observations of the interior. A few wells drilled by petroleum com-panies have penetrated between 20,000 and 25,-000 feet of the crust, but these barely scratch the outermost layers. It is 3,959 miles from the center of the earth to the surface. The deepest wells penetrate about one-thousandth of this distance.

Crust of Earth

THE INTERIOR OF THE EARTH HAS OFTEN been defined as that part of the planet that lies below a depth of 10 miles. When this def-inition was formulated the interior was visu-alized as being composed of concentric shells of material, the outermost shell being the crust. In recent years the lower boundary of the crust has been redefined as the depth at which there is a sharp break or discontinuity in the velocity with which shock waves are propagated through the earth. Of the many seismic discontinuities known, none is better documented than one named for its discoverer, *Mohorovičić*. This dis-continuity is usually called *Moho*, or *M* for short. Moho is recognized by the sudden in-crease in the velocity of compressional shock waves from about 6.5 to 8 km. per second at the discontinuity. It almost certainly marks a change in the type of rock.

Moho is not found at the same depth under oceans and continents. Although investigation of its exact depth throughout the world is far from complete, there is enough information to suggest a general pattern. As was pointed out earlier, it is at greater depths under continents than it is under oceans, and it is deeper under mountains than it is under plains. It appears that the configuration of the underneath side of the crust of the earth is almost a mirror image of the surface (Fig. 22–1).

Direct Observation of the Interior

OUR BEST OPPORTUNITIES TO STUDY ROCKS that have been buried at great depths in the crust are provided by cores of folded mountain belts. These belts are great upbuckles in the crust. The stratified layers of sedimentary rocks near the surface are folded and faulted. The lower, older metamorphic and igneous rocks are likewise deformed and uplifted high above sea level. Once this mass of crust is elevated, erosion of it is accelerated and younger units are cut away, exposing successively older beds. It is possible to approximate the depth of former burial of any exposed rock by measuring the thickness of sedimentary rock units overlying it. If the youngest sedimentary strata are marine sediments they were deposited at or below sea level. At that time the oldest unit was buried at a depth equal to the thickness of all of the intervening strata. On this basis we can say that the rocks exposed in the Blue Ridge Mountains were covered by a thickness of more than 35,000 feet of sediments. Even this great depth is less than half the distance to the Moho under the mountain range. Thus the subcrust, or *mantle*, is not exposed even in the deeply eroded folded-mountain belts (Fig. 22–2).

The best evidence of the nature of the interior that can be obtained through direct observation is found where materials from below Moho have been intruded into the crust, or where deep-seated volcanism brings lavas and blocks up to the surface from below Moho, or through drilling through the crust.

The existence of such intrusions has been recognized for many years. They are composed of *peridotites* (a general term for essentially nonfeldspathic plutonic rocks consisting of olivine with or without other mafic minerals, such as amphiboles, pyroxenes, or micas). Peridotites are frequently altered by hot waters to *serpentine*.

FIG. 22–1. / *Crustal structure. The thickness of the crust of the earth is shown for a number of locations. Note the great thickness under continents as compared with the thickness under ocean basins. The solid black represents part of the mantle beneath Moho. (From G. P. Woollard, Trans. Am. Geophysical Union, v. 36, No. 4.)*

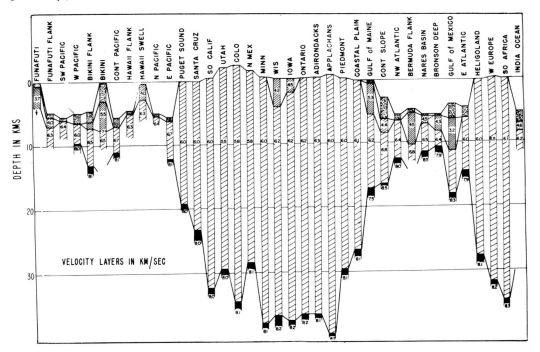

These deeply intruded peridotites are located in central parts of complexly folded mountain belts like the Alps. Since the core of folded belts, now exposed through erosion by glaciers, weathering, and running water, has been uplifted great distances, it is probable that peridotites which were intruded there came from below the Moho.

Alpine peridotites occur in two belts, about 120 miles apart, extending the length of the mountain system (Fig. 30–4). So close is the relationship between these peridotites and the alpine type of mountain belt, that the presence in the earliest Precambrian rocks of peridotites showing a similar alignment is taken as an indication of the probable existence of ancient alpine mountain systems which have been almost completely destroyed by erosion, metamorphism, and subsequent deformation.

Blocks of peridotite and lavas extruded from deep-seated volcanoes have offered the only other means of determining directly the composition of the rocks below the crust. Moho is at a much shallower depth under the deep-ocean basins than it is under continents, thus rock melted below the crust would more likely find its way to the surface beneath the deep oceans than to the surface on the continents. Apparently this has actually happened. There is a distinct difference in the composition of the lavas extruded from volcanoes in the Pacific basin from those extruded around the margins of the Pacific. The lavas in the deep ocean are composed of olivine basalt, while those of the boundary zone are andesite or rhyolite (silica-rich). Blocks of peridotite found in the basalt are probably derived from subcrustal layers.

Mohole Project

IN 1961 drilling operations were begun on one of the most ambitious projects yet undertaken in earth science—drilling through the earth's crust. This project was sponsored by the National Academy of Science and the National Science Foundation. Our knowledge of the interior of the earth is almost altogether derived from indirect methods. By drilling a series of holes through the crust, geologists would for the first time have an opportunity to examine rocks from a number of complete sections through the crust, through the M discontinuity, and into the outer mantle. The first holes drilled did not penetrate through the crust. They were drilled to study the feasibility of drilling a later series of deeper holes. Drilling through the crust is not a simple matter. It was decided early in the study that the Mohole would have to be drilled in the sea, to take advantage of the relatively shallow depth of the Moho there. Drilling at sea by oil companies is confined to the continental shelves, but drilling to Moho will have to be undertaken in deep water. This presents a number of problems, some of which have already been solved. The test drilling in 1961 demonstrated that a well could be drilled from a floating barge through thousands of feet of water. The problems here are to maintain the position of the barge over the hole and to arrange a method for re-entering the hole when drill bits have to be replaced. Both of these problems were overcome in what actually constitutes a major engineering advance—one of the side benefits of this program.

In the 1961 operation five holes were drilled in 3,100 feet of water off La Jolla, California. The holes penetrated to over 1,000 feet in the sea floor. This was followed by five more holes drilled in waters 11,600 feet deep with penetration of 600 feet. The second set of holes was drilled near Guadalupe. Here the drilling penetrated some 600 feet of Miocene sediments and then went into a basalt layer. Drilling penetrated only 40 feet into the basalt. It could be that this is a thin layer of basalt in a thicker section of sediment, or it could possibly be the upper portion of a second layer in the crust, but well above the Moho.

Plans are now being made for more drilling to greater depths. Specialized drilling equipment and ships are being designed and built. Hopefully these will be used to drill holes into and through the crust in many parts of the oceanic crust. In the meantime scientists are concerned with where to drill to obtain the most information. Among the most probable sites are one on

FIG. 22-2. / *A sharp downward pitch in an anticline on the west side of the Big Horn Mountains in Wyoming. Folded structures of this nature indicate the magnitude of forces which deform the earth. The oldest rocks are exposed in the core of the fold. (Photo by courtesy of the U.S. Geological Survey.)*

the rise just north of the Puerto Rico Trench and a second on St. Paul's Rock where sub-crustal rocks may be exposed. Comprehensive studies of these and other areas are now being made with seismic and other geophysical tools.

The cost of this operation will be many millions of dollars, but the potential it offers for providing data is very great. Complete sections through the ocean floor sediments will provide information concerning the age of the ocean basins, whether or not the continents have drifted, past temperature changes in the ocean, rates of marine sedimentation, extent of turbidity current deposits, amount of extraterrestrial material in the ocean sediments, and the nature and extent of deformation of rock units in the oceanic crust. Deeper holes would reveal the nature of the Moho discontinuity, and would

answer questions as to what causes the discontinuity—a change in composition of the rocks, or a change in the phase or atomic packing of minerals making up the rock. Important information will continue to come for a long period of time from holes drilled because they can be equipped to record seismic disturbances, variations in magnetic fields, and heat flow measurements. These are but a few of the problems which may be studied through deep drilling in the ocean. If plans continue on schedule the next phase of the drilling will start in 1965 or 1966 (Hedberg, 1963).

Seismology

MOST OF WHAT IS KNOWN ABOUT THE interior of the earth is obtained through the exacting work of seismologists. Unlike most other major branches of natural science, seismology (the study of earthquakes) dates back less than a century. The first effective records were not obtained until the latter part of the nineteenth century, and application of seismology to exploration for oil and other natural resources did not occur until after World War I. Japanese scientists have carried on much of the work on earthquake waves in hope of finding a way to predict earthquakes, which have taken such heavy tolls of life and property in Japan and other Asian countries. Most earthquakes are caused either by failure (breaking) of rocks of the crust or by explosions of volcanoes. Sudden impulses generated in earthquakes expand and distort rocks near the fault or explosion, and these impulses are propagated through the interior of the earth and along its surface, because the materials of which the earth is composed are highly elastic. These impulses or shock waves travel with different velocities through rocks with different elastic properties. Part of the energy of a wave may be reflected or refracted where it comes to the contact between different types of rocks. Many of these waves are intense enough to go through or completely around the earth. The job of the seismologists is to devise means of detecting waves, of recognizing different types of waves, and of interpreting their significance.

Causes of Earthquakes

ROCKS, BEING ELASTIC, CAN WITHSTAND A certain amount of stress without deforming permanently, but if stress is continued for a long period of time, or if it is increased in magnitude, rocks first take a permanent deformation or strain and eventually rupture. A *fault* is a break or fracture in the materials of the earth along which there has been displacement (Fig. 22–3). When rupture occurs, rocks on either side of the fault tend to return to their original shape because of their elasticity, and an elastic rebound occurs. It is this rebound that sets up seismic waves. The magnitude of

faulting is highly variable. Some faults are nothing more than slight displacements. Others extend for hundreds of miles, and have accumulated displacements amounting to many miles. The San Andreas fault in California is one of the longest. A movement along it was responsible for the San Francisco earthquake of 1906. The crust was visibly rent for a distance of 270 miles, and displacements in that zone amounted to as much as 20 feet. Movement along the fault was primarily a horizontal shifting, with minor vertical displacement. That this fault has been active for a long period of time is shown by displacement of streams and other physiographic and geologic features. All of these features are offset to the right on opposite sides of the fault.

Volcanic Earthquakes

EARTHQUAKES ASSOCIATED with volcanoes are more localized, both in extent of damage and in intensity of shock waves produced, than are those associated with faults. In some regions, particularly in the circum-Pacific belt, volcanic activity and active faulting are closely associated. Nevertheless, it is possible to distinguish some earthquakes as being caused by activity due to volcanic phenomena not associated with major breaks in the crust. A shock may be produced by any of the following mechanisms:

1. Explosion of the volcano upon release and expansion of gases and lavas.
2. Faulting within the volcano resulting from pressures in the magma chamber.
3. Collapse of the volcano into space formed by extrusion of gases and molten matter.
4. Harmonic tremor due to rising magma.

Kwanto Earthquake

ONE OF THE GREATEST earthquakes on record occurred about 50 miles from Tokyo, Japan, on September 1, 1923. Estimates of the loss of as many as a quarter of a million lives have been made. The earthquake occurred shortly before noon, and much of the damage was caused by fires which swept through the ruins afterward. Fires were started because so many families were cooking at the time of the earthquake. Buildings collapsed and ignited, and water mains were broken, making the extinguishing of the fires impossible. Half a million buildings were shaken down in the region around Sagami Bay, and much of this damage was concentrated in the heavily populated cities of Tokyo and Yokohama. Hydrographic resurveys of the bay shortly after the earthquake revealed changes in the shape and depth of the bottom of the bay of such magnitude that most geologists attribute part of the change to errors in the earlier survey. If the figures of both surveys are taken at face value, some areas of the bay were lowered more than 650 feet and other areas were raised more than 800 feet. Even allowing for errors in surveying, the magnitude of the changes was exceptionally great. Most of the sediments in the bay came from eruptions of the famous volcano Fujiyama. It is likely that these unconsolidated sediments shifted or slumped during the earthquake, which was caused by movement along a major fault. Waves on the surface of the bay attained a height of 35 feet during and shortly after the earthquake, and more than 1,000 aftershocks of minor intensity followed the main shock, which lasted only a few minutes.

Assam Earthquake

THE INDIAN EARTHQUAKE WHICH occurred in the range of mountains south of the Himalaya Mountains and north of the Bay of Bengal in 1897 is probably the most violent in recorded history. The quake occurred when the mountains, which are formed of large blocks of the crust tilted along faults, were shifted northward and uplifted as much as 35 feet in places. Faults that opened in the surface were traced for more than 20 miles into the jungle. Drainage of some streams was stopped, lakes formed, and large areas were flooded. In other areas lakes and swamps were drained. Many fissures opened in the ground. Almost all masonry buildings in the mountains were leveled. The region of complete destruction covered nearly 9,000 square miles; extensive damage was done in an area of 150,000 square miles; and the earthquake was felt over an area of ¾ million square miles.

Chilean Earthquakes of 1960

AT 6 A.M. on May 21, 1960, a sharp earthquake was felt in the region around Concepcion, Chile. Considerable property damage was caused by this movement and most of the people in the region affected were so frightened that they ran out of their houses. This quake, which was later determined to have originated at a depth of 50 km., was followed by small aftershocks for all of the next day. Then on the next day at 3 P.M. a second sharp shock

FIG. 22–3. / *Ground fractures. These fractures opened in the ground near a fault scarp which resulted from the Montana earthquake of August, 1959. (Photo by the author.)*

came and was followed fifteen minutes later by the most severe shock of what was to be a long period of violent earth movements. The center of this shock was almost 300 km. south of Concepcion, but it affected an area 150 km. by 1,600 km along the coast of Chile.

When the second and third shocks came, waves were visible in the streets and on the ground. Trees and telephone poles swayed back and forth, loud noices were heard coming from the ground, and cracks formed. Cars were tossed back and forth across streets and some fell into fissures. Almost all man-made structures in this region were damaged and many were totally destroyed. Landslides caused by the violent motion buried parts of a number of cities. The strongest shocks were felt at Isla Chiloe, where trees were snapped off, the ground cracked open, highways were split, road fills gave out, and soils became liquid and flowed.

After the main shocks the sea retreated well below low tide and came back 20 minutes later as a tsunami between 4 and 11 meters high, destroying parts of many towns. In one alone, five hundred people were drowned. These waves were set up by subsidence of parts of the coast, in places amounting to two meters. Wave motion caused by this subsidence crossed the Pacific and destroyed towns in Hawaii and in Japan. On May 24 an explosion occurred on the side of one of the large active volcanoes in Chile. Ash, steam, and finally lava poured from a fissure about a hundred meters long.

Earthquakes continued in Chile for several months. These were responsible for billions of dollars in property damage and loss of more than 5,000 lives in what may have been the most severe earthquakes of this century.

Modified Mercalli Intensity Scale

G. MERCALLI MADE STUDIES OF INTENSITY and regional effects of earthquakes between 1890 and 1901. He found that some regions suffered much more intense shocks than others.

His work called for an accurate scale of intensity, and he devised such a scale. At that time few seismographs were in existence, and the scale had to be based on readily obtainable information. The Mercalli scale (below) is still in use today. (Nicholas H. Heck, *Earthquakes*, Princeton University Press, 1936.)

1 — Not felt except by a few under especially favorable conditions.

2 — Felt only by a few persons at rest. Delicately suspended objects may swing.

3 — Felt quite noticeably under favorable circumstances. Standing automobiles may rock slightly.

4 — Felt by many or most persons, some being awakened. Dishes, windows, and doors are disturbed, walls crack. Sensation like a heavy truck striking the building.

5 — Some dishes and windows break. In a few instances plaster cracks. Unstable objects move.

6 — Felt by all; many are frightened and run outdoors. Some heavy furniture moves. A few instances of fallen plaster or damaged chimneys.

7 — Everyone runs outdoors. Damage is negligible in buildings of good design and construction, slight to moderate in well-built ordinary structures. Some chimneys break. Noticed by persons driving cars.

8 — Panel walls are thrown out of frame structures. Many chimneys, factory stacks, columns, monuments and walls fall. Heavy furniture overturns. Sand and mud are ejected in small amounts through fissures in unconsolidated sediments.

9 — Buildings shift off foundations. Ground cracks conspicuously. Underground pipes break.

10 — Ground is badly cracked; rails are bent; landslides from river banks and steep slopes are considerable. Water is splashed over banks.

11 — Few masonry structures remain standing. Bridges are destroyed. Broad fissures open in the ground. Earth slumps in soft ground.

12 — Damage is total. Waves occur in ground surfaces. Lines of sight and level are distorted. Objects are thrown into the air.

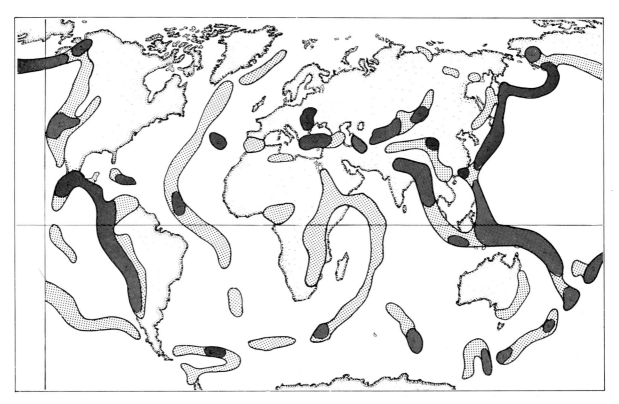

FIG. 22–4. / *Distribution of earthquakes. Belts of moderately intensive activity are lightly stippled. The darker portions are zones of most intensive earthquake activity. These belts coincide with folded mountain belts and midocean ridges. (After Yu. A. Meshcheryakov, American Geological Institute, International Geology Review, v. 1, No. 8, August, 1959, pp. 48–49.)*

Distribution of Earthquakes

As DATA HAS SLOWLY ACCUMULATED IT has become apparent that earthquakes occur most frequently in certain belts of the crust (Fig. 22–4). Some areas, the stable continental shields and the abyssal plains of the oceans, have almost no earthquakes. Other areas have typical seismic characteristics. The circum-Pacific belt is one of the most active zones. Most of the shallow earthquakes and almost all deep ones occur in this belt. Young, folded mountain belts are sites of many shallow earthquakes, as is the midocean ridge. Other earthquakes are associated locally with volcanoes and rift zones like the Red Sea.

Shock Waves

ROCKS POSSESS ELASTIC PROPERTIES WHICH enable them to transmit seismic waves. A perfectly elastic material is one which returns to its original form when a deforming force is removed. A rock behaves elastically within a certain limit. If *strain* (change in shape) of the rock exceeds that *elastic limit*, the rock cannot fully recover after the deforming force is removed. If strain greatly exceeds the elastic limit, the rock may rupture. Strains are caused by *stress*, force applied to the rock. Several types of stresses are recognized. An elevator cable tends to pull apart; it is under what is called *tensile stress*. Elongation of the cable resulting from the stress is a *tensile strain*. A different type of stress is found in the drive shaft of an automobile, which is twisted and said to be in *torque*; it is under *shearing stress*. If a nail is driven into a board with a hammer, with each blow the nail is shortened under *compressive stress*. Still another type of stress is found in bodies submerged in a liquid or in rocks buried under great thickness of rock. The term *hydrostatic pressure* is applied in cases where objects are submerged in water, and *rock pressure* is the corresponding term designating pressure in the interior of the earth.

When an earthquake occurs, a sudden movement of rocks in the crust takes place. This movement may be elastic rebound resulting from release of stresses on either side of a fault when rupture occurs, or compression created inside a volcano by an explosion. This impetus given to the rocks in the immediate vicinity of the earthquake is transmitted through the crust. If crustal rocks are homogeneous, identical reactions to the initial shock move outward from the point of origin in spherical shells. Because rocks are rigid, strain produced in one place is transmitted to the other parts very rapidly, and shock waves travel great distances before the energy is expended. Two types of waves, *dilational waves* and *shear waves*, are set up by quakes.

Dilational waves are also known as *P-waves*, *compressional waves*, and *longitudinal waves*. They involve changes in volume of the rock through which they are transmitted. Sound waves are typical of this type of wave motion. Sound travels through any compressible medium such as water or rocks. A vibration is set by motion of the object sending the sound, as in the motion of the surface of a drum after it is hit. As the face of the drum moves out on each vibration it forces air away from it, compressing the air in immediate contact with the drum face. This layer of compressed air in turn compresses the layer of air next to it, and so the wave is transmitted. Each time the drum face moves in, the air next to it is pulled in. This pull is transmitted to the next layer of air and follows the compressed layer outward as an expanding spherical shell. Vibration is along the path of travel of the wave front—hence the name "longitudinal." *Shear waves* are known as *S-waves* or *transverse waves*. They vibrate perpendicular to the direction in which the wave

front is moving, and they are caused by the transmission of shearing stresses like the twist in a bar. No volume changes are associated with them, but other distortions of shape are.

In addition to P- and S-waves, more complicated wave motion is produced and propagated along the surface of the earth. Lord Rayleigh was the first to recognize this special wave type on the surfaces of bounded elastic solids. In the propagation of a *Rayleigh wave*, motion is vertical and in the direction of motion of the wave front. Each particle involved in this motion follows an elliptical orbit in retrograde motion (along the bottom of the ellipse the motion is in the direction of propagation and at the top in the opposite direction). A. E. H. Love later demonstrated the probable existence of another type of wave which travels at the surface, with displacements being transverse to the direction of motion of the wave front. These two wave motions move along the ground surface.

Velocity of Shock Waves

THE VELOCITY OF seismic waves through a rock is determined by the rock's elastic properties and density. Both S-waves and P-waves increase in velocity as rocks become more rigid and velocity is decreased as rocks become more dense. However, a shear wave cannot travel through media which cannot be sheared, such as liquids, whereas a P-wave does continue through liquids because it depends on compressibility of the medium.

Bending, Reflection, and Refraction

SEISMIC WAVES ARE BENT as they pass through layers that gradually increase in rigidity with depth. Waves are *reflected* and *refracted* (Fig. 22–5) at boundaries between layers with different elastic properties or densities. When a shock wave reaches a *discontinuity* (a change in elastic properties), part of the energy of the wave is reflected back toward the surface. The velocity of the reflected wave remains unchanged, but the remainder of the energy passes through the boundary and continues as a wave with increased or decreased velocity, according to the qualities of the new layer. Because the velocity is changed, the path of the wave is changed. When the wave passes from one layer to another of lower rigidity (and therefore lower velocity), the wave front is bent down. The reverse occurs when waves pass from a less rigid to a more rigid layer. Thus the gradual increase in rigidity of rocks with depth causes the velocity to gradually increase and the paths of shock waves to be curved upward.

Detection of Seismic Waves

MOTION OF THE GROUND SURFACE resulting from an earthquake depends on how deep and how far away the *focus* (where an earthquake originates) is located. Near the *epicenter* (the point on the ground directly over the focus) ground motion may turn buildings on their foundations or throw objects into the air, but at great distances from the earthquake center the motion consists of small displacements far less than the jar resulting from blasting in a quarry. The *seismograph* is an instrument designed to detect the magnitude and direction of these minute displacements. Any quantity such as force or acceleration that has magnitude and direction can be resolved into three mutually perpendicular components. For this reason most seismograph stations employ three instruments to record components of ground motion along three mutually perpendicular lines—horizontal motion along north-south and east-west lines, and motion perpendicular to the earth's surface. The principle on which most seismographs operate is very simple. The perfect seismograph is one in which it is possible to isolate a mass and measure the motion of the ground in relation to that stationary mass. In essence this is how a seismograph works. A mass is delicately suspended by springs so it is relatively unmoved during the quake. In many modern instruments a magnet is used for the mass, and a coil of wire is anchored to the ground so that it moves past the magnet when the ground is in motion (Figs. 22–6 and 22–7). The two are isolated so

FIG. 22–5. / *Schematic illustration of the reflection and refraction of a shock wave along a contact between two rock units of different materials. The wave represented by the vertical ray passes through the boundary without reflection or refraction. The second ray is bent into the lower unit at the contact. Part of the energy is reflected back up into the top unit. The third ray is shown approaching the boundary at what is known as the critical angle. Part of the energy is reflected back into the top unit, and the remainder is refracted along the contact. All along the contact energy continues to be refracted back into the top unit. The wave energy which is reflected and refracted into the top unit from the boundary may be picked up by geophones placed on the ground surface.*

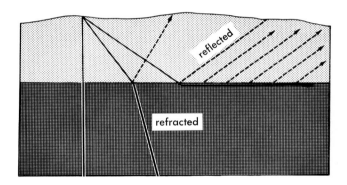

that they do not touch one another at any time. During an earthquake the coils move through the magnetic field surrounding the magnet, which induces an electrical current in the coils. The magnitude of the current is a function of the speed and distance of the coils' motion and thus of the ground motion also. The current is then recorded by the seismograph as a measure of the earthquake's intensity. A radio at the seismograph station receives time signals from the United States Naval Observatory or other stations broadcasting Greenwich Standard Time (this is used at seismograph stations throughout the world to avoid confusion in timing the occurrence of an earthquake). This time signal is converted into a small current impulse marking the exact time on the seismogram.

FIG. 22–6. / *Receiving component of a Wilson-Lamison seismometer. (Photo by courtesy of the U.S. Coast and Geodetic Survey.)*

FIG. 22–7. / *A simple seismograph. The mass suspended on the wire tends to stand still while the support and drum move during an earthquake. This instrument would measure motion in the direction perpendicular to the page.*

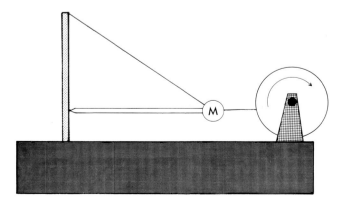

Interpretation of Seismic Waves

WHILE THE SEISMOGRAPH IS IN OPERATION, the trace indicating the earth's motion is rarely at rest. Movements of trees, waves breaking along the seashore, and even trucks passing on nearby highways are picked up by the more sensitive instruments. These minor movements are called *microseisms*. With the arrival of the first shock wave from an earthquake the trace is suddenly displaced from its sinuous path. This break is indicated by a sudden change in the direction of the movement and increased amplitude of the swing of the trace. The key to identification of arrival of subsequent waves is also change in direction and amplitude of the movement. The time of arrival of each wave at the station varies according to the path traveled by the wave in coming to the station and the velocity of the wave motion. The first wave to arrive is one which travels the most direct path with the highest velocity. That wave is usually the P-wave. It is followed by the S-wave traveling the same path. The time required for a wave to travel from the earthquake to the station is called the *travel time* for that wave (Fig. 22–8). The travel time for P- and S-waves is not known at the seismograph station because neither the location nor the distance to the epicenter is initially known. These can be calculated, however, because P and S travel the same path and with known velocities. The longer the path the two have traveled the farther P will be ahead of S; thus the time interval between their first arrivals is a function of the distance they have traveled. Three seismograph stations pool their calculated distances to the epicenter. The distance from each station to the earthquake is laid out on a globe as an arc, and the point of intersection of the three arcs is the epicenter of the earthquake (Fig. 22–9).

Most interpretations of the structure of the interior of the earth from seismograms are based on changes in travel times and amplitudes of waves reaching stations located at various distances from an earthquake (Fig. 22–10). Evidence for the first discontinuity below the Moho

FIG. 22–8. / *Travel time curve. The ordinate is time in seconds. The absissa is distance in degrees. From this graph it is possible to predict what seismic waves will reach a station at a given distance from the earthquake epicenter, and the time of arrival of each of those waves. P is for compressional waves, S is for shear waves. Subscript c as in PcP means the wave was reflected from the core. K indicates that the waves passed through part of the core. (After Jeffreys, The Earth, Cambridge University Press, 1952.)*

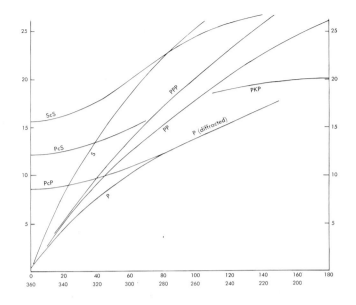

FIG. 22–9. / *Location of epicenter of an earthquake is obtained by use of distance determinations from three seismograph stations.*

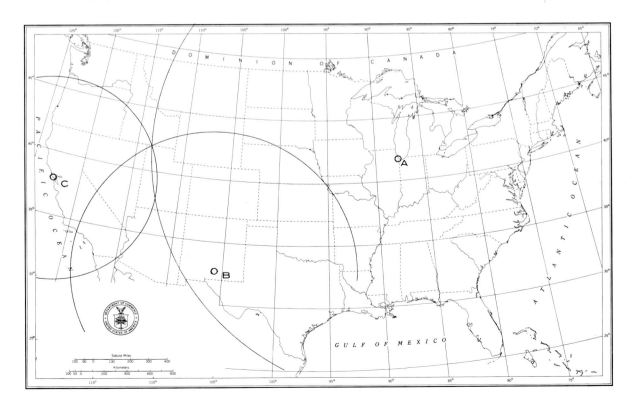

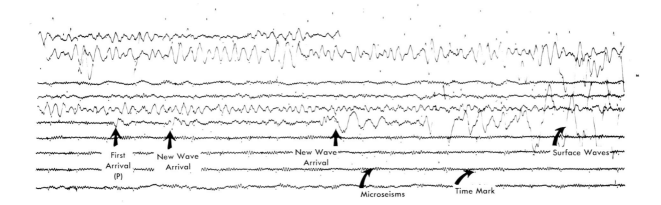

FIG. 22–10. / *A seismogram. The minor fluctuations in the trace are called microseisms. They are received almost continuously. The first break in the trace marks the arrival of the wave which traveled the most direct path with the greatest velocity. This is the P, or compressional, wave. The sheer wave which arrives some time later started at the same instant as the P wave and travels the same path but at a lower velocity. The spread between the arrival of these two waves is a measure of the distance to the focus.*

is found on records of stations located between 15 and 22 degrees from the epicenter. At these distances the velocities of P and S increase considerably—P goes up to 9.1 km./sec. from the normal 8.1 km./sec., and S up to 5.3 km./sec. from 4.5 km./sec. Sir Harold Jeffreys interprets this as a change brought about by passage of the waves through a zone in which the rate of change of velocity with depth increases. He postulates that the depth of this zone is about 400 km.

Beyond 22 degrees from the epicenter the velocity of P- and S-waves increases continuously (Fig. 22–11). This holds for all stations located up to a distance of 103 degrees from the epicenter. Beyond 103 degrees the amplitude of P- and S-waves decreases, or they are not recorded at all. This decreased amplitude is observed by stations in the area, called the *shadow zone*, between 103 and 143 degrees distant. Beyond 143 degrees amplitude increases for compressional (P) waves, but shear (S) waves have disappeared altogether. These observations lead to identification of the outer boundary of the core. No records, or at best only poor records, are obtained between 103 and 143 degrees because waves approaching the boundary of the core along a line tangent to the boundary are refracted into the core and through it in such a way that they return to the surface and are recorded at stations between 143 and 180 degrees distant (Fig. 22–10).

Some P-waves have been identified in the shadow zone. They are due to a small inner core with a higher velocity than the outer core. This inner core has a radius of 1,300 km. and is more rigid than the outer core. The core as a whole has a radius of 2,900 km.

So far no mention has been made of waves that are reflected and refracted from each of the discontinuities above. They are observed at seismograph stations and serve to confirm the interpretations made from first arrivals of P- and S-waves. Some paths and the travel-time curves are illustrated (Figs. 22–8 and 22–11). After arrival of the shear wave, motion of the ground often becomes so complex that correct identification of many of these phases is impossible. None of them can be identified after the surface waves arrive. Usually a state of resonance is set up in the ground with the arrival of the surface wave, producing long-period waves that are easily identified on the record by their amplitude.

FIG. 23–1. / *Gravity corrections. In* a *three masses are shown. If the gravity meter were located at the center position the attraction on the meter by the two other masses would be equal and directed in opposite directions. The two attractions would balance one another. In* b *a second mass is shown in a position above one on the ground. The solid arrows represent the direction along which the forces act. The effect on the mass at the ground surface is the same as it would be if two forces shown by the dashed arrows were acting on it. Thus part of the pull on a meter in this position by the earth would be offset by the upward force due to the second mass. This situation is essentially that caused by the sun, moon, or segments of the topography located above the position of a gravity meter. In* c *a gravity meter is shown set up at some elevation above the geoid. In this case the reading must be corrected for the effect of the topography, the distance the meter is above the geoid, and for the attraction of the plate of rock between the geoid and the gravity meter.*

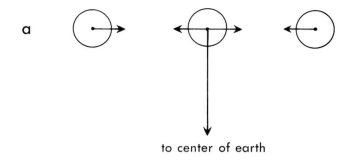

a

to center of earth

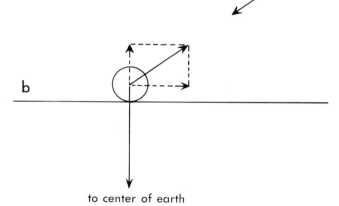

b

to center of earth

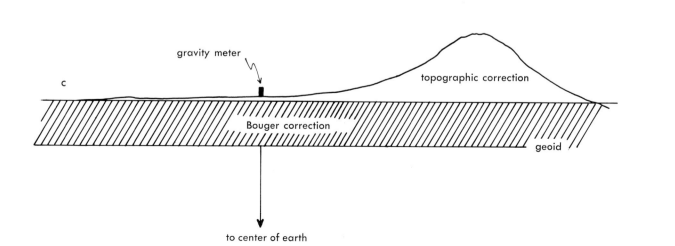

c

gravity meter

topographic correction

Bouger correction

geoid

to center of earth

tion of the elongation is needed. A number of different methods are used to obtain these magnifications. The instruments are calibrated to read in terms of units of force. One of the standard procedures for checking the calibration is to take readings with the instrument on various floors of a building. The readings can then be checked against the theoretical changes arising from differences in elevation.

Gravitational force may be thought of as a pull exerted between two objects. It acts along a line connecting the two objects, and it has a certain magnitude. When several objects are mutually attracting one another the effects on any one of them may be additive or may tend to cancel each other out, depending on the position of the bodies as shown in Fig. 23–1.

Causes of Variation in the Earth's Field

BECAUSE SUCH PRECISE MEASUREMENTS can be made, great care must be taken in analyzing gravity measurements. Gravity should be a constant value everywhere on the surface of an isolated, homogeneous, perfectly spherical earth, but the earth is none of these. It is possible, however, to calculate what the force of gravitational attraction would be if the earth were isolated from the pull of other planets, the sun, and the moon, and if the mass of the earth were incorporated in a homogeneous, spherical body without irregularities on the surface. The following factors cause deviation from such a theoretical gravity field.

1. Deviation of the earth's shape from that of a sphere. The earth's form closely approximates a sphere, but its radius is 21 km. longer at the equator than it is at the poles, and it is slightly pear-shaped. The earth behaves as a fluid balanced between gravitational forces, tending to make it spherical, and centrifugal forces, tending to flatten it. The force of attraction at the equator is less than at the poles for two reasons:

The surface of the earth at the equator is farther away from the center of mass.

Centrifugal acceleration of the earth at the equator is outward and opposite in direction to gravitational acceleration. Because the poles are not involved in the rotation there is no centrifugal acceleration there.

2. Attraction of extraterrestrial bodies. In a sense every body in the universe exerts some attraction on the earth, but since the force of attraction varies as the square of the distance between the bodies, it is unnecessary to consider the gravitational effect of bodies outside the Solar System. Effects of the sun and the moon are the most notable. They not only produce such familiar phenomena as tides in the oceans, they also distort the shape of the "solid" earth. Likewise they exert a pull on the instrument being used to measure the earth's field. If the lines of attraction pass through the earth, a high value for the field will be obtained; if the pull is opposite, it will tend to reduce the observed value of the force of gravity. This variation changes from hour to hour and with the seasons as positions of the moon and sun change.

3. Variation with elevation. Because a point on a mountain is farther away from the center of the earth than one at sea level, the force of gravitational attraction on objects there will be lowered if the effect of increased elevation alone is considered.

4. Variation due to attraction of surface material. In considering the effect of elevation we neglected to take into account the attraction that the mass of material between sea level and the top of the mountain is going to exert. This is known as the *Bouguer effect*. Not only that surface material which is directly below the point at which we want a measurement will affect the reading, but mass in the surrounding topography will also exert an attraction on the instrument.

Negative Anomaly

average specific
gravity 2.4
of sediments

specific gravity
2.15

Salt

Reduction of Gravity
Observations to Reveal Anomalies

THE INSIGHT WE GAIN INTO THE STRUCTURE of the earth's crust and interior comes mostly from interpretation of the places where acceleration of gravity deviates from the normal. These anomalies may be obtained by making corrections in the observed value for the effect of latitude, terrain, the Bouguer effect, *free-air* (elevation above sea level), and the attraction of the sun and moon. The observed value is thus reduced to what it would be at sea level at that position if all the terrain above sea level were removed and the pull of the sun and moon were nullified. If the resulting corrected value still deviates from the theoretically calculated value

FIG. 23–2. / *A profile of the force of gravity over a salt dome. Note the marked decrease in the force of attraction over the salt. Salt has a specific gravity of 2.15 as compared with an average value for the unconsolidated sediments of 2.4. A negative anomaly is seen over the salt. A positive anomaly would appear if the profile had been run over a body of high-density rock.*

FIG. 23–3. / *A gravity maximum appears here over the crest of an anticline because a high-density limestone is brought close to the surface in the anticlinal structure. The extension of the springs represents the force of attraction on a mass at the surface. (By courtesy of* The Oil and Gas Journal, Tulsa, Oklahoma.*)*

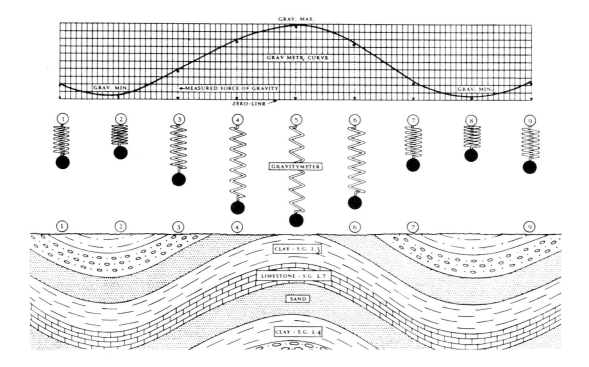

GRAV. MAX.

GRAV METR CURVE

GRAV. MIN. ←MEASURED FORCE OF GRAVITY GRAV. MIN.

ZERO-LINE

GRAVITYMETER

CLAY - S.G. 2.3

LIMESTONE - S.G. 2.7

SAND

CLAY - S.G. 2.4

for a homogeneous earth, the difference in the two values is the amount of the anomaly. Anomalies may be either positive or negative.

Negative anomalies are found over bodies of salt under the Gulf Coast (Fig. 23–2). Over two hundred of these salt plugs are known. They have been prolific oil–producing structures and are well-known from well data. The typical plug is about a mile in diameter, located a few hundred to a few thousand feet deep, and shaped somewhat like a carrot. Because salt has a lower density than sediments in which these plugs are intruded, the plugs are readily located by gravity measurements. Positive anomalies are found where metallic ore bodies are located in less dense country rock. Other anomalies help locate faults or folds in which high density rocks have been offset, as is indicated in Fig. 23–3.

Unlike seismic methods, gravity measurements do not give exact information about the depth or shape of the buried rock masses they suggest. A small body of high density ore buried at a shallow depth might give the same anomaly as a much larger but more deeply buried mass. Thus other geologic considerations and methods must be used to suggest the most probable actual circumstance. Gravity anomalies do not have unique solutions.

Isostasy

THE THEORY OF ISOSTASY POSTULATES A system for large-scale distribution of material in the earth's crust and interior. The theory is based on, and explains, observed gravity values. We can, of course, measure the density of rocks exposed at the surface and in wells, but these give only an idea of the outermost part of the crust. Rocks making up continents are generally found to be of lower density than those in the ocean basins. The difference is essentially that between basalt and granite. This does not answer the important question: How are continents supported so high above the level of the ocean floors (Fig. 4–19)? Is the earth's mantle rigid and do continents simply rest on a solid platform, or is this weight of the continents buoyed up in some way? This problem concerned Leonardo da Vinci in the sixteenth century. He expressed the opinion that the mountains were lighter than the plains and that this was in part responsible for their relative elevations. As early as 1749, Pierre Bouguer, who was a member of a French expedition sent to Peru to establish by survey the length of a meridian arc, expressed the opinion that the Andes have less mass than had been expected. An explanation offered soon after this was that mountains have less density because they represent material that has risen as a result of thermal expansion of rocks at depth.

The next major advance came one hundred years later, in 1850. Another survey was being made to establish the length of a meridian arc. This time the survey was being conducted in India and one of the geodesists was a man named G. Everest for whom Mt. Everest was named. Two methods were used to determine the difference in latitude between two cities in the mountains. One was careful surveying on the ground and the other was use of astronomical observations. When the work had advanced far enough it was discovered that there was a difference in the latitude measurements made by these two methods that amounted to 5¼ seconds of latitude in a distance of only 375 miles. No errors could be found in either set of data to explain such a large difference. One of the men who studied the data was J. H. Pratt, who was living at Calcutta at the time. He studied the measurements and concluded that the error had been introduced because the leveling system used to set up the telescope to make the astronomical observations had been thrown off by the mass of the Himalayan Mountains. He calculated what the deflection should be at each of the two stations, taking into consideration the mass of the nearby mountains. He concluded that the two readings should have been off by nearly 16 seconds instead of 5¼ seconds. This surprising discovery—that the mountains did not cause as much deflection of a plumb bob as they should—left him with the conclusion that part of the attraction must be compensated for within or under the mountains by a mass deficiency. Pratt developed and expanded the idea that mountains are caused by expansion from depth of rocks of high density. This model allowed the mountain range to have lower density, accounting for the observed deflection of the plumb bob (which was deflected toward the mountains, but not as much as it should have been). He held that this thermal expansion gradually decreased at depth under the mountains in such a way that eventually a depth was reached at which density would be essentially the same, regardless of the differences between areas at the surface. He calculated that at a depth of about 100 miles the surficial differences in gravity would be evened out. This depth would thus be a depth at which compensation occurs.

Within a few months of the time Pratt submitted his paper to the Royal Society of London another scientist, G. B. Airy, submitted a paper on the same subject. But Airy had a different idea of the mechanism of density distribution.

I conceive that there can be no other support than that arising from the downward projection of a portion of the earth's light crust into the dense lava; the horizontal extent of that projection corresponding rudely with the horizontal extent of the table-land, and the depth of its projection downwards being such that the increased power of flotation thus gained is roughly equal to the increase of weight above from the prominence of the table-land. It appears to me that the state of the earth's crust lying upon the lava may be compared with perfect correctness to the state of a raft of timber floating upon the water; in which, if we remark one log whose upper surface floats much higher than the upper surfaces of the others we are certain that its lower surface lies deeper in the water than the lower surface of the others.

It will be remarked that the disturbance depends on two actions; the positive attraction produced by the elevated table-land; and the diminution of attraction, or negative attraction, produced by the substitution of a certain volume of light crust (in the lower projection) for heavy lava.

The diminution of attractive matter below, produced by the substitution of light crust for heavy lava, will be sensibly equal to the increase of attractive matter above (Airy, 1855).

Thus was originated the idea that mountains have roots.

About thirty years later C. E. Dutton defined the term *isostasy* in terms of the figure of the earth, as follows:

If the earth were composed of homogeneous matter its normal figure of equilibrium . . . would be a true spheroid of revolution; but if heterogeneous, if some parts were denser or lighter than others, its normal figure would no longer be spheroidal. Where the lighter matter was accumulated there would be a tendency to bulge, and where the denser matter existed there would be a tendency to flatten or depress the surface. For this condition of equilibrium of figure, to which gravitation tends to reduce a planetary body, irrespective of whether it be homogeneous or not, I propose the name isostasy. . . . We may also use the corresponding adjective, isostatic. An isostatic earth, composed of homogeneous matter and without rotation, would be truly spherical. . . .

But if the earth be not homogeneous—if some portions near the surface are lighter than others—then the isostatic figure is no longer a sphere or spheroid of revolution, but a deformed figure, bulged where the matter is light and depressed where it is heavy. The question which I propose is: How nearly does the earth's figure approach to isostasy?

Modern measurements show the answer to Dutton's question to be that the earth as a whole approaches the condition of *isostatic equilibrium* very closely. The original models of Pratt and Airy have been modified, but regardless of which of these models is used, the conclusion is reached that the earth is essentially in a condition of isostatic equilibrium.

Pratt assumed that the boundary between upper light material and lower dense rocks is at a uniform depth, called the *depth of compensation*. He further postulated that there are variations in the density of the lighter layer which are related to the elevation of the surface. Lighter material lies under mountains, and heavier material under oceans. The weight of columns of rock extending from the surface to the depth of compensation in different parts of the earth is thus the same. The United States Coast and Geodetic Survey uses as the depth

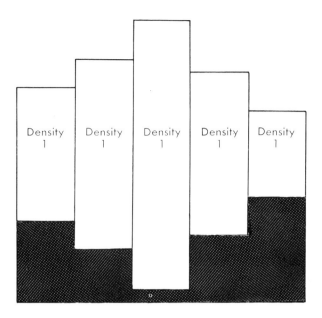

FIG. 23–4a. / *Airy's theory of isostasy. This illustrates one way in which isostatic equilibrium might be obtained if the crust of the earth consisted of an essentially uniform density unit of different heights. Airy would account for the mountains by the presence of deep roots of crustal material extending down into the high-density mantle. This actually represents a case of flotational equilibrium. The mantle rock is plastic and can flow.*

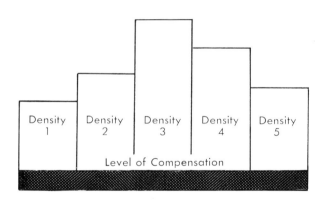

FIG. 23–4b. / *Pratt's theory of isostasy. Pratt recognized that the crust of the earth is not made up of materials of uniform density. He visualized isostatic equilibrium as being the result of density. The low-density materials would represent the continents and the high-density materials, the ocean. He postulated a depth or level of compensation at which the effects of different densities above were balanced.*

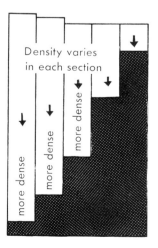

FIG. 23–4c. / *Heiskanen's theory of isostasy. He combines the assumptions of both Pratt and Airy. According to this theory density varies both between columns and within each. The higher densities are represented by the shorter columns and toward the bottom of each column. This theory accounts for the roots of mountains, and for the variations in density in different parts of the crust.*

of compensation 113.7 km. This figure is obtained by calculating isostatic anomalies for stations at a large number of different elevations, using different depths of compensation. The depth that gives the smallest average anomaly is considered the most probable actual depth of compensation (Fig. 23–4).

Heiskanen's Modifications

Airy postulated that columns of rock are nearly the same in density, floating like blocks in a fluid. Pratt suggested that different segments of the earth are of different densities, but that the differences are compensated at a certain depth. A third hypothesis has been formulated by Heiskanen (1933). He combines the assumptions of both Airy and Pratt (Fig. 23–4). It has been observed that rocks at sea level are more dense on the average than those at higher elevations (2.76 gm/cm^3 at sea level down to 2.70 gm/cm^3 at elevations in high mountains). He assumes that this change continues downward, tending to make deeper rocks more dense than shallower ones in all sections of the earth's crust. In addition, different sections have different densities and different lengths. Heiskanen's theory has the advantage of being based on actual knowledge of density variations that can be obtained by direct measurement, and when it is applied to the observations we now have on the gravitational field it yields very low isostatic anomalies.

Application of Isostasy

According to all three of these theories the earth's crust is approximately in a state of equilibrium, meaning that there are few large imbalances in the distribution of mass. Most geologists and geophysicists support either Pratt's or Heiskanen's theories or some modification of them. If either is correct, then we have an extremely valuable tool which may be used to explain large-scale crustal features and to predict behavior of the earth's crust in response to changes in the distribution of mass brought about by such processes as volcanism, mountain

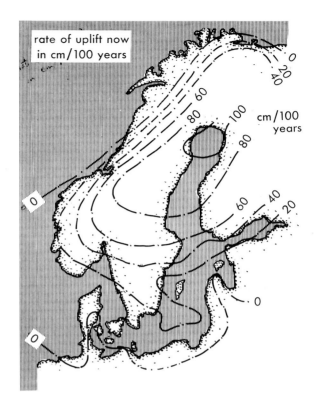

FIG. 23–5. / Rate of uplift in Scandinavia. During the ice ages this part of Scandinavia was covered by great thicknesses of ice. The weight of the ice caused the crust to be depressed as the additional weight was compensated for by subcrustal movement of materials. When the ice melted away readjustment started and is still going on. This map shows the present rates of uplift in centimeters per 100 years. (After Beno Gutenberg.)

building, and erosion. Undoubtedly the crust and interior of the earth down to the depth of compensation have some strength and rigidity which enable them to support loads of rock for at least short periods of time, but over long periods of time a state near compensation appears normal.

The theory of isostasy holds meaning both for the interior and for the crust of the earth. If a zone of compensation does exist, then the rock below that zone must be in a plastic or pseudo-viscous state in order to maintain compensation as loads on the crust are shifted from one place to another. Tops of mountains are eroded rapidly, and this debris is transported away by mass wasting, running water, and glaciers. As more and more mass is moved, the column of rock through the crust under the mountain is lightened in relation to other columns in the crust. Since pressure at the zone of compensation is due to the weight of the column of rock over it, the pressure under the mountain would be lessened. This would cause material below the zone of compensation to move toward that position and raise the column of rocks under the mountains again. Thus mountains tend to rise as they are eroded away.

Though most of the crust is in a state of isostatic equilibrium, the three per cent that is not provides some interesting applications of the theory. Among the most striking of these are the isostatic anomalies associated with the regions which during the Ice Ages were the sites of thick accumulations of ice, in some cases more than a mile thick. These areas include the portion of the Canadian Shield around Hudson Bay, and the Fennoscandinavian Shield region. Careful level surveys have been made across both areas in recent years. Results show that portions of Scandinavia are being uplifted at rates of as much as a centimeter each year (Fig. 23–5). Marks made at sea level in the region hundreds of years ago confirm that this uplift has been going on for a long time (since the ice melted). These same regions are sites of negative gravity anomalies. There is a deficiency of mass under them. This can be interpreted in terms of movement of subcrustal rocks. When the ice was present plastic flowage in the subcrust took place out and away from the centers of ice accumulation. The ice melted more rapidly than compensation by return flow took place. Flowage back into the areas is still going on. The size of the anomalies is an indication of how much more movement must take place before the areas are compensated again. One estimate is that parts of Scandinavia will be uplifted by close to 200 meters before compensation is complete. In Canada we can predict on this basis that Hudson Bay will slowly disappear as the continent rises. Similar adjustments have taken place around the Great Salt Lake (Fig. 23–6).

Positive anomalies are often found over volcanoes. The anomaly indicates that the volcano has a surplus of mass, and that it is not underlain by a void. It also indicates that the crust is locally strong enough to hold up the mass of the volcano.

Another example is found in the Mississippi Delta, where large quantities of sediment are being deposited annually on the continental shelf. These deposits might be expected to increase the mass of that segment of the crust, but measurements in the region reveal no positive anomaly. It appears that this is a region where compensation is taking place.

FIG. 23–6. / *Isostatic deformation of Lake Bonneville. Lake Bonneville was one of the great periglacial lakes of the Basin and Range Province. Salt Lake is a remnant of it. These two diagrams depict the present elevations of one of the former shorelines of Lake Bonneville (lower right), and depth of water in the lake in feet (top left). As the water has slowly evaporated the lake has been uplifted deforming the former shorelines. The shorelines have been elevated most in those areas formerly covered by the greatest depth of water. (After Crittenden, U.S. Geological Survey Prof. Paper 454D and E.)*

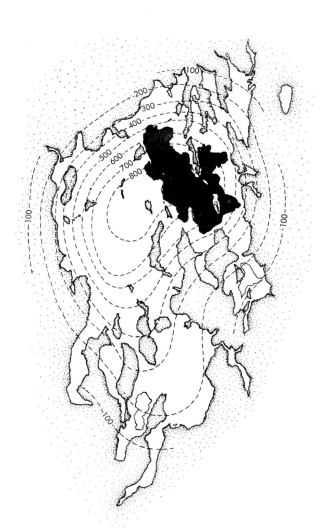

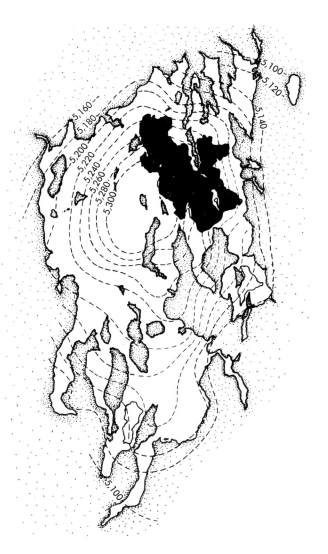

FIG. 24–1. / *The magnetometer. This instrument measures variations in the earth's magnetic field. These variations offer clues to the structure of the earth. This magnetometer is being used at sea where it is towed behind the ship. Magnetometers are also used from airplanes. Measurement by magnetometer is one of the many indirect methods of investigating the crust of the earth. (Photo by courtesy of the University of California, La Jolla, Scripps Institution of Oceanography.)*

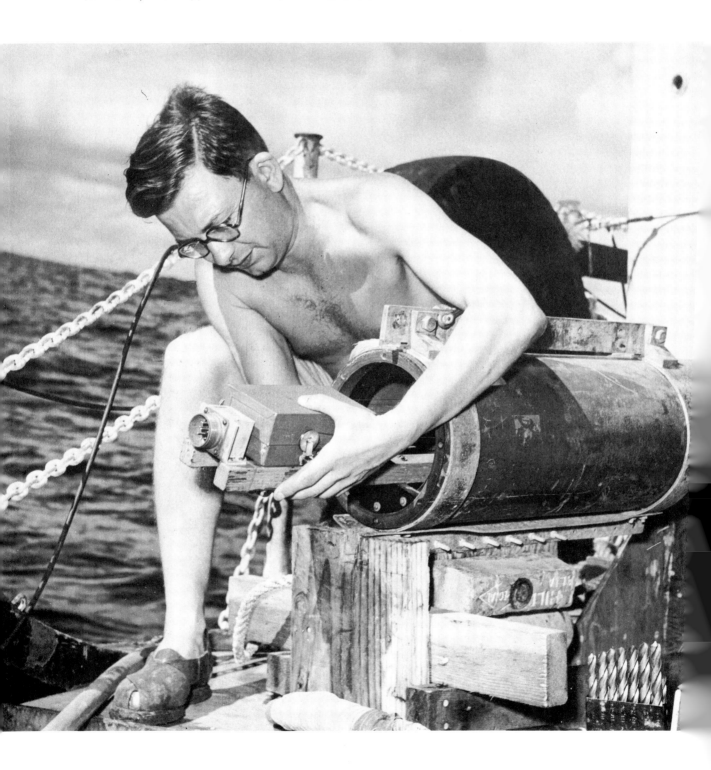

Earth's Magnetic Field

THE CHINESE ARE CREDITED WITH THE DIS-
covery of the phenomenon of magnetism, and
some historians believe they had made this discovery as early as 2000–3000 B.C. It is known
with greater certainty that the Greeks knew of
the magnetic effect of lodestone by the sixth
century B.C. and primitive compasses were in
use by the Arabs and the Chinese by A.D. 1000.
William Gilbert (1540–1603) was the founder
of the field of geomagnetism. He was the first
to show that the earth as a whole behaves like
a great bar magnet. Even at the time of Gilbert
much was known of magnetic phenomena.
Among the elemental knowledge were these
observations:

1. Certain rocks are natural magnets. The rock
   is known as lodestone, which is composed of
   the mineral magnetite.
2. Several other materials, including steel, may
   be made into magnets by being held close to
   lodestone. When a bar-shaped magnet of
   steel is placed in a pile of iron filings the filings will be attracted to the steel, with more
   being attracted to the ends of the bar than
   to the middle. The points where the most
   filings are held are called the *poles* of the
   magnet.
3. If a steel needle is magnetized and placed
   carefully on the surface of water so that it
   floats, it will rotate until one end always
   points North and the other always South.
   The two ends are known as the *north* and
   south poles of the magnet.
4. If two such magnetic needles are brought
   close together, opposite poles are attracted to
   one another, similar poles repel one another.
5. The force of attraction or repulsion between
   two magnetic poles is directly proportional to
   the product of their pole strengths and inversely proportional to the square of the distance between them.

The similarity of magnetic, static electric,
and gravitational phenomena are quite striking.
In 1820 Hans Oersted made public his discovery of an important relation between electric
and magnetic fields. He had placed an electric
wire in which a current was moving over a compass needle and discovered that the needle rotated until it was oriented at right angles to
the wire. Many had thought that the two types
of phenomena were entirely separate. He showed
instead that electric charges not only have electric fields associated with them, but also when
the charge is in motion it sets up a magnetic

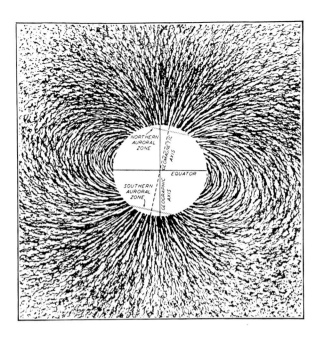

FIG. 24–2. / *The magnetic field of the earth.* (*From Vestine, 1960.*)

FIG. 24–3. / *Lines of equal intensity of Earth's magnetic field. (After E. H. Vestine, et al.)*

field oriented perpendicular to the direction of motion of the charge. This connection between electric and magnetic fields set the stage for some modern ideas about the origin of the earth's magnetic field, but before turning to these let us examine the nature of the field (Fig. 24–2).

Gilbert thought that the earth behaved as a magnet because there was a large body of permanently magnetized rock like lodestone buried deep in the earth. There are several imperfections in such a picture, however. First, the bar would not pass through the center of the earth —it would miss the center by almost 600 miles. Secondly, the North Magnetic Pole is not situated at the north geographic pole, but in northern Canada at about latitude 75° N. The South Magnetic Pole is located at latitude 68° S., south of Australia. The positions of the poles are known to shift. Some of the shifts are periodic, but others appear to be a permanent drifting.

The nature of the field is depicted in maps showing lines of equal inclination of the field

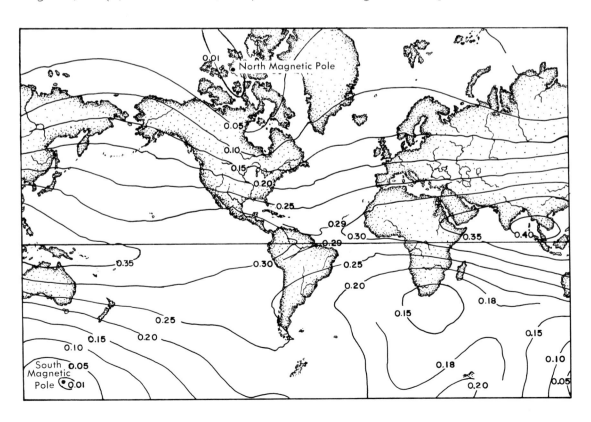

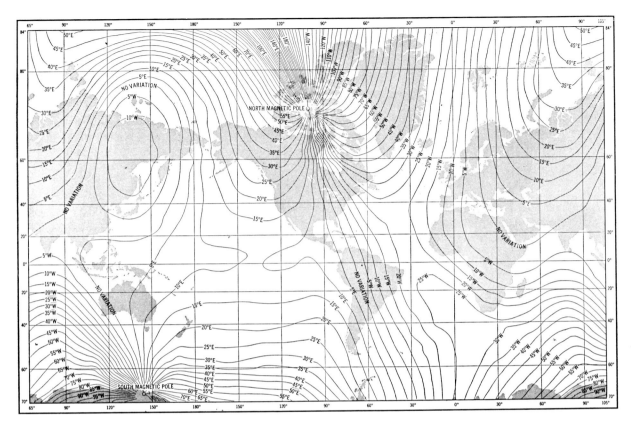

FIG. 24–4. / *World map of magnetic declination D; lines connect points of equal variation of compass from geographic north, 1955. (E. H. Vestine, by courtesy of U. S. Hydrographic Office and Encyclopedia Britannica.)*

in relation to the earth's surface, lines of equal intensity or strength, and lines of equal declination of the magnetic pole from the geographic pole (Figs. 24–3, 24–4, and 24–5). In understanding these maps it is important to remember certain features of the field. The magnetic field may be visualized by drawing a series of imaginary lines showing the direction in which a compass would point if held at any given point on or above the earth. The needle would point toward the magnetic poles, but it would be inclined if suspended from a string (note that compasses have weights on one end of the needles to hold them nearly level). So with a needle it is possible to determine the horizontal direction of the field and the angle of inclination of the field. The angle between arcs connecting any location with the magnetic pole

and the geographic pole is the declination at that place. Fig. 24–4 shows a hypothetical scheme of these lines. It was pointed out earlier that the poles of a bar magnet will attract more iron filings than the sides. This is an indication of the variation of strength of the field. The strength of the earth's field is determined by finding the force of attraction at a given place. As expected, regions near the poles have the highest magnetic intensity, but the South Magnetic Pole is slightly stronger than the North, suggesting that the center of the earth's field is somewhat closer to the surface at the South Magnetic Pole.

While Gilbert was wrong in thinking that the earth's field was due to buried magnets, it is now known that rocks differ in their magnetic properties. Some rocks contain large proportions of magnetite, and a great many other minerals are slightly magnetic. When sufficiently accurate maps of the earth's field are prepared, irregularities due to distribution of these rocks of differing magnetism show up. This fact has proved to be a most useful tool in exploration for economically important iron ore and other mineral deposits that have magnetic minerals associated with them.

Variations in the Field through Time

DETAILED STUDY OF THE MAGNETIC FIELD has been in progress for over ninety years. Although the great bulk of the data has been collected recently, there have been enough data collected over a long enough period to show clearly some of the variations that take place through time. These variations include some that are periodic and others that are irregular. Some of the variations occur within the period of one day. These have been shown to be related to solar radiation; consequently they vary from night to day and with the season of the year. In addition to these daily variations there are

monthly and annual cycles related to motions of the sun and moon. These variations occur with fixed periodicity and can be predicted with accuracy. Irregular variations are due to such phenomena as sunspot activity, during which high-energy particles from the sun bombard the earth; at these times auroral activity is at a maximum and it may extend even to the middle and low latitudes.

In addition to short-term variations, certain long-term changes have been noted. As early as 1635 Gellibrand noted that the position of the North Magnetic Pole was shifting. It was later suggested that the magnetic pole may be moving in a circle about the geographic North Pole, but such a simple explanation does not satisfy the observation that the period of this motion is different as observed at different locations on the earth. Indeed, it appears that the magnetic field is influenced by local or regional conditions. Such regional characteristics would reflect differences in the physical properties of the material deep in the earth's interior.

FIG. 24–5. / *Lines of equal inclination of the magnetic field.* (*After A. E. Vestine,* et al.)

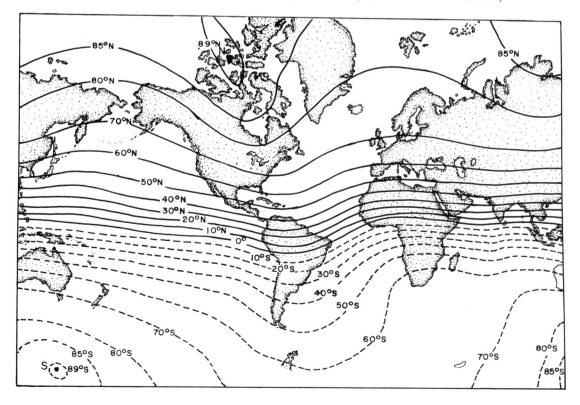

We will return to these long-term shifts of the magnetic field in our consideration of continental drift and the shifting of the earth's crust.

Origin of the Earth's Field

SOME OF THE BAFFLING CHANGES OBSERVED in the field are easier to understand if we think of it as surrounding electric currents rather than a magnet. It has already been shown that the core of the earth behaves as a liquid, and that indications of the composition of that liquid interior are that it is a nickel-iron compound of some type. Both of these qualities would promote the existence of electric currents in the interior. The remaining condition necessary for the development of a magnetic field would be to start such an electric current and then to sustain it in motion. There are several ways electric currents might have begun in the interior of the earth. They could be due to chemical processes similar to those in a battery. Other students of the earth's magnetic field point to the possibility of slow movements due to slight differences in chemical composition within the melt or the chance that the core has not yet reached a condition of stability. Once electric currents started they would be amplified if movements in the interior were taking place. Motion would logically arise from heat differences between the inner and outer parts of the core. As a result of these differences in temperature there should be *convection* (a slow, boiling-like motion) within the molten material. Few earth scientists doubt the existence of some form of motion in the interior, their principal argument regards the amount and intensity. But even very

FIG. 24–6. / *Magnetic anomaly map of Florida and the Bahamas. Local variations in the earth's magnetic field such as these are valuable in making interpretations of the structure of the earth's crust. (From C. L. Drake, et al.,* Jour. Geophysical Research, *1963.)*

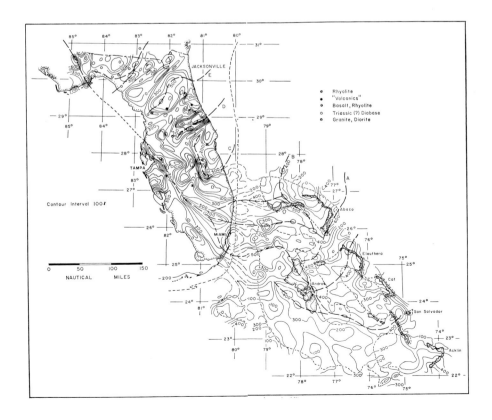

slow motion could create electric currents of sufficient magnitude to account for the observed magnetic field.

How well does such an explanation fit the observations? First, it certainly agrees with our knowledge of the interior derived from seismology. Furthermore, it explains the cause of the variability of the earth's magnetic field. If there are many small, eddy-like convection currents within the interior, and if electric and magnetic fields are associated with these, then we should find corresponding local variations in the observed field at the earth's surface, as we do (Fig. 24–6). That these many small magnetic fields do not show up more distinctly is due to the rotation of the earth as a whole. This imparts a general pattern of symmetry to the entire field and causes the alignment of the fields of convection cells; thus what we observe at the surface is the net over-all effect of the fields, with some minor variations superimposed.

Radiation Belts

The Aurora

MOST DRAMATIC of the effects of the earth's magnetic field are the *auroral displays*. These are sometimes visible as far south as the southern United States, and are consistently seen in the Arctic and Antarctic with displays being most common and most pronounced in belts located 23 degrees from the earth's axis in what are called the *auroral zones*. Auroras take on many patterns and colors, but the most common are pale glows that are greenish, or yellow, with occasional brighter-colored greens, yellows, reds, and even blues. The form of the aurora may be that of arcs of diffuse color slowly rising from the horizon in the direction of the magnetic pole and moving toward the zenith along lines approximately parallel to lines of the magnetic field. Several of these arcuate clouds of color may succeed one another through the night. At other times the arcs break up into rays or even into bands of rays that resemble folded draperies

or curtains. Usually these rays move about and pulsate, and generally they indicate the breaking up of the auroral display.

It is generally agreed that the aurora is definitely connected to the magnetic field of the earth because the auroral zones are located at those places where the lines of the earth's magnetic field converge and dip into the earth toward the core (Fig. 24–7). It is also well-known that there are fluctuations in the intensity of the magnetic field that accompany the waxing and waning of the aurora. The most widely accepted explanation of the cause of the aurora connects it with solar activity and the earth's magnetic field. Protons and electrons from the sun bombard the atmosphere, exciting oxygen and nitrogen atoms in the upper atmosphere to a state of luminescence. That this activity is connected with the sun is shown by the eleven year period of increasing and decreasing auroral display which parallels the eleven-year cycle of sunspot activity. It has also been observed that the most prominent auroras follow periods of solar flares. There is a slight lag, suggesting that the greater part of the ionized particles move from the sun to the earth at a speed of about 1,000 miles per second, taking almost a day to reach the earth. Some invisible clouds of particles, known as *plasma clouds*, continue to arrive for several days. Knowledge of these clouds is now being derived largely from artificial earth satellites. When one of these clouds of ionized particles reaches the outer parts of the earth's magnetic field it causes the field to be deformed, bending it in toward the earth. This would account for the presence of auroral displays at low latitudes on such occasions, and account for some of the *magnetic storms* on earth which interrupt radio communication.

The auroral displays are normally located in the polar regions because the ionized particles that give rise to them are influenced by the lines of force of the earth's magnetic field. Particles which approach the earth are deflected into paths roughly parallel with lines of the magnetic field, and are thus funneled toward the magnetic poles.

FIG. 24–7. / *Auroral displays taken during IGY 1957–58 at the University of Alaska. (Courtesy of U.S.N.C.–I.G.Y., N.A.S.)*

Van Allen Belts

ONE OF THE VERY important discoveries made through the use of artificial earth satellites is that there are two very large belts of intense radiation surrounding the earth. These were unknown until rockets were put to use to investigate the space immediately surrounding the earth. The first indication of radiation belts came from high-altitude balloon and rocket studies in 1952–53, when James Van Allen and a number of co-workers were studying the cosmic ray intensity in the atmosphere of the Arctic region. A few of their records showed abnormally high readings for the radiation in a zone starting about 30 miles high. Several years later it was established with the use of rockets that a similar belt of high intensity radiation existed in the Antarctic. At about the same time (1958) Carl McIlwain discovered that the radiation includes protons (hydrogen nuclei) and electrons. The greatest advances after this came during the

International Geophysical Year, when a number of satellites were put into orbit about the earth. The most detailed pictures of the radiation belts were yielded by Explorer IV and Pioneer III. Data from these showed that the earth is surrounded by two belts of radiation shaped somewhat like hollow doughnuts, one inside the other (Fig. 24-8). These concentric doughnuts are oriented so that they are in the plane of the earth's magnetic equator. The inner belt lies above altitudes of 500 miles and extends to about 34° north and south of the equator. The peak in this belt occurs at about 2,000 miles above the earth. The peak of the outer belt lies at about 10,000 miles. Beyond that the intensity drops off and falls to a low level at 40,000 miles. The intensity of radiation in the belts is about 25,000 counts per second, which is estimated to represent bombardment by some 40,000 particles per square centimeter per second.

The explanation advanced to account for this radiation is that the particles originate from the sun; they are injected into the earth's magnetic field and there deflected into corkscrew paths which follow to some extent the lines of the magnetic field. Once in the field they are trapped, but not permanently. As the number of particles increases some are lost—particularly in the auroral zones, giving rise to the displays observed there. Some normally escape, causing the phenomenon known as airglow—a faint illumination of the night sky. Another possible origin has been suggested. In this alternative theory, neutrons, released in the upper atmosphere by bombardment of atoms by cosmic rays, decay into protons and electrons, which are trapped in the magnetic field. It is agreed that this process does take place, but there is some doubt that a sufficiently high number of particles could be produced in this way.

FIG. 24-8. / *Schematic representation of the Van Allen radiation belts, and a representation of the relations between the sun and the earth's magnetic field. (Courtesy of U.S.N.C.–I.G.Y., N.A.S.)*

FIG. 24-9. / *Schematic representation of the interactions between the sun and the earth's magnetic field. (Courtesy of U.S.N.C.–I.G.Y., N.A.S.)*

VAN ALLEN RADIATION BELTS

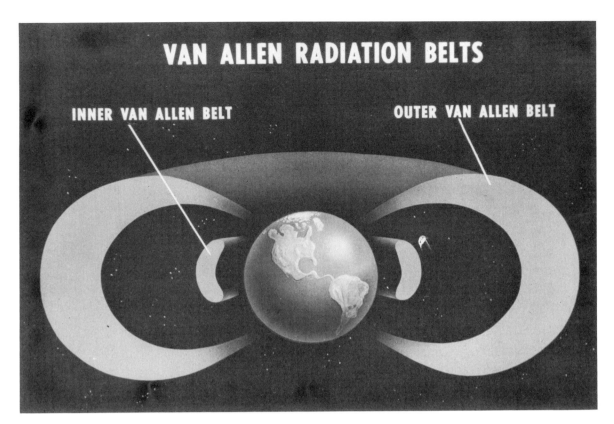

INNER VAN ALLEN BELT

OUTER VAN ALLEN BELT

EARTH AND SUN

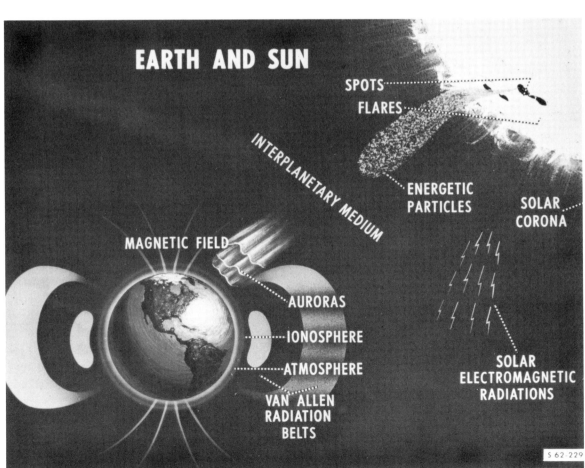

SPOTS
FLARES

INTERPLANETARY MEDIUM

ENERGETIC
PARTICLES

SOLAR
CORONA

MAGNETIC FIELD

AURORAS

IONOSPHERE

ATMOSPHERE

VAN ALLEN
RADIATION
BELTS

SOLAR
ELECTROMAGNETIC
RADIATIONS

S 62-229

25 / Structure of the Crust

SEDIMENTARY ROCK UNITS LIKE THOSE WHICH cover continental shelves are found folded and broken as though they were shoved together with tremendous force. In other places coasts with sandy "beaches," scattered shell fragments, or wave-cut cliffs and terraces have been lifted high above the level of the modern oceans. We can only conclude that the oceans have either gone down or that the former beaches have been lifted up. Thus there is much evidence that the crust of the earth is not nearly as stable as it may appear.

Epeirogeny and Orogeny

TWO ESSENTIALLY DIFFERENT TYPES OF deformation are in evidence. The first type, broad uplifting or downwarping, is called *epeirogeny*. These movements affect all or a large part of a continent or sea bottom. Strata of sedimentary rocks are not strongly folded in this type of deformation, although they may be tilted, or "warped" (bent in broad, gentle curves without strong folding or faulting).

A second type of deformation is *orogeny*. In orogenic deformation strata are folded; they are broken by low-angle faults along which they are displaced laterally over many miles. Usually orogenic movements affect long, narrow belts of the crust.

Evidence of Epeirogeny

IN THE SIXTH CENTURY B.C. A LARGE CITY was built on the shore of the Bay of Taman on the northern shore of the Black Sea. Remains of this city, named Phanagoria, are now being excavated. Excavations reveal that some streets of the city now lie under the sea. Thus it appears that the region has been lowered in relation to sea level since the city was built. Similar evidence is found near Naples, Italy, in the ancient Roman public market known as the temple of Jupiter Serapis. Here marine gastropods have bored holes in columns 18 feet above the floor of the temple. Remains of some of these gastropods are still found in the holes. It is evident that the shore was submerged beneath the sea after the Romans built the temple and then again rose above sea level, where it stands today.

Aristotle and other Greek philosophers noted evidence of large-scale movements of the crust, but one of the first efforts to measure the rates of such movements came in 1731, when special marks were made on rock cliffs along the coast of Sweden at sea level. These marks are now almost eight feet above sea level. Such a rise is extremely rapid and could easily account for great uplifts of large areas if continued for long periods of geologic time. Now careful surveys of sea level are made and checked from year to year to determine rates of changes in the level of continents as a whole in relation to sea level, and movements of parts of continents in relation to one another. Examples of the results are the discoveries that the Gulf Coast of the United States is subsiding at the rate of 6.6 mm. per year, the coast of Newfoundland is rising .8 mm. per year, the shield of Scandinavia is rising about 7 mm. per year, the eastern coast of Australia is rising at the rate of .4 mm. per year, and the eastern coast of India is subsiding at the rate of 1.2 mm. per year.

In 1946 a large number of flat-topped sea mountains were discovered submerged in the Pacific. These mountains, called *guyots*, are probably extinct volcanoes. The most logical explanation for their flat tops is that they were eroded off by wave action. Along the northern coast of Africa row on row of wave-cut terraces are found above the level of the sea. Their step-like pattern shows a history of repeated uplift, temporary stability while a new terrace was cut, then renewed uplift. Either of these examples taken alone might be explained as a change in the level of the sea rather than epeirogenic deformation of the crust, but the relative movements in the two are in opposite directions, making sea-level movements alone an impossible explanation (Fig. 25–1).

The level of the seas has changed as a result of the quantity of water in the oceans. There is enough ice on land to raise sea level 70–150 feet. More ice has been stored on the continents at times during the last million years. Sea level is estimated to have been as much as 300 feet lower. Thus shifts in relative positions of continents and seas result from two major processes, change in the quantity of water in the oceans, and deformation.

Grand Canyon and Epeirogeny

ONE OF THE MOST REMARKABLE records of epeirogenic movement is found in the section of strata exposed in the Grand Canyon (Fig. 25–2). Near the bottom of the canyon rocks more than half a billion years old are exposed. They were folded and metamorphosed in an orogeny. Following this mountain building there was a long period of erosion. Then marine sedimentary layers were deposited across the edges of the older eroded rocks. During the millions of years represented by the strata exposed in the canyon, the region was beneath or just at sea level most of the time. Occasionally the strata were uplifted, and some of the sediments were eroded off, but during most of that time new sediments accumulated on top of the older ones, which continued to subside slowly. Today the marine sediments found in the walls of the canyon nearly a mile above sea level are as flat-lying as you might expect them to have been when they were initially deposited in the sea. Here, then, a segment of the earth's crust has been uplifted more than a mile without orogenic deformation of the rocks within the block.

Epeirogeny and Isostasy

THE THEORY OF ISOSTASY provides the best explanation of the cause of epeirogenic uplifts. The crust of the earth is known to be of variable thickness, of variable composition, and of variable density. Shifting of loads of rock on the surface as a result of weathering, erosion, transportation, and deposition is constantly in progress. Over a long period of time mass is shifted mainly from high mountains to lower elevations. Volcanoes and lava plateaus are constructed through igneous activity, and mountains are formed through orogenies. These processes throw up large masses of rock in spaces previously unoccupied by them.

According to the theory of isostasy the earth approaches isostatic equilibrium. Loads on the crust are approximately balanced. If mass is removed from a certain part of the earth's surface, equilibrium is upset. Within the earth's interior,

FIG. 25–1. / *Uplifted wave-cut terrace. Epeirogenic deformation of the crust often elevates portions of the sea floor as it has here along the California coast where a wave-cut terrace has been uplifted. (Photo by the author.)*

the mantle rock behaving like a plastic flows and exerts a pressure on the crust, tending to elevate the area from which mass has been removed and to restore equilibrium. Rates of epeirogenic uplift of the Canadian and Finnoscandinavian shields may be explained in these terms.

Strength of the Crust

COMPENSATION for uplift and subsidence of the crust in accordance with the theory of isostasy could take place only if rocks in the interior of the earth behave as plastics. Rocks at the surface are hard and strong materials. Examine the cross sections through the Alps and Appalachians (Fig. 25–3). In these the strata are folded and contorted in a way we might ordinarily think impossible for rocks as hard and solid as limestones, sandstones, and meta-

morphic rocks. Yet the evidence is conclusive. Massive units of rock have been contorted and deformed more like wet clay than like hard, brittle rock. We are forced to conclude that rocks do not always behave the way they do at the surface, and that, while individual hand specimens may be hard and brittle, sections of the earth considered as a whole are not.

Both field and laboratory studies confirm that rocks do, in fact, flow and behave as plastics when they are subjected to high confining pressures and high temperatures. Although the essential character of rock deformation is known with confidence, there are certain problems that make complete understanding of the behavior of rock materials in orogeny difficult to obtain. The highest pressures that can be produced in the laboratory are equivalent to the confining pressure at a depth slightly into the mantle. Laboratory studies must necessarily be confined

FIG. 25–2. / *The Grand Canyon of the Colorado River. The Colorado River and many of its tributaries are deeply entrenched in nearly flat-lying strata. These strata provide a record of the history of this region for a period of more than a billion years of earth history. Some of the rock units exposed near the rim of the canyon contain fossils of marine invertebrate animals. That the rim is now about a mile above sea level indicates that the region has been uplifted in relation to the sea. In the distance the extinct volcanoes of the San Francisco Mountains of central Arizona are visible.* (Photo by Union Pacific Railroad.)

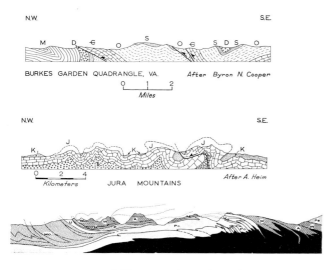

N.W.　　　　　　　　　　　　　　S.E.

BURKES GARDEN QUADRANGLE, VA.　　After Byron N. Cooper

0　　1　　2
Miles

N.W.　　　　　　　　　　　　　　S.E.

0　2　4
Kilometers　　JURA MOUNTAINS　　After A. Heim

FIG. 25–3. / *Cross sections through parts of three folded mountain belts. The section at the top is across the Appalachian Mountains, that in the center is across the Jura Mountains, and that at the bottom is typical of the Himalayas and Alps. (After Billings.)*

to small specimens, while mountain ranges are of a vastly larger scale and are much more heterogeneous. The time involved in orogeny is measured in millions of years, while experiments are rarely extended over more than a few years. Although we have been forced to work within these limitations, our knowledge of orogeny has nevertheless been steadily increasing.

FIG. 25–4. / *Strike of a rock unit is the compass direction of horizontal lines on the unit. The dip is the angle between the horizon and the surface of the unit measured at right angles to the strike.*

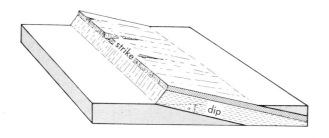

Structures Resulting from Diastrophism

STRUCTURE REFERS TO THE CONFIGURATION in space of rock units or features of rock units. Many structures originate when the rock is formed. Sedimentary rocks, for example, may contain ripple marks, cross-bedding, or other primary features that give them certain shapes (Figs. 13–7 through 13–14). Such primary features are not products of diastrophism, but are due to certain conditions which prevailed during the initial formation of the rocks.

In describing diastrophic structures it is necessary to use some method of specifying positions of planes and lines in three-dimensional space. A line can be described by giving the compass direction of its horizontal projection (i.e., N 20° E) and its inclination or *plunge*—the angle (measured in a vertical plane) between a line and the horizon (Figs. 25–4 and 25–5). A plane is readily described by strike and dip: *strike* is the compass direction of any horizontal line on the plane; *dip* is the angle between the plane and the horizon, measured in a vertical plane at right angles to strike. Dip of a plane corresponds to plunge of a line. Thus dip may also be described as the plunge of a line on the plane at right angles to the strike. In addition, other structural features are imparted to rocks when they are subjected to deforming stresses. There are four major groups of these—folds, faults, fractures, and unconformities.

Folds

FOLDS ARE SIMPLY bends, but they exist in many types and form under varying conditions which give indications of their mode of origin.[1] On the basis of their outward appearance it is easy to classify folds into two groups—those with some regular geometric form, and those with highly irregular form. Geometrical folds

[1] Many large-scale structural features are shown on the geologic maps of the Bighorn Mountains area and the eastern United States at end of book.

usually result from deformation in which layers in a sedimentary rock sequence undergo flexure or shearing. In *flexure folding* one layer simply slips over others, as in a bent deck of cards (Fig. 25–7). In *shear folding* rock layers have been fractured and movements have occurred along closely spaced *rock cleavages* or fractures (Fig. 14–3). When the form of a fold or fold system is highly irregular, it usually signifies that plastic behavior has been a factor in the formation of the fold. *Flowage* and *plastic deformation* are characteristic of many folded meta-

FIG. 25–5. / *Dip face of a sedimentary layer exposed in a Pennsylvania quarry. (Photo by the author.)*

FIG. 25–6. / *Block diagram of folded structure suggesting flowage in Farm Blasskranz, Africa. (From Korn and Martin, Bull. Geol. Soc. Am., v. 70, 1959.)*

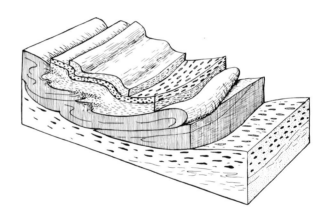

FIG. 25–7. / *Flexure folds. (Crown Copyright.)*

morphic rocks and unconsolidated sediments (Figs. 25–6 and 25–8).

Folds are readily described in terms of their shape. Parts of folds, the *axial plane, axis, limbs, crest,* and *trough,* are illustrated in Fig. 25–9. When two limbs of a fold are nearly mirror images of one another the fold is *symmetrical,* and when this is not the case it is *asymmetrical.* When the axial plane is inclined so that one limb lies over the other the fold is said to be *overturned.* If the axial plane is flat-lying the fold is said to be *recumbent.* The imaginary line formed where the axial plane intersects the bedding is called the *axis* of the fold. The axis or hinge, as it is sometimes called, is located where the curvature of the beds is greatest. This axis may be horizontal for great distances, but folds must eventually die out and then the axis becomes inclined. (Since the axis is a line, the angle of its inclination is called the *plunge* of the axis.)

The principal fold types are defined on the basis of their shapes and the direction of inclination of their limbs (Figs. 25–10 through 25–14). Definitions of the main types are:

Anticline—an upfold in which the limbs dip away from the fold axis.

Syncline—a downfold in which the limbs dip toward the axis.

Dome—a circular uplift.

Basin—a circular or elliptical downwarp or structural depression.

Monocline—uniformly dipping beds on a flexure.

Folds of varying orders of magnitude are found in the crust. In folded mountain belts they may measure many miles across and extend for as much as a hundred miles. Such folds with associated low-angle faults are characteristic products of orogenic deformation. They are found in all orogenic belts.

Faults

FAULTS IN THE SOLID crust of the earth are breaks of the earth along which there have been displacement of the two sides. Long after move-ments cease they may still be recognized. Some of the criteria for recognition are:

Displacement of physiographic features. Streams, mountains, hills, and other topographic features may be offset where they cross a fault.

Fault scarps. Small escarpments mark the position of displacements where one side moved up in relation to the other.

Displacement of geologic structures. The outcrop of uniformly inclined strata may be displaced, or a structure such as a fold may appear distorted or offset across a fault.

The *fault plane* is the zone within which the two sides have moved. It may be a smooth plane produced by a sharp break or it may be a wide zone of distortion as much as several hundred feet thick. Within the fault plane, crushed and brecciated rock is usually present. Sometimes crushing is so complete that *breccia* is reduced to a powdery-textured material. Striations and grooves, called *slickensides,* appear where the two sides moved across each other. A fault may die out, pass into a fold, or intersect another fault. Faults locally divide the crust into blocks. If the fault is not vertical, one of these blocks must lie above the fault. The upper block is called the *hanging wall,* a mining term derived from the fact that a miner standing in a mined-out fault zone finds one of the blocks hanging over his head. He stands on the other block, so it is called the *foot wall.*

If the fault is inclined, any movement within the fault can be described in the following terms. If the movement of two points originally adjacent on opposite sides of the fault is traced, it will follow one or a combination of these paths. If there is no vertical component—that is, all motion is horizontal along the strike— the fault is called a *strike-slip fault.* If movement was at right angles to the strike—that is, all motion was parallel to the dip—the fault is a *dip-slip fault.* An *oblique-slip fault* results if the displacement is partially up or down dip and partially along strike, or if oblique movement occurs. *Rotation* of the blocks in relation to one another is also possible, in which case the motion is scissor-like.

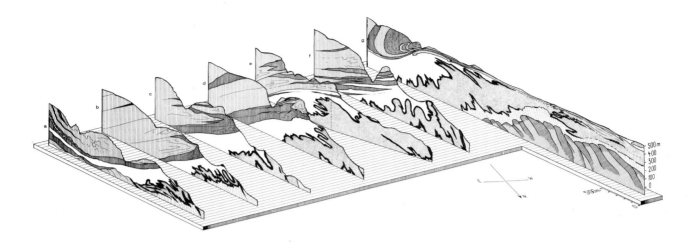

FIG. 25–8. / *Profiles of the mountain face, Farm Blasskranz, Africa. Note the flowage-type structure which is characteristic of many orogenic belts. (From Korn and Martin, Bull. Geol. Soc. Am., v. 70, 1959.)*

FIG. 25–9. / *Block diagram illustrating various types of folds.*

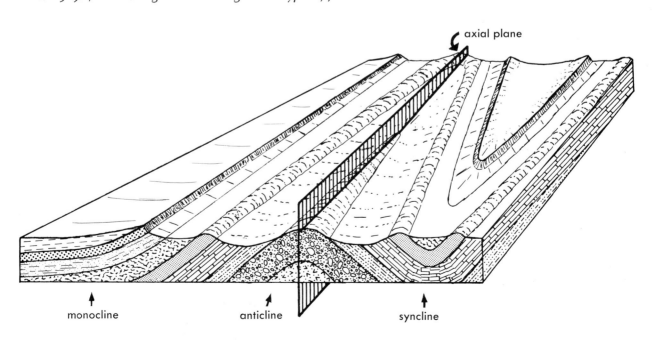

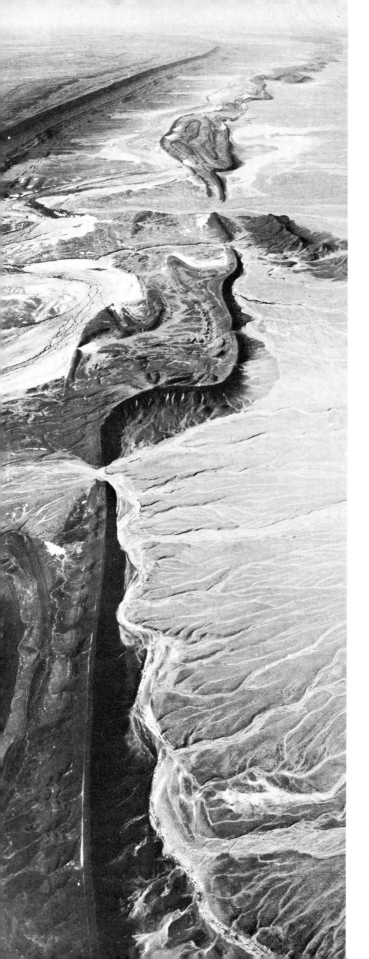

FIG. 25–10. / *Belt of folded mountains in Africa (Atlas Mountains). Deformation and uplift of the crust of the earth is one of the main factors in maintaining parts of the crust high. Already these mountains have been deeply dissected. Note the erosion products of the mountains which lie on the flanks of the ridges. (Photo by courtesy of the U.S. Air Force.)*

FIG. 25–11. / *The Colorado Front Range. The structure of the strata along the margin of this range has been etched out by stream erosion, and the streams have become adjusted to the structure. In the distant background the mountain tops appear at about the same level indicating the presence of a widespread erosion surface. The landforms in the central part of the picture are called hogbacks. (Photo by T. S. Lovering, U.S. Geological Survey.)*

esses that bring about other deformations of the crust.

Rock cleavage (Fig. 25–21) is another form of fracturing. Cleavages are closely spaced fractures. The best examples of rock cleavage are found in folded shales and slates. The cleavage in these is oriented approximately parallel to the axial plane of the folds. Rock cleavage is a plane of weakness, but it should not be confused with mineral cleavage (Fig. 25–22), which is determined by atomic arrangements and not by deformation.

Unconformities

UNCONFORMITIES ARE SURFACES of erosion or nondeposition separating younger strata from older rocks. Unconformities may be caused by either epeirogenic or orogenic deformations, but different types of unconformities result, reflecting different forces. If intense deformation precedes the development of the unconformity, an *angular unconformity* will be formed (Fig. 25–23).[2] The contact is called an angular unconformity if the beds beneath the erosion surface are folded or tilted so that they form an angle with the overlying younger strata. But if there is no folding or faulting in connection with the unconformity, strata below and above may have nearly identical attitudes. The unconformity is called a *disconformity* if young units are laid down parallel to the older units below the erosion surface. Frequently in these cases

[2] See geologic maps of Wyoming and northeastern United States at end of book.

FIG. 25–19. / *Shells of rock being split up into joint blocks by frost action. Note the tendency to develop joints in parallel sets in a rock which not long ago was essentially structureless and exfoliated freely in any direction parallel to an exposed surface. (Photo by courtesy of the U.S. Geological Survey.)*

it is possible to recognize the break if part of the old topography is buried by the young sediments. If no such features can be found the disconformity may be recognized by the presence of an old soil profile, by differences in ages of strata on either side of the disconformity, or by identification of old stream channels or other features that might be expected on an erosion surface.

Stable Crustal Elements

Continental Shields

WITHIN THE BOUNDARIES of each continent there are large areas of exposures of very old rocks formed during that portion of geologic time known as the Precambrian.[3] The term *shield* is applied to those areas which have not been folded or complexly deformed since the end of the Precambrian, about 600 million years ago. They have not always been stable, for structural evidence of old mountain systems is still found in every shield. Undoubtedly they were strongly deformed at one time, perhaps one billion years ago or more. The important thing about them is that, unlike most of the surrounding continental masses, they have been stable since the end of the Precambrian. Precambrian rocks underlie the rest of the continents, but they have yielded to subsequent deformation more than the shields.

Precambrian rocks are complex. Because they are old, there has been more opportunity for them to become deformed and for more alteration of them to take place. This alteration has been twofold—removal of material by erosion and weathering, and change through metamorphism. Most Precambrian rocks have been metamorphosed. Large portions are granitic in composition, and, although some of these are now known to be granitized sedimentary rocks (rocks altered to granitic composition and texture), others are of igneous origin. The largest shield areas are:

[3] Refer to Part II or chapter 27 for a discussion of the geologic time scale.

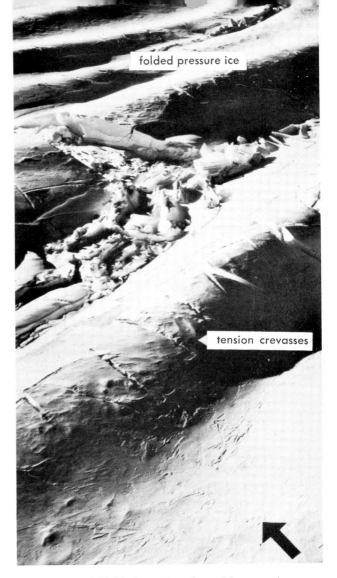

FIG. 25–20. / *Folds in an ice sheet. Note particularly the regularity of the fractures on the crest of the fold. (Photo by courtesy of the U.S. Navy.)*

FIG. 25–21. / *Steeply dipping beds cut by cleavage and joints. (Crown Copyright.)*

The Canadian Shield, covering most of central Canada and extending into the northern United States. The central part of the United States is covered by a few thousand feet of sedimentary rocks, but large parts of it have been relatively stable since the Precambrian and should be considered as an extension of the shield area.

The Baltic Shield, located in northern Europe and including Sweden, Finland, and most of the Baltic Sea.

The Central African Shield, located in the southern and central parts of Africa.

The Brazilian Shield, which makes up most of the area of Brazil.

The Australian Shield, located in the western part of that continent.

The Angara Shield of northern and eastern Siberia.

Exact margins of the shields are not easily determined. Marginal areas are usually covered by thick, often undeformed sequences of sedimentary rocks.

Shields are subject to erosion. As a result of their long-term stability they contain very few mountains. Most of them are well above sea level, but physiography is that of gently rolling hills and isolated physiographic features etched out by long years of erosion on rocks of different resistance. Their stability is marked by the absence of volcanism, active deformation, or earthquakes within their boundaries. From the point of view of stability they resemble the deep plains of the ocean basins.

Nature of Orogenic Belts

BEFORE REVIEWING THE MORE SIGNIFICANT hypotheses that have been advanced to account for orogeny, we should take note of certain facts which must be explained concerning mountain belts .[4]

1. Strata in every orogenic belt are folded and contain low-angle thrust faults. Movement

[4] Parts of the Appalachian and Rocky Mountain orogenic belts are illustrated at end of book.

FIG. 25–22. / *Mineral cleavage in calcite with hornblende crystals. (Photo by courtesy of the U.S. National Museum.)*

FIG. 25–23. / *Unconformities. The block diagram at top depicts an angular unconformity. That at the bottom is a disconformity. The topographic forms shown are only two of many possible landforms which might develop.*

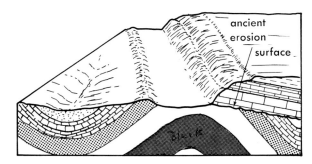

ancient erosion surface

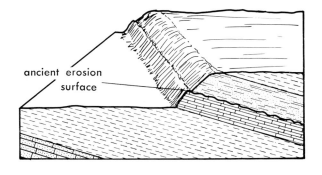

ancient erosion surface

FIG. 25–24. / *Asymmetric, overturned fold in siliceous moines.* (*Crown Copyright.*)

along faults was directed away from the central part of the mountain system toward the margins. Folds and thrusts were produced under compression. Thus there is at least local compression of the crust of the earth within orogenic belts during part of the orogeny.

2. In mountain belts there is what appears to be a shortening of the crust, an apparent reduction in the circumference of the earth, forcing the crust to pile up in folds and faults to fit into less area. The word "apparent" must be emphasized because the effects of crustal shortening might be caused by some other process.

3. Mountain belts are characterized by their eminent heights above their immediate sur-

FIG. 25–25. / *Sharp, asymmetric fold at Sandy Mouth, Cornwall.* (*Crown Copyright.*)

roundings. The amount of their uplift may reach at least 30,000 feet, the height of Mt. Everest.

4. Mountain belts are large features. Their lengths may be measured in thousands of miles and their widths in hundreds. Stresses sufficient to lift masses of rock of this size must be accounted for in any acceptable theory.

5. Sedimentary rocks found in folded mountains are of all types, but shallow-water marine sediments are most common.

6. One of the most common sedimentary rocks found in belts of mobility is graywacke, formed of sandy sediments containing mixtures of feldspars and various minerals of volcanic origin. Stratigraphic sections of at least parts of all major mountain systems contain considerable quantities of volcanic debris and lava flows. Many of these flows are pillow-shaped masses thought to form when lava is extruded under water.

7. In addition to shallow-water sediments, some deep-sea deposits are found. These include such sediments as siliceous radiolarian oozes.

8. Mountain ranges are sites of most large-scale igneous activity outside the ocean basins. Large batholiths occur in folded mountain belts.

9. The core of highly deformed mountains is a metamorphic complex usually intruded by magmas. Original structures may no longer be apparent. These zones are characterized by considerable alteration, flowage, and distortion.

10. Orogenic belts contain ultrabasic intrusions. These may be peridotites, dunites, or serpentines. The few isolated intrusions known are aligned to form two parallel rows about 100 miles apart on either side of the axis of the mountain system. They occur persistently in orogenic belts and not outside them.

11. Sedimentary units are thicker in mountain belts than outside. It is apparent that most sediments now exposed in mountain chains were deposited in elongate troughlike depressions called geosynclines. Before an orogeny the thickness of accumulation in a geosyncline reaches 50,000 or more feet, as compared with the 2,000 or 3,000 feet of sediment which might have accumulated outside the geosyncline during the

same period of time. Geosynclines obviously subsided during the time preceding the orogeny, because shallow-water sediments usually occur all through the sequence. Geosynclinal accumulations presently lie off the eastern and Gulf coasts of America under the continental shelves and continental slopes.

12. Near margins of most mountain belts folding is less intense; strata are only slightly folded or flexed. Toward the center of the belt folding becomes increasingly intense, and folds become more asymmetrical toward the margins. In the central part of the belt folding is largely due to flowage.

13. The pattern of entire mountain chains is complex. They are relatively continuous structures, but their paths are by no means straight, and structures in one part of a range may differ from those in another part of the same chain. The over-all geographical pattern of many such chains may be drawn as a connected series of arcs.

14. The position of many of the youngest mountain ranges along continental borders may be a significant fact, particularly since island arcs also occupy this position.

15. Island arcs are sites of present-day orogeny. For that reason they are of special interest and importance in the theory of orogeny. They are sites of igneous activity and volcanism, earthquakes and seismic instability, major fault zones which dip under the continents, and deep-sea trenches.

16. Study of the older mountain systems indicates that orogeny involves million of years. Activity may be dated by the presence of angular unconformities. There are usually many of these in any major mountain belt, and they are not all of the same age. Deformation does not take place simultaneously throughout the belt.

17. There appear to be several stages in the history of most folded mountains. The first is formation of a geosyncline, subsidence, and accumulation of sediments. Second comes an orogenic episode in which the geosyncline is intruded, folded, faulted, and uplifted. This may be followed by a long interval of erosion and

perhaps one or more renewals of uplift. Toward the end of the orogeny high-angle normal faults cut older structures and displacement forms graben and horst structures.

Geosynclinal Theory

IN THE PRECEDING DISCUSSION WE HAVE seen that the mobile belts of the world are geosynclines—long, narrow, deeply subsiding troughs which have often been uplifted, folded, and faulted to form folded mountain belts. The concept of the geosyncline was proposed to explain the formation of the Appalachian Mountains and subsequently other mountain belts as well. The history of the development of this theory and its application to the Appalachians is interesting because it shows how this important concept underwent a series of modifications as knowledge of the geology of the Appalachians increased. The character of the Appalachian geosyncline is not completely settled even today and we shall examine some of the current arguments.

With the introduction of geosynclinal theory we are confronted with a problem involving historical interpretation. We have seen that mountain belts undergo long periods of sedimentation in their early history. Later they are uplifted, folded, faulted, and eroded. The history of the events as well as the processes by which they were accomplished is of great importance in understanding the formation of the folded mountain belts. Such understanding is complete only in the light of historical interpretation. In the next few chapters we will examine the principles of historical interpretation as they are applied in geology.

The concept of the geosyncline was originated by one of the most colorful and productive of early American geologists, James Hall. Born in Massachusetts in 1811, Hall was educated at a school, recently formed by Stephen Van Rensselaer, where science was taught through field and laboratory studies. On fossil collecting trips Hall discovered the study to which he was to make great contributions for the rest of his life. Following graduation he remained at the school and became a teacher for a short time before joining the newly formed New York State Geological Survey. Early in his career he discovered some of the prolific fossil localities of the state and began what was to become a lifetime of work describing, illustrating, and studying fossil invertebrates. The results of his work, which covered sixty-two years, were published in thirteen large volumes. Hall was forty-five years old when he first publicly proposed his concept of the geosyncline and the importance of geosynclines in earth history. He had studied sections of fossiliferous rocks as far south as Virginia and into the midwest. He selected as his presidential address to the American Association for the Advancement of Science the geological history of the North American continent. In this address he outlined the view that the Appalachians had been formed through long-continued accumulation of sediments in shallow seas in the Paleozoic Era. As limestone, sand, and gravel deposits derived from the land filled in these seas the deposits had gradually subsided until nearly 40,000 feet of sediment had accumulated. Hall recognized that all of this sediment was deposited in shallow water, shown by the ripple marks and marine plant fossils found in many parts of the section.

Thickness of strata was greater within the trough of subsidence than along the side (in the Midwest) where the same rock units could be traced. It followed in his argument that along the trough where thickness and subsidence were greatest, strata were folded into complex folds and broken by faults. Thus Hall visualized that folding and faulting associated with mountain belts take place during subsidence of the trough. As one opponent to this view put it, Hall had a theory of mountain-making with the mountains left out. But Hall recognized this objection and proposed that mountains as physiographic features resulted from erosion after the folded and faulted pile of sediments was uplifted as part of a general continental rise. However, this view has never been widely accepted.

Hall extended this idea of the formation of folded mountain belts to all such belts, saying

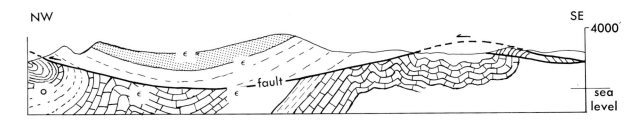

FIG. 25–26. / *Section of thrust fault. A thrust fault in southern Virginia has carried a slab of Cambrian strata out to the northwest more than twenty miles over Cambrian and Ordovician strata. This sheet is one of several similar though not quite so extensive sheets in the Appalachians. The section is taken along the Virginia-Tennessee state line and shows the structure of the Pine Mountain thrust. (After P. B. King.)*

that mountains could not take form without long-continued accumulation of sediments. With the statement of these ideas the world was presented with a controversy regarding mountains that has continued as a most lively one to this day. That geosynclines exist much as Hall described them is not disputed, but the cause of subsidence, character of the region on the seaward side of the geosyncline, and the time and cause of the folding and faulting in the geosyncline's history are all topics of current debate. Folded mountain ranges have been developed over long periods of time. The Appalachians, for example, was a region of marine sedimentation during most of the Paleozoic, a period of nearly 400 million years. Mountains rose within the Appalachian geosyncline during that time, and the mountain system as a whole was an active belt for at least that length of time. Any acceptable theory of the mechanism or cause of orogeny and the formation of folded mountain systems must not only explain the present structure and composition of the mountains, but it must be compatible with the factual knowledge we have concerning the history of folded mountains. This is an example of the importance of historical interpretation in the development of geologic thought. As an example of the history of a folded mountain belt, the history of the Appalachians is presented in chapter 30. The history of a mountain range is interpreted from the existing structure, the nature of the rocks of which it is composed and by which it is surrounded,

and by the evidence from radioactive dates of its thermal history as expressed in metamorphism and igneous activity. Most geosynclines have had somewhat similar histories, as outlined in the section on the nature of orogenic belts, item 17.

One particularly important aspect of the histories of folded mountain systems concerns the nature of the margins of the geosynclines. It is generally agreed that most ancient geosynclines formed in positions along the margins of continental shields, though a few developed between two shields. The side of the geosyncline adjacent to the continent is usually well preserved, and here we find that the sedimentary layers from the geosyncline thin out over the shield. But, unfortunately, the side of the geosyncline adjacent to the ocean is often either so strongly deformed or covered by younger rocks that the nature of that margin before and during the orogeny is obscured. Many geologists have supported the idea that extensive land areas occupied this oceanward side of the geosyncline during its early history and provided a source from which sediments found in the geosyncline were eroded. Other geologists have proposed that this margin of the geosyncline was essentially similar to the modern island arc system. Some of the arguments on this point are brought out in chapter 30. The character of this oceanward side of the geosyncline is of critical importance in judging the acceptability of theories of the cause of orogeny.

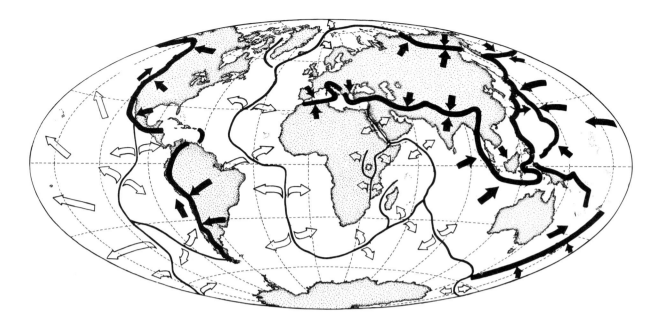

FIG. 25–27. / *Rift zones, folded mountain belts and hypothetical convection currents. The heavy solid lines are modern folded mountain belts. The lighter lines mark positions of the major crusted rift zones. Arrows indicate general patterns of convection in the earth's interior based on the hypothesis that mountain belts and island arcs form where currents sink and that the rifts indicate upwelling. (Based on illustrations by J. T. Wilson with permission.)*

FIG. 25–28. / *Cross sections across the Rhine Graben. The Rhine River flows down a down-dropped troughlike depression called a graben (German for grave). Normal faults form both sides of the graben. (From Billings, 1960; after Dorn.)*

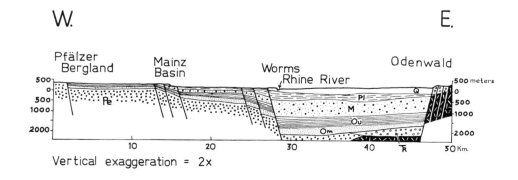

Theories of Orogeny

IT IS HARDLY SURPRISING THAT NO SINGLE theory has been devised to account for all the varied and complex observations above. Their complexity, coupled with the lack of information about the lower portions of the crust and subcrust, makes the explanation of orogeny most difficult. Of course, it is possible that mountains may be formed under different circumstances in different parts of the crust, instead of by orogeny from a single cause. However, many geologists feel that there must be a fundamental cause of orogeny because of the remarkable similarity of orogenic belts throughout the world. Theories reviewed here have been offered to explain certain specific aspects of orogeny.

Theory of the Contracting Earth

ONE OF THE FIRST attempts to explain mountain-building processes was based on the assumption that the earth is cooling, and as a result contracting. This theory is tied in with another widely assumed hypothesis that the earth was pulled out of the sun as a molten mass and that it has been cooling ever since. Accordingly, the crust represents the already cooled portion of the earth, and the hot interior is part of the original molten mass. As the interior of the earth cools, the volume of the interior decreases, and the outer crust is forced to accommodate itself to a sphere of smaller radius. This is accomplished by wrinkling or folding of the crust. The beauty of this theory is that it explains the compressional features found in the crust. But in recent years the fundamental assumptions of the theory have been questioned. With the discovery of great quantities of radioactive minerals in the crust, the question arises as to whether the interior is actually cooling and contracting, or heating and expanding, for radioactive decay is accompanied by the release of heat. In either case the rate is too slow for us to make any direct observations to determine expansion or contraction.

A second major problem as yet unexplained in terms of this theory is the existence in the crust of features that originate through tension. Block fault mountains and grabens are most readily explained in terms of tensional stresses (Fig. 25–28). The rift zone that follows the crest of the Mid-Atlantic Ridge has been traced along other midoceanic ridges and through several of the largest grabens known in the crust (Fig. 25–27). It appears from this pattern that large portions of the crust are experiencing or have in recent times experienced tensional forces that have created this system of rifts.

Tectogene Hypothesis

VENING MEINESZ made extensive gravity surveys in the southwestern Pacific Ocean, particularly around Java and Sumatra, during and after World War II. He demonstrated that large negative gravity anomalies exist over deep-sea trenches (Fig. 25–29). A negative anomaly at a location indicates a deficiency of mass there as compared with an ideal homogeneous earth. The negative anomaly persists even after corrections are made for differences in density between rock and sea water in the trench. The interpretation of this anomaly has been that low-density rocks project down into the more dense subcrust under the island arc. Meinesz postulates that lower-density rocks, the sialic part of the crust, have been pulled into a downbuckle. Such a feature is called a *tectogene*.

The force required to form the downbuckle is provided by convection currents, which exist in mobile fluids when there are temperature differences in different parts of the fluid. In the earth the interior is hotter than the surface and there may be locally high temperature gradients established by concentrations of radioactive minerals (possibly under the continental margins). Convection could not exist in the earth's crust because it is too rigid, but within the mantle and core, where the material is thought to be in a plastic (pseudoviscous) state as a result of high temperature and confining pressure, convection is possible. Postulated convection cells somewhat like those illustrated in Figs. 25–30.

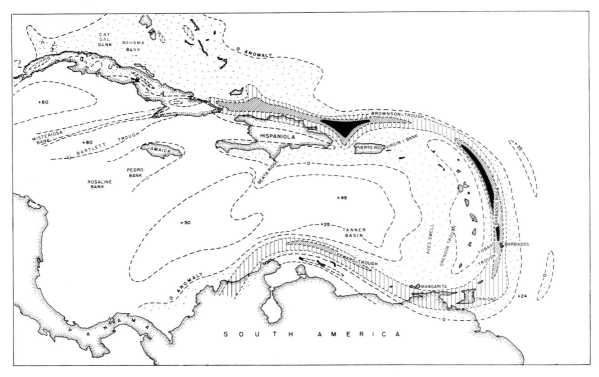

FIG. 25–29. / *Gravity anomalies in the Caribbean. The black and diagonally lined areas are negative anomalies where there is a mass deficiency. Such negative anomalies are associated with deep-sea trenches in the island arc systems of the Pacific also. (From A. J. Eardley, 1957.)*

and 25–31 would exert a frictional drag on the solid crust of the earth, and in areas where two cells converge and move down the crust is pulled down as a tectogene into the mantle. As this downbuckle is pulled farther down the deeper portions are heated, folded, and highly metamorphosed; magmas are created and then intrude the mass. Eventually the downbuckle is so pressed together that part of the material in it is forced upward to become a folded mountain range. Thus the hypothesis successfully explains many observed features of folded orogenic belts.

In recent years measurements have been made of the rate of heat flow from the interior of the earth to the surface. One of the most interesting of the preliminary conclusions is that the rate of heat flow is abnormally low in island arcs and abnormally high in the vicinity of the midocean ridges. This lends support to the tectogene hypothesis, and offers convection cells as a possible explanation of the upbulge in the midoceans. Midocean ridges might be caused by upwelling of convection currents. The

crust becomes cracked open along these ridges under tensional stresses.

Although the convection current hypothesis is not universally accepted, it does explain more of the structure of the crust and more of what we know of mountain building than any other single integrated hypothesis.

Gravity Tectonics

THERE HAS BEEN unusual interest in recent years in the depth of the intricately folded and faulted sedimentary rock masses. Such structures might be created in several ways. They could result from shortening of the crust of the earth. Measurements in the Appalachians show that nearly two hundred miles of crustal shortening would have to take place in order to create the folds found there. However, there are other alternatives. One of these is that the folding that is so striking in its surface expression is actually only a "skin-deep" type of deformation. This could be produced by slippage of a sedimentary veneer over crystalline basement rocks or along faults that parallel original bedding surfaces. Such slippage is thought by many to be due primarily to the force of gravity. Slippage is facilitated by presence in the sequence of units composed of clay, gypsum, or other soft and weak materials on which sliding could occur. Such sliding is visualized as taking place after uplift in major orogenic belts. It would affect primarily marginal portions of deformed belts. Probably one of the best examples of the shallow depth of deformation is found in the Pine Mountain overthrust of the Cumberland Mountains in the Appalachians (Fig. 25–26). Here a large section of sedimentary rocks has been thrust to the northwest along a fault which lies flat and nearly parallel to flat sedimentary rocks below, as shown in the cross section.

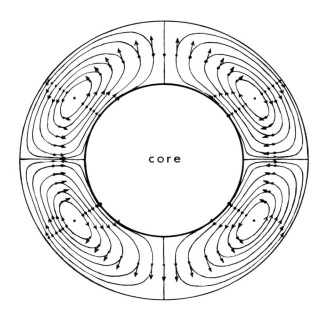

FIG. 25–31. / *Convection cell pattern. Length of the arrows indicates relative rates of movement. (After Pekeris, 1935.)*

Continental Drift[5]

STUDENTS OF THE EARTH HAVE LONG BEEN intrigued by the striking similarities in the shape of the eastern coast of North, Central, and South America and the western coast of Europe and Africa, but the theory that the continents have actually drifted apart was advanced by Alfred Wegener only in 1922. Since the theory was first advanced, the question of permanence of continents and ocean basins has been intensively debated. Within the last decade the conceptual schemes of continental drift and shifting poles have been increasingly accepted

[5] A review of modern work may be found in *Polar Wandering and Continental Drift*, ed. A. C. Munyan, Soc. Eco. Paleo. & Min. Spec. Pub. 10, 1963.

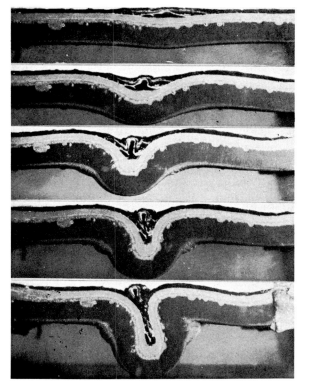

FIG. 25–30. / *Experiment in the formation of a tectogene. A floating plastic layer is shown as it is compressed. According to Vening Meinesz the down-buckle may be formed by drag of convection currents on the crust. These photographs, representing five successive stages, were taken during an experiment by Ph. H. Kuenen. (From Vening Meinesz, Geol. Soc. Am., Special Paper 62.)*

as explanations for a broad spectrum of data. When Wegener advanced the idea of continental drift, it was to explain anomalous distribution of ancient climatic belts. Today supporting evidence is found mainly from the study of paleomagnetism, paleobotany, paleoclimatology, and crustal structure. At the present time all of the data from these various lines of investigation cannot be fit into a unified and unconflicting picture of movements of the poles and continents, but each line of evidence points to such shifts and many geologists expect that in time the causes of present inconsistencies in the data will be explained and corrected.

Wegener attempted to fit all continents into a single protocontinent called "Pangea" (Fig. 33-4), and the close fit of the coasts on either side of the Atlantic remains a convincing line of evidence for continental drift, but other evidence, particularly paleomagnetic, is more responsible for the current interest in the problem.

Paleomagnetism

THE GENERAL CHARACTER of the earth's present magnetic field was discussed in chapter 24. A means has now been found which makes it possible to reconstruct the magnetic field as it existed at various times in the past through the study of remanent magnetism found in ancient rock units and masses. Remanent magnetism of rocks is mainly due to the iron oxide and sulphide minerals. Such magnetic minerals may obtain a preferred directional magnetism as they crystallize from magma, through chemical precipitation or reaction at low temperatures, or through alignment of magnetic particles when they are deposited as a sediment. In each case the preferred alignment is due to the local direction of the magnetic field of the earth at the time the rock is formed. Some minerals lose their preferred directional magnetism in time and the effects may be completely destroyed if the rock is subsequently metamorphosed or subjected to heat. But the direction of the poles from a given locality at the time of formation of a particular rock containing such magnetized minerals can be determined if the preferred di-

rectional field strength remains strong enough in the sample. Obviously the effects of any later tilting or folding must be accounted for in orienting the specimen as it was at the time of formation of the magnetized minerals.

Many studies have now been made of remanent magnetism for rocks of various ages and rocks of the same age located in different areas. The results indicate that the position of the poles has not remained constant through time. This is shown by studies of rocks of different ages on a single continent. For example, studies in North America indicate that the position of the North Pole has shifted along the line indicated, (Fig. 25-32), from a Precambrian location in the central Pacific to a Triassic position in Siberia and then to its present location. This then suggests a shifting of the pole in relation to modern geographical distribution of land.

When paleomagnetic data from Europe are plotted on the same diagram a similar shift of poles is indicated, but the lines of shift are not coincident as they should be if the geographic positions of Europe and North America had remained fixed relative to one another. This is evidence for continental drift. Similar studies from other continents likewise reveal shifting of continents in relation to one another.

The nature of paleoclimatic and paleobotanical evidence supporting the theory of continental drift is pointed out in chapter 33.

Structural Implications

IF THE CONTINENTS ARE DRIFTING then there should be resulting large-scale structural features which can be related to the movements. Furthermore the nature of the structure and strength of the continental and oceanic crustal segments must be such that these movements are possible. We have already seen, in our examination of the theory of isostasy, that the crustal segments are in a type of floatational equilibrium on the subcrustal materials and that the subcrustal materials must be capable of flowing. Movement of a rigid continental mass over subcrustal materials that yield by flow is therefore feasible. Furthermore we have seen that dis-

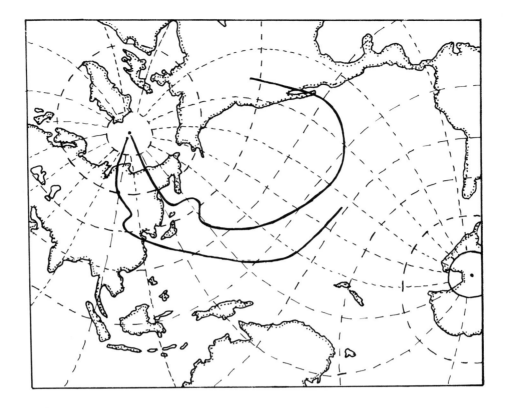

FIG. 25–32. / *Traces of the movement of the position of the North Pole from the Precambrian to the present, as determined by paleomagnetic studies of rocks on North America (western line) and from Europe (eastern line). (Modified after S. K. Runcorn, in* Polar Wandering and Continental Drift, *1963, Soc. Eco. Paleo. and Min., spec. pub. no. 10.)*

tinct differences exist in the nature of the continental and oceanic crusts. The continents are characterized by their stable shield areas and marginal folded geosynclinal belts. The oceans in turn have midoceanic rises composed of extruded volcanic materials the crests of which are broken by globe-encircling zones of tensional faulting. At the margins of the Pacific Ocean basin we find island arcs and their associated structural features. One of these is a major fault system that is inclined from the vicinity of the trenches toward and under the adjacent continents, making it appear that the continents are moving out over the oceanic crust.

Convection currents in the earth's interior can be used to explain certain aspects of continental drifting. Upwelling of these currents has been postulated to coincide with the midoceanic rises, accounting for the tensional faults, volcanic activity, seismic activity, and high heat flow rates associated with the rises. From these areas the currents must spread out laterally until they merge from opposite directions and start down. During this lateral movement the currents might bring compressional pressures to bear on the margins of the continents which, because the continents are composed of lighter materials, extend down into the more dense materials on which they are floating. This compression would account for the development of the apparent movement of the continent over the ocean basin along a fault, just as the downward movement of the currents has been postulated to explain the formation of the tectogene and the island arc system. Thus the oceanic crust could be essentially spreading and thereby exerting a force on the continents causing them to move. It is still much too early to tell if this theory or even a substantial part of it will stand the test of time, but it is an engaging idea and brings together many diverse results from a great variety of geologic investigations.

VIII / ANALYSIS OF EARTH HISTORY

26

Early History and Basic Concepts of Historical Geology

THE EARTH'S HISTORY AND ITS PHYSICAL NATURE have been subjects of man's interest since classical times, but serious attempts to make observations and piece earth history together in an orderly manner date primarily from the seventeenth century.

One of the first attempts to classify the rocks of the earth's crust was made by Johann Lehmann in 1756. Lehmann, teacher of mineralogy and mining in Berlin, divided the various types of rock units he observed into three groups:

Primary rocks, crystalline rocks containing no fossils—"formed at the beginning of the earth."

Secondary rocks, consolidated and stratified rocks in which fossils could be found—"formed during the Flood."

Alluvial rocks, unconsolidated sediments and loosely consolidated material—"formed since the time of Noah's Flood."

Soon after Lehmann, Giovanni Arduino proposed another classification. Arduino was a prominent geologist in Venice, where he served as professor of mineralogy and metallurgy. He is credited with being the first to recognize that many crystalline rocks are of volcanic origin, and that paleontology can be applied to the chronology of the formations. He recognized a fourfold classification of the crust:

Primary mountains—those containing metallic ores and crystalline rocks.

Secondary mountains—those built up of marble and limestone.

Low mountains and hills—those generally composed of gravels, sand, clay, and volcanic materials.

Earthy and rocky materials—those resting upon all the preceding alluvial material.

Law of Superposition

AMONG THE MOST BRILLIANT OF THE SEVenteenth century scientists was the Danish geologist Nikolaus Steno (1638–87). He made a number of astute observations about the formation of sedimentary rock strata, and from these he formulated a group of laws governing the formation of the stratigraphical succession. These laws include the following:

1. A definite layer of deposit can only form upon a solid basis. (It is now known that layers can form on unconsolidated sediments also.)
2. The lower stratum must therefore have consolidated before a fresh deposit is precipitated upon it. (This is known to be wrong.)
3. Any one stratum must either cover the whole earth, or be limited laterally by other solid deposits.
4. During the period of accumulation of a deposit there is above it only the water from which it is precipitated; therefore the lower layers in a series of strata must be older than the upper.

The first three of these laws are not entirely accurate, but the fourth is one of the underlying principles of historical interpretation in geology, known as the *"law of superposition"*—in a normal, undisturbed sequence the oldest strata lies below younger strata. Steno recognized that stratigraphic sequences are not always found undisturbed. He cited a number of examples of local "crust-inthrow," places where the strata had been thrown into a perpendicular position or arched upward in folds. Thus he recognized the possibility that sequences could be turned upside down, in which case the law does not apply. He went further, to suggest that the arching and "faulting" might originate from uplifting due to volcanic activity. In many instances this is true.

Neptunism vs. Plutonism

ABRAHAM G. WERNER WAS BORN IN PRUSsian Silesia in 1749. He became interested in earth science as a child in playing around the mines near his home. While studying at the University of Leipzig he wrote his first important work, a new method of mineral description. At the age of 25 he became an instructor at the university and soon initiated many new ideas on techniques of instruction. He introduced

TABLE 9 / *Life spans of some of the most famous early geologists*

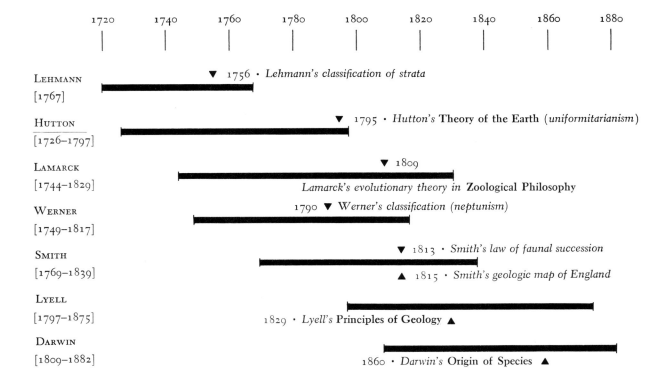

practical demonstrations as a part of training in the natural sciences. Werner asked his students questions continuously, took them on field trips, and invited them into his home. Undoubtedly he was one of the most effective teachers in the history of earth science. So popular and brilliant a man was he that his teachings dominated geologic thought for almost 40 years. His ideas were rigidly based on fact at a time when most of what was written and taught was based on pure speculation. Unfortunately, Werner misunderstood what he observed in a number of instances, and his persuasive ability made it difficult for others to correct the misinterpretations that became so firmly entrenched in the minds of his followers. Werner's basic concept was that the ocean had gradually receded from the continents to its present position, and that the oceans had deposited all the rocks visible in the crust. Hence the name "Neptunists" was applied to Werner and his followers.

We are also convinced that the solid mass of our globe has been produced by a series of precipitations formed in succession; that the pressure of the materials, thus accumulated, was not the same throughout the whole; and that this difference of pressure and several other concurring causes have produced rents in the substance of the earth, chiefly in the most elevated parts of its surface. We are also persuaded that the precipitates taking form from the universal water must have entered into the open fissures which the water covered.

In 1790 Werner modified Lehmann's classification to:

Primitive series—chemical precipitates from the ocean deposited before emergence of the land. (Igneous and metamorphic rocks.)

Transition series—consolidated sedimentary rocks deposited in layers which extend without interruption around the world. These we now know to be nonexistent.

Stratified series (*Secondary*)—these are the stratified fossiliferous rocks. Werner thought these were products of erosion of mountains which emerged as seas receded.

Alluvial series—poorly consolidated rocks formed after the oceans had withdrawn.

Volcanic series—Werner thought these were of minor importance, representing nothing more than local effects of burning coal beds.

Werner taught that the ages of rocks could be recognized everywhere by the nature—lithology—of the rocks, an idea we now recognize as false. He failed to observe the great variety of rocks being formed even in his own lifetime.

Opponents of Werner's views of all rocks as sedimentary in origin included James Hutton, a Scotsman who was a contemporary of Werner. Unfortunately Hutton did not have the personal appeal of Werner and even with the aid of conclusive and sound arguments he was very slow to convince the Neptunists of their error. Hutton was able to establish that the primary rocks of Werner's classification were, in fact, of igneous origin. Hence those who favored the igneous origin of primary rocks were called plutonists. Slowly Hutton's views, on the importance of volcanism (igneous activity) as the process by which many crystalline rocks are formed, came to be accepted.

Uniformitarianism

GEORGES FUSHSEL, A FRENCH PHYSICIAN who was a contemporary of Lehmann, described and subdivided a large stratigraphic sequence near Paris. He went so far as to propose time units for the series of rocks, assuming that each rock unit was formed during a different time. Among Fushsel's outstanding accomplishments was the construction of a geologic map and cross sections. The greatest contribution made by Fushsel to the young science of geology was the first statement of the *principle of uniformitarianism*: "Indeed, the manner in which nature at the present time is still acting and producing things must be assumed as the rule in our explanation; we know no other." In order to make sure that his work would be available to educated men of all nations he wrote it in Latin. As a result his work was ignored not only by scientists of other nations, but by those of his native country as well. This was a most unfortunate circumstance, because it held back for many years our understanding of the nature of the stratigraphic record of time. Werner's influence and opposition was one of the main factors in the suppression of Fushsel's work.

James Hutton's observations not only led him to the conclusion that many crystalline rocks are of igneous origin, but also enabled him to state clearly the principle of superposition and the principle of uniformitarianism. Though both of these important ideas had been advanced earlier, they were not widely accepted during Hutton's life. Most students of the earth subscribed to the idea that the earth was no more than a few thousand years old, and that its history had been punctuated by one or more catastrophies during which all living beings had been wiped out and newly created beings followed. Such catastrophic events were widely accepted as the explanation of the formation of mountains and other natural features. This view survived into the nineteenth century, as is shown by the following writing in 1818 of the prominent American geologist Amos Eaton:

Our present continents may now be supported in the same way and the meeting of the edges of segments form the granitic ridge which extends from Georgia to the Frigid Zone—that is to say, that which forms the Appalachian Mountain System.

In whatever manner the ancient world was supported, it is evident that when the wickedness of man drew down the vengeance of the Almighty, its foundations gave way and it sank to the bottom of the ocean never to be again uplifted. . . .

While this tremendous crash of Nature was going on, scales of various thicknesses from the various strata were shot up, detached and broken, which gave formation to our surrounding hills, the ragged cliffs of the Catskill and the bleak brow of the Andes. Some were formed at the bottom of the sea by volcanic fires; others have arisen from various causes since the great deep retired.

One of the foremost exponents of the theory of uniformitarianism was Charles Lyell (1797–1875). The following quote from his textbook (1833) summarizes his reasoning regarding the uniformity of earth processes.

By these researches into the state of the earth and its inhabitants at former periods, we acquire a more perfect knowledge of its present condition, and more comprehensive views concerning the laws now governing its animate and inanimate productions. . . .

If we reflect on the history of the progress of geology, we perceive that there have been great fluctuations of opinion respecting the nature of the causes to which all former changes of the earth's surface are referable. The first observers conceived the monuments which the geologist endeavors to decipher to relate to an original state of the earth, or to a period when there were causes in activity, distinct, in kind and degree, from those now constituting the economy of nature. These views were gradually modified, and some of them entirely abandoned, in proportion as observations were multiplied, and the signs of former mutations more skillfully interpreted. Many appearances, which had for a long time been regarded as indicating mysterious and extraordinary agency, were finally recognized as the necessary result of the laws now governing the material world; and the discovery of this unlooked-for conformity has at length induced some philosophers to infer, that during the ages contemplated in geology, there has never been any interruption to the agency of the same uniform laws of change. The same assemblage of general causes, they conceive, may have been sufficient to produce, by their various combinations, the endless diversity of effects, of which the shell of the earth has preserved the memorials; and, consistently with these principles, the recurrence of analogous changes is expected by them in time to come.

. . . By degrees, many of the enigmas of the moral and physical world are explained, and, instead of being due to extrinsic and irregular causes, they are found to depend on fixed and invariable laws. . . .

Now the reader may easily satisfy himself, that, however undeviating the course of nature may have been from the earliest epochs, it was impossible for the first cultivators of geology to come to such a conclusion, so long as they were under a delusion as to the age of the world, and the date of the first creation of animate beings. . . .

If we could behold in one view all the volcanic cones thrown up in Iceland, Italy, Sicily, and other parts of Europe, during the last five thousand years, and could see the lavas which have flowed during the same period; the dislocations, subsidences, and elevations caused during earthquakes; the lands added to various deltas, or devoured by the sea, together with the effects of devastation by floods, and imagine that all these events had happened in one year, we must form most exalted ideas of the activity of the agents, and the suddenness of the revolutions. Were an equal amount of change to pass before our eyes in the next year, could we avoid the conclusion that some great crisis of nature was at hand? If geologists, therefore, have misinterpreted the signs of a succession of events, so as to conclude that centuries were implied where the characters imported thousands of years, and thousands of years where the language of Nature signified millions, they could not, if they reasoned logically from such false premises, come to any other conclusion than that the system of the Natural world has undergone a complete revolution.

The concept of uniformitarianism is that the same processes and principles that govern natural changes on the earth today have acted in the past to produce similar changes. In other words, *"the present is a key to the past."* Since there is no way for us to actually observe that uniformity has prevailed, this concept must be considered an assumption. It is one of the most important, fundamental assumptions of geology. The strength of an hypothesis, or for that matter of a whole science, is based on the strength of its basic assumptions. Therefore it is worthwhile for us to examine this assumption. There are two reasons for its general acceptance among geologists.

First, in the time that man has been actively observing and recording the nature of natural processes, there appears to be no evidence of any change in the way in which they operate. The so-called laws or principles governing physical and chemical reactions and interactions have remained constant. Thus we assume that they may be applied as well to events of the past as to those observable in the present. We see no reason to think that the law of universal gravitation was in any way different during the Cambrian Period from what it is now. It seems logical to assume that limestone exposed at the ground surface during the Silurian Period or any other time was dissolved by rainwater carrying carbon dioxide in solution just as it is today. This does not mean that we assume that there was necessarily the same amount of carbon dioxide that we find in the rainwater today, or that limestones were as widely distributed as we now find them.

Second, geologists feel that further proof of the validity of uniformitarianism is found in the ease with which the geologic record of the past can be interpreted by its use. This in itself may not be a very persuasive argument, but it is hard to dispute the fact that when several lines of investigation are used they inevitably all lead to the same or compatible conclusions about a past event. An example will serve to illustrate the point. Exposures of limestone are common in many parts of this country. Assume that you study one such outcrop and find fossil remains of some invertebrate animals. If these particular animals presently live only in marine waters, then you have one line of evidence pointing to a marine origin of this limestone unit. If this limestone is a form now deposited only in the sea, you have a second line of evidence pointing to a marine origin of the unit. These different lines of evidence point to a marine origin for the limestone unit. Both of them are based on the assumption that the present is a key to the past.

By using uniformitarianism it is possible to make remarkable restorations of conditions long past. Past climatic conditions may be postulated. Positions of coastlines and mountains, and depth and even temperature of water at a given time in the past may be judged. What can be learned of past geologic ages must be obtained from the rocks formed during those ages and preserved

FIG. 26–1. / *A massive layer of sandstone exposed in a cliff in New Mexico. Such strata are commonly found to extend for many tens or even hundreds of miles. They reflect very continuous conditions of sedimentation at the time they were formed. (Photo by courtesy of the New Mexico State Tourist Bureau.)*

since that time. This imposes several restrictions on our interpretations and makes the problem a much greater challenge. How can we possibly discover whether or not there was a mountain range in a certain area 100 million years ago, if the mountain range itself disappeared from the face of the earth 90 million years ago? The answer is that the material removed from the mountain was deposited on its flanks and in the areas around it. If it was located near a sea, it is probable that the sediment accumulated there. The presence of the mountains will have to be inferred from the character of the deposits in the sea. Thus the nature of sedimentary deposits is extremely important, and in order to understand them we must know the conditions under which they were formed. The solution to this situation is found in the theory of uniformitarianism.

By studying environments in which present-day sediments are deposited we know how to interpret those of the past. It is worthwhile not only to study the type of sediment that is formed in a certain place, but to consider the animals that live there. These animals die, and their remains become incorporated in the sediment. Just as different animals live in different climates or regions on land, so certain marine organisms live in particular marine environments. The fauna and flora of a swamp are strikingly different from those of the continental shelf or those of the deep-sea floor. Some marine organisms live only in warm waters, others only in cold water. Some require currents to bring them food, others move about and collect their food. Thus a valuable means of interpreting past environments lies in knowing the environments in which similar animals and plants live today.

Limitations of Uniformitarianism

LIMITATIONS THAT MUST be placed on the concept of uniformitarianism depend largely upon its interpretation. There is no need to limit its application if it is used only in the strictest sense of its meaning, that the nature of processes and physical and chemical laws have remained constant throughout time. This does not imply that because we have ice caps at the poles today there have always been ice caps at the poles, nor does it suggest that sea level has always tended to rise, or that climatic variations have always been as great as they are now. An example of how the concept of uniformitarianism may be somewhat stretched is the use of rates of sedimentation to judge the length of time involved in the formation of a sedimentary rock. The present rate of accumulation for a particular sediment type is measured, then the thickness of an ancient deposit of similar nature is measured and, by assuming that the same rates of sedimentation applied in the past, the length of time required to form the ancient deposit is calculated. The adherent to a strict interpretation of the concept of uniformitarianism will not accept this line of reasoning. Uniformitarianism may be used to evaluate the mechanism or mode of deposition, but not its rate. The rate would depend on many other factors. Conditions have certainly not been the same throughout the earth's history. During the greatest part of its history, there were no land plants and very few land animals. When the plant cover is lost from an area today erosion is accelerated. If this condition existed in the past for continents as a whole, the amount of sediment flowing into the oceans may have been much greater than it is today. This certainly would have affected the rate of sedimentation.

Uniformitarianism vs. Catastrophism

ONE OF THE FIRST principal objections to uniformitarianism was the amount of time required for completion of all the work accomplished by natural processes. In the eighteenth century most people believed that the earth was no more than 6,000 years old. This would hardly leave time enough for a feature the size of the Grand Canyon to be formed by a stream cutting in the manner and at the rate of the Colorado River. Even if we accept the possibility that the river might have cut more rapidly in the past than it is now cutting, 6,000 years is not conceivably enough time. One apparent solution to the problem is to accept the principle of uniformitarianism, but with a modification. That modification is that the earth has from time to time experienced great catastrophies. It has even been proposed that the Grand Canyon is a huge rift in the earth's crust, torn apart in as short a time as a day or a week, and that the rift has simply been modified by subsequent erosion. However, there is no field evidence of any such catastrophic event.

Periods of mountain formation mark breaks between some of the major divisions of geologic time. Many have envisioned these mountains as rising rapidly, in a matter of a few hundreds of years. With the advent of accurate dating methods and with a greatly improved idea of the age of the earth, it is unnecessary to call on catastrophic events to explain these. Upuifts of as little as a fraction of an inch a year may eventually create mountains. That slow rates of this order of magnitude have been the usual order of mountain formation is demonstrated by unconformities that characteristically occur around the margins of major uplifts. Instead of sudden uplift, mountains rise slowly. They may become stable for a period of time while they are eroded, and products of that erosion are laid down as sediments around the mountains. Then, when uplift is renewed, sediments are uplifted, then beveled off by erosion, and new sediments from the mountains are laid down over them. Thus a series of angular unconformities are formed at the margins. From observations of erosion and deposition of sediments in the present, we can say that the amount of time involved in these events is great. Radioactive dating in the Rocky Mountain folded belt shows that the mountains continued to be actively formed over millions of years. This is typical of all the major mountain belts.

Uniformitarianism and Catastrophism

IF WE MUST CHOOSE between these two concepts, then uniformitarianism is the obvious choice. The very word "catastrophism" has a bad connotation for most earth scientists. They are so adamant in refuting the more extreme views of catastrophists that they prefer not to use the word at all. However, minor catastrophies are rather common on earth today. The earthquakes which struck Agadir, Africa, and Chile in 1960, the 1963 landslide in Italy, and the typhoon that hit Japan in 1959 are examples. The effects of such minor catastrophies are pronounced. Each of the following occurs many times during every year:

Rivers flood and wash away huge amounts of topsoil.

Hurricanes hit coasts, storm beaches are formed, and ordinary beaches are washed away.

Torrential rainfall causes alteration of desert landscapes.

Strain is built up on opposite sides of faults for periods of many years; then release of this energy and subsequent displacement takes place in a matter of a few hours.

Volcanoes may stand dormant for many years and suddenly begin to eject great quantities of lava, dust, or other pyroclastic material.

Tsunamis break up rocks along the sea cliffs around the oceans of the world and inundate lowland areas in short periods of time.

Masses of loose sediment or decayed rock stand on steep slopes for years until they become unstable, then the slightest disturbance sets huge landslides in motion. The counterpart of this process in the oceans is the turbidity current. Some occur with the seasons, after large quantities of sediment have been deposited on the steep submarine slopes off the mouths of rivers.

These serve to illustrate the importance of minor "catastrophic" events in accomplishing erosion and deposition. The cumulative effects of the constant downslope creep of soil, the gradual decay of rocks in the atmosphere, and the gradual removal of material by streams hour after hour, day in and day out, over millions of years are probably much greater than the effects of these minor catastrophes. Nevertheless, minor catastrophes should not be discounted. To understand the nature of the operation of natural processes today it is necessary to employ the concepts of both uniformitarianism and catastrophism.

The Law of Faunal Succession

Fossils have long attracted the attention of man, but their nature has not always been as obvious as it may appear to today's students. The fifteenth century marked the start of a long debate about the origin of fossils. Some scientists believed that they grew from seeds, others interpreted them as marine organisms laid on the surface of the earth during Noah's Flood, and still others had suggested that they were placed in the rocks by the Devil to confuse man. Leonardo da Vinci was one of the first to recognize fossils as remnants of marine organisms deposited in the seas at a time when the seas were higher or the land lower. Robert Hooke, who is famous for his work in physics, is credited with being the first to suggest that fossils might be used in the study of the earth's history. He pointed this out in 1688 in a paper on earthquakes.

John Woodward (1665–1722), an English paleontologist, strongly opposed the religious dogma of the period, which held that all fossils were remnants of the Flood. Woodward considered fossils to be remnants of flora and fauna that lived in the distant past. His writings reveal that he correctly identified and interpreted widespread sedimentary strata.

The Result of this was that in time I was abundantly assured that the Circumstances of these Things in remoter Countries were much the same with those of ours here: that the Stone, and other terrestrial Matter, in France, Flanders, Holland, Spain, Italy, Germany, Denmark, Norway, and Sweden, was distinguished into Strata, or Layers, as it is in England; that those Strata were divided by parallel Fissures: that there were enclosed in the Stone, and all the other denser kinds of terrestrial Matter, great numbers of Shells, and other Productions of the Sea; in the same manner as in that of this Island.

The importance of this insight lies in that it opens the way to consider the possibility of correlation of events in historical perspective.

Undoubtedly the most significant conclusions regarding the value and use of fossils were recognized by William Smith. Smith (1769–1839) was a man with an insatiable curiosity and a habit of taking notes on nearly everything he observed. His life's work was engineering, and to it he brought an immense amount of imagination and skill. He was employed to drain swamps, locate canals, and restore springs. He realized that an understanding of rock units was of great value in accomplishing these tasks. His success in these projects put him in such great demand that he was called to all parts of England. Often he traveled as much as 10,000 miles a year, and on all these trips he kept careful notes of the types of rocks he saw. Probably his most important contribution was the observation that certain rock units can be identified by the particular assemblages of fossils they contain. This led to the formulation of the *"law of faunal succession."* These important findings of Smith first appeared in a paper written by his friend Rev. Joseph Townsend. Oddly enough the paper was entitled "The Character of Moses established for Veracity as an Historian, recording events from Creation to the Deluge." Later Smith published three volumes describing the fossil content of the strata that outcrop in England. In 1815 he published a geologic map of the entire country to the scale of 5 miles to an inch, and this map has not been substantially changed since then.

27

Geologic Time Scale

THE FIRST APPEARANCE OF A GEOLOGIC TIME scale similar to that used today was in 1833 in a textbook by Charles Lyell, *Principles of Geology* (Table 10). Lyell's classification has a threefold subdivision, Primary, Secondary, and Tertiary. But the meaning given to these terms in 1833 was completely different from the meaning initially assigned to the same terms by Lehmann. Lyell's time scale was devised to include both rock units identified by William Smith and others that had been identified in Europe. Within each of the major divisions of the scale there are *groups* of strata of similar lithology. Not all of the strata recognized by Smith outcrop at the surface in any single locality; therefore, considerable time elapsed before the correct positions within the sequence could be established for some units. Studies of the fossil fauna and flora paralleled the studies of rock lithologies. Smith had recognized that different rock groups contain different fossil assemblages. The observed differences were so great in some cases that the idea that there had been a number of catastrophes in the past which destroyed most forms of life became accepted and was used as a basis for subdividing the rock record. It was noted that these marked changes in the

forms of life often occurred where the rocks of one group or series were deposited on those of an earlier sequence which had been folded or warped, causing angular unconformity between strata of the two groups.

It was soon discovered that it was possible to correlate groups of strata by their position in relation to these unconformities. The same rock units containing almost identical fossils were found immediately above an angular unconformity in many localities in Europe and England. Eventually it was shown that similar units and fossils had identical relations to unconformities in North America. The evidence suggested that there had been a number of periods in the geologic past when the entire earth's crust was strongly deformed. As a result of these periods of deformation, mountains formed, climates changed, seas withdrew from the continents, and whole populations of animals died out.

Many geologists consider that such widespread deformations of the crust are the ultimate basis for correlation of geologic events throughout the world (Fig. 27–3). But the question of whether there are periodic earth movements affecting large parts of the earth's crust almost simultaneously is still subject to debate. We do know that world-wide correlation on this basis is not a simple process. Complications are found as stratigraphic study is pursued in greater detail. At the present time thousands of geologists are working on problems related to this question. They are making more exact correlations between rock units, fossil assemblages, and geologic time, and their relation to deformation of the crust. In general, their findings seem to point to major errors in earlier concepts based on the belief that geologic time may be divided into several major eras separated by almost catastrophic periods of deformation. Mountains are found to develop slowly over periods of millions of years. Even changes in forms of life characteristic of different eras seem to be much less drastic than formerly thought.

The Modern Time Scale

Eras

PROMINENT UNCONFORMITIES separate Primary, Secondary, and Tertiary groups of Lyell's classification in many places. From the abundance of paleontologic data on the rocks of the three groups paleontologists learned that certain fossil animals dominated each group. Primary rocks were found to consist of two parts—unfossiliferous crystalline rocks and sedimentary rocks characterized by fossils of invertebrates and fishes. The Secondary group was characterized by remains of certain mollusks (cephalopods, ammonites) and reptiles, including dinosaurs; the Tertiary group by mollusk and mammal remains. The prominence of unconformities and impressive changes in faunas between these divisions led to their acceptance as "eras" of geologic time. They were given names which reflect the stages of the development of life in each—*Paleozoic* (old life), *Mesozoic* (middle life), and *Cenozoic* (modern life).

Periods

WITHIN ROCK UNITS of each era other unconformities and noteworthy changes in faunas and floras are observed. Many of these breaks can be recognized in different parts of the world and therefore have come to be generally accepted. The largest of these subdivisions of time is called a *period*. Rock units formed within periods are called *systems*. Systems and periods are usually given the same names. These are names of the locality in which the system was first recognized and described. This locality is called the *classic locality* or *type section* for rocks of that period. Ages of other rocks which are to be classified in the same period must either be correlated with the rocks of that type section or be shown to have formed during a

TABLE 10 / *Geologic time scale of Lyell.*

POST TERTIARY		
PLIOCENE		
MIOCENE	TERTIARY *or* CENOZOIC	
EOCENE		NEOZOIC
CRETACEOUS		
JURASSIC	SECONDARY *or* MESOZOIC	
TRIASSIC		
PERMIAN		
CARBONIFEROUS		
DEVONIAN	PRIMARY *or* PALAEOZOIC	PALAEOZOIC
SILURIAN		
CAMBRIAN		
LAURENTIAN		

FIG. 27–1. / *Lower Old Red Sandstone conglomerate resting unconformably on folded and eroded slates and limestones, Argyll, England. (Crown Copyright.)*

time when no deposits were formed in the type section.

The Paleozoic Era is divided into seven periods: Cambrian, Ordovician, Silurian, Devonian, Mississippian, Pennsylvanian, and Permian. In Europe the Pennsylvanian and Mississippian are combined into what is known as the Carboniferous Period. The Mesozoic Era is divided into three periods: Triassic, Jurassic, and Cretaceous. The Cenozoic Era, the one in which we live, is divided into two parts, Paleogene and Neogene, or Tertiary and Quaternary. The exact equivalence of these terms is shown in Table 11. Younger rock units overlie older strata and tend to cover them up. Younger units are more widespread, are better exposed, and can be studied in greater detail than older units. Thus they can be subdivided more readily.

FIG. 27–2. / *Angular unconformity between Upper Old Red Sandstone beds on vertical Silurian beds, Siccar Point, Berwickshire. (Crown Copyright.)*

TABLE 11 / *Chart of geologic time scale in millions of years. The Precambrian is often known as the Cryptozoic Eon and is subdivided into the Archean (older) and Algonkian Eras. The Paleozoic, Mesozoic, and Cenozoic Eras are known collectively as the Phanerozoic Eon. Note the alternate names for the periods of the Cenozoic Era; the preferred usage in this book is Paleogene and Neogene Periods.*

CENOZOIC ERA (63 M)	QUATERNARY PERIOD (1–2 M)	Last 10,000 Years (Recent) Pleistocene Epoch	NEOGENE PERIOD (25 M)
	TERTIARY PERIOD (62 M)	Pliocene Epoch Miocene Epoch	
		Oligocene Epoch Eocene Epoch Paleocene Epoch	PALEOGENE PERIOD (38 M)
MESOZOIC ERA (167 M)	CRETACEOUS PERIOD (72 M) JURASSIC PERIOD (46 M) TRIASSIC PERIOD (49 M)		
PALEOZOIC ERA (370 M)	PERMIAN PERIOD (50 M) CARBONIFEROUS PERIOD (65 M) { PENNSYLVANIAN PERIOD / MISSISSIPPIAN PERIOD DEVONIAN PERIOD (60 M) SILURIAN PERIOD (20 M) ORDOVICIAN PERIOD (75 M) CAMBRIAN PERIOD (100 M)		
PRECAMBRIAN ERA (about 4.5 Billion Years)			

The lower part of the Primary series in the classification of Lyell is composed of igneous and metamorphic rocks that contain few identifiable fossils. These rocks represent more than three-quarters of the earth's history. It is probable that they include as much as seven-eighths of the record, yet the exact position of the division in relation to overlying divisions is often unclear. They are more complicated than younger rocks. They are poorly exposed, and where they are exposed they yield very little information in return for a great deal of hard work. Undoubtedly one important reason for the disregard of these rocks is the fact that very little oil and gas is found in rocks older than the lowest part of the Paleozoic Era, the Cambrian Period. Nevertheless, these rocks, the Precambrian units, are receiving considerable attention at the present time. They will become increasingly important in the future as we are forced to search more intensively for new mineral resources to maintain the industries of the world.

Geologic Concept of Time

THE GEOLOGIC CONCEPT OF TIME IS ONE of the most difficult ideas for the beginning student to grasp. We must learn to think in terms of lengths of time that so far exceed our common experience that we tend to lose their significance. It is a simple matter to be aware of the fact that the earth is thousands of millions of years old, and to know the approximate time of many events in the earth's history. It is not so easy to comprehend or appreciate fully the implications that these great spans of time hold for the processes acting on the surface of the earth and within its interior. For example, rises in sea level too small to be detected within the span of recorded history might flood most of

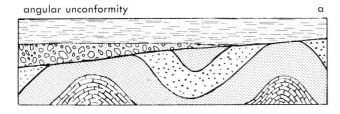

angular unconformity   a

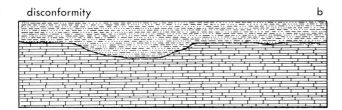

disconformity   b

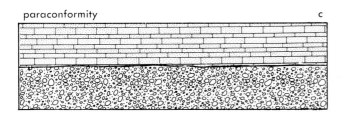

paraconformity   c

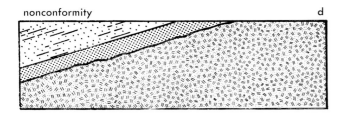

nonconformity   d

FIG. 27–3. / *Unconformities. Four types of breaks in the rock record are depicted below. In* a *there is an angular discordance between the strata above and below the unconformity. The older folded strata have been subjected to erosion and were planed off before the younger strata above the erosion surface were deposited. Note the basal conglomerate unit directly above the break. Similar types of breaks appear in* b *and* c *except that part of the topography was buried in* b *while the contacts between the units in* c *are almost perfectly parallel. The nonconformity in* d *at the bottom is the break between the older igneous mass and the overlying strata which have been tilted. The igneous mass was intruded, solidified, uplifted, and eroded before the deposition of the sandstone unit over it.*

the continents of the world if continued over a period of a few million years. Although this example is purely hypothetical, there is positive, undeniable evidence that seas have invaded the continents in the past and have, in fact, covered almost all the land surface of the world. Some areas are being slowly submerged today, while others are emerging, perhaps to rise eventually as mountains. As a second example we may cite the Grand Canyon. How could a canyon several miles wide and as much as a mile deep have been formed? Without an understanding of the time involved it is a perplexing problem. But to those who know how streams erode and transport rock debris it is not at all difficult to visualize the formation of the canyon over a period of millions of years as the rocks exposed in the walls of the canyon gradually crumble, break away, and fall into the Colorado River, which transports them to the sea. In other words, the canyon is being enlarged today, right now, in just about the same way and perhaps as fast as it ever has been in the past. The face of the earth has never before looked exactly the way it does right now. It will never be the same again. It is not even the same from day to day, but the changes are so slow that we generally fail to perceive them at all. In the short term these changes seem insignificant; in the long term they may convert seas into mountains and mountains into plains. The examples cited above serve to emphasize that it is the cumulative effects of natural processes over periods of geologic time that have brought about the record of change that is the history of the earth.

Very few people actually seem to enjoy learning historical dates just for the fun of knowing them. Often they are even looked upon as stumbling blocks to learning the "interesting" parts of history. You can never appreciate the value of dates until you try to unravel history without knowing them. Imagine attempting to reconstruct the history of some part of the world you have never seen, nor even heard of, from an accumulation of undated newspapers, and you will understand something of the problem confronting the student of the earth's history. Eventually you would be able to piece together the history by establishing sequences of events and by finding an occasional date recorded. While this technique is time-consuming and sometimes difficult, it does offer a definite challenge and often leads to fascinating solutions.

There are essentially two techniques by which geologic time can be measured. The first is by observing some feature of a rock that gives evidence of the existence in the past of a process that was unidirectional and nonreversible. The movement of the hands of a clock is such a process, although it can hardly be used for the geologic past. The clock would be of no use if you could not depend on the hands to move in one direction all the time. It has the added advantage of moving at a constant rate in that one direction. Some "geologic clocks" do not proceed at constant rates, therefore they cannot be used to tell absolute time. Nevertheless, they are useful in fixing the time of one event in relation to the time of some second event. Some of the unidirectional, nonreversible processes in nature include:

Decay of radioactive substances. This is the best "geologic clock" because the rate of decay is constant and dates obtained are absolute dates.

Evolution of life. Evolution has proceeded since the first forms of life appeared on earth. Evidence of the process is found in the fossil record. Many of the same phyla or types of animals are represented through long periods of time, but, as a group, fossils of any one time are a unique assemblage. There is nothing about these assemblages that automatically tells us how old they are, but they provide a reference system for determining the order of succession of geologic events, as will be explained. Fossils are by far the most widely used means of determining sequences of events.

Accumulation of sediments.

Erosion of the land surface.

Increase of the salinity of the oceans.

A second technique by which geologic time is measured is analysis of the record of events that have resulted from processes which recur with a fixed periodicity. Such processes are not uncommon within small areas, but there is disagreement among geologists on the question of the existence of such processes on a world-wide scale. Locally, seasonal variations in climate influence the rate of deposition and types of sediments deposited in lakes. This results in the formation of finely banded or *varved deposits.* Some geologists believe there is evidence to support the existence of periodic changes of great extent. Some of these pulsations may include:

Periodic changes in the world climate, bringing periods of glaciation in high latitudes.

Periodic movements within the earth's crust, causing deformation and formation of mountain ranges.

Because of uncertainty about the validity of these periodic changes, they are of little value in working out the history of the earth.

Decay of Uranium to Lead

URANIUM-238, LIKE MOST OTHER radioactive substances, is transformed into a stable substance, lead-206, only after passing through a number of other radioactive isotopes. Radioactive decay occurs in such a way that half of the radioactive substance decays in a given period of time; that period, called the *half life,* is a constant for a given isotope. The half life of uranium-238 is 4.56×10^9 years. One million grams of uranium-238 will produce $1/7,600$ gram of uranium lead per year.

During a period of diastrophism magma may be intruded into the deformed rocks. Let us suppose that one of those minerals that crystallizes from the magma contains uranium-238. As soon as it has crystallized nuclei of uranium-238 atoms begin to disintegrate. A certain percentage of the atoms disintegrate every minute. After 4,560 million years, half of them will have disintegrated. As the uranium-238 disintegrates, helium and lead-206 are formed as end products of decay. Both of these are stable and undergo no further change. Thus the ratio of helium and lead-206 to the amount of uranium-238 bears a definite relationship to the age of the mineral in which it is found and, therefore, to the time of its formation. In our example the rock was formed during a period of deformation, so the age of the rock is the age of the deformation.

A number of other radioactive substances have proved useful in determining the age of geologic events. Noteworthy among them are decay of rubidium to strontium and decay of potassium to argon.

Carbon-14

THIS METHOD of dating is well known for its use in dating archaeological findings. The method depends on the presence of radioactive carbon, carbon-14, in organic matter (Fig. 27–4). Carbon-14 is formed in the upper atmosphere when nitrogen is bombarded by cosmic rays. Nitrogen, when hit by a cosmic ray, emits a proton, and becomes carbon-14. Carbon-14 combines with oxygen to form carbon dioxide, which is absorbed by all living matter. When the plant or animal dies it stops absorbing carbon-14, and carbon-14 present in the organism begins to decay, forming nitrogen again. The half life of carbon-14 is about 5,600 years. In order to date the remains of the plant or animal the amount of carbon-14 in the organic matter is measured and compared with the amount found in living matter today. The ratio is a measure of the length of time carbon-14 in the dead matter has been decaying, and therefore of its age. For example if we find exactly half as much carbon-14 in a piece of wood that has been buried in an old river deposit as we find in living trees, then the age of the old wood can be estimated. Assuming that the old wood had the same concentration of carbon-14 in it when it was living as the present-day trees, then one half has decayed. Thus the age is equal to the half life of carbon-14, or 5,600 years.

Although radioactive methods of dating are the best we have for obtaining absolute ages of rocks, there are certain limitations to their usefulness. These are limitations implicit in the mode of occurrence and nature of the radioactive isotopes.

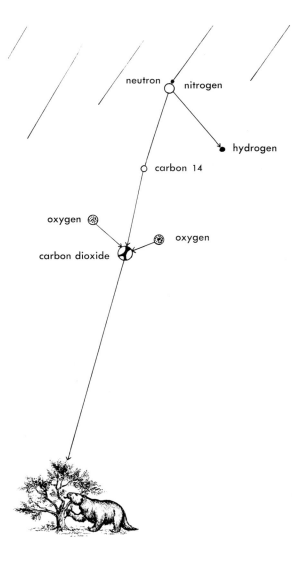

FIG. 27–4. / Carbon-14. Cosmic rays bombard the upper atmosphere, producing neutrons. When these neutrons collide with nitrogen in the atmosphere small amounts of carbon-14 and hydrogen are yielded. The carbon-14 combines with oxygen to form carbon dioxide. The carbon dioxide containing carbon-14 is absorbed by plants and eventually animals feeding on the plants add carbon-14 to their bodies. When the plant or animal dies it ceases to absorb additional carbon-14, and that in the dead remains begins to decay. Half of the remaining carbon-14 decays every 5568 years.

1. The half life of carbon-14, 5,600 years, is so short that most of it decays after about 50,000 years. Therefore it is of no value in dating older forms of organic matter.

2. Carbon-14 is confined to organic matter and provides no means of dating rocks that do not contain organic matter.

3. Uranium-238 is largely confined to igneous rocks, particularly pegmatites. Potassium-argon dating is useful in dating micas of metamorphic rocks. But occurrence of uranium is not sufficiently widespread to solve more than a small fraction of all dating problems. Micas are largely confined to igneous and metamorphic rocks, so there is little opportunity to date by these means the most commonly found rocks, those of sedimentary origin.

4. Where uranium is found in igneous rocks and dated, we learn the age of the igneous rock. If that igneous body has intruded a sedimentary rock unit it proves only the minimum age for the unit.

5. Dates are accurate within about .10 per cent, but even this is a long time when you are dating rocks that are billions of years old.

6. All radioactive dating methods are time-consuming, difficult, and expensive. They require special laboratory equipment and cannot be used in the field.

7. Radioactive decay can be interrupted by re-crystallization of the rock. This amounts to resetting the "radioactive clocks."

28

Nature of the Rock Record

It is not clear whether the earth was in a molten or solid state at its creation, but molten rocks are being formed within the earth today, and they are intruded and extruded through the solid crystalline rocks of the earth's crust. We may assume that it has not been substantially different in the past. As soon as the earth developed an atmosphere, solid rocks on the surface were weathered and eroded by processes similar to those acting today. Disintegrated and dissolved rock material was then transported by water, ice, or air, and eventually settled out to form layers. The type of sediment formed in each layer depended to a large extent on the environment in which it was deposited. Life began, and the remains of the dead became incorporated in the rocks being formed. The impression created by the great movements of the unstable crust is also left as a dynamic record in the rocks. The earth has been gently warped upward in some places, exposing areas that were sea bottoms. In other areas, downwarping has submerged parts of the continents below the waters of the ocean. Occasionally the crust has been intensely folded into long chains of high mountains. The discovery and explanation of the earth's history await investigation and interpretation of the rock layers. Their composition, structure, variations in thickness, distribution—all these furnish part of the details of this story. With painstaking care geologists are able to piece this information together and decipher the long record. If they are lucky, they will be able to reconstruct a large part of the story. They may be able to describe the evolution of life and the changing form of the continents during much of the earth's history. At the present time a relatively accurate and complete record is available for the past half billion years.

The story is not without flaw, and obviously it is incomplete in places, but it is known in far greater detail than most people realize. Imperfections in our knowledge result largely from the almost unbelievable complexity of the rock record. First we must learn to interpret rocks that are being formed today. This gives us a clue as to how the environment of deposition leaves its imprint in rock and provides the basis for interpretation of similar impressions in older rocks. Trouble may arise as soon as we first attempt to apply this simple procedure. In some areas of the world, sedimentary layers are flat-lying. In such places the history of the area

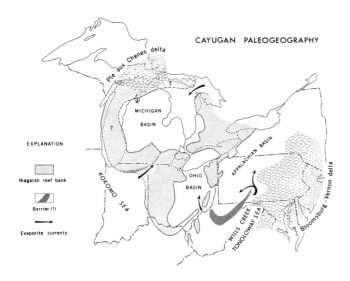

EXPLANATION

Niagaran reef bank

Barrier (?)

Evaporite currents

FIG. 28-1. / *Paleogeography during the Cayugan. The limits of the reconstruction are governed by the extent of Silurian outcrops. Through well-cutting within the region of Silurian outcrop, it has been possible to reconstruct the position of extensive Niagaran reef banks, possible land barriers, and inlets through which marine waters entered the evaporite basins. (From L. I. Briggs.)*

during the time of formation of the surface layer can be found by analysis of the layer. But more commonly sedimentary or metasedimentary rock units and igneous rock bodies of various ages are exposed in an area as a result of a long history of events which may include sedimentation, uplift, folding, faulting, igneous activity, and erosion. In such an area the sequence of events must be established and the rocks formed during each interval of time must be located and identified before details of the history of a given time can be found by hypothetically restoring the area to its condition during that time.

Exploring the Geologic Past

THE FIRST IMPORTANT REQUIREMENT IN exploration of the geologic past is to learn to determine the age of certain bodies of rock. They alone hold the key to the riddle of these ancient times. If we want to reconstruct a region or a continent as it was at a particular

time in the past, we must first know what rocks were formed at that time. Reconstruction is complete only after the geography, climate, ecology, and stability of the crust at that time are known. We can go a long way toward obtaining this goal by studying surface outcrops, but the picture is often incomplete until there is a good sampling of subsurface data to supplement surface observations. The first step is to find rocks that were formed during the time in which we are interested. This can be done by such methods as radioactive dating or the use of guide fossils. Once the age of a few strata has been determined, others are dated by various techniques of correlation. This eventually leads to relatively complete knowledge of the distribution of rocks of this particular age. Geologic maps (see end of book) are constructed to show the distribution of these rocks at the present time. Then to this outline symbols can be added to indicate different rock types and their locations. Thus sandstones of this age would be differentiated from igneous rocks, shales, limestones, conglomerates, and other rocks. From our understanding of conditions under which these various types of rocks are formed today, we begin to see certain possible correlations between present conditions and those prevailing in the past.

Careful analysis of rock units and of their

FIG. 28-2. / *North America 70 million years ago. This outline map of North America shows outcrops of Upper Cretaceous (Campanian) strata in black. Because these strata contain marine fossils and are composed of sediments such as those now formed in the sea the position of the Upper Cretaceous Seas on the continent may be approximated. This was the last time seas spread extensively across the continental interior. The exact borders of the sea are exact only where ancient beach deposits are found. There are few such exposures, but the type of sediment and the fossil assemblages it contains are an indication of the water depth and distance from shore. (Reprinted with permission from Charles Schuchert,* Atlas of Paleographic Maps of North America, *John Wiley & Sons, Inc., 1955.)*

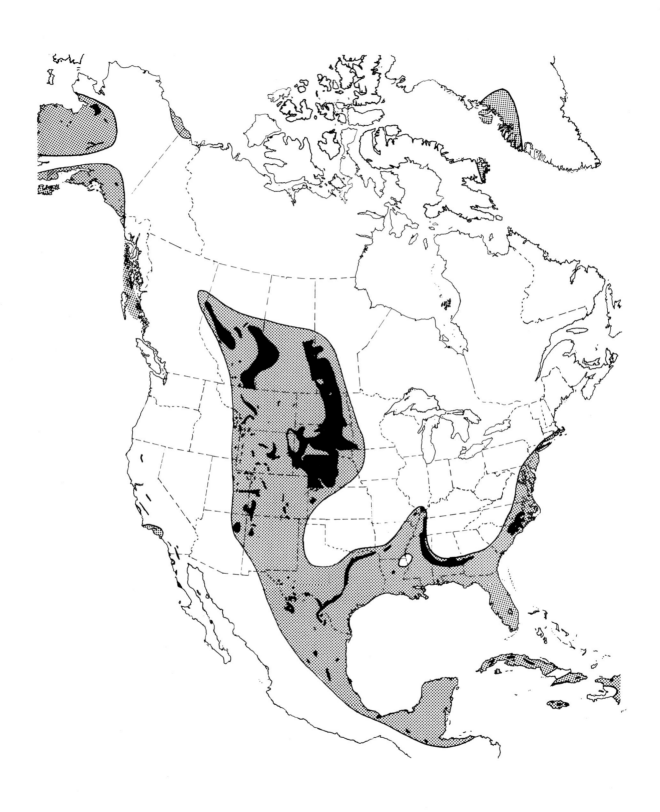

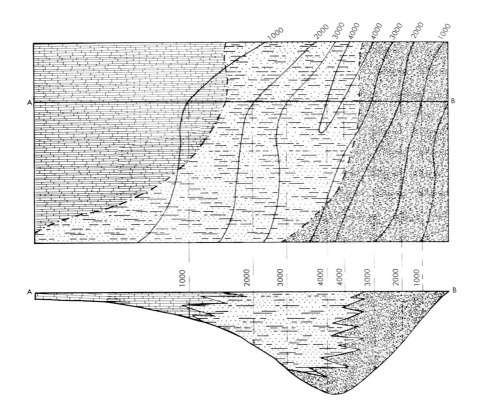

FIG. 28–3. / *Isopach map. The distribution of rock types is shown as an overlay on an isopach map. The top section is a map view on which the isopachs are drawn and labeled. They are somewhat similar to contours except that they represent lines of equal thickness of a particular rock or time-stratigraphic unit. Below is a cross section showing the variations in thickness along the line A-B on the map. The top of the unit is drawn here as horizontal and thicknesses are plotted directly below. When the isopachs and nature of the rock types are considered together we get a good indication of the conditions which prevailed when this section was deposited. The coarse conglomerates on the east side must have been eroded from a highland area. Further out sands and shales were laid down in a zone that was subsiding. In the west limestones were deposited in shallow relatively clear waters on the stable shelf. Here the geosynclinal accumulation trended north northeast.*

fossil content is necessary to obtain all the information possible about climates and ecology of this period. From this we construct a *paleogeographic* map (Fig. 28–1), one showing the geography of this period of time. It should include continental margins and features found along them, such as beaches, offshore bars, continental shelves, continental slopes, swamps, deltas, and reefs. It may reflect the general nature of the land masses near shorelines such as mountains, swamps, and plains or lowlands. Definition of the physiography farther inland from the continental margins is generally poor. Paleontologic studies can reveal the correlation between the fossils and various environments in which they lived. From them we may learn something of temperatures, depths of water, and strength of currents in the seas. It is sometimes possible to infer climatic conditions from the nature of the sedimentary deposits, as we will see in chapter 33.

Another important aspect of history concerns stability of the crust during the period in question. It is not an easy matter to determine what happened in areas that were uplifted, since they received no deposits and were usually areas from which material was derived to be laid down elsewhere. But where regions subsided and accumulated sediment it is possible to determine the extent of the deformation. This may be done by measuring thicknesses of rock units laid down during the time. These thicknesses are recorded on the map already constructed to show the distribution. A map showing thicknesses may be prepared by drawing *isopachs*, lines connecting points of equal thickness. The result looks something like a topographic contour map (see end of book). Lines are labeled systematically in the same manner as contour lines, at a definite interval; the difference is that the interval is an increase of thickness instead of elevation. Where lines are close together units thicken rapidly. Where lines are widely spaced, thicknesses vary only slightly. Such a map is called an *isopach map* (Fig. 28–3). The isopach

designated zero separates units of this period from those that are older. Positions of deep accumulation are obvious in such a representation, and this, combined with a map showing distribution of different rock types, may be extremely useful in interpretation. Assuming that there has been no later erosion, areas covered by thin sediment were relatively stable. Those areas in which great thicknesses accumulated were near an abundant source of sediment, such as a mountain range. Great thicknesses of sediment indicate great subsidence or rapid accumulation of sediment.

If the time being investigated lies far back in geologic history, it is highly probable that at least part of any large area, especially one approaching continental dimensions, will have

FIG. 28–4. / *Reconstruction of strata. The folded, faulted, and tilted section at the top may be returned to its position at various times in its past history by determining the sequence of events and then systematically removing the effects of each. The first step is to reconstruct conditions before faulting, and then to reconstruct the eroded units and tilt section back to a nearly horizontal position such as that at the time of deposition of the top sedimentary sequence on the angular unconformity. Reconstruction might be continued by removing the top strata, and then proceeding to reconstruct the conditions before folding.*

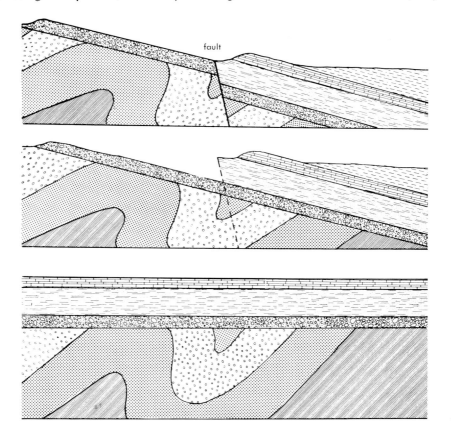

been deformed since the end of the period. This means that before it is possible to construct an accurate paleogeographic map or isopach map, effects of deformation must be removed. This requires determination of exactly what happened during deformation. If, for example, a large fault has displaced the strata formed during the time under study, the original position of the strata is found by hypothetically moving the displaced strata back into their original position, as in Fig. 28–4. Likewise, if strata were thrown into folds, the strata must be restored by removing the folds. If deformation has been complex and extensive this reconstruction is likely to be difficult or perhaps even impossible.

The remainder of this chapter deals with some of the more important considerations involved in historical interpretation. The character of the mappable rock layers, the relationship between these and the enclosed fossils, and the reliability of rock layers and fossils as indicators of time are discussed. The balance of the chapter explains how rock units and events are correlated from one area to another. Correlation is extremely important in obtaining and understanding a broad picture of the historical evolution of a large area or the earth as a whole.

Rock Units

THE STORY OF THE PAST IS TOLD BY UNITS of rock. Because continents are continually undergoing erosion and removal of material, most of the record is contained in rocks formed in seas. Occasionally continental deposits are covered by advance of a sea over land, but the greatest part of the record consists of sands, silts, clays, and limy muds deposited in oceans. The original site of deposition of most of the strata now exposed on the continents was much like the shallow continental shelf and continental slopes which border land masses today.

Marine sediments form through settling of matter through water to the bottom, where a layer is built up. If material being supplied or physical, chemical, or biological factors influencing the environment change, the nature of layers being formed also changes. This brings into existence a feature known as *stratification*, a characteristic produced by deposition of sediments in beds, layers, laminae, lenses, wedges, and other essentially tabular units. Sediments may be fragmental or crystalline, formed from settling of solid insoluble debris, products of chemical precipitation, or composed of organic remains. Resulting layers can be traced and identified. Stratification results from variations in color, texture, density, composition, and fossil content. Rock units resulting from stratification can be subdivided and recognized on the basis of objective criteria. They can be identified and mapped as units.

Differentiation and recognition of rock units are so important that much attention has been given to formulation of a system of nomenclature to be used in describing them. The basic unit is the *formation*, a lithologically distinctive product of essentially continuous sedimentation selected from a local succession of strata as a convenient unit for purposes of mapping, description, and reference. Formations are usually given two names. The first is the name of the locality where the unit was first described or a place where it is exceptionally well exposed, called the *type section*. The second name gives the rock type if the formation is composed of a single type of sediment (i.e., Martinsburg shale or Tuscarora sandstone). If the lithology is not distinctive the geographic name is used alone.

When a number of formations are related to one another by lithologic characteristics, the entire sequence of formations may be called a *group*. The term group always follows the geographic name, usually of the type section, i.e., Clinton Group and Medina Group. Breaks used to separate groups may be unconformities, but most groups are composed of formations that are related to one another lithologically or genetically and are not separated by unconformities.

Where mapping is done in detail it is possible to make subdivisions of existing formations. These small subdivisions are called *members* if they extend over a large area, *lentils* or *lenses* if they are only locally distributed, and *tongues* or *wedges* if they wedge out in one direction between sediments of different lithology. The terms *beds* and *laminae* are also used for these smallest subdivisions.

Biostratigraphic Units

A BIOSTRATIGRAPHIC UNIT CAN BE DISTINguished by the assemblage of fossil animals or plants which it contains. A designation different from that applied to rock units based on lithology is required for these units, because boundaries of units containing certain assemblages of fossils do not always conform with physically distinguishable characteristics of formations, members, or even small beds or lenses. The fundamental biostratigraphic unit is the *zone*, which is named for one of the fossils found in it.

Zones are characterized by the assemblage of fossils found in them—not just by the fossil for which the zone is named. If some of the fossils making up the assemblage are known to have existed only a short time, geologically speaking, then the zone may approximate a time marker. In a sense all zones are time markers, but some define a much shorter interval than others. If the interval is very short, the zone may be found to cut across stratification boundaries (Fig. 28–5), but if the fossilized animals lived in only one type of sedimentary environment their remains may be confined to a single type of sediment.

Sedimentary Facies

THE REEF COMPLEX SHOWN IN FIG. 28–7 serves to illustrate the meaning of *facies*. Here within relatively short distances very different types of sediments are being formed. At the time illustrated, mud, coral sand on beaches and other varieties of sand under water, coral rubble, and coral rubble with algal remains in it are all being deposited. From the cross section it is obvious that this situation has continued for some time. Contemporaneous deposition of a

number of different sediments undoubtedly occurred in the past. These deposits vary in thickness and interfinger with one another. Imagine that this reef exists in a sea in which mud is being deposited. After many years mud encroaches on the reef and finally covers it. The reef becomes part of the mud-rock unit. Some millions of years later the compacted mud-rock unit, a shale, is uplifted, eroded, and exposed at the earth's surface. The extensive layer of mud is given a formation name. It reflects the environment in which it was deposited, but within this shale formation there exist rocks of the coral reef. They are a complex group which interfinger with shale and with one another. Each of these rock types reflects something of the very localized environment in which it was formed, and each is genetically related to those about it. Each may be called a *sedimentary facies*.

From the foregoing discussion two interpretations of the meaning of facies are possible. First, the reef and its sedimentary products may be thought of as representing a "reef facies" that would be similar to other reef facies. The shale would represent a "shale or mud facies." In this sense "facies" means a recognizable rock record of some particular type of depositional or organic environment. An alternative approach is to consider that the shale is the main rock unit and the reef is a part or "facies" of the shale unit. It is easy enough to see that when many rock units laterally change character parallel to stratification, such lateral variations are facies changes reflecting changes in depositional environments during sedimentation. It is not always easy to pinpoint the cause of such changes.

Time-Stratigraphic Units

ALTHOUGH ROCK UNITS EXPOSED IN AN outcrop or across a region may appear to be an orderly "layer cake" succession it does not necessarily follow that each of those layers is exactly the same age throughout. Consider first the situations in which a layer would be of uniform

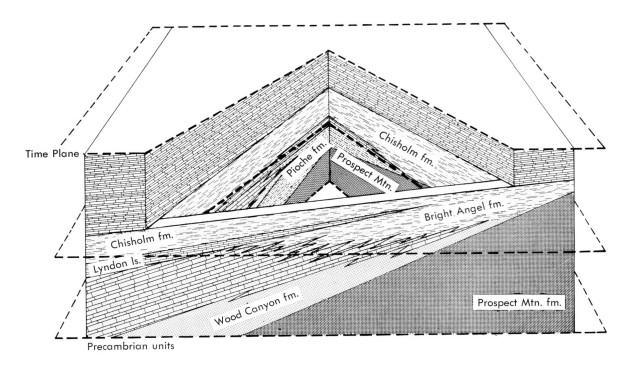

FIG. 28–5. / *Temporal transgression and the Bright Angel group. This triangular diagram is a schematic representation of the variations in space and time of the Bright Angel group. Sections are shown at three different localities. Note the lithologies vary from one of these places to another. The rock unit lines cut across the time lines (black).*

FIG. 28–6. / *Cross section across the Guadalupe Mountains. These mountains, including the famous El Capitan, are composed of the reefs which existed along the borders of the Permian basins. In front of the reef, fragments broken off by wave action accumulated and graded into finer sediments which were being laid down in the basins. Behind the reef water circulation became restricted and the rate of evaporation was great, resulting in deposition of quantities of dolostone and evaporites. (After N. Newell.)*

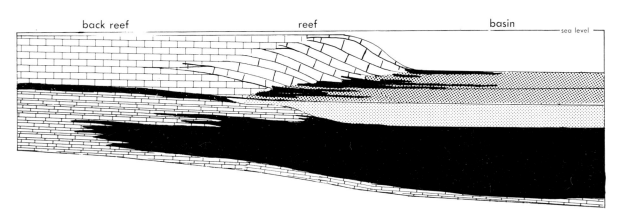

age. Glacial lake *varves* approach this condition about as closely as anything can, as they may extend over the entire area of a large lake. During the winter a thin layer of dark sediment may settle over the entire lake bottom. For an earth that is four billion years old the period of one winter is such a small portion of time that the dark layer formed essentially in an instant, thus every point on the layer formed contemporaneously. The boundary between two varves thus corresponds to a particular time in the earth's history. A similar situation holds for parts of the deep-ocean basins where sedimentation consists essentially of the remains of animals of microscopic size which slowly settle to the bottom and build up layers of calcareous and siliceous oozes. Ash layers approach this condition of "instantaneous" deposition also.

In the second case, time lines cut across rock-unit boundaries. Assume that sea level is rising along a shoreline of moderate relief. Waves break up rocks exposed along a sea cliff. These materials are washed back and forth in the wave motion and gradually are broken into finer and finer sizes. The finer sizes are washed out toward the sea or carried along parallel to the shore by longshore currents. Several miles out, deposits are predominantly mud or limy muds containing remains of small animals. As sea level rises the coastline moves inland and environments are shifted toward the continent, until limy muds are being deposited above the coarse fragments broken from the sea cliff earlier. If transgression of the sea across the continent continues for a long period of time, gravels, sands, and muds deposited offshore will constitute extensive deposits. If there are no reversals during transgression the layer of gravel formed may appear to have a uniform sharp contact against the overlying sand, and similarly sand may appear in sharp contact with the muds. Except for the section near the shoreline, mud will appear to overlie sand, and sand will appear to overlie gravel throughout their extent. There may be no immediately obvious evidence to suggest that all three were formed at the same time. The time line actually cut across the rock-unit boundaries in this case.

FIG. 28–7. / *Reef facies. The sediments associated with the reef are surrounded by muds which are being formed contemporaneously. It is apparent that a number of different types of sediment are being produced and deposited simultaneously. The reef, coral sand, and coral rubble make up facies of the mud unit. They reflect particular environments of deposition. This reef is at Batavia Bay, Java. (Modified after R. C. Moore.)*

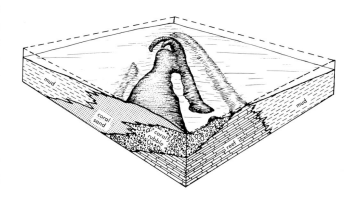

Because boundaries of rock units are not always "time marker" horizons, care must be taken to differentiate them when accuracy is required. A rock unit is defined by its lithology; a zone by a particular assemblage of fossils; a time unit by its absolute length. A time-stratigraphic unit is composed of the rock units and parts thereof formed during a particular time.

Correlation

CORRELATION IS THE PROCESS OF SHOWING the connection between two related things, but it is more specifically used in geology to mean "the determination of equivalence in geologic age and stratigraphic position of two formations or other stratigraphic units in separated areas; or, more broadly, determination of contemporaneity of events in geologic histories of two areas" (A. G. I. Glossary). This definition implies the real reason for the importance of correlation in geology. It is necessary to be able to relate widely separated and dissimilar bodies of rock in order to establish connections between sequences of events in different places. Significance of a local sequence of events is often lost if its relation to surrounding areas is not known. Ideally we would like to be able to reconstruct what was happening over the entire face of the world during each of the major periods of geologic time.

Correlation is used for a variety of purposes. It may be used to throw light on development of continents, movements of seas, or evolution of life. It is of vital importance in locating mineral deposits. For example, formation of coal was widespread in rocks of certain ages, particularly in the Carboniferous Period. This knowledge is of great importance in directing the search for coal in unexplored regions. Efforts can be concentrated in areas where rocks of Carboniferous age occur.

An interesting example of the use of a knowledge of age relations is found in occurrence of gold as placer deposits along streams in California. Gold was deposited in stream valleys formed during the Eocene Epoch. Following the Eocene, volcanic activity filled old valleys with dust, ash, and lava, and the streams of this time formed new valleys on the surface of these volcanic rocks. These rivers changed their courses as new ash deposits dammed or filled some of the valleys. The present stream patterns were not established until volcanism had subsided. These modern streams have cut down through volcanic rocks and exposed the gravel deposits formed in older valleys. An estimated $600,000,000 worth of gold is to be found in Eocene stream valleys, but only a minute amount of gold occurs in valleys formed during the period of volcanic activity. Obviously it is extremely important to know the age of the gravels before you start digging in one of the old, partially exposed stream deposits. A lot of time, money, and effort has been lost digging in gravels of the wrong age.

Correlation is particularly important in exploration for petroleum. Once a rock unit is known to contain oil in several places, it is highly probable that the same unit will contain oil in other nearby areas which have a similar history. Thus it becomes important to be able to recognize the same rock units. Of course, occurrence of oil in numerous places in one unit does not insure its occurrence throughout the unit.

Methods of Correlation

WHEN CORRELATION OF STRATIGRAPHIC sections in one area with those in another was first started, it was generally believed that boundaries between rock units were all "time lines." Consequently, correlation came to be looked on primarily as a means of correlating events in time. As the true nature of the differences in rock units and time units became clarified, the need for different types of correlation became obvious. Following is a brief summary of methods used in correlation of rock units, biostratigraphic units, and time-stratigraphic units.

Rock Units
a. Continuity of contacts between units.
b. Lithologic similarity.
c. Stratigraphic position of a unit in a sequence of strata.
d. Well logs.
e. Structural characteristics.

Biostratigraphic Units
a. Stage of evolution of the fauna.
b. Guide fossils.
c. Faunal resemblance (assemblages of fossils).
d. Position in a biostratigraphic sequence.

Time-Stratigraphic Units
a. Quantitative chronology—radioactive dating methods.
b. Eustatic (worldwide) changes in sea level.
c. Paleontology.

Correlating Rock Units

THE SIMPLEST and most straightforward method of correlation is to find the contact between two distinct lithologic units and trace

FIG. 28–8. / *Monument Valley. (Photo by Chuck Abbott.)*

out that contact (Fig. 28–10). In some cases this can be done for many miles. Aerial photographs often show contacts because of visible differences in the way units weather or in types of soil developed on different types of rock. Units of differing resistance to erosion and weathering are particularly prominent in arid and semiarid regions. Where more rainfall occurs or when erosion has continued for millions of years, contacts may not be exposed. In these areas deep soils are likely to cover rock units and geologists may have to rely on soil types and the presence of certain plants restricted to soils of particular rock types. This method of correlation is used in swampy areas of the Gulf Coast.

Position in a stratigraphic sequence is significant in the recognition of strata with distinctive lithologic characteristics arranged in a systematic order. If the sequence is found to be the same over a large area, then it may be possible at other localities within and near the area to recognize a particular unit by its relation to others in the sequence.

It is sometimes possible to identify rock units by the relation they bear to older, folded strata, as in angular unconformities.

Any method that employs physical and chemical criteria for identification of a rock unit may be used for purposes of correlation. It is necessary that the unit have some unique characteristics, or at least a certain group of characteristics, which make it possible to distinguish it from others. Correlation by lithologic similarity is extensively used in petroleum exploration. In drilling wells, it is necessary to recognize rock units being penetrated in order to calculate depth to the zone or trap which is thought to contain oil, and also to compare the actual stratigraphic section at the well location with that predicted from sections observed at

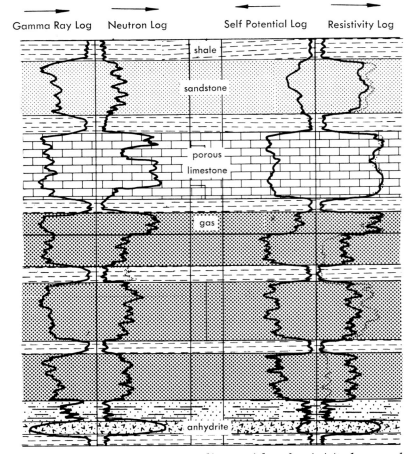

Gamma Ray Log   Neutron Log   Self Potential Log   Resistivity Log

shale

sandstone

porous
limestone

gas

anhydrite

FIG. 28–9. / *Well logging. Gamma-ray, neutron, self-potential, and resistivity logs are shown for a hypothetical section to illustrate how various common sedimentary rock units might appear on well logs. Both the radioactivity log and the electric log reflect the lithology of the units.* (Modified after Oil and Gas Journal *drawing.*)

the surface and those taken from nearby wells. Rock units can change in lithology in short distances, as in facies changes. There may be other changes caused by deformation or compaction of loose sediments. These must be taken into account if the well is to be successfully completed. As a well is drilled, samples of rock are collected. These may be rock fragments or solid cores taken by means of special core drilling. Much information can be obtained from a core, but the process of collecting the core is expensive. It usually necessitates taking all the pipe, or drill stem, out of the well, putting on the coring tube, lowering this tube, cutting and collecting the core, withdrawing all the pipe again to take the sample out, and then lowering all the pipe into the well again to continue drilling (in drillers' parlance, called "making the trip"). Because of the expense of this process other methods are often used. These include use

of the fragments of ground rock that are carried to the surface in mud used as a lubricant in drilling. This mud is forced down the drilling pipe and out through holes around the drill bit. Pressure causes it to return to the surface through the space left between the pipe and the wall of the hole. This mud serves several purposes; it not only cools and lubricates the pipe and bit as they turn in the hole, but also removes ground-up rock and tends to stabilize walls of the drill hole in unconsolidated sediments. When samples are collected they may be tested in the following ways:

1. Analysis of the mineral assemblage to obtain percentages of different minerals present.
2. Chemical analysis of the rock.
3. Analysis of size and shape of fragments which make up the rock. Such observation helps in the interpretation of the conditions under which the sediment was deposited.

4. Examination of rock by etching with strong acids to reveal small structures or acid-resistant components.
5. X-ray analysis of clays to determine which clay minerals they contain.
6. Differential thermal analysis. Measurement is made of physical and chemical reactions induced in a mineral assemblage by change in temperature.
7. Thin-section study. Petrographic microscopes are designed for study of polarized light transmitted through a section of rock. Polarized light is used to identify mineral constituents of the rock.
8. Radioactive minerals. If the rock unit being correlated contains radioactive minerals it may be possible to recognize the unit by this means.

Well-logging methods of correlation have become important because of their widespread use in correlation of subsurface units. Well logs are records showing variation in conditions found in wells. These records may include electrical, radioactive, temperature, and drill-time logs.

Electrical logs record *resistance* of rock units to the passage of electric currents through them, and *self-potential* (the spontaneous potential difference in the well opposite a rock unit) (Fig. 28–9). In resistance-type logs a current is generated and applied to drilling muds in the hole. In the second case no artificially generated current is used. The self-potential is caused by salinity contrast between mud in the hole and fluids in the rock unit. The amount of self-potential depends on the nature of beds and the solutions they contain. A dry rock ordinarily does not conduct electricity; neither does oil or gas. But water is a conductor, and the more chemicals there are in solution the more conductive it is. Factors which affect resistance most are relative amounts of oil, gas, water, and concentration of salts in water of the rock units.

There are two principal types of radiation logs. One measures natural radioactivity of the rock unit, *gamma-ray logs,* and the second measures effects of bombarding the unit with neutrons from an artificial source. Different kinds of rocks have different amounts of natural radioactivity and therefore emit different amounts of gamma rays. When a rock unit is bombarded by neutrons, gamma rays are artificially produced. Hydrogen has the effect of absorbing gamma rays, and thus low readings will be obtained opposite units containing abundant hydrogen atoms. Materials that contain an abundance of hydrogen include water, oil, and shales.

Methods of Correlation by Fossils

METHODS OF CORRELATION of biostratigraphic units are easily understood in principle. Processes of evolution have brought about changes in populations of animals that have inhabited the earth throughout geologic time. As a result of these changes, different populations of animals are preserved in sedimentary rocks of different ages. Of course, animals and plants are not evenly distributed over the face of the earth today. Some forms, such as corals, live primarily in warm, agitated, and clear waters, while others require the frigid temperatures of the Arctic. For this reason the same assemblage of animals is not found in all rock units of any single age. Fossil assemblages of any past geologic age are related not only to the time in which they lived but also to the environment they inhabited.

Histories of different groups of animals are highly varied. A few groups represented in the oldest fossiliferous rock units survive to this day. Some apparently survived for millions of years with little change in the over-all size of their populations. Then they began to expand rapidly in size and diversity, only to become extinct a short time later. Others expanded in numbers through long periods of time before starting a gradual decline which eventually led to their extinction. Still others appeared and disappeared from the fossil record in relatively short spans of time.

Those groups of animals and plants that were relatively abundant and possessed distinctive, readily preserved hard parts have been used as *guides to biostratigraphic zones.* The span of time from the first appearance of a particular group to its extinction is known as the *"range"* of the group. Obviously the most useful guide fossils are those that are widely distributed, easily recognized, abundant, and have a short range.

In summary, biostratigraphic units, or zones, are correlated on the basis of the presence of certain guide fossils or more generally on the basis of the similarity of assemblages of fossils (Figs. 28–10, 28–11, and 28–12). Correlation may also be established by the position of a zone in a sequence of biostratigraphic zones.

Methods of Correlating Time-Stratigraphic Units

A TIME-STRATIGRAPHIC UNIT is a sequence of strata deposited during a given span of time. Relatively few rock units qualify as time-stratigraphic units. Only a few biostratigraphic units can be rigidly considered as time-stratigraphic markers. But they ordinarily come much closer to meeting the requirements than rock units do. Therefore, in practice, biostratigraphic zones are often considered as time markers. Several factors prevent a zone from being a time marker. New species are not simultaneously evolved in all parts of the world, since time is required for a newly evolved species to migrate throughout the world. Environmental conditions may prevent or at least limit inclusion of certain animals in the sedimentary record.

An animal or plant which tends to migrate rapidly, lives in many environments, and has a short range can approximately represent a time marker, in which case it is a *guide fossil*. If such a guide fossil is quite widely distributed in rocks of a certain age, it may be called an *index fossil* and used as a key to that age. In this respect several groups are particularly important. These include free-swimming (nektonic) and floating (planktonic) marine organisms. Another outstanding group is the animals living in the waters of continental shelves. Marine invertebrates are particularly abundant among index fossils, and of these protozoans stand out.

Radioactive dating methods serve as checks on other means of time-stratigraphic correlation. Radioactive dating as a means of correlation has been used extensively in igneous and metamorphic rocks which contain few fossils. Carbon-14 is coming into widespread use for dating units less than 50,000 years old.

Eustatic (worldwide) changes in sea level occur as glaciation causes the volume of water in the oceans to be reduced. They may also be brought about by changes in shape of ocean basins or warping of the sea floor. Whatever the cause, there is good evidence to suggest that fluctuations in sea level throughout the world have occurred many times in the geologic past. We are now experiencing such a change as ice caps melt, adding more and more water to the oceans. When a eustatic rise occurs, seas begin to advance across continents. When a eustatic lowering takes place, seas retreat. Turning points in these advances and retreats serve as approximate time markers. However, complexities are introduced by the fact that local deformation of continents may cause part of a continent to rise. If the continent rose without an accompanying rise of the sea level, the effect would be a relative lowering of sea level in that locality.

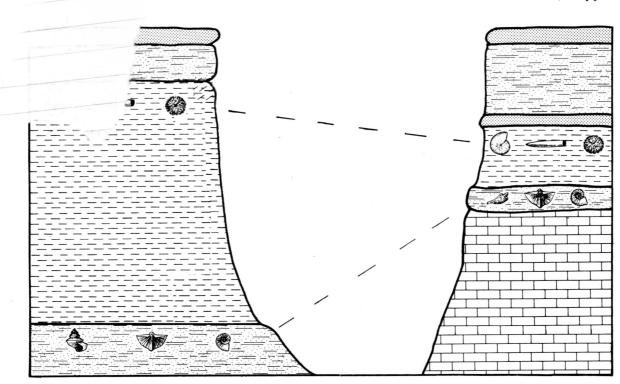

FIG. 28–10. / *Correlation by zones. Zones are not characterized by certain lithologies nor are they separated by identical thicknesses of rock units in various places.*

FIG. 28–11. / *Correlation of zones. A zone may be defined as a bed or group of beds characterized by one or several special fossils, which serve as indices. In some zones almost identical assemblages of fauna may be found. In others a few species are representative, but a great variety of others may or may not be present. Study the two sections to see how the zones may be used for the purpose of correlation. Notice that the lithologies in the two top zones are not identical.*

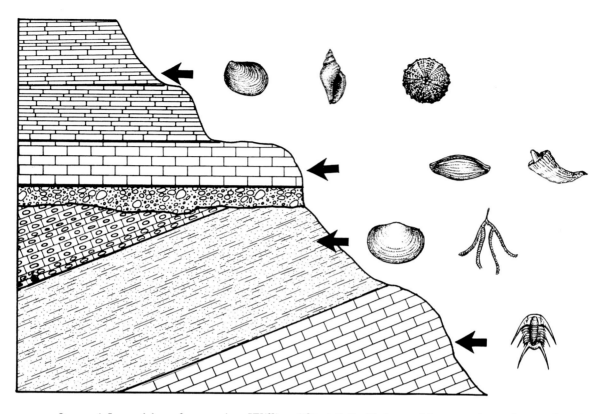

FIG. 28–12. / *Law of faunal succession. William "Strata" Smith learned to recognize various rock units by the particular assemblages of fossils which they contained. In this case it would be possible to recognize the angular unconformity by the difference in the inclination of the beds above and below the break in the record. If the assemblages in these units were known it would be possible to recognize the break by the fact that the assemblage in the concealed unit is missing in the exposure. This would be particularly applicable in discovering a break in a well when there are no surface exposures.*

IX /

SKETCHES FROM
GEOLOGIC HISTORY

29 /

Precambrian History

Origin of Continents

Two of the most important obstacles encountered in the search for the first continents are the extreme antiquity of any such feature, and the consequent probability that it has been altered beyond recognition, and that its remains are now covered by younger sediments. The age of the earth is estimated to be approximately 4½ billion years. The oldest rocks that have been dated by radioactive decay techniques are 3⅓ billion years old. That leaves a period of slightly more than a billion years for which we have no positive evidence of a rock record. It is almost certainly within this period of time that continents first began to appear on the earth.

The oldest theory of the origin of continents maintains that they originated as outer parts of the molten earth, cooled, and solidified. They were what might be considered an end product of the process of gravitative separation. Throughout the cooling history of the earth various minerals crystallized at different temperatures. When heavy minerals crystallized they sank toward the earth's interior. When lightweight minerals crystallized they rose to the surface, if they were less dense than the melt. This action

created a crust composed of minerals that were of low density or that had crystallized after temperatures dropped. This explains why continents are composed of sialic rocks. The most common minerals in principal rock types of continents are feldspars and quartz. These crystallized at relatively low temperatures and are of lower density than the minerals of the mantle. Thus, according to this theory, continents are supposed to be large platelike or raftlike accumulations of these minerals, floating on a more dense, basaltic subcrust.

At the other extreme is the idea that the original solid crust was entirely basaltic. In places this crust was fractured during and following consolidation. Breaks through the crust provided zones through which gases, lavas, and solutions could come out of the mantle. As soon as the atmosphere and oceans began to develop, materials extruded on the earth's surface were affected by weathering and erosion. Effects of chemical weathering, such as carbonation, oxidation, and hydration, combined with addition of silica from solutions brought out from the mantle, led to differentiation of basaltic lavas and pyroclastic debris and formation of granitic rocks. These early lands may be visualized as somewhat like present-day island arcs. According to this theory continents grew by successive addition of new sedimentary rocks at margins of the land. One chain of island arcs after another developed along the margins and eventually became incorporated into the continents by diastrophism. Those who support this general point of view call our attention to the following:

> The island arc systems are located around margins of continents today, and they are currently characterized by diastrophism.

> Many of the oldest rocks dated by radioactive methods lie in central parts of continental shields.

> Young folded mountain belts generally lie along margins of shields or continents.

> There is also a tendency for successively younger belts of folding to be located at progressively greater distances from the centers of shields.

Origin of the first continents, along with development of the atmosphere, oceans, and even the first forms of life, took place during the first billion years of the earth's history. No positive evidence in the form of a record left from these times exists. We must infer the early history and development of the earth from what we know of the past three billion years and from information we can learn through geochemical and geophysical studies. The earth's history as deciphered by interpretation of the sedimentary rock record begins only after the surface had cooled and after weathering, erosion, and sedimentation had begun to take place. These processes require the presence of an atmosphere and large quantities of water. The oldest rocks in Southern Rhodesia, dated at 3⅓ billion years, are conglomerates formed through erosion and sedimentation in water.

Origin and Development of the Hydrosphere and Atmosphere

THE ATMOSPHERE IS BOUNDED ABOVE BY space. Below, at the earth's surface, it is in contact with the ocean, with sediments and rocky crust, and with animal and plant life. Chemical reactions take place between the atmosphere and all of these, and there is an exchange of materials. Thus the composition of the atmosphere has not necessarily remained constant through time. A record of its changes may be left in sediments formed at different times. The problem is to find out how these changes are recorded and then to piece the information together. To accomplish this we must recognize that certain characteristics of rocks are related to the presence of particular elements in the atmosphere. For example, the presence in a sedimentary unit of fossils of animals that require oxygen to sustain life must mean that the atmosphere contained oxygen at the time those animals lived. If we find oxidized minerals of Precambrian age, there must have been oxygen in the atmosphere when those minerals were oxidized.

As in dealing with such questions as the origin of the earth, of life, of continents, and of the atmosphere, we are forced to rely largely on indirect evidence usually capable of two or more interpretations. Even though the same data and observations may be analyzed, varied interpretations usually arise as a result of the use of different basic assumptions.

Hypotheses advanced to explain the origin of the atmosphere and oceans fall into two groups. One group is based on the assumption that the earth was once a molten, globelike mass of gases and liquids which derived from the sun and cooled first to a liquid, then slowly developed a solid crust. The atmosphere and oceans, according to this theory, are residual materials from the primitive atmosphere which enveloped the earth; thus the earth has had an atmosphere almost from the beginning, with additions and losses of gases through time.

A second theory is derived from the idea that the earth was formed by accumulation of small bodies called *planetesimals* which were in a cool, solid state when they accumulated. According to this theory the atmosphere was created by "degassing" of the earth's interior and by chemical reactions that took place when the solid planetesimals accumulated. The heat required to melt the earth's interior would have come from decay of radioactive minerals.

Residual Atmosphere Hypothesis

IF THE EARTH FORMED from a part of the sun which was separated in a gaseous state, as is assumed in the Dynamic Encounter theories, it would be logical to assume that the early atmosphere was similar to that indicated by spectra of the sun and other stars. Most elements found in the sun are known on earth; however, the relative abundance of some of the elements is notably different: hydrogen, helium, xenon, and krypton all are less abundant on earth than they are in the sun.

Amounts of hydrogen and helium in the sun greatly exceed all other elements in abundance. Therefore, a large quantity of these would be predicted for the primitive atmosphere of the earth. Methane (CH_4) and ammonia (NH_3) are the most abundant gases in atmospheres of several major planets. Since both of these gases are stable in the presence of hydrogen and helium, it is predicted that they were present in the primitive atmosphere. Nitrogen and water vapor are also thought to have made up a part of the early atmosphere.

At first there would have been considerable loss of those gases too light to be held by the earth's gravitational attraction. Hydrogen and helium would be among these. The rate of loss would decrease with time. As the earth cooled, compounds would form, and these would retain hydrogen in the crust. Helium, because it is an inert gas, does not form compounds. As cooling continued, gases were gradually transformed into liquids, and these in turn into solids, which formed near the surface where the rate of cooling was most rapid. This idea provides a ready explanation for existence of a molten core: it is simply a residual liquid from initial stages of the earth's formation. Cooling of gases to liquids would not completely remove all gases. Some remained as a primitive atmosphere, and these underwent changes through losses and additions.

These changes are treated separately, since they are independent of the initial stages in formation of the atmosphere.

Accumulated Atmosphere Hypothesis

DATA BECAME AVAILABLE about 1960 strongly supporting the theory that the atmosphere accumulated gradually as a result of "degassing" of the interior and is not, in fact, a residual mass of gases (Fig. 29–1). Much of this evidence has been derived from studies of the moon's shape and distribution of its surface features. Both Russian and American astronomers have seen "smoke" rising from craters on the moon. This indicates that the moon is volcanically active. Other studies have shown the surface is covered by a layer of dust. It is easy to see that this dust could be dust and ash from volcanoes. Great quantities of dust have come from some eruptions on earth. Rays that extend out from craters may actually be faults or fractures. Many craters are aligned, suggesting that they may be related to the rays (faults). If there were random impact of meteorites on the moon and if rays were shatter fractures radiating from the center of craters, there should be no alignment of craters and rays. Alignment suggests that craters are volcanic in origin and that molten rock and gases came up along fractures. This is supported by the observation that many of the moon's craters lie at the intersection of two or more aligned fracture zones.

If the atmosphere were derived from accretion of planetesimals it would appear unreasonable to assume that it ever had exceedingly large concentrations of hydrogen and helium, since these would have been lost more readily from small planets than from large ones. It is particularly noteworthy that even heavier, inert gases might be lost from small planetesimals. This could be the explanation for the deficiency of krypton and xenon on earth. These two inert gases are thousands of times less abundant on earth than are some of their close, nongaseous neighbors in the periodic table.

What, then, would the initial composition

of the earth's atmosphere have been? Since planetesimals would be meteorites, analysis of gases in meteorites should give some ideas. Meteorites yield carbon dioxide and nitrogen. A second source of information might be the composition of gases coming from volcanoes today. The main constituents are water vapor, carbon dioxide, and oxides of sulfur.

Oxygen in the Atmosphere

NITROGEN IN THE ATMOSPHERE is easily explained by either theory. It is present in meteorites and in volcanic gases, and it could be derived from decomposition of ammonia.

The history of oxygen is more debatable. The earth's atmosphere consisted primarily of carbon dioxide, nitrogen, and relatively little free oxygen two billion years ago. This conclusion is based on studies of oxygen-bearing compounds in rocks of Precambrian age. From studies of compounds formed in rocks of different ages it is possible to estimate the partial pressure of oxygen in the atmosphere at the time of formation.

The first oxygen in the atmosphere was probably freed from water vapor in upper layers of the atmosphere by solar radiation, a process called *photochemical dissociation*. This process is taking place today at a rate which, if continued throughout geologic time, would provide several times the amount of oxygen presently found in the atmosphere. Some of the oxygen produced in the past has been incorporated in minerals.

A second source of oxygen is *photosynthesis* by green plants. In photosynthesis, the process by which plants manufacture carbohydrates, carbon dioxide is taken from the atmosphere and oxygen is released as a waste product. This process may be responsible for maintaining the present oxygen content of the atmosphere, but it could not account for oxygen in the Precambrian atmosphere, because plants which produce oxygen by photosynthesis did not appear in abundance until the Devonian Period. Lower plants which might have been present in Precambrian time absorb oxygen and expire carbon dioxide.

FIG. 29–1. / *Origin of the atmosphere. Water vapor, carbon dioxide, and nitrogen are shown coming from a volcano. The water vapor is broken down by photochemical processes high in the atmosphere—oxygen is liberated and hydrogen, being light, is lost.*

Thus this process does not explain the observed oxygen content of the Precambrian atmosphere.

Losses from the Atmosphere

Through rock-weathering processes the atmosphere and crust react. These reactions tend to remove certain constituents from the atmosphere as they combine to form compounds. Examples of some of these losses are:

1. When the partial pressure of carbon dioxide reaches a certain level, reactions which may be symbolized as follows begin:
   $$CaSiO_3 + CO_2 = CaCO_3 + SiO_2.$$
   Stated without chemical formula, the carbon dioxide of the atmosphere reacts with minerals formed from crystallization of rock melts to produce carbonate rocks, such as limestone and dolomite, and free silica. Rubey (1955) defines steps symbolized in the equation above:
   a. Carbon dioxide, sunlight, and water favor growth of plants on land and in the sea.
   b. Plants support growth of all other organisms.
   c. Decaying organic matter yields carbon dioxide which, dissolved in ground water, forms carbonic acid.
   d. Common rock-forming minerals in crystalline rocks and carbonates in sedimentary rocks are decomposed by weak solutions of carbonic acid, with formation of clay minerals and release of calcium into solution.
   e. Ground waters carrying calcium and other dissolved materials discharge into streams and so into oceans, where solar evaporation causes gradual concentration of $CO_3^=$ ions in sea water.
   f. When the solubility product of calcium ions and carbonate ions exceeds a certain value, limestone is deposited.
2. Carbon dioxide is taken out of the atmosphere as plants and some animals use it. They in turn may be transformed into coal, petroleum, or disseminated carbon in rocks.
3. Oxygen combines with other elements through oxidation.
4. Light gases are lost from the earth's gravitational field (notably hydrogen and helium).
5. Nitrogen is removed by bacteria in soil to form oxides of nitrogen.

Residual Hypothesis Summary

According to the residual atmosphere hypothesis, the original atmosphere consisted of water vapor, hydrogen, nitrogen, ammonia, and methane. It underwent evolution through photochemical reactions, degassing of the interior by volcanic activity, and finally photosynthesis by green plants. Oxygen developed through photochemical decomposition of water vapor and later by photosynthesis. Carbon dioxide, nitrogen, and hydrogen were formed through oxidation of methane by water vapor and decomposition of ammonia. Hydrogen escaped into space. When the level of carbon dioxide reached a certain point, reactions began to take place with silicate minerals leading to production of limestones.

Degassing Hypothesis Summary

The atmosphere slowly accumulated from gases given off through volcanism, according to the accumulated atmosphere hypothesis. These gases were nitrogen, carbon dioxide, water vapor, and a number of others in minor quantity. Oxygen was produced first by photochemical reactions and later by photosynthesis by green plants. Absence of oxygen at first gave the earth a reducing atmosphere, which gradually changed to an oxidizing atmosphere with the increased addition of oxygen (reduction occurs when oxygen is released in chemical reactions; in oxidation oxygen combines with other elements).

Origin of the Oceans

Origin of water in general and oceans specifically must be closely related to origin of the atmosphere. Water was present on earth as soon as temperatures of the surface cooled down to 365° C., the critical temperature for water, above which it cannot exist as a liquid regardless of the pressure exerted upon it. We cannot say exactly when this happened, but we find

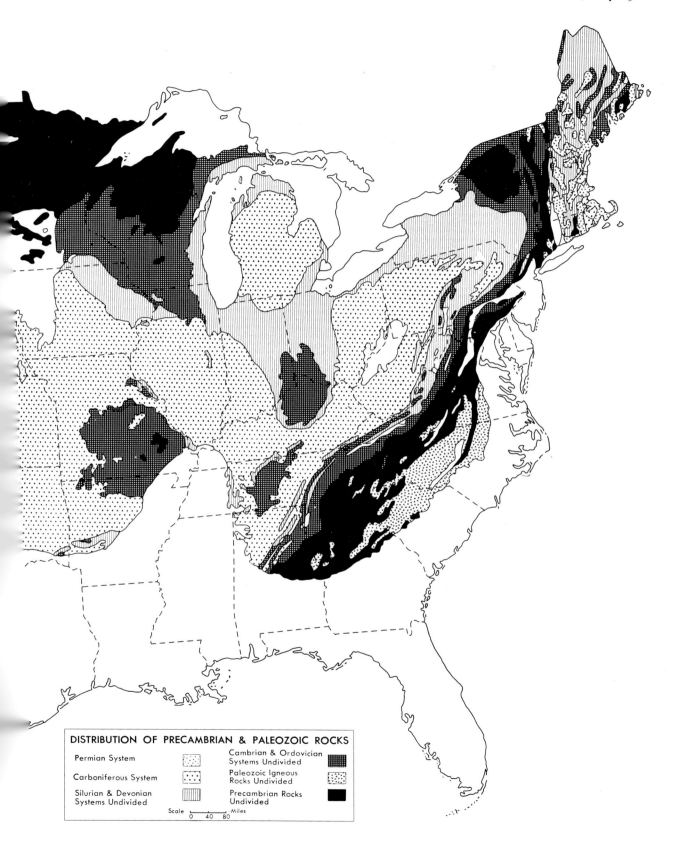

DISTRIBUTION OF PRECAMBRIAN & PALEOZOIC ROCKS

Permian System

Carboniferous System

Silurian & Devonian
Systems Undivided

Cambrian & Ordovician
Systems Undivided

Paleozoic Igneous
Rocks Undivided

Precambrian Rocks
Undivided

Scale Miles
0 40 80

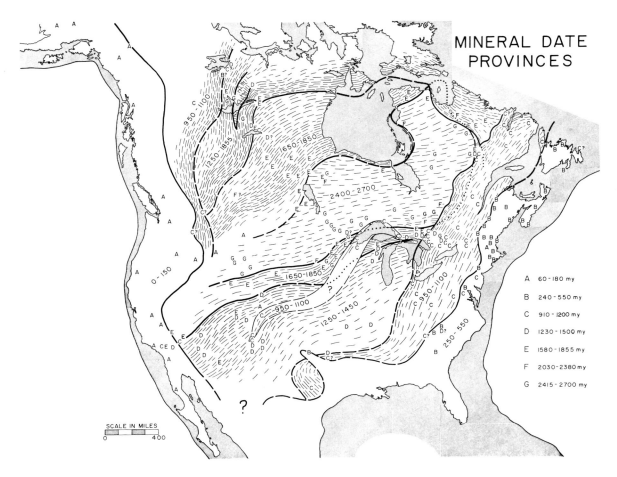

MINERAL DATE
PROVINCES

A   60 - 180 my
B   240 - 550 my
C   910 - 1200 my
D   1230 - 1500 my
E   1580 - 1855 my
F   2030 - 2380 my
G   2415 - 2700 my

FIG. 29–4. / *Precambrian orogenic belts of North America. Age ranges for each belt, obtained by radio-active dating methods, are indicated in millions of years. (Courtesy of Dr. Gordon Gastil.)*

throughout the shield, then there must have been a period of extensive uplift over a vast area at that time. Otherwise we are seeing evidence that different parts of the shield were elevated and eroded at various times before relatively less altered units were laid down. Subdivisions in the Middle Precambrian are known as *Huronian*; these were deformed and intruded by granites that are 1,400 million years old. Overlying these with angular unconformity is the Upper Precambrian, exposed around Lake Supe-

rior, where it is known as the *Keweenawan* series. This thick series of lava flows, intrusive rocks, and sedimentary rocks is broken by faults, but it has never been subjected to strong folding. The igneous rocks are perhaps 1,100 million years old. This leaves a gap in the history of the region between the Precambrian and Cambrian systems that amounts to half a billion years. This is about equal to all the time since the first abundantly fossiliferous units were deposited.

Lower Precambrian

TIME REPRESENTED BY THE Early Precambrian is extremely long, and both the history and rocks preserved from that time are quite complex. Over the vast area of the Superior Province the most exposed rock is composed of granite and granitic gneiss, some of which may be metamorphosed or granitized sediments, but large parts are true igneous rocks. Exposed in elongate patches scattered across this surface are strongly-folded and highly-altered sedimentary rocks and lava flows that trend roughly east–west. It is difficult to correlate these units from one place to another. Most distinctive of these are Keewatin lava flows, actually greenstones, a dense greenish rock formed by metamorphism of basalt. Many of these flows are made up of the pillow-shaped masses thought to form where lava is extruded under water. Ash and poorly sorted sediments including ironstones and cherts are associated with them.

Most sedimentary rocks found below Keewatin volcanics are called "Coutchiching." Those above are called "Knife Lake" or "Timiskaming." There is no certainty that all units below Keewatin-type sequences are the same age. It could be that there were several periods of outpourings of similar lavas at widely separated times. If this is the case, then Coutchiching of one area may be the same age as Knife Lake or Timiskaming of another locality.

One outstanding characteristic of these rocks —Coutchiching, Knife Lake, and Timiskaming —is that they contain large quantities of feldspar mixed with sands and gravels. This signifies either a rapid rate of subsidence and sedimentation or dry deposition, because feldspar decays into clay in water or humid climates. Rates of deposition may have been very rapid with little time for sorting of sediments. A great variety of metasedimentary rocks is found—quartzites, conglomerates, slates, schists, and gneisses. At Lake Timiskaming they contain pebbles of Keewatin-type volcanic rocks. These units overlie Keewatin volcanic rocks nearby. Thus in this type section the Timiskaming series is younger than the Keewatin.

There must have been igneous activity at many times during the Early Precambrian (Table 12). Two names are most frequently applied to these granitic intrusions. Where two periods of intrusion are seen in a single area the older one is called "Laurentian," and the cross-cutting granite is called "Algoman."

Middle Precambrian

MOST UNITS OF THIS AGE are deformed and slightly altered, but not so extensively as those below them. The name Huronian is frequently applied to all or parts of the Middle Precambrian. This name is taken from the type locality near Lake Huron. Similar units are found farther west, around Lake Superior, where they are divided into three groups separated by unconformities. Around Lake Huron, Middle Precambrian is divided into *Upper*, *Middle*, and *Lower*

TABLE 12 / *Subdivisions of the Precambrian of the Canadian Shield.*

PRECAMBRIAN	UPPER	*Keweenawan Series*	*Killarney Granite*
	MIDDLE *or* ALGONKIAN	Upper Huronian* Middle Huronian* Lower Huronian*	Animikie Series Cobalt Series Bruce Series
		Major Angular Unconformity	
	LOWER *or* ARCHEAN	Timiskaming Series* Keewatin Lava Series* Coutchiching Series*	*Algoman Granite* Knife Lake Series *Laurentian* (?) *Granite*

* These series are not exact time equivalents.

FIG. 29–5. / *Early Precambrian units intruded by later granites. These units are exposed in this vertical photograph of the region near Duncan Lake, Northwest Territories. The early Precambrian sediments are dark in color. They have been intruded by granite in bodies up to one-half mile in size. Note how the light-colored dikes have filled fracture and fault patterns in the lower part of the photograph. This establishes the age of the fracture pattern. Late Precambrian diabase dikes shown in dark grey cut across both the early Precambrian metasedimentary rocks and the granites. The irregular black areas are lakes. (By courtesy of the Royal Canadian Air Force.)*

Huronian. But in Ontario the divisions are called *Animikie, Cobalt,* and *Bruce* series. The subdivisions of the Middle Precambrian in these two localities are not time equivalents.

One of the most important events of the Middle Precambrian was deformation of Middle Precambrian rocks as well as the underlying units. They were sharply folded and uplifted to form a major mountain range trending east–west across the Great Lakes region. This ancient mountain range is known as the *Penokean Range.* Folds of the range were intruded by granitic rocks near the close of the Middle Precambrian. Some of these intrusions contain radioactive minerals, which have been dated as 1,400 million years old. Deformation was less intense to the north and west, where the same units are only slightly tilted instead of folded.

Sandstones, slates, conglomerates, dolomites, and lava flows are all present in quantity. Those formed just before the orogeny contain units that are indicative of crustal activity, such as lava flows and graywackes. Among the most interesting and economically important parts of the sequence are iron formations.

Iron Formations

THESE DEPOSITS have been extremely important in the development of the American industrial society. Iron ore mined from localities in Minnesota and northern Michigan has been the principal raw material for the steel industry in Pennsylvania. Most famous of these mining districts are Mesabi, Cuyuna, Vermilion, Gogebic, Marquette, and Menominee ranges. Occurrence of iron is essentially the same in all. One widely accepted theory is that during the Middle Precambrian streams carried products of decomposition of older igneous and metamorphic rocks into seas of that time, and silica-rich shales and iron-bearing cherts were deposited. Iron was derived from iron-bearing minerals (augite, hornblende) in the older rocks. When the region was later deformed these were partly metamorphosed, and a rock known as *taconite* developed. Still later the taconite became exposed at the surface and was subjected to weathering and erosion. Over a long period of time leaching by ground water concentrated iron near the surface. This rich ore is about 60 per cent iron. Pure hematite occurs with jasper, a hematite-rich chert. These ores have been important for many years, but with the present high rates of consumption they will be depleted in the foreseeable future. Attention is now being given to the commercial development of taconite, which contains up to 30 per cent iron.

Upper Precambrian

THE NAME *Keweenawan series* is generally applied to rock units formed during the late Precambrian. Lower parts of these are thick, basaltic, lava flows and intrusions of basalt and its coarse-grained equivalent, *gabbro*. These were followed by a thick sequence of conglomerates, sandstones, and shales apparently laid down on land, since the sands contain ripple marks indicating strong currents like those common in streams, and shales and silts contain mud cracks formed where muds were periodically dried. A tidal zone or lake bottom might also contain these features. Many of the sediments are stained by iron oxide, suggesting that they were oxidized. These sediments and the igneous ac-

FIG. 29–6. / *Precambrian geology in the Western Great Lakes region. (From Goldich, et al., Minnesota Geological Survey, Bull. 41.)*

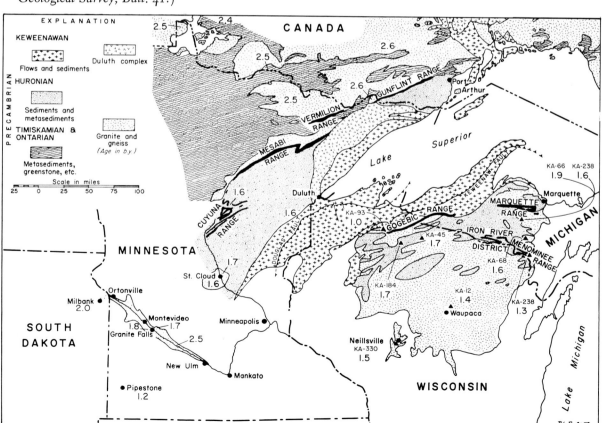

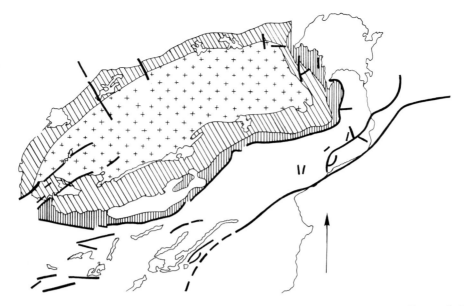

FIG. 29–7. / *Sudbury Intrusion, Ontario. The world's richest nickel deposits occur in Precambrian rocks here. The heavy lines are faults; the Sudbury intrusion, a lopolith-like body, is indicated by diagonal rulings; ancient Precambrian granites and gneisses occupy clear areas; and younger metamorphic rocks have a cross pattern. (From H. C. Cooke, 1948.)*

tivity may have been related to the Penokean orogeny.

The Keweenawan series is confined to the area around Lake Superior. It is within a structural basin and probably never extended far beyond present boundaries of this down-warped area. The amount of magma involved in the igneous activity of this time amounted to thousands of cubic miles. Surface flows aggregated more than five miles in thickness in many areas, and in addition there were huge intrusions. Of the latter, the large *lopolith*, a funnel-shaped intrusion, that is exposed along the western end of Lake Superior, the *Duluth lopolith* (Fig. 29–6), is almost 50,000 feet thick and more than 140 miles long. This body is dated as 1,100 million years old. This may well be the age of a large part of the igneous activity. A second important intrusion is found at Sudbury, Ontario (Fig. 29–7). Composition of this intrusion is slightly different; it is a norite, a gabbro containing a special type of pyroxene mineral. Associated with it there are rich deposits of nickel ore that is the principal source of this metal in North America. Another important mineral resource produced from the Keweenawan sequences is native copper. The main source is

the Keweenaw Peninsula of northern Michigan, where native copper fills vesicles left in ancient lava flows by escaping gases. It also occurs as a filling around pebbles of some conglomerates that lie above the lavas. The copper was probably brought in and deposited by hot solutions after lavas and conglomerates had formed.

Precambrian History of the United States

IT WILL BE MANY YEARS BEFORE IT IS POSsible to piece together an integrated and meaningful history of the United States during Precambrian time. Exposures are scattered (Fig. 29–3) but lie primarily in three areas—the central portion of the Appalachians near the Canadian border, where the Canadian Shield comes into this country, and cores of mountain ranges of the Rockies. Precambrian exposures in the Rockies are of two principal types, older rocks which have been thoroughly metamorphosed, and younger, less metamorphosed sequences whose original sedimentary character is still clearly evident in stratification and the presence of primary sedimentary structures. In a number of places, notably the Grand Canyon and the northern Rocky Mountains, less metamorphosed sequences (called *Belt* in the north and *Grand Canyon Series* in Arizona) clearly rest unconformably on highly metamorphosed basements. This suggests a twofold division of Precambrian time, but it may yet be shown that some of the less metamorphosed sedimentary sequences are as old as the metamorphic complexes. Radioactive dates obtained through the Rocky Mountains give a wide range of ages, but these cannot always be accepted at face value. Radioactive dates provide minimum ages —not maximum. It has already been established that there were several periods of orogeny and intrusion during Precambrian time in the United States. Effects of these may have included "resetting of clocks" through recrystallization of minerals undergoing radioactive decay. As in the Canadian Shield, histories for Precambrian time can be worked out in detail over areas with relatively continuous outcrop, but correlation between such areas is subject to considerable question. Details of two widely separated areas are given for comparison.

Precambrian of Arizona

PRECAMBRIAN ROCKS are exposed at the bottom of the Grand Canyon, where the Colorado River has cut through almost a mile of Mesozoic and Paleozoic sedimentary rocks. The river is now entrenched in Precambrian metamorphic and igneous rocks in the inner gorge.

There is no doubt about the original sedimentary character of metamorphic rocks in this region, or about the igneous origin of the granites which intrude them. Deposition of chemical sediments and fine muds occurred at a time of considerable volcanic and igneous activity. Basic lava flows intermittently poured out over the sediments. The fine-grained character of the sediments suggests that they must have been laid down at a great distance from any source of coarse debris, such as a high mountain range. The first change in conditions is indicated by a corresponding change in coarseness of sedi-

ments. Gravels, sands, and muds indicate that the region was becoming less stable. There was a land area above sea level nearby. This land continued to rise. Rapid erosion of it created very coarse sediments, including conglomerates that contain boulders of the earlier volcanic rocks. Uplift was accompanied by extensive igneous intrusion. Great quantities of siliceous lava (rhyolite) poured out, forming widespread lava flows that were later tilted and folded.

Following this first orogenic episode there was a return to the quiet conditions which had characterized the first known event. Uplifted areas were eroded down and finally the sea returned. Sediments were again laid down, this time on top of the deformed conglomerates, rhyolites, and intrusives. The region might be visualized as a broad continental-shelflike environment.

Later, deformation took place again, and volcanic activity was resumed. Again conglomerates and volcanic rocks became intermixed and interbedded. Igneous activity gradually increased until huge intrusions invaded the older rocks, metamorphosing and assimilating them. Some of these magmas broke through to the surface, giving rise to extensive ash deposits. Most of these magmas were granitic in composition. The end of this activity marks the close of the Early Precambrian interval.

A long interval of erosion followed before younger, now relatively unmetamorphosed sediments were deposited, forming a major angular unconformity. The first of these sediments were coarse conglomerates, but later finer sediments were also laid down. Before the start of the Paleozoic there was another disturbance of the region. This time there was uplift and tilting, but relatively little folding or igneous activity. Cambrian strata are now found deposited across the beveled edges of these tilted Upper Precambrian deposits (Fig. 29–8).

Beartooth Mountains

THE STORY OF INVESTIGATIONS of the Beartooth Mountains is of importance because it illustrates continual re-evaluation of accepted

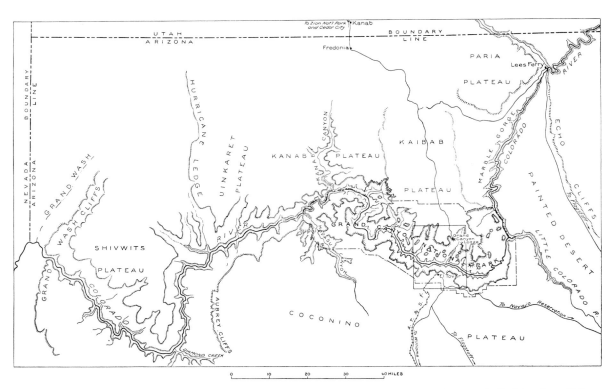

FIG. 29–8a and b. / *Map and geologic cross section of the Grand Canyon. (From F. E. Matthes, U.S. Geological Survey Topographic Map.)*

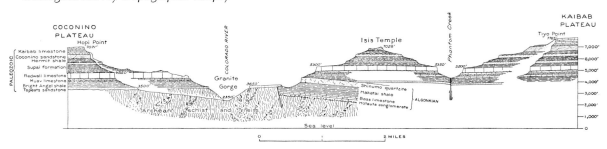

ideas, and the methods used are strikingly different from those used in analysis of the history of rocks younger than Precambrian. This range is one of the most extensive exposures of Precambrian rocks in the Rocky Mountains.

Precambrian rocks of the Beartooth Mountains consist mainly of granitic gneisses. Throughout the Paleozoic and Mesozoic eras this region, south-central Montana and northern Wyoming, was buried under great thicknesses of sediment. Toward the end of the Mesozoic the whole Rocky Mountain system began to be uplifted. In that part of the system known as the Middle Rocky Mountains uplift took the form of displacements of huge blocks of the crust. A number of large, elongate blocks were uplifted along faults, and adjacent blocks were depressed, forming basins. Like other blocks of this region the Beartooth block was eroded as soon as it was uplifted above the level of the sea. Erosion was accelerated during the ice ages, when glaciers carved huge valleys in the mountains. Eventually sediments that had been deposited during the Paleozoic and Mesozoic were eroded away, leaving a bare exposure of the older rocks in the core of the range.

The origin of crystalline rocks here has been a subject of debate for many years. Because they contain the same mineral assemblages found in igneous granites, and because the texture is very much like that of granites, the rocks were called granites, and the core of the range was mapped as a batholith. These rocks are very much like granitic gneisses of the Canadian Shield. Most of them are faintly banded. In places they contain lenses of a darker rock known as amphibolite, which contains a large quantity of hornblende. These lenses are often contorted and drawn out. They were originally interpreted as blocks of country rock into which the batholith was intruded. It was assumed that they were broken off the top or sides of the magma chamber during intrusion. After falling into the hot magma they were partially melted or assimilated. In addition to granitic rocks and darker lenses of amphibolite, a number of different sets of dikes were known to cut through the Precambrian. Some of these are basaltic dikes, and others are light-colored porphyry dikes composed of quartz and feldspars.

Early in 1950 a more intensive and more detailed study was started. Methods employed consisted of very detailed mapping. Each outcrop was examined, and distribution of even the most minor variations in rock types was mapped. Where granitic rocks appeared, massive orientation of the flakes of mica was recorded. All rock types were sampled and studied with a petrographic microscope;[3] some were analyzed to establish their exact chemical compositions. Maps of the central core reveal a pattern that resembles a plunging system of folds in sedimentary rocks. Detailed mapping of true igneous intrusions elsewhere show structures with eddy-like flow patterns such as would be expected in a viscous magma as it is intruded. These foldlike structures suggest, then, that the granitic rocks of the Beartooth are not of an igneous origin. They appear to be highly altered sedimentary rocks. That folds exist indicates that this region was deformed in the Precambrian. This might very well have been part of a high, folded mountain belt that rose during the Precambrian, but vanished before the beginning of the Paleozoic Era. That such a mountain range had disappeared before the Paleozoic is shown by the angular unconformity between

3 Microscopes designed for study of thin sections of rock.

the lowest Paleozoic rock unit and the Precambrian granites. The contact between them is almost perfectly even. It is undoubtedly an erosion surface created sometime before the end of Precambrian time.

Existence of these folded structures is an indication that the rocks were originally sedimentary, but it is not necessarily a conclusive argument. Another method used was to study the minerals in the granitic rocks. Zircon makes up a small portion of the rock. It occurs as very small crystals which can be separated from other minerals by crushing the rocks and placing the crushed minerals in a dense liquid to separate out lightweight feldspar and quartz. Zircon is further separated by use of a strong magnetic field. The reason for making this separation is to study the shape of the zircon crystals (Fig. 29-9). Like quartz, zircon is insoluble in water and does not dissolve when it is transported in a stream; it usually is deposited in small amounts in sand. Zircon originates in igneous rocks, in which it is one of the first minerals to crystallize. Since it is present in small quantities it tends to crystallize into a small, perfect crystal. The zircon is freed through weathering processes, and it is carried along in running water just as quartz is. As it is transported the small crystals are broken and rounded, and eventually rounded zircon becomes part of a sedimentary deposit. So the shape of zircons in a rock is one key to the history of the rock. If its zircons are rounded, it is sedimentary; if they are crystals, it is likely that the rock is igneous. Zircons in granitic rocks of the Beartooth Mountains are rounded.

What happened to the original sedimentary units to transform them into granitic rocks? They were highly metamorphosed under conditions which led to "granitization." A thick sequence of sedimentary shales, limestones, and silts has the same bulk chemical composition as granite. It is likely that they were deeply buried and that they were subjected to high confining pressures. They were heated to high temperatures. Although temperatures were high, nearly 600° C, they were not sufficient for the mass to be a magma. Under these conditions the

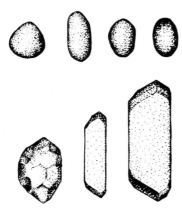

FIG. 29–9. / *Zircons from metamorphic rocks. The top row of zircons were removed from a granitic gneiss, and the bottom row came from a porphyry dike. That the gneiss was originally sedimentary, not igneous, is indicated by the rounded shape of the zircons. They were transported in a stream and rounded like sand grains before they were deposited and incorporated in the sediment. Later the deposits were metamorphosed and transformed into a granitic rock, but the zircons remained relatively unchanged. Zircons like those in the bottom row crystallize early in the cooling history of a magma. They tend to form euhedral, perfectly shaped, crystals. (Redrawn from R. Harris.)*

minerals of the original sediments became unstable and underwent changes, recombinations of their elements, which brought about the development of a rock composed essentially of feldspar, quartz, and biotite. During this process of granitization pegmatites formed. Some of these contain uranite, a radioactive mineral. This has been dated as 2,700 million years old. Because the pegmatite is related to granitization, we know the age of this process, and because the granitization is related to the deformation, we have a good idea of the age of this orogenic episode in the history of the earth. The age of these activities makes them the oldest known events in the history of the United States.

An Outline of the Precambrian History of the Beartooth Mountains

1. A thick sequence of sediments was deposited in a shallow sea. Cross-bedding is found in some quartzite units, which indicates deposition of sand in a current. The sediments were probably composed of sandstones and silts.
2. Deposition was followed by an undetermined period of time for which there is no record.
3. Then ultramafic magmas, rich in iron and magnesium, were intruded into the sediments.
4. Shortly after intrusion of the ultramafic rocks the sediments and the intrusions were deformed and folded.
5. About 2.7 billion years ago the deeper zones in the crust of this area were transformed into granitic rocks. Older dikes and intrusions were metamorphosed, and pegmatites formed.
6. Then came another long period about which we have no knowledge.
7. In the Late Precambrian the region was uplifted a second time, and rocks were faulted and fractured. Swarms of basaltic dikes were intruded. These dikes are not metamorphosed, and they cut across the older ones and the granitic rocks. Chilled contacts, where magma was cooled quickly by contact with the country rock, are found along some of these later dikes.
8. Following the Late Precambrian disturbances there was a long period of erosion. This removed the top part of the mountains and elevated parts of the area. It may have required millions of years for a nearly flat surface to be developed across the region.
9. In the Early Paleozoic a shallow sea transgressed the region, leaving a flat-lying layer of sand.
10. Much later the region was again deformed and uplifted, and the present Rocky Mountains began to take shape in the Cretaceous Period.

The Beltian System

Many of the spectacular mountains in the Northern Rockies are composed of Upper Precambrian sedimentary and volcanic rocks that are part of the Beltian System. These units were deposited in a broad, subsiding trough that must have been several hundred miles wide and may have extended in length all the way into the southwestern United States. Almost 35,000 feet of sediments accumulated on the western side of this geosyncline, while the eastern side received about 12,000 feet. Sediments consist of red, green, and black mudstones, thick sections of limestone, quartzite, and in places large amounts of basaltic lavas. Some basalts were extruded as flows on the surface; others were intruded into older sediments as sills and dikes.

Where it is exposed the lower part of the Beltian System is composed of conglomerates. These contain pebbles of older Precambrian rocks now exposed in cores of nearby mountain ranges. This suggests that a source area of this type of rock stood open to erosion and decay during the time that the Belt was deposited. Since the units are much thicker on the west, it is probable that the source lay to the west of the geosyncline. Some of the fine-grained clastic sediments are cross-bedded. From these it is possible to determine the direction in which water currents were moving. Studies of these confirm the existence of a western source, but it is apparent that other sources existed from time to time. Muds and shales contain mud cracks and ripple marks as well as cross-bedding. These prove that shallow water conditions existed at the time. Limestones of this age contain large cabbage-shaped masses of calcareous algae that grew in great quantities almost like reefs (Fig. 29–10).

FIG. 29–10. / *Calcareous alga,* Cryptozoon proliferum. *This reef of alga is exposed near Saratoga, New York. The surface of the reef has been scoured by continental glaciers providing a beautiful cross-sectional view of the reef. (Photo by the author.)*

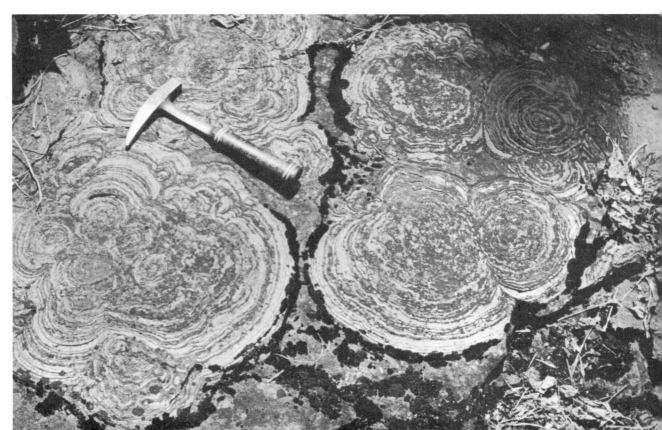

30 / Appalachian Mountains

Geologic Setting of the Appalachian Geosynclinal Belt

IN THE FOLLOWING DISCUSSION WE TAKE a broad view of the Appalachian geosyncline, the deformed belt that extends from Newfoundland through New England to Alabama, where a significant break occurs between the Appalachian Mountains and the Ouachita Mountains of Arkansas and Oklahoma.[1] The system thus defined is long and characterized by varied geologic structures and history. Our treatment will bring out some of the most significant parts of the vast store of factual knowledge which has been accumulated about this area, and will also outline the theoretical interpretations placed on these observations. Two major schemes have been advanced to explain the nature of the geosyncline, but in order to understand these and the reasoning on which they are based it is necessary to establish the limits to observation, the character of rock units, and the nature of structures in the Appalachian geosyncline.

[1] Refer to the Geologic Map of the United States at end of book for a portion of this belt.

Nature of the Continental Margin

SINCE GEOSYNCLINES WERE FIRST recognized in America it is appropriate that we examine the history of the development of the geosynclinal theory and its application to the American continent.

Interior areas of most of North America exhibited remarkable stability throughout the Paleozoic. Most of the continent was low-lying, and during most of the time it was near sea level. Shallow seas spread over parts of it, covering all of it at times. Because the seas were shallow and land had low relief, a slight change in sea level or a slight warping of the continent affected the shape of the seas. These slow changes went on almost continuously. During most of this time a few areas tended to rise and remain higher than surrounding plains. These areas included regions of the Adirondacks, the Cincinnati Arch, the Wisconsin Upland, the Ozark Mountains, and probably a large part of Canada. Geosynclines existed in areas now occupied by the Appalachian Highlands and its northern extension into Newfoundland, by the Ouachita Mountains, and by the Rocky Mountains. Great thicknesses of sediments accumulated within these geosynclinal belts.

At this point general agreement as to the nature of the pattern ends. Several views are held regarding the nature of the continental margins during the Paleozoic. Two hypotheses which are most commonly held are:

Borderland theory. Continental margins outside geosynclines consisted of crystalline continental borderlands.

Island arc theory. The geosyncline consisted of two parts, a shallow trough near the continent and oceanward a more deeply subsiding trough in which chains of volcanic islands stood. These are thought to have been very similar to modern island arc systems.

Before going into the evidence for *borderlands* and *island arc* related geosynclines let us examine the circumstances that allow two such strikingly different concepts to exist. This is a case of insufficient data and inconclusive facts. The main argument concerns the nature of the region that was located on the oceanward side of the present Appalachian and Rocky Mountain systems when the sedimentary rocks now found deformed in these belts were being deposited. The data are insufficient because in the case of the Appalachians the region to the east is covered by sea water or younger sedimentary rocks. What remains of the Paleozoic sedimentary sequences in the area to the east has been altered and complexly deformed through metamorphism and orogeny. On the west coast we also find few rocks of Paleozoic age exposed. They have been covered by younger sedimentary sequences.

The Borderland Hypothesis

THE FRAMEWORK OF the North American continent as postulated by Charles Schuchert is sketched in Fig. 28–2. The main elements include a central stable region; two major geosynclines, the Appalachian in the east and Cordilleran of the west; two embayments, the Ouachita and Sonoran; and a number of con-

tinental land masses, Appalachia, Llanoria, Cascadia, and others.

Schuchert's borderland hypothesis followed the failure of two earlier concepts of the continental margins, devised by J. D. Dana, to explain all the facts known at that time about the stratigraphy of the margins.

Marginal Reefs

THE FIRST OF DANA'S ideas, presented in 1856, was that in the early Paleozoic a great reef or sand bank lay off the eastern shore of the main North American continent, separating the Atlantic Ocean from a vast lagoon along the edge of the continent. He suggested that the southward-flowing Labrador Current carried most of the sediment deposited along the eastern shores of the continent during the Paleozoic. When the structure and stratigraphy of the eastern United States had been studied in sufficient detail, it became apparent that the Green Mountains of Vermont had been formed during the Paleozoic. These lie exactly in the path Dana postulated for the Labrador Current, blocking the course the current had to follow to bring in sediments now exposed in the region south and west of New England. Recognizing that his earlier theory was wrong, Dana formulated a new hypothesis.

Marginal Crystalline Ridges

IN PLACE OF THE marginal reefs Dana postulated that marginal crystalline ridges of Precambrian rocks rose before the start of the Paleozoic Era. He suggested that these occupied the position of the large exposures of crystalline rocks in the Sierra Nevada and Rocky Mountains and in the Blue Ridge and Piedmont. These old uplifted areas were supposed to be the sources of sedimentary rocks now found in the Appalachian and Cordilleran geosynclines. Unfortunately this theory met with failure also. It turns out that most of these crystalline rocks are not even Precambrian in age, that Dana's marginal ridge on the eastern coast did not rise until the end of the Paleozoic, and that the

Present Profile

Pacific — Sierra Nevada — Rockies — plains — Appalachians — Atlantic

Profile in Cambrian (Schuchert & Dunbar)

Pacific — Cascadia — continental interior — Appalachia — Atlantic

Profile in Cambrian (Kay)

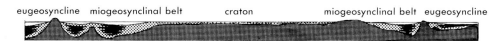

eugeosyncline miogeosynclinal belt craton miogeosynclinal belt eugeosyncline

FIG. 30–1. / *Cross sections across North America. The top section depicts the present topography. The second profile is drawn to represent a section during the Cambrian Period according to the theory of borderlands. The bottom section represents a profile in the Cambrian according to the island arc hypothesis. (After Marshall Kay and Schuchert and Dunbar.)*

ridge on the west coast was not uplifted until late in the Mesozoic Era.

Borderlands

IT WAS AT THIS TIME that the borderlands were first postulated. They were postulated in order to provide a source area for sediments laid down in the geosynclines. Why should such borderlands be located off the coasts? Many of the clastic sediments that are found in these geosynclinal accumulations thicken toward the east along the east coast. Such eastward coarsening is found in beds of Ordovician, Silurian, and Devonian age at various places in the eastern United States. In 1897, to account for these sediments, Dr. H. S. Williams first postulated a now lost land mass which he called *Appalachia*. Appalachia was located in a very convenient position off the eastern coast out on the continental shelf. In this position Appalachia could easily provide an explanation for the observed gradation in size of sediment. The absence of a comparable land mass in that position today was accounted for by postulating that it had either subsided or been removed by erosion and buried under more recent sediments.

One of the leading proponents of borderlands was Charles Schuchert. His concepts of these lands have been widely accepted. The eastern borderland, Appalachia, occupied the area of the present Piedmont and coastal plains and extended out into the Atlantic Ocean an indeterminate distance. Cascadia occupied the area of the modern coast ranges of the west and extended out into the Pacific Ocean. A third major borderland occupied the present site of the Gulf Coast and Gulf of Mexico. According to Schuchert these elements persisted as dominant features of the continental framework throughout all of the Paleozoic Era.

Theory of Marginal Volcanic Geosynclines and Island Arcs

FOR MANY YEARS the concept of marginal borderlands had few vocal critics, although even as early as 1856 Dana rejected it:

On the idea that the rocks of our continent have been supplied sands and gravel from a continent now sunk in the ocean . . . the whole system of progress . . . is opposed to it. The existence of an Amazon on any such Atlantic continent in Silurian, Devonian, or Carboniferous times is too wild an hypothesis for a moment's indulgence.

Hans Stille was the first to recognize the existence of two belts along the Appalachian Mountain belt, one of which contains primarily nonvolcanic sediments and a second, located farther out from the continent, which was the loci for volcanic intrusions and extrusions of great magnitude. He proposed the term *"eugeosyncline"* for the deeply subsiding belts containing the volcanic rocks. Figures 30–2 and 30–3 show a generalized location for the two early Paleozoic geosynclinal belts which bordered North America during the era according to this hypothesis.

The position of these belts changed later in the Paleozoic. On both coasts inner belts are characterized as long, narrow, troughlike depressions containing accumulations of marine sediments thicker than those typically found in the interior, but not as thick as those sections deposited farther out in the eugeosynclines. These inner belts, called *miogeosynclines,* are further distinguished by the absence of volcanic sediments. They contain thick sections of sandstone, shale, and limestone. Eugeosynclines are located farther out from the *craton,* the name applied to the central stable region of a continent. They more or less parallel miogeosynclines but are much more active belts in which subsidence is more pronounced, allowing more sediments to accumulate. These belts are distinguished by the presence of igneous intrusions and extrusions. According to this view, North American continental borders in the Paleozoic Era resembled one of the island arc systems of the Pacific Ocean today. Perhaps deep-sea trenches extended along the eastern margin of a festoon of volcanic islands like the Aleutians and were separated from the main continent by a relatively shallow sea. Evidence in support of the eugeosynclinal theory has been rapidly expanded in recent years. Detailed measuring of sections of the rock units indicate that the thickness of sediments in eugeosynclinal belts is greater than that in miogeosynclines. Products of volcanism—lava flows and ash deposits—have been found in great quantity in the position of the postulated eugeosynclines. Further studies of sandstones in the miogeosynclinal belts have revealed that at times during the Paleozoic the source of sediments was from the west in the Appalachians, making an eastern source area unnecessary.

The boundaries of the deformed geosynclinal belt as it exists today are shown in Fig. 30–4. This is not a map of former limits of the geosyncline, of course, but it does show the area now available for us to study and interpret. Northern and western edges of the belt are well preserved. In Canada the Appalachian belt is bounded on the west by the St. Lawrence River, which separates it from the older group of Precambrian igneous and metamorphic rocks in the Grenville Province of the Canadian

FIG. 30–2. / *New York to Maine. Section across the eugeosynclinal and miogeosynclinal belts from New York to Maine in the middle of the Ordovician Period, according to Kay. (After Marshall Kay.)*

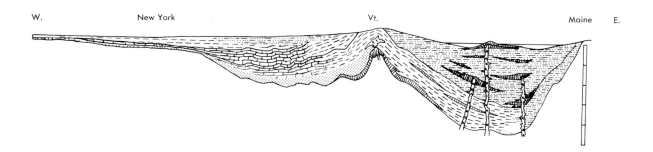

W.   New York   Vt.   Maine   E.

Shield. The Adirondacks of New York form a sharp western edge for the belt. Here a dome of Precambrian gneisses stood high even during early stages of deposition in the geosyncline. If the Appalachian Plateau is considered as part of the geosyncline, the western margin extends westward from the Adirondacks, then follows two long arches, Findley and Cincinnati, south from the western tip of Lake Erie through Cincinnati and then through the Nashville Dome. Along this line structural arches have been prominent since early Paleozoic times. Many Paleozoic rock units thin out over these arches, making this a reasonable western margin for the geosyncline. Near the Alabama-Mississippi-Tennessee corner, the line of these arches is covered by younger Coastal Plain sediments. To include the Ouachita Mountains as part of this system the western boundary must be traced under the Coastal Plain sediments of the Mississippi Embayment (that part of the Coastal Plain that extends up the Mississippi Valley to Cairo, Ill.) northwest to central Arkansas. The Ozark Mountains lie north of the line. The boundary then extends west along the edge of

FIG. 30–3. / *Island arc hypothesis. The alternative to the borderland hypothesis is a theory that the craton, the stable continental interior, was separated from the deep-ocean basins by miogeosynclinal belts in which sandstones and limestones accumulated. Further from shore in the eugeosynclinal belt great thicknesses of graywacke, sandstones, lavas, limestones, and shales accumulated. Island arcs similar to those of the Pacific and Caribbean occupied these outer belts. (After Marshall Kay and E. Raisz.)*

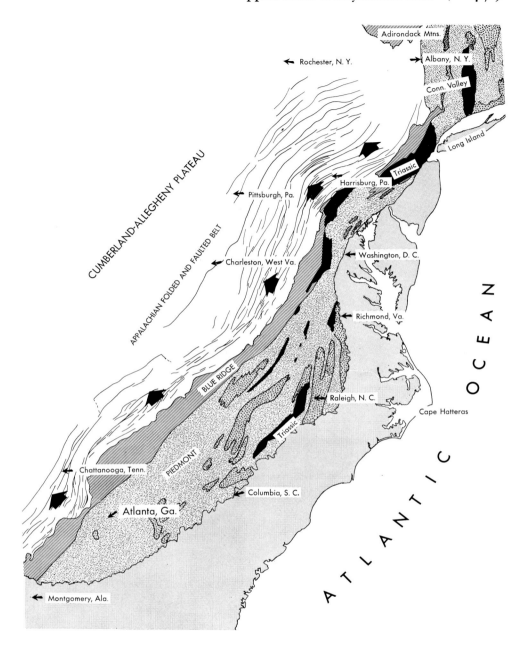

FIG. 30–4. / *Appalachian Provinces. The Coastal Plain is underlain by extensive sheets of semi-consolidated sediments laid down as wedges during the Mesozoic and Cenozoic Eras after the Appalachian orogeny had ended. The Piedmont and New England areas are covered by complexly deformed igneous and metamorphic rocks of Precambrian and early Paleozoic age. The Blue Ridge is partly composed of the rocks of the Piedmont and partly of Cambrian rocks. The northern extension of the Blue Ridge is known as the Reading Prong of the New England Highlands. In the Valley and Ridge Province, Paleozoic strata are folded and cut by thrust faults which have moved the sections northwestward. The most intense zones of folding and faulting are along the Blue Ridge. Farther to the northwest the folded strata are less deformed and in the Appalachian Plateau they are gently tilted westward. The black areas are basins bordered by normal faults which were dropped down on one or both sides during the Triassic after the Appalachian orogeny was over. Continental deposits are found in the Triassic basins. (After the Tectonic Map of the United States.)*

the Arkansas Valley and swings back to the south in eastern Oklahoma, where it disappears under the Coastal Plain sediments again. There are two other places where deformed rocks may represent parts of the same geosynclinal belt. These are in the Llano Mountains and the Marathon Mountains of central and west Texas. They are separated from the Ouachita belt by over a hundred miles of Coastal Plain sediments.

Along most of this western margin of the Appalachian-Ouachita geosynclinal belt the character of the belt is preserved, so we have a means of studying relationships between the geosyncline and the stable central interior of North America. However, because the rock units are less deformed—indeed they are gently warped along this margin—and consequently very few strata are exposed, drilling is needed to establish the nature of the stratigraphic section at depth and the structure of the layers hidden from view. The eastern margin of the geosyncline is quite different. In Canada and down as far as Long Island, the ocean covers the geosynclinal rocks; what we know of them, therefore, must be derived from geophysical studies or drilling. From New York City south and west, the southern margin of the belt is covered by Coastal Plain sediments. These are Cretaceous and younger in age. They are broad sheets of unconsolidated or semiconsolidated sediment lying unconformably on older Paleozoic rocks of the Appalachians and the Ouachitas (Fig. 30–4). These sediments, which have a wedge-like shape, thicken slightly toward the ocean and Gulf. They also dip slightly toward the ocean (Fig. 30–4). Though drilling has been quite extensive in Louisiana, Mississippi, Arkansas, and Texas, very few wells have been drilled far enough to penetrate Paleozoic rocks; consequently our knowledge of the eastern and southern edge of the geosyncline is very slight. This lack of data accounts for the controversy surrounding the nature of this seaward margin.

Present Subdivisions of the Geosyncline

THE GEOSYNCLINAL BELT IS DIVIDED INTO a number of parts that are geographically distinct and to some extent geologically different. That part north of the New York–Pennsylvania state line is called the *Northern Appalachians*; that from New York south to Alabama is called the *Central* and *Southern Appalachians*, with no distinct boundary between these last two.[2] The similarly deformed belt in Arkansas and Oklahoma is called the *Ouachita Mountains*.

The Central and Southern Appalachians contain four physiographic divisions (Fig. 30–5). Physiography is often due to the character of underlying rocks, which is the case here. The *Piedmont* is low, rolling country often covered by red soil developed on crystalline igneous and metamorphic rocks. The deep soil offers relatively few outcrops. This factor has been important in retarding our understanding of this metamorphic complex, but it is currently being studied intensively. The Piedmont is bounded on the south and east from New Jersey to Alabama by the Coastal Plain. At the western side it slopes up to the *Blue Ridge Province*.

The *Blue Ridge Mountains* are a distinct ridge that can be followed almost continuously from Maryland southward to the Great Smoky Mountains. Along a considerable portion of its length it has a fault on its western side, and in places erosion has worn through the overthrust sheet, exposing rocks beneath the Blue Ridge and proving that it has been moved several miles, perhaps as much as 20, to the northwest. Rocks that make up the Blue Ridge vary, but most represent metasediments (partly metamorphosed sedimentary rocks) deposited during later parts of Precambrian time and the earliest part of the Cambrian Period. These rocks include metamorphosed basalt flows and intrusions in addition to quartzites, sandstones,

[2] See geologic map of this area at end of book.

FIG. 30–5. / *Physiographic divisions of Appalachians.*

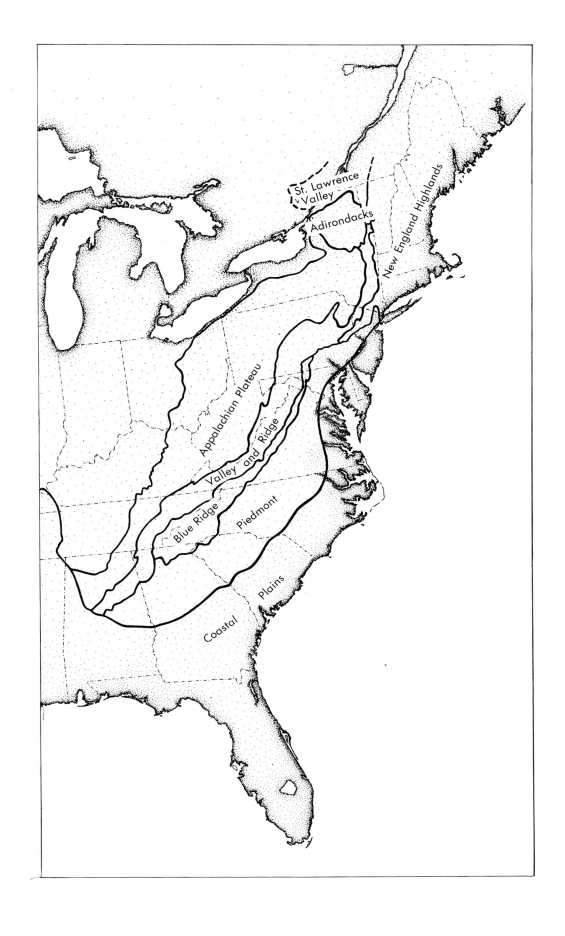

St. Lawrence
Valley

New England Highlands

Adirondacks

Appalachian Plateau

Valley and Ridge

Blue Ridge

Piedmont

Coastal Plains

shales, graywackes, and schists. The northwestern edge of the ridge, often a prominent scarp, overlies a thick section of hard, resistant quartzite which differs greatly from limestones of the valley to the west.

Between the Blue Ridge and the Appalachian Plateau there is a long valley broken up by ridges that run parallel to it and the Blue Ridge. It is called the *Valley and Ridge Province*. This belt varies from a few to more than fifty miles in width and can be traced from Pennsylvania into Alabama. Rock units in it range in age from Cambrian to Pennsylvanian. Ridges are usually capped by Silurian sandstones and quartzites, while valleys are formed in shales, limestones, and dolomites. It is the counterpart of this belt that makes up the Ouachita Mountains (there is no equivalent of the Piedmont related to the Ouachitas). Sedimentary units are thick in this province and are complicated structurally as a result of one or more periods of deformation. Strata have been deformed into folds that range from broad, open features to very tightly folded and overturned structures. In many places the section of rock is broken by faults along which the units have been displaced toward the northwest. Exposure of these thrust faults is more common in the Southern than in the Central Appalachians.

The Northern Appalachians consist of several subdivisions which are in some ways similar to those farther south. The Blue Ridge terminates to the north in the South Mountain fold in Maryland, but the folded belt of Paleozoic rocks on the west side of the Blue Ridge continues through Pennsylvania into its northern counterpart, which runs first on the western side of the *New Jersey Highlands*, then up the Hudson River due north through the Champlain Valley, and finally as a much broader belt on the eastern side of the St. Lawrence River. Similar rocks appear in the western part of Newfoundland and extend into the North Atlantic Ocean. Bedrock of New England, New Brunswick, Nova Scotia, and eastern Newfoundland are northern equivalents of the igneous and metamorphic rocks of the Piedmont.

Igneous and Metamorphic Rocks of the Appalachians

METAMORPHIC COMPLEXES ARE FOUND IN Newfoundland, New England–New Brunswick–Nova Scotia areas, and in the Piedmont. Similar complexes are assumed to lie buried under at least part of the Atlantic and Gulf Coastal Plain. A number of special problems are encountered in working out the history of such metamorphic complexes. Exposures are generally poor and discontinuous, particularly in areas where thick soil is developed. Metamorphic rocks do not often contain recognizable fossils even if the units were originally fossiliferous; this makes correlation with fossils impossible or at best unlikely. A third problem involves the origin of gneisses. Large areas of the world's metamorphic provinces are composed of gneisses of granitic composition. These have been interpreted as intrusives by some workers, as metamorphosed sedimentary rocks by others. Methods are now available by which the two may be distinguished, but much work remains to be done before all of the relations will be known. One of the chief means of making correlations within metamorphic and igneous rocks is through use of radioactive dates. Even here there are some serious complications. Dates obtained by analysis of one of these series depend on the time at which the radioactive mineral was formed, but dates obtained are not always completely reliable. It is possible for the process to be interrupted by metamorphism—which may bring about recrystallization and thereby "reset the radioactive clocks."

Piedmont and Blue Ridge

PRECAMBRIAN ROCKS are exposed in a long, relatively narrow belt in the Blue Ridge Mountains (Fig. 30–5). In the Great Smoky Mountains these include a thick section of clastic sedimentary rocks, mainly the Ocoll series. Precambrian crystalline rocks of a wide variety (granites, gneisses, metamorphosed basalt lava flows, and schists) are common. Radioactive dates indicate two periods of thermal activity, one about 1,130 million years ago and another between 800–900 million years ago. The remainder of the crystalline rocks of the Piedmont are now thought to be Paleozoic in age.

Most prominent of the metamorphic rocks is schist, which contains metavolcanic rocks (partly metamorphosed volcanic rocks) in places. While the age of these schists is still somewhat uncertain, it seems increasingly likely that they are Early Paleozoic in age and thus equivalents of sedimentary sequences of the Valley and Ridge region. The grade of metamorphism (the degree generally reflecting temperature and pressure conditions) increases to the southeast from the Blue Ridge, reaching a peak in the central portion of the Piedmont. This may well correspond to the central core of the Appalachian geosyncline. Southeast of this line, rock masses have been less metamorphosed and less deformed. This zone is represented best by slates, graywackes, and volcanics of the *Carolina Slate Belt*. A few metamorphic rocks have established Paleozoic age. *Arvonia* and *Quantico Slate Belts* of Virginia contain Ordovician fossils (they lie unconformably on older slates). In addition there are several belts of metamorphic rocks of a lower grade of metamorphism than those surrounding them, indicating that they were formed after an earlier metamorphic event.

Batholithic intrusions of granitic rocks are known in the Piedmont. These are so widespread that many geologists think that metamorphism of the Piedmont is due to intrusion of these bodies. These intrusives are now established as also being Paleozoic in age (Devonian and Carboniferous).

New England Crystalline Complex

PRECAMBRIAN IGNEOUS and metamorphic rocks have large surface exposures in the New Jersey Highlands and in the Green Mountains. Smaller areas of outcrop occur on Cape Breton Island. A section of Precambrian slates, graywackes, and sandstones nearly six miles thick

makes up eastern Nova Scotia. Similar Precambrian sections occur in Newfoundland.

With the exception of a few basins, such as the Boston and Narragansett basins, where late Paleozoic sediments are found, and the Connecticut River valley where Triassic sediments cover older rocks, most of New England is composed of crystalline rocks. Four major series of igneous intrusions have been described:

> White Mountain magma series
>   (youngest, possibly Triassic)
> New Hampshire magma series
>   (Late Devonian–Early Mississippian age)
> Oliverian magma series
>   (probably Mid-Late Devonian age)
> Highlandcroft magma series
>   (probably Late Ordovician)

That these intrusions were quite extensive is indicated on the map (Fig. 30–6).[3] Intrusion of magma undoubtedly was a contributing factor in metamorphism of older sedimentary country rocks. Metamorphism can be shown to become more intense toward contacts of these intrusions. Of the intrusive series, the New Hampshire series appears to have played the most important role in bringing about alteration.

Among metamorphic rocks one series in New Hampshire is particularly important. It consisted originally of some 8,000 feet of limestone and shale and 4,000 feet of volcanics, all of which was deposited in the Ordovician in what is called the *New Hampshire eugeosyncline*. Another thick sequence of more than 10,000 feet of sandstone, shale, and volcanic material was deposited during the Early Devonian.

Ultrabasic Intrusives

THOUGH THEY ARE of small outcrop extent, a large number of bodies of ultrabasic rocks have been found in the Appalachians. These bodies are often altered to serpentine, but where unaltered they are dunite (all olivine), peridotite, or other rocks made up largely of iron

[3] See geologic map of northeastern U. S. at end of book.

and magnesium-rich silicates. They form well-defined linear zones (Fig. 30–7) which parallel belts of crystalline rocks. The best defined of the two parallel belts of ultrabasics is on the western side. Harry Hess has interpreted these belts, where they appear in the Appalachians and other highly deformed mountain belts, as lying close to the axis of the orogenic belt and as defining the core zone of the orogenic belt.

History of the Appalachian Sedimentary Provinces

STRATIGRAPHICALLY ABOVE THE IGNEOUS and metamorphic rocks of the Blue Ridge and below the first fossil-bearing sandstones of Cambrian age there lies an unfossiliferous sequence composed of sandstones, shales, graywackes, silts, conglomerates, layers of volcanic ash, and metamorphosed basalt flows. Most of these clastic sediments represent erosion products from land. Their coarse texture suggests that the land from which they were derived stood not far from where they were deposited. These thick sequences make up a large part of the Smoky

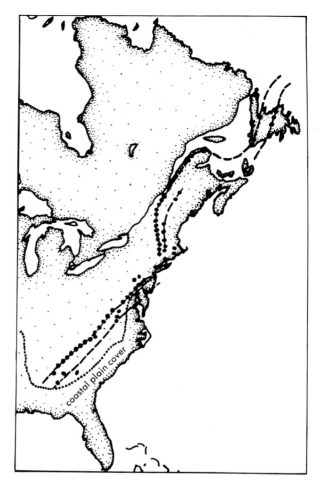

FIG. 30–7. / *Ultramafic intrusive belts in the Appalachians. (After H. H. Hess).*

Mountains. They indicate that the Late Precambrian or earliest Cambrian time was one of volcanism and erosion from a high mountainous area located southeast of the modern Appalachians.

The first Cambrian rocks are identified by the occurrence of recognizable fossil remains. The lowest unit is a massive, thick sequence of sandstones and quartzites. These sands, like those below them, contain ripple marks, cross-bedding, and other features which identify them as sediments deposited in shallow water. Some

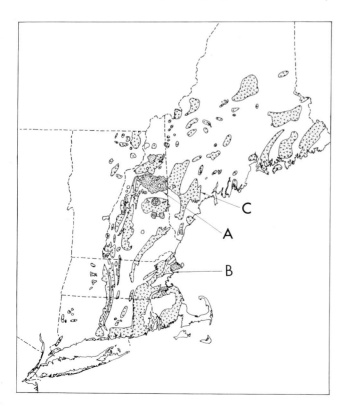

FIG. 30–6. / *New England intrusives. Pattern A indicates areas of exposure of Paleozoic and Mesozoic rocks with alkalic composition. Pattern B indicates Paleozoic mafic intrusive bodies. Pattern C indicates Paleozoic felsic intrusive bodies. These are Late Ordovician, Middle Devonian, and Late Pennsylvanian age. Some of those in eastern Massachusetts may be Precambrian. (After the Tectonic Map of the United States, American Association of Petroleum Geologists).*

FIG. 30–8. / Fossil of a graptolite. This group is extinct. It is thought to be related to the hemichordates. (Photo by courtesy of the U.S. National Museum.)

of them are so thoroughly washed and rounded that it has been suggested that they might be windblown sands redeposited as marine sedimentary rock units.

Sandy beaches and possibly sand dunes occupied the Blue Ridge region. Conditions of clastic sedimentation gave way during the Cambrian to the formation of mud and lime deposits that later became shales, slates, limestones, and dolostones. These rocks underlie the valleys of Virginia, Pennsylvania, and their continuations south toward Alabama and north—the Hudson, Champlain, and St. Lawrence valleys. Rocks of similar character were deposited up and down a belt nearly 2,000 miles long. This does not mean that exactly the same type of sediment was deposited all through this belt at any given time. Up and down the belt there were lateral variations in thickness and in sediment type. These shales and calcareous sequences, deposited in the Cambrian and Ordovician, have an estimated thickness of over 10,000 feet. Some of the limestones and shales are black and almost barren of fossils, suggesting that they were deposited under stagnant water conditions, perhaps in seas with poor oxygen circulation. Some of them contain mainly fossils of organisms that floated on the surface, graptolites (Fig. 30–8). Other parts of the sequence are light-colored beds so richly fossiliferous that they may best be thought of as reefs. Among the fossils in these beds are trilobites (Fig. 30–9), animals that groveled in the bottom sediment for their food. Since many trilobites had eyes, these sediments probably accumulated in shallow water, for light penetrates

FIG. 30–9. / Trilobites. These fossils of the species Olenoides serratus were collected from the Burgess shale which is of Middle Cambrian age. They are typical of the near perfect preservation of fossils in this famous collecting locality in British Columbia. (Photo by courtesy of U.S. National Museum.)

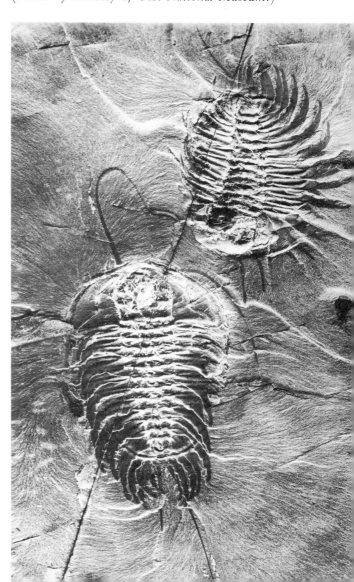

FIG. 30–10. / *Source areas of the great clastic wedges in the Appalachian geosyncline. Cambrian sources are indicated in A. Ordovician sources are depicted in B. (After P. B. King, 1959.)*

into the sea only about 600 feet and eyes are consequently useless in deeper water. There are also layers in which freshly deposited sediment was disturbed by wave action and broken up into an irregular conglomerate. During the millions of years in which these limy deposits accumulated there was some deformation in the geosyncline. Even at this early time muds flooded into the shallow sea. Most probably they came from raised portions of the geosyncline or from distant land areas. Such muds thicken toward the source, forming wedge-shaped bodies in cross section and are somewhat like huge, low alluvial fans (Fig. 30–10).

The Taconian Orogeny and Queenston Delta

TOWARD THE END OF THE ORDOVICIAN A major mountain system began to rise along the northeastern coast of North America. This, the Taconic Mountain Range, ancestor of the present-day Taconic Mountains of western Massachusetts and Vermont, may have resembled the modern Alps. Most evidence of this great upheaval is found in New England and farther north in eastern Canada. The sedimentary rocks of the geosyncline were thrusted and folded toward the continental interior. Before it started to rise, North America was probably more nearly a featureless continent than it ever has been since. Most of it was covered by shallow seas at that time, but as mountains rose in the east sediments were eroded and transported off into these seas and a huge deltaic deposit, the Queenston Delta, was built across the eastern United States.

The classic area for the study of the Taconian orogeny is illustrated in Fig. 30–16. Sedimentary rock units that had been deposited in seas of the Cambrian and earlier Ordovician were involved in the diastrophism. These are now exposed in a narrow belt extending down the Hudson Valley and southwestward.

The most prominent structures of the Taconian orogeny are extensive thrust sheets. Several large sheets of Cambrian and Ordovician rocks were thrust westward and lie on top of younger formations. Some sheets are now isolated from the area from which they came and are completely surrounded by younger formations. Such a mass, lying on younger strata and separated from other strata of the same age, is called a *klippe*.

The Queenston Delta

As soon as mountains began to be uplifted in eastern North America they were subjected to increased erosion, and erosion products were carried out into the seas that lay on either side of the mountains. Those that were carried

FIG. 30–11. / *Geologic map of Silurian and Devonian exposures in the northern United States. The exposures of Devonian strata here are the most extensive in the United States. Many of the units are richly fossiliferous. The Catskill Mountains are composed largely of debris eroded from a mountain range which stood along the eastern coast during the Middle Devonian. The debris was deposited in a large delta, part of which is still preserved as the now deeply dissected Catskill Mountains. (After the Geologic Map of the United States.)*

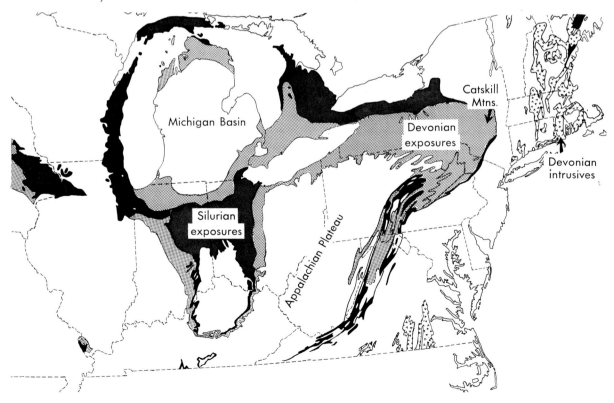

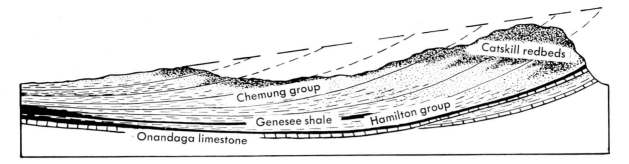

FIG. 30–12. / *Cross section across the Catskill Mountains. Notice how the units grade into one another. It was once thought that each unit was of a different age from the others. More detailed study has shown that they were laid down almost simultaneously.*

to the west and deposited are still preserved in the eastern United States. These deltaic deposits began to be built toward the end of the Middle Ordovician. At that time sedimentation in the eastern United States changed from predominantly limestone, as it had been throughout most of the earlier part of the Ordovician, to shales and clastic sediments. By the start of the Late Ordovician, muds were being distributed over most of the sea floor in the eastern seaways. The source lay to the east in the mobile belt situated in parts of eastern New England, eastern New Jersey, and on the continental shelf farther south. Muds derived from this land were spread westward. Black muds were formed east of the western edge of the present-day Appalachian Plateau, and limestones were formed beyond, over the interior of the continent.

Through the Late Ordovician, sediments in the east became increasingly coarser. Eventually coarse, clastic sands gave way to conglomerates and finally to nonmarine debris. As mountains rose, coarser sediment was spread over older, finer sediments. At first the landward part of the delta was small, but as uplift continued streams brought down more debris than the seas could distribute and the delta expanded. It forced the shoreline to retreat westward eventually as far as the Niagara River.

In the following period the land areas were eroded. Most of the rocks that comprise the Silurian system (Fig. 30–11) are clastic and resemble the Cambrian clastic sequence in composition and in that they were deposited in

shallow water. In some places in the geosyncline these Silurian clastics lie only a few miles horizontally from outcrops of the Early Cambrian clastics. Thus while Silurian sediments were formed in shallow water, as indicated by ripple marks and cross-bedding, the top of the Cambrian sands must have been buried at a depth very nearly equal to the thickness of the intervening limes and muds (on the order of two miles). The limes and muds are thinner to the northwest, and either nonexistent, or so highly metamorphosed that they cannot be recognized, to the east in the Piedmont.

One notable characteristic of the Silurian sands is that during the later part of the period iron compounds were deposited with sand, which eventually led to the formation between the sand grains of cement composed of the iron oxide hematite. Hematite also formed sand-shaped particles and replaced shells of marine invertebrates. In places these sands contain so much iron that they are mined for use in making steel. This hematite-cemented sand is the iron ore at Birmingham and at other places up and down the Appalachians as far north as New York.

Acadian Orogeny and Catskill Delta

THE CLASSIC AREA FOR STUDY OF THE DEvonian in the eastern United States is located just west of the Hudson River in New York.[4]

[4] See geologic map of northeastern U. S. at end of book.

The Hudson now flows through a valley of Cambrian and Ordovician limestones and shales. West of the valley rises the escarpment of the Catskill Mountains. Along this escarpment and in valleys cut into the mountains, sediments of Devonian time are beautifully exposed. These sediments, like those of the Queenston Delta, are erosional products from a high mountain range which lay east of the present Devonian outcrops. How sediments of the Catskill Mountains have survived removal by erosion in the time since the end of the Devonian, while the higher central core of the Acadian Mountains has been removed down to Cambrian-Ordovician units, is a puzzling question. This range must have been a very prominent mountain range to supply enough sediment to build a delta more than 12,000 feet thick on its flanks.

Middle Devonian rock units give the first indication of the uplift in the Acadian Mountains which culminated later in the Devonian, at which time the Catskill Delta was formed. The following, based on the work of Dr. George H. Chadwick (New York State Museum Bulletin 336) outlines the development of thought on the nature of the Catskill Delta.

It was formerly supposed that the Upper Devonian strata of New York consisted of four successive formations each with a characteristic lithology and fauna or flora. These are the Genesee, a black shale; the Portage, an olive shale containing thin sandstone layers; the Chemung, a unit of sandy shales and sandstones; and the Catskill formation, composed of red shales and interbedded sandstones. A unit of white sandstone and conglomerate, the Pocono formation, was thought to lie over the above strata. In some places these five units can be seen in succession one above the other, but in other localities each can be seen to grade laterally into one of the others. After much field work and long years of disagreement it was finally established that all five of these types of sediments were laid down contemporaneously on a large alluvial fan and its deltaic extension into the shallow sea that covered the eastern interior United States. The white sands and conglomerates, the Pocono formation, were deposited high in the alluvial fan. The red muds that were washed down from the high parts of the fan covered the lower slopes of sand, forming the Catskill beds. Debris that was carried into the marine waters soon lost its red color as a result of reduction in the shallow warm waters of the littoral zone in which the Chemung formation was formed. The finest debris remained in suspension and was carried farther westward into deeper waters where it was deposited as the Portage formation. Far out where the main source of sediment was organic material, the Genesee formation, a limestone, was formed.

The apparent superposition of these deposits was brought about by long-continued uplift in the Acadian Mountains and consequent building westward of the alluvial fan and delta. As the delta built westward each zone or facies of sediment overlapped the one next to it. Eventually the Pocono was being deposited over the first-formed Genesee.

Carboniferous History

MISSISSIPPIAN UNITS are exposed mainly on the western edge of the folded belt and in the Appalachian Plateau. Sections are thick, indicating a continuation of the subsidence of the geosyncline and of the long period of sediment accumulation that started in the Precambrian. Thicknesses in the more complete sections are in excess of 6,000 feet in eastern Tennessee and nearly 4,000 feet in Virginia–West Virginia, Maryland, and Pennsylvania. The bulk of the sediment is shale, but there are interbedded sandstone and limestones (some up to 800 feet thick are known in the Central Appalachians). Coal is also found interbedded with the sands and shales. Coal forms in swamps; fossils of plant matter are abundantly preserved in coal deposits of the Mississippian and Pennsylvanian. Marine fossils in limestones interbedded with coal indicate that these particular swamps were located close to sea level. There were fluctuations in level of the land—a sort of gentle warping of the vast region of the Appalachian Plateau and the eastern part of the continental platform. Cyclic sedimentation giving rise to the development of cyclothems (Fig. 30–13) continued through the Pennsylvanian. The chief difference between Mississippian and Pennsylvanian sequences lies in increased amounts of coal and in predominance of sandstone over

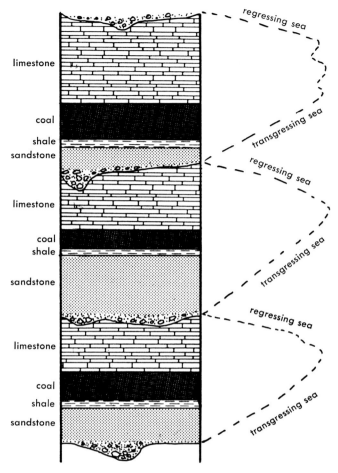

limestone

coal

shale
sandstone

limestone

coal
shale

sandstone

limestone

coal
shale

sandstone

regressing sea

transgressing sea

regressing sea

transgressing sea

regressing sea

transgressing sea

FIG. 30–13. / *Cyclothems, depicted in this illustration of rhythmic sedimentation. Seas slowly transgressed and retreated from the shallow swampy continental interior, giving rise to systematic variations in the type of sediment forming. Starting with the erosion surface at the bottom, three complete cycles are shown. During the first part of the cycle continental deposits of conglomerate, sands, and muds cover the lowland regions. When this land is close to sea level, swamps form in which plant growth is abundant. The plant remains form a layer of peat which is covered by the first strata, a shale containing marine fossils. As the water becomes deeper some limestone becomes mixed with the shale and finally limestones deposited far from shore are laid down. These often contain fusulinids. When the sea begins to recede the character of the sediments change again back toward shaly limestone and shale. Then comes the next unconformity. During the interval of erosion part of the last shale and limestones may be removed. When the seas begin to advance again the cycle is repeated.*

shale in the Pennsylvanian units. Pennsylvanian sequences alone amounted to over 5,000 feet of sediment in West Virginia.

Only a small area of the eastern United States contains any Permian rocks. These are shales and limestones found in Ohio and West Virginia. Erosion removed any other Permian rocks that may have been laid down there or elsewhere in the eastern United States. The nearest remaining outcrops are found in Kansas. This erosion took place following the last of the major episodes of folding in the Appalachians.

Appalachian Orogeny

THICK SEDIMENTARY SECTIONS OF PALE-ozoic units, which had been deposited within the southern part of the Appalachian geosynclinal belt, were strongly uplifted, folded, and faulted during Late Paleozoic deformation. Sediments that were deposited in the eugeosynclinal belt were altered by metamorphism and overlain by younger Mesozoic and Cenozoic sediments in the Coastal Plain. Northwest of the western edge of the Piedmont the exposed sedimentary rocks are strongly folded and thrust-faulted. Folds are asymmetric toward the northwest, and low-angle thrusts are inclined southeast, suggesting that the whole geosyncline was moved toward the stable continental interior from the southeast toward the northwest. Intensity of folding dies out toward the northwest across the Appalachian Highland into the Appalachian Plateau, which was only warped into a broad, open syncline. The eastern edge of this syncline makes the escarpment of the Allegheny and Cumberland Plateaus. Some of the

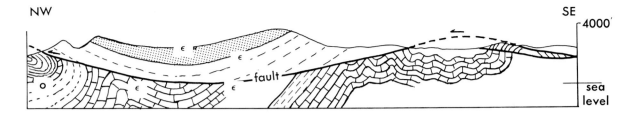

FIG. 30–14. / Section of thrust fault. A thrust fault in southern Virginia has carried a slab of Cambrian strata out to the northwest more than twenty miles over Cambrian and Ordovician strata. This sheet is one of several similar though not quite so extensive sheets in the Appalachians. This section is taken along the Virginia-Tennessee state line and shows the structure of the Pine Mountain thrust. (After P. B. King.)

structures formed during this orogeny are illustrated (Fig. 30–14).

Triassic sediments in the region are nonmarine sands, gravels, and lake deposits trapped in down-faulted troughs along the Appalachian Highlands. Even today these troughs are lower than their surroundings. They include the Connecticut Valley, the New Jersey lowlands (which are continuous with a valley in southeastern Pennsylvania), the Richmond basin, and numerous other troughs found southward into South Carolina (Fig. 30–16). These troughs subsided as sediments accumulated within them. Faulting and subsidence were accompanied by intrusion of basalt, which came up along high-angle faults that form boundaries of the troughs on at least one side and spread out into the accumulated sediments as sills. The *Palisades sill*, which forms a scarp along the western edge of the Hudson River in New Jersey, is the thickest of these sills. Deformation that accompanied the faulting and intrusion is called the *Palisades disturbance*.

Ouachita-Marathon Orogenic Belts

THERE IS MUCH EVIDENCE TO SUGGEST that the Ouachita Mountains of Arkansas and Oklahoma and the Marathon Mountains of southwestern Texas are part of the same system as the Appalachian geosyncline. In all three areas there are thick geosynclinal accumulations of Paleozoic age; all three were affected by orogeny during the later part of Paleozoic time; the pattern of deformation in all three is similar, since in each case deforming forces created asymmetric structures directed toward the continental interior; and the fossil record suggests that there were interconnected waterways between the three areas during the time when sediments were being deposited. A tectonic map (Fig. 30–18) shows the geographic relations of these belts. The Ouachitas are separated from the Appalachians and the Marathons by embayments of the Coastal Plain in which younger

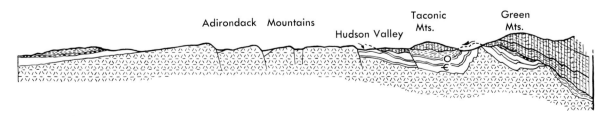

FIG. 30–15. / Cross section of the Taconic, Green, and Adirondack Mountains. The heavy line in the Taconic and Green Mountains shows low-angle thrust faults. (After Kay, 1942.)

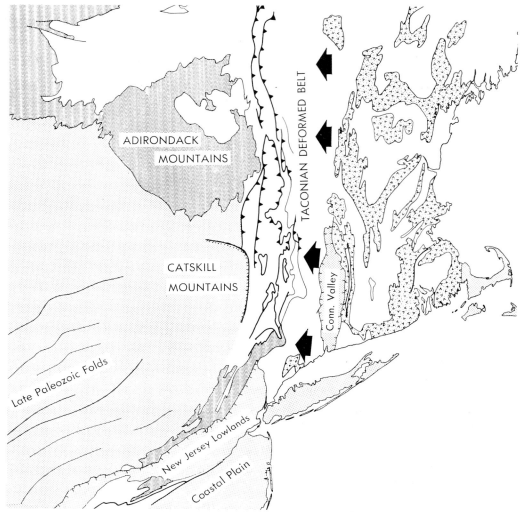

FIG. 30–16. / *Tectonic sketch map of the northeastern United States. The heavy barbed lines are thrust faults formed during the Taconian Orogeny. Within the same belt the strata are complexly folded and faulted. To the southwest in Pennsylvania fold axes of a much later deformation are found. Likewise the down-dropped fault troughs are of Triassic age. The region affected by the deformation at the end of the Ordovician lies east of the Adirondacks and extends both northeastward and southwestward. (After the Tectonic Map of the U.S.)*

sediments have been deposited unconformably on the folded and faulted orogenic belts. Trend directions of folds and faults in the Appalachians and Ouachitas provide one of the most serious problems in connecting them (Fig. 30–18). In order to connect the fold belt of the Ouachitas with the fold belts of the Appalachians it is necessary to postulate in the fold system (Fig. 30–18) a major bend of a sort that is not present elsewhere in this geosyncline; however, bends of this magnitude are present in the Alps.

Precambrian sequences are not present in either the Ouachitas or Marathons, but the Paleozoic sequences are similar to those of the Appalachians. In both areas Cambrian, Ordovician, Silurian, and Devonian sequences are only a few thousand feet thick, and in both areas they are characterized by unusual quantities of chert, such as the famous Arkansas *novaculite* (a special variety of chert). Thick layers of sediment were deposited in the Mississippian and Pennsylvanian (18,000 feet in the Ouachitas, and a similar amount in the Marathons) when

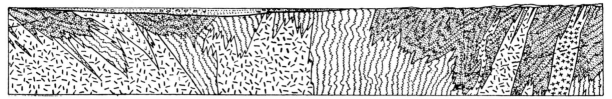

At the beginning of Triassic sedimentation

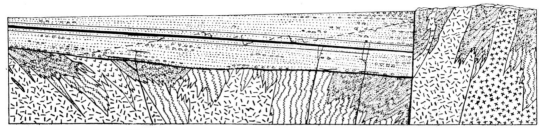

At the close of the Triassic

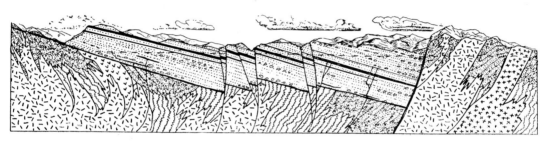

In the Jurassic

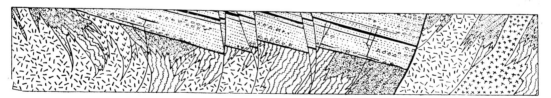

In the Cretaceous

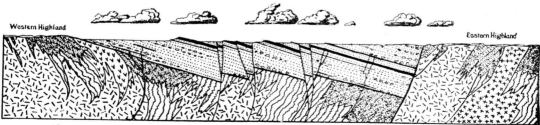

Present

FIG. 30–17. / *Evolution of the Connecticut lowland from the Late Paleozoic to the present. (After J. Barrell.)*

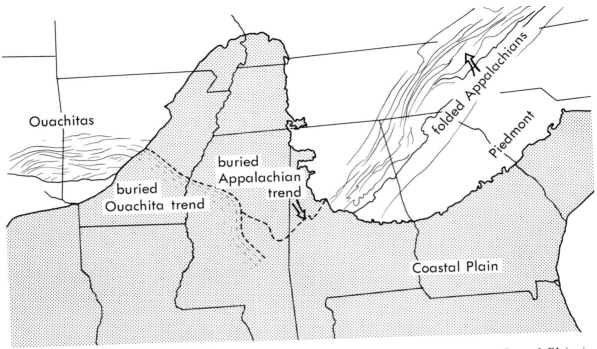

FIG. 30-18. / *Connection between the Ouachita and Appalachian Mountains. The Coastal Plain is shown covered by a dot pattern. Projected subsurface trends of the Ouachita and Appalachian folded belts are shown under the Coastal Plain sediments. The exact nature of the intersection is unknown. (After the Tectonic Map of the United States, American Association of Petroleum Geologists.)*

clastic materials flooded into the geosyncline. It is notable that thicknesses similar to this are found in the Appalachians (Mississippian strata in eastern Tennessee reach 6,000 feet in thickness, and Pennsylvanian deposits in Alabama are close to 10,000 feet thick). In all three regions the Upper Paleozoic sediments are clastics.

Deformation in the Ouachitas probably started in the Mississippian and had three phases, two in the Mississippian and the third in the Pennsylvanian. Many students of the region believe the Pennsylvanian phase to be the most important of the three. Deformation took the form of uplift, folding, and development of low-angle thrusts (Fig. 30-19).

A much smaller portion of the Marathon deformed belt is exposed. The folded and faulted Paleozoic sequences are surrounded by Cretaceous sedimentary units which have been locally removed by erosion in the center. Most

of the folding and overthrusting here seems to be Pennsylvanian in age.

Paleozoic History of Newfoundland

NEWFOUNDLAND MAY BE DIVIDED INTO four northeast-trending belts (Fig. 30-21). The eastern and western belts are made up of Precambrian metamorphic and igneous rocks. The central belts were sites of large-scale sedimentation and deformation during the Paleozoic. Exposed rock units range in age from Cambrian to Pennsylvanian, and like those of the geosyncline farther south reveal deposition of large quantities of sandstone, shale, and limestone, but in addition great quantities of lava were intruded and extruded in parts of the section, so that some sedimentary units are composed

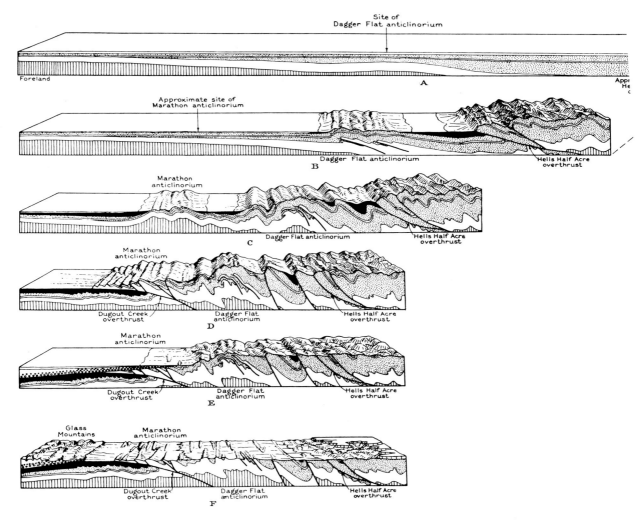

FIG. 30–19. / *Hypothetical block diagrams showing progressive development of structural features in the Marathon Region of Texas. (Modified after P. B. King.)*

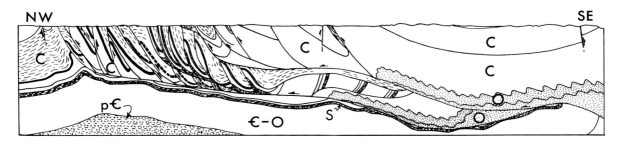

FIG. 30–20. / *Ouachita structures. Cross section near the western end of the Ouachita Mountains. The symbols are for Cambrian, Є, Ordovician, O, Silurian, S, and Carboniferous, C. (After Hendriks, 1943.)*

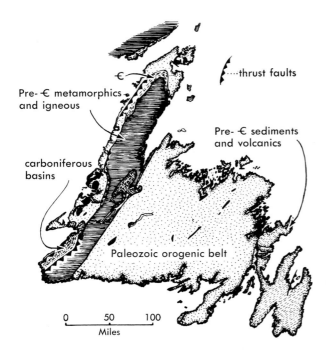

Pre- Ꞓ metamorphics
and igneous

carboniferous
basins

····thrust faults

Pre- Ꞓ sediments
and volcanics

Paleozoic orogenic belt

0   50   100
Miles

FIG. 30–21. / *Sketch map of Newfoundland. (Modified after Snelgrove, Newfoundland Geological Survey.)*

largely of volcanic ash and debris. Volcanic lava flows are found underlying the Cambrian system. The greatest quantities of volcanics are found in Ordovician sections, but they also are known in sections of Silurian, Devonian, and Mississippian age. A large part of the central portion of Newfoundland is composed of metamorphic rocks. In recent years fossil plants indicating a Devonian age have been found in some of the slates. It now seems likely that most if not all of these metamorphics are of Paleozoic age.

31

Sketch of the Physical History of Western North America

KNOWLEDGE OF THE EARLY HISTORY OF WESTERN North America is limited by the small number of exposures of rocks of this age. Large areas are covered by Cenozoic lava flows, Cenozoic basin fill, and stream deposits. Other large areas are Mesozoic batholithic intrusions. Precambrian rocks are found in high portions of the Rocky Mountains and in scattered exposures in the southwest. Paleozoic exposures are most commonly found along flanks of the mountain uplifts, as in the Rockies (Fig. 29–3). Much of what is known is obtained from drilling in the western oil-producing areas. Huge parts of the western portion of Canada and Alaska are still largely unknown.

Sufficient mapping has been done to support a twofold division of the western region during the Paleozoic. The region now known as the *Cordilleran geosyncline* consisted of a western eugeosyncline and an eastern miogeosyncline. These two can be traced through the United States and Canada into Alaska. Differences in the two are thick masses of volcanic debris and lava in the eugeosyncline and absence of such sediments and intrusives in the miogeosyncline. The eugeosyncline has a more complex history of orogeny and many of the rocks are metamor-

phosed. Early Paleozoic rocks are unknown from the eugeosynclinal portion in the United States, but in Alaska there are thick volcanic sequences of this age. It seems likely that these early sequences in the United States have been so metamorphosed that they are no longer recognizable.

Orogenies may have taken place in the eugeosyncline early in the Paleozoic, but the earliest conclusive evidence for such deformation comes in the Devonian. At that time the margin between the eugeosyncline and the miogeosyncline became active. The belt of activity extended from central Nevada through eastern Oregon and Washington into British Columbia (Fig. 31–2). Orogenic activity along it continued intermittently from the Late Devonian through the Permian. A second belt of deformation lay west of the first during the Late Paleozoic. The two may have been separated by a basin in which sediment accumulated. The entire region was affected by orogeny during the Permian. There was particularly great igneous and volcanic activity at this time, as is shown by accumulations of nearly two miles of ash at places as widely separated as California and Alaska. This belt of orogeny is known as the *Antler orogenic belt*. The miogeosynclinal

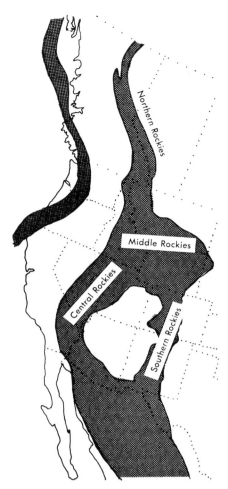

FIG. 31-2. / Belts deformed in the Laramide orogeny. (After A. J. Eardley.)

trough is characterized by a large number of basins, uplifts, and arches that shifted position from time to time during the Paleozoic. Some of these are illustrated in Fig. 31-4.

Nevadan Orogeny

THE PACIFIC BORDER OF THE UNITED States is typical of the long, narrow belt of deeply subsiding geosynclines that extended northward along the western coast of British Columbia and into Alaska. Probably similar features continued southward also. Within this belt deep subsidence, volcanic activity, and orogeny mark Jurassic history. The Nevadan orogeny occurred in the Late Jurassic. It so altered the structure, depositional patterns, and physiography that it is a natural dividing line in the history of the west. Before the Nevadan orogeny a geosynclinal belt occupied the region of western California and eastern Nevada. This subsiding trough was continuous into Oregon and Washington. It received sediments almost continuously through the Early Jurassic in California, but in Oregon there was deformation within the trough before the first Jurassic sedi-

ments were deposited. These preliminary movements of the orogeny which was to follow resulted in folding, faulting, and formation of coarse conglomerate on the flanks of uplifts. Chains of island arcs west of the geosyncline supplied volcanic debris to the trough. Volcanics are most abundant (12,000 feet thick) in California and southwestern Oregon. The lavas were extruded under water, forming pillow lavas of all types from rhyolites to basalt. Centers of volcanic activity can be recognized in places by preserved volcanic necks and unusually thick concentrations of flows and coarse agglomerates. Large masses of molten rock were

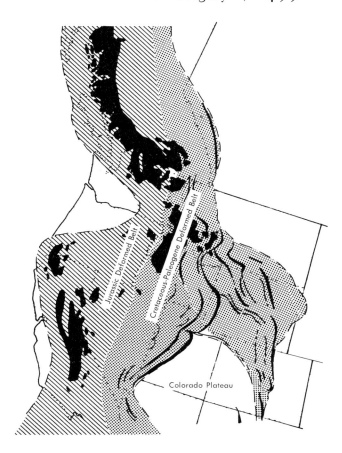

FIG. 31–3. / *Orogenic belts of the Jurassic and Cretaceous. The black areas are exposures of igneous intrusions, most of which are granitic batholiths of Jurassic age. The diagonal belt was deformed in the Nevadian orogeny while the region covered by dots was affected in the Laramide orogeny. The heavy black lines indicate the position of major folds. Note that the Laramide belt goes on either side of the Colorado Plateau. (After A. J. Eardley.)*

FIG. 31–1. / *The Sierra Nevada seen from the east. (Courtesy of U.S. Geological Survey.)*

intruded into the geosynclinal accumulations and cooled below the surface. This volcanic activity was followed by a period of relative calm in which a great thickness of muds with some greenstones and volcanic dust accumulated.

The Nevadan orogeny uplifted and violently deformed sediment that had accumulated. Rocks formed in the preceding periods of time were folded into overturned and recumbent folds. Major thrust faults moved the folded Paleozoic rocks in the western part of the geosyncline over Jurassic units on the eastern side of the belt. Contemporaneous with this deformation deep-seated igneous activity was resumed, but instead of taking the form of extensive volcanic extrusions it resulted in many intrusive bodies. The largest batholith in America, the *Sierra Nevada batholith* which makes up the core of the present-day Sierra Nevada Mountains, is one of these intrusions. Others are exposed in British Columbia. Similar intrusions in the early part of the Cretaceous now form the peninsula of Baja California.

Following the orogeny, a new geosyncline formed along the western coast in the position of the modern Coast Ranges. Most of the sediments exposed in the Coast Ranges are those deposited within this geosyncline. The source of volcanic activity that had supplied tuffs and lava flows to the pre-Nevadan geosyncline continued to exist again west of the new geosyncline. These volcanoes provided a large part of the more than 20,000 feet of sediments that went into this geosyncline. Following this, another orogeny, the *Diablan*, affected this new geosyncline. Folding, faulting, and intrusion accompanied this orogeny as it had in the Nevadan.

In the Rocky Mountain region (western Montana, Idaho, Wyoming, eastern Utah, Colorado, and New Mexico) Early and Middle Cretaceous time was characterized by irregular subsidence and uplift. Considerable thicknesses of terrigenous material were brought into the geosyncline from elevated areas to the west. At the same time the Rocky Mountain geosyncline,

FIG. 31–4. / *Sketch map of the main structural elements in the mid-western United States during the late Paleozoic.*

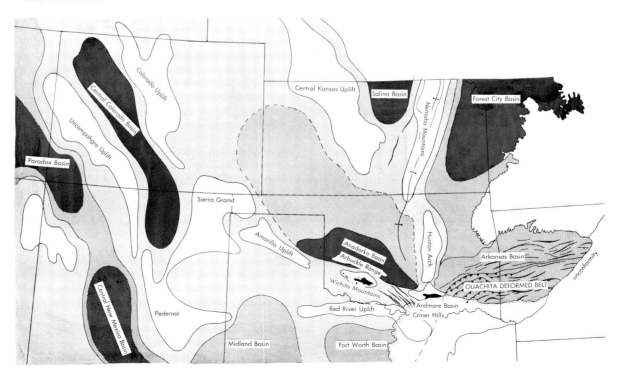

which occupied the area of the present-day Rocky Mountains, formed and collected Middle Cretaceous sediments before it was uplifted in the Late Cretaceous. Just before this uplift began, an extensive alluvial deposit of sandstone, the Dakota formation, was laid out into the Plains States. At first sediments came from west of the present Rockies, but the front of the uplifted area moved eastward until the present Rockies were elevated. The flood of debris from this uplift forced the seas to retreat and finally filled them. This orogeny, which started in the Late Cretaceous and continued on into the Cenozoic, is the *Laramide orogeny*.

Laramide Orogeny

THE LARAMIDE OROGENY WAS NOT A SINGLE uplift or compression within the crust of the earth. Most orogenies have long, complex histories. One phase of an orogeny may be the most intense part, but when sufficient data are available it is possible to demonstrate that orogeny began quietly with uplift within a geosyncline and continued through a long period of time marked by intermittent activity that uplifted, fractured, folded, faulted, severely distorted, and altered the sedimentary sequences. Igneous bodies intruded the more deformed parts of the belts, entering along deep-seated faults and fracture zones. Deep parts of the belts are metamorphosed. Structures formed during early phases of an orogeny are later distorted and altered by continued diastrophism, and, as uplift proceeds, higher portions are subjected to erosion and are beginning to be destroyed even as they form. Sediments from these uplifted areas seek a lower level, where after depositon they may in turn be deformed by a later phase of the orogeny.

The Laramide orogeny started toward the end of the Cretaceous and in places continued well into the Cenozoic. The area affected in North America may be divided into four major parts—the Northern Rockies, Middle Rockies, Southern Rockies, and Central Rockies.

Northern Rockies

THE NORTHERN ROCKIES INCLUDE eastern parts of the Canadian Rockies and their southern continuation into northern Montana. The western part of the Northern Rockies was deformed in the Nevadan orogeny of the Jurassic. The eastern part is Laramide. Rock units exposed in these rugged ranges include Late Precambrian, Paleozoic, and Mesozoic sedimentary rocks. This part of the Rocky Mountains is bounded on the east by a zone of thrust faults that have carried Paleozoic formations eastward out over the Cretaceous formations. The Lewis overthrust in northern Montana is a notable example of these thrusts. A number of remnants of these overthrust sheets, such as Chief Mountain, still re-

FIG. 31–5. / *Chief Mountain, Montana. This large block of Precambrian units has been thrust out on Cretaceous shales. The block is now completely isolated, forming a klippe. (Photo by courtesy of the Montana Highway Department.)*

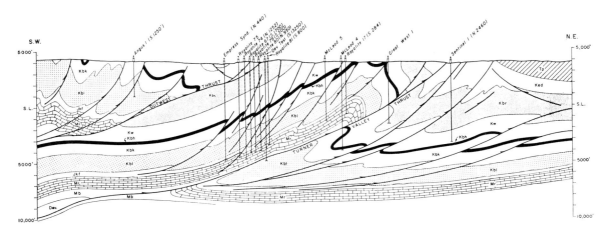

FIG. 31–6. / *Cross section across the central sector of the Turner Valley. Two large thrust faults and a number of smaller thrusts are shown. (From F. G. Fox, Bull. A.A.P.G., v. 43, 1959.)*

main (Fig. 31–5). Many thrust faults along the eastern margin exhibit what is known as *imbricate structure*; that is, a number of thrust planes, all approximately parallel, have developed. Many of these planes probably extend into a single plane of movement at depth (Fig. 31–6). There is folding in the high mountains and in Cretaceous sections along the foothills to the east. Folds in the foothills developed under the weight and northeastward movement of the high mountains.

Middle Rocky Mountains

THIS PART OF THE ROCKIES is located in south-central Montana and Wyoming.[1] It is characterized by large blocklike uplifts rather than the long folded and faulted belts found in the Northern and Central Rockies. Fig. 31–7 shows one of these big uplifts, which are separated by deep basins. Some blocks have not continued to rise since the Laramide and have been almost buried in their own debris and alluvial deposits of other nearby ranges. Most of the blocks are bounded by high-angle faults. They have risen so high that post-Laramide erosion has bared Lower Precambrian rocks on their summits. Paleozoic and Mesozoic sections of sedimentary rocks are found on the flanks. Uplift dominated movement in the Middle Rockies, while thrusting and folding controlled formation of

[1] See Geologic Map of Wyoming at end of book for one of these ranges.

structures in other parts of the Rockies. The explanation for this difference in behavior may lie in the fact that the Northern and Central Rockies had been occupied by deeply subsiding geosynclines through parts of the Paleozoic and Mesozoic. The Middle Rockies are located on a shelflike separation between these belts and the continental interior. Thinner sections of sediment covered the shelf. When diastrophism began to affect the Cordilleran geosyncline, zones of thick sediment accumulation yielded by folding and faulting; but the shelf, which was underlain by metamorphic and igneous rocks, was too strong to yield in that manner. Instead it broke along fracture and fault zones that had formed in the Precambrian. Blocks outlined by these zones of weakness moved with respect to one another.

Southern Rocky Mountains

THIS SECTION INCLUDES central Colorado and New Mexico. The uplift known as the *ancestral Rockies* was covered by Cretaceous sediments before it was uplifted as the Colorado Front Range. The Front Range is the largest single element of the Southern Rockies. It is over 200 miles long, extending almost north-south from Canyon City, Colorado, to the Laramie Range in Wyoming. Along the eastern margin this range rises abruptly from the plains. In places sedimentary units are overturned, but along most of it monoclinal dips mark the eastern edge of this large, elongate upwarp. The western edge of the Front Range is bounded by an eastward-dipping thrust fault. To the west of the Front Range three synclinal basins, called *parks*, separate the Front Range from a second elongate uplift with a Precambrian core, the Park Range. West of this second uplifted mass of Precambrian lies the central Colorado Basin. To the south, in southern Colorado and New Mexico, ranges with Precambrian cores were uplifted along high-angle faults which are locally thrust eastward.

Central Rockies

THIS PART INCLUDES deformed areas in southern Idaho, western Utah, and eastern Nevada, and continues southward into Arizona (Fig. 31–2). It is the most complex of the four divisions, and its history is more difficult to decipher because much of it was broken up by block faults in the Cenozoic. The result of this later faulting was to shift some blocks up and drop others down, making an extensive pattern of grabens and horsts. Down-dropped blocks are

FIG. 31–7. / *The Grand Tetons of northwestern Wyoming. These mountains are one of the ranges of the Middle Rocky Mountains which have been uplifted along high angle faults. This side of the range rises very abruptly from Jackson Hole. The western slope of the range is gentle. Faulting movements during the Neogene have raised the block to its present height. It has been dissected in the Pleistocene. Note the river terrace in the alluvial fill of the basin. (Photo by the author.)*

filled by alluvial debris from uplifted blocks. A second complicating factor is absence of Cretaceous sediments in the western part of the Central Rockies. Structures in this area are complicated by effects of the Jurassic Nevadan orogeny. Patterns of deformation resemble those of the Northern Rockies in that thick accumulations of sediments were complexly folded and faulted throughout the area as they were forced toward the craton to the east.

Cenozoic History of the Western United States

THE CENOZOIC HAS BEEN A TIME OF GREAT crustal activity and volcanism in western parts of the United States. Changes there have been even more dramatic and far-reaching than those of other parts of the country. Deformation is still in progress, and the freshness of lava flows in many places makes it seem probable that volcanism stopped only recently.

The region can be subdivided into a number of large provinces (Fig. 31–8). These are:

1. Coast Ranges
2. Valleys and basins (i.e., San Joaquin, Ventura, Los Angeles, and Sacramento)
3. Cascade Mountains
4. Columbia Plateau
5. Klamath Mountains
6. Sierra Nevada
7. Basin and Range Province

The Colorado Plateau and folded belts of the Laramide orogeny are located east of these provinces.

Coast Ranges

THESE MOUNTAINS BOUND the western coast of the United States. They contain thick sections of deformed Cenozoic sediments resting on several types of basement rocks, including highly altered, intruded, and metamorphosed rocks of the eugeosynclinal belt of the Nevadan orogeny. Such crystalline rocks compose the Sierra Nevada and Klamath Mountains, and

make up the Transverse and Peninsular Ranges south of Los Angeles (Fig. 31–8).

In other places basement rocks are parts of a group of formations known as the *Franciscan group*. Units of this group are highly deformed. They include graywackes, shales, cherts, limestone lenses, and interbedded basaltic lava flows. This eugeosynclinal accumulation has been cut by serpentine intrusions and partially metamorphosed to schist. The sequence is largely unfossiliferous, making it difficult to determine its age; however, it is certainly pre-Cenozoic.

During the Cenozoic thick sedimentary sections have been deposited over at least parts of these basements and have been deformed almost continuously. Stratigraphic sections contain many angular unconformities, particularly near margins of subsiding basins. There appear to be two major periods during which deformation was stronger than at other times. These were during the middle of the Miocene and about the middle of the Pleistocene. During the first of these many major folds were formed, and during the latter most of the region was brought above sea level.

California Basins

A NUMBER OF BASINS in California are closely associated with Coast Range deformation (Fig. 31–10). These include the Great Valley of California and the Los Angeles and Ventura basins. They have been rapidly deepened and filled with vast quantities of sediment in the Pliocene and Pleistocene epochs. In the Los Angeles basin there is about 40,000 feet of marine deposits, in the Ventura there is nearly 35,000 feet, and in the San Joaquin there is about 20,000 feet of marine clays, shales, and sand in the Miocene and Pliocene series, and an additional 9,000 feet of nonmarine deposits of Pleistocene age. The trend of sedimentation within these basins has been toward deposition in progressively shallower water. In the mid-Pleistocene they were steeply folded; upper Pleistocene units lie nearly flat across eroded upturned edges of older units.

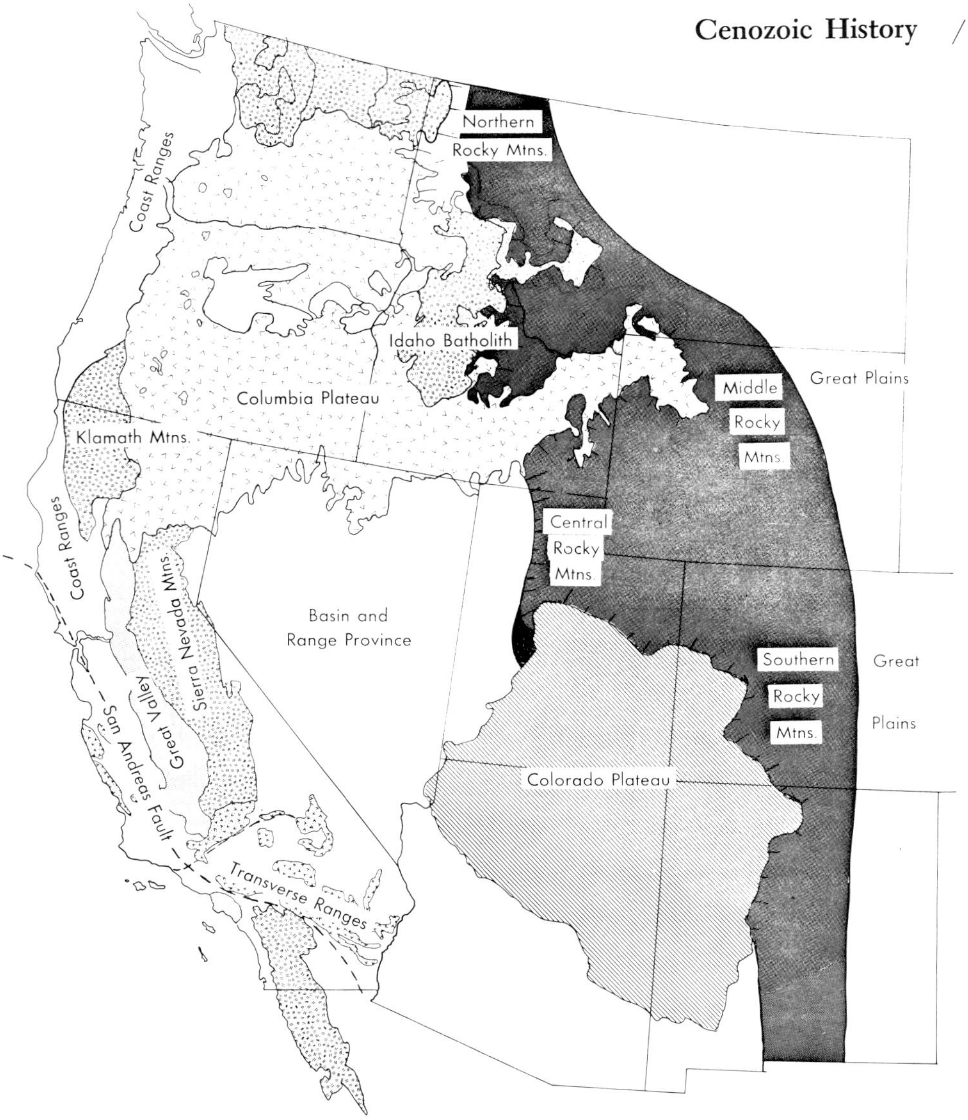

FIG. 31–8. / *Sketch map of the geologic provinces of the western United States. See the text for descriptions of the Cenozoic history of each.*

Faulting

THE SAN ANDREAS RIFT FAULT is one of a system that strikes northwestward along the coast (Fig. 31–11). Movement along it is strike-slip, the oceanward side moving northward in relation to the continent. This and the system of faults that cut across southern California have made possible shifting of blocks of the crystalline basement, such as the Transverse and Peninsular Ranges, northward along the faults. It is possible to estimate the position of the two sides of this fault system at times in the past by reconstructing strand lines (coastlines) of the period, shifting the blocks back to a position at which the strand may be traced continuously across the fault. A 65 mile shift is necessary to re-establish the position of the two sides near the end of the Miocene. The total displacement may amount to over 300 miles.

Cascade Range

THE CASCADE MOUNTAINS start near the northern border of California between the Klamath and Sierra Nevada mountains (Fig. 31–

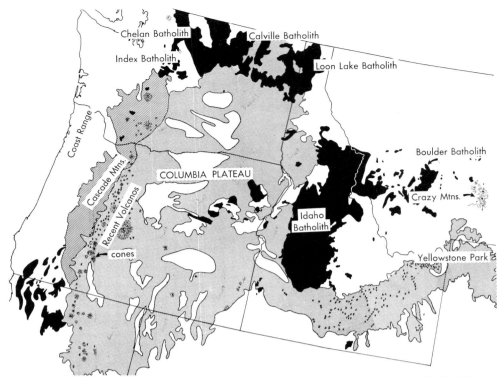

FIG. 31–9. / *Distribution of volcanic and igneous intrusions in the northwestern United States. (After the Tectonic Map of the United States.)*

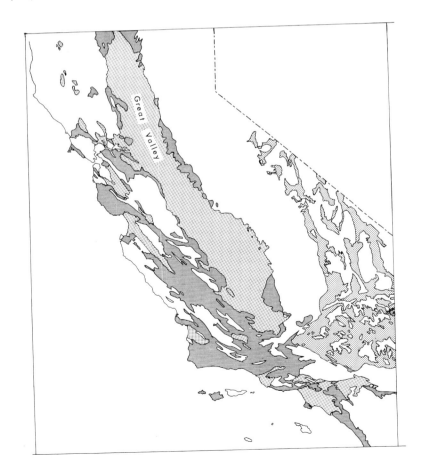

FIG. 31–10. / *Cenozoic sedimentary basins of California. The dot pattern indicates the quaternary and upper Tertiary deposits in structurally negative areas. These rocks are mainly non-marine. The areas covered by the lined pattern are Tertiary sedimentary rocks largely of marine origin. (After the U.S. Tectonic Map of the American Association of Petroleum Geologists.)*

9). They extend northward as a narrow belt through Oregon and Washington into Canada. The range is separated from the Coast Ranges by a large synclinal valley. This range, which is famous for its beautiful high and rugged mountain peaks, is composed almost entirely of volcanic rocks with an estimated volume of 25,000 cubic miles. In the northern part of the belt volcanic rocks are situated on a basement composed of crystalline rocks of the Nevadan orogenic belt, but southward we find only a thick sequence of Cenozoic igneous intrusives and extrusives. These include breccias, tuffs, mudflows, and andesite lavas. Ages of these extend over a large part of Cenozoic history, and most seem to be contemporaneous with Columbia River basalts that lie east of this belt (Eocene to Pliocene in age). The main differences in the two provinces are found in the quantity of volcanic rocks, their composition, and amounts of intruded material. The Cascades are an uplifted belt that has been the site of excessive volcanic activity. Basaltic lavas of the Columbia Plateau are uniform. Intrusions and extrusions of the Cascade Range are varied in composition, including andesites and granodiorite intrusives. These might be formed by partial melting of lower parts of the continental crust. They contain sialic material, in contrast to the Columbia Plateau basalts.

During the last stages of the Pleistocene, activity in the Cascades has been extrusion of great quantities of lava, ash, and construction of a series of large composite cones. These cones include Mt. Baker, Mt. Rainier, Mt. Hood (Fig. 31–13), Mt. Lassen, Mt. Shasta, Mt. Washington, Mt. Jefferson, and Mt. Mazama. The last of these, Mt. Mazama, exploded, blowing the top of the mountain off, then other parts of it subsided to form the caldera in which Crater Lake is found (Fig. 31–12).

FIG. 31–13. / *Mt. Hood. This mountain is one of the Neogene volcanoes which stand upon the axis of the Cascade Range. (Photo by the author.)*

FIG. 31–12. / *Profile through Crater Lake including the Watchman, Wizard Island, and Mount Scott. (From F. E. Matthes, U.S. Geological Survey, Crater Lake Quadrangle.)*

Columbia Plateau

THE COLUMBIA PLATEAU is directly east of the Cascade Mountains (Fig. 31–8). It includes most of southeast Washington, northeast Oregon, and parts of northern California and Idaho. The region has been the site of volcanic activity during most of the Cenozoic. The first outpourings of lava began in the westernmost parts of the region. These older lavas are largely covered by later flows and deposits. The main flood of basalt came in the Miocene. Flows cover about 100,000 square miles with an estimated 35,000 cubic miles of basalt. There are many flows, one on the other, aggregating thicknesses of as much as 5,000 feet, with some individual flows several hundred feet thick. All of the flows are nearly the same in composition.

Miocene eruptions came from a number of large fissures located in southeastern Washington and northeastern Oregon. The lava must have been very fluid, for individual flows can be traced over great distances and tops of individual flows are nearly flat over large areas. As this tremendous quantity of lava poured out the surface warped downward into the vacated space below, creating a basin-shaped regional structure.

Activity continued into the Pliocene and Pleistocene, with flows pouring forth in the eastern part of the province, covering the Snake River plain and Yellowstone Park region. The province is a plateau; however, parts of it are folded and faulted. In the southeastern edge there are broad warps and folds that parallel the direction of Jurassic deformation. Along the southern edge the margins are involved in the faulting of the Basin and Range province.

Basin and Range Province

THIS PROVINCE, characterized by high mountain ranges separated by broad, nearly flat basins (Fig. 31–14), is found in a wide belt from southern Oregon, covering all of Nevada and parts of Utah, Arizona, New Mexico, southern California, and Mexico. Almost all of this region is arid or semiarid. Included in the province is the Great Basin, an area of internal drainage which has no rivers flowing out of it into the ocean. Rainfall is sparse, since most of it falls in ranges along the western coast before it reaches this region.

In the Early Cenozoic, following the Nevadan orogeny, this region was eroded down to a broad, low surface. Similar erosion surfaces were produced farther east in the area that had been uplifted in the Laramide orogeny. Fossils of deciduous trees have been found in Miocene sediments at an elevation of 9,000 feet on the sides of the Sierra Nevada. These plants do not grow at elevations above 2,500 feet, so this represents a maximum elevation for the highest of the ranges of this province at the beginning of the Miocene.

Early in the Miocene, lavas and tuffs erupted and flowed out across the western and northern parts of the province. This was the period in which so much volcanic activity took place in the Cascades and the Columbia Plateau. Following this volcanism, faulting and tilting of some of the blocks began. The Sierra Nevada began to be tilted up and may have risen several thousand feet at this time. One reason for believing this is the presence in Nevada of a Pliocene flora that now characterizes savannas and grasslands, where rainfall is on the order of

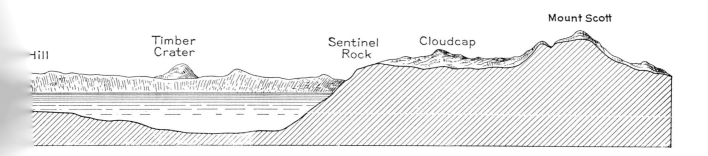

15 inches per year. Thus, by Pliocene time, western ranges had risen high enough to intercept a large part of the moisture coming inland from the ocean.

During the Pliocene and Pleistocene block faulting continued and accentuated the region's topographic relief as block mountains were uplifted in relation to the adjacent basins. Some of these basins moved downward. Death Valley is one such example. Here sediments of marine origin are depressed over 200 feet below sea level. Normal faulting in these later periods has created graben and horst structures. Although the topography is similar throughout the province, the topography does not reflect structures that existed before normal faulting occurred. At least three very different types of older structures are found in the block mountains—those that were part of the geosynclinal accumulation deformed in the Nevadan orogeny; deposits that were laid down on the continental shelf and have been only slightly deformed; and those that are part of the Columbia Plateau province.

Margins of many ranges in the Basin and Range province are faults. Along some, recent faulting has produced fresh scarps. Along a few ranges old structures parallel mountainsides and may simply have been etched out by erosion following general upwarping of the region that occurred during the Cenozoic. Still other ranges are bounded by scarps that most likely have been produced by retreat of original fault scarps, which is typical of erosion in arid and semiarid climates.

FIG. 31–14. / *A mountain range of the Basin and Range province. The mountain peaks rise sharply above the gently sloping alluvial fans at the base. Many such ranges have bordering high angle faults along which they have been uplifted. The flat surfaces extending out into the basins are pediments close to the mountains. Internal drainage characterized this region; playa lakes are often found in the center of the basins. This view is in southern Nevada. (Photo by the author.)*

32

The Coastal Plain

THE COASTAL PLAIN OF THE UNITED STATES extends from Cape Cod through New York City, west of Chesapeake Bay, and south along the eastern edge of the Piedmont Province to Alabama. In Alabama Coastal Plain sediments lie over the folded belt of the Appalachians, where the edge of these younger sediments bends northwest. A major embayment follows the Mississippi River Valley as far north as Paducah, Kentucky. On the western side of the embayment Paleozoic folded mountain belts of the Ouachitas are partially covered. The margin then follows a southwest path around the Llano Mountains of Texas and into Mexico (Fig. 32-7).

On the continent side Coastal Plain sediments lie with unconformity on rock units and structures of a great many ages and types.[1] On the seaward and Gulf side these sediments may be traced out under the continental shelves and pass into the somewhat obscure transition zone between continental and oceanic segments of the crust.

The Coastal Plain is a physiographic province distinct from surrounding provinces, although it includes a wide variety of physio-

[1] See Geologic Map of the U. S. at end of book.

graphic features. It is characterized by low, flat to rolling topography, beaches, swamps, low-gradient rivers, coastal terraces, deltas, and lagoons. Where Coastal Plain sediments lie unconformably on rocks that are resistant to erosion, as along the margin of the Piedmont, waterfalls and rapids are found in the rivers. These mark the inner extent of navigation on many major rivers in the east. The line of these rapids and falls is called the *fall line*.

Similarities in topography through the Coastal Plains reflect certain similarities in geology of underlying rock types, structure, and history. The unconformity around the Coastal Plain is one of the most prominent unconformities in the world. The oldest rock sequences in the Coastal Plain are of Cretaceous age. Along most of the margin these rest on Paleozoic units. In a few places they lie on Triassic units. So the time separation between Coastal Plain units and adjacent units ranges from 25 million to more than a billion years. A series of major events took place between formation of these units—final orogenies of the Appalachian, Ouachita, and Marathon geosynclines.

Major effects of the Late Paleozoic orogenies were over in the Triassic, but at no place in the

Coastal Plain are rocks of the following period, Jurassic, exposed. No Jurassic is known along the Atlantic seaboard even at depth, but in the Gulf Coast deep drilling has revealed Jurassic sedimentary rocks as far north as southern Arkansas. These units include salt and gypsum, possibly deposited in a shallow sea with restricted circulation. Geophysical data indicate that these same units thicken greatly to the south.

The Cretaceous marked a great advance of seas into eastern parts of North America. The surface over which the seas advanced is exposed at the continental margin of the Coastal Plain, and although few wells have been drilled to this surface a number of seismic profiles have been made across it (Fig. 8–4). In profiles it appears that the surface was characterized by slight topography. There was certainly sufficient time for erosion by streams and mass wasting to have reduced the once high Appalachian Mountains to an erosion surface of low relief. Almost certainly the sea contributed further to leveling the land by wave action as the seacoasts gradually moved farther and farther inland. It has been suggested by some students of Appalachian geomorphology that this sea actually covered a very large part of the region now known as the Appalachian Highlands. The principal reason for this contention is that peaks and tops of ridges in the southern and central Appalachians are so nearly equal in altitude that they may be visualized as representing remnants of a regional erosion surface. If Cretaceous seas advanced over this region it was, of course, much lower than it is now, and the advance was followed by regional uplifting. Unfortunately for those who support this view, no remnants of Cretaceous sediments of any type have been found far from the present-day outcrop belt.

Pattern of Sedimentation in the Coastal Plain

MOST OF THE ROCKS ARE UNCONSOLIDATED or semiconsolidated sediments. They represent a wide variety of sediment types, reflecting varia-tions in sedimentary environments. During the Mesozoic and Cenozoic the position of the coastline shifted. Some of these shifts were of great extent. In the *Mississippi Embayment* and in Virginia and North Carolina, Tertiary sediments overlie Cretaceous units along the margin of the Coastal Plain. These movements of the coast and changes in the shape of the seas, together with localized upwarping and downwarping, have created a great number of unconformities and disconformities in the sequences. Orogenic-type folding is absent from the Coastal Plain, but there has been considerable differential warping superimposed on a broader pattern of subsidence and deposition. Accumulations of geosynclinal proportions are now known in the area of the continental shelf and Coastal Plain from Newfoundland to Honduras. Thickness measurements show that the centers of maximum deposition have shifted. Since the Jurassic, the zone of maximum deposition has tended to shift seaward along the Gulf Coast (Fig. 32–1). Sedimentary units are generally thicker toward the ocean and the Gulf throughout the Coastal Plain.

Some sedimentary units may be considered regional in extent, but there are enough data from deep wells to reveal that the over-all picture of units in the Gulf is one of complex interfingering of sedimentary facies. Patterns like those illustrated in Fig. 32–5 are common in many of the rock units.

Gulf of Mexico Geosyncline

THE CENOZOIC HISTORY OF THE GULF OF Mexico and surrounding coastal plains is of particular interest because sedimentary deposits there have become sites for accumulation of vast stores of petroleum. This is one of the most prolific oil producing areas of North America. The Gulf is also the site of a modern-day geosynclinal accumulation of sediments.

The pattern of sediment distribution and the structures of the Gulf are relatively simple (Fig. 32–7). Outcrop patterns in the Coastal Province reveal a sequence of Mesozoic and

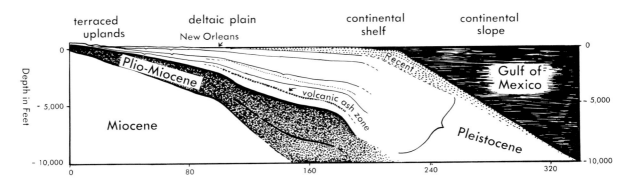

FIG. 32–1. / Cross section across the Gulf Coastal Plain through New Orleans (After McFarland.)

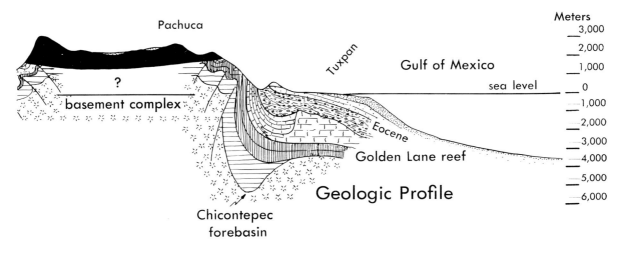

FIG. 32–2. / Cross section of the southern margin of the Gulf of Mexico. (After Woolard and Caldera, 1956.)

Cenozoic sediments exposed in successive belts. Progressively younger beds are exposed toward the coast. These sediments dip toward the Gulf, and most of them are wedges that thicken toward the Gulf. Seas transgressed the continental borders near the beginning of the Cenozoic, and since that time the broad pattern of deposition is that of a regressing sea.

Most important feature of the history of the Gulf is development of the Gulf Coast geosyncline. The axis of this deeply subsiding belt trends almost east–west and extends parallel to the edge of the continental shelf along the northern side of the Gulf. Parts of the section in this geosyncline are well-known from deep drilling in exploration for oil. Geophysical studies have provided information about deeper portions within the crust. In general, toward the axis of the geosyncline Cenozoic sediments of this region change from dominantly nonmarine

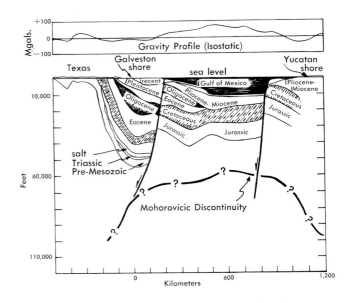

FIG. 32–3. / Generalized cross section and gravity profile across the Gulf of Mexico. (After Ewing et al., 1955.)

sands and shales to marine facies. Among the most prominent of these are deltaic deposits of the Mississippi River. These and other older deltaic deposits are lens-shaped bodies that thin both toward the continent and toward deeper parts of the Gulf. In cross section the entire sedimentary sequence in the Gulf geosyncline is lens-shaped (Fig. 32–1). Units thin northward and thicken southward to the edge of the shelf. Then they thin out again to the south. Deepest subsidence has taken place from the northern coast out to the edge of the continental shelf. In this region alone, Cenozoic sediments reach to a depth of about 45,000 feet. One trend that is apparent from the history of the geosyncline is that the position of greatest accumulation of sediments has tended to shift toward the Gulf.

The center of the Gulf is the deepest part, known as the Sigsbee Deep. It is an abyssal plain at approximately 12,000 feet depth. Below this plain the top of the Mesozoic section is buried under about 10,000 feet of sediment, and the crystalline basement, which is presumably Paleozoic, is at a depth of nearly 32,000 feet.

Very little is known about the southern side of the Gulf. We do know that the sea floor rises sharply from the Sigsbee Deep up to the continental shelf and that there is approximately 4,500 feet of sediment between the surface and the top of the Cretaceous units. It is another 3,500 feet to the top of the crystalline basement. Thus on the southern side of the Gulf there is apparently a large fault along which the Gulf floor has been dropped downward in relation to the continent.

Oil in the Gulf Coast has been concentrated in a variety of structures, of which salt domes are among the most important. In addition there are major fault zones that parallel the outcrop patterns, notably the Balcones Zone. Most of these zones are located inland 200 or even 300 miles from the coast. Faults in these zones are all normal faults. The Gulf side has generally moved down in relation to continental masses around the Gulf. Other notable structures are nonorogenic folds, domes, and basins. Many of these trend or are aligned almost perpendicular to the coast (Fig. 32–7).

Gulf Coast Salt Domes

TWO BELTS OF SALT DOMES CAN BE RECOGnized in the Gulf Coast region of the United States. Both belts are essentially parallel to the coast. One runs close to the coast, and the other

FIG. 32–4. / *Cross section of the Coastal Plain drawn through Memphis and Natchez. (After Fisk, 1944.)*

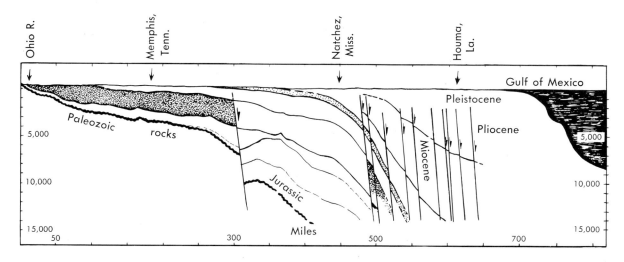

is about 200–300 miles inland. Combined, they contain over 200 salt plugs, and there is every reason to expect that a good many more will be found in sediments underlying shallow waters of the Gulf of Mexico.

A typical salt dome is a mile in diameter and about 20,000 feet or more in height. Many of them appear to have the shape of a carrot, with the top being broadened. Some taper off at depth, but others are nearly cylindrical all the way down to the source bed of salt, which is believed to be within the Jurassic or Cretaceous sedimentary sequences now deeply buried

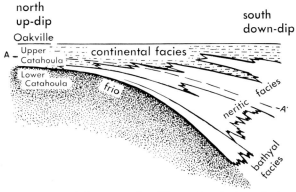

FIG. 32–5. / *Cross section illustrating facies relations in the Gulf Coastal Plain. (After Lowman, 1949.)*

FIG. 32–6. / *Geologic sketch map of the Gulf of Mexico coastal plains in the United States, Mexico, and Latin America. (After the Geological Map of North America.)*

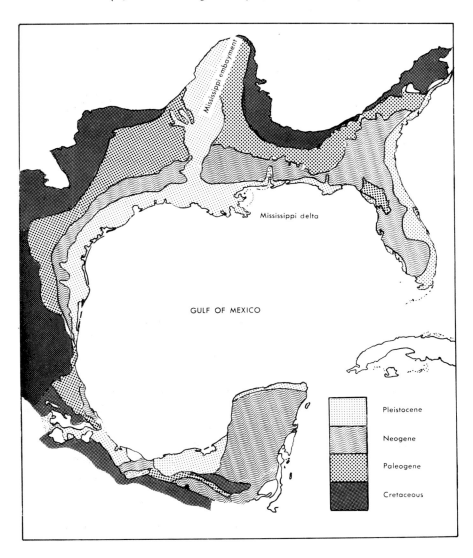

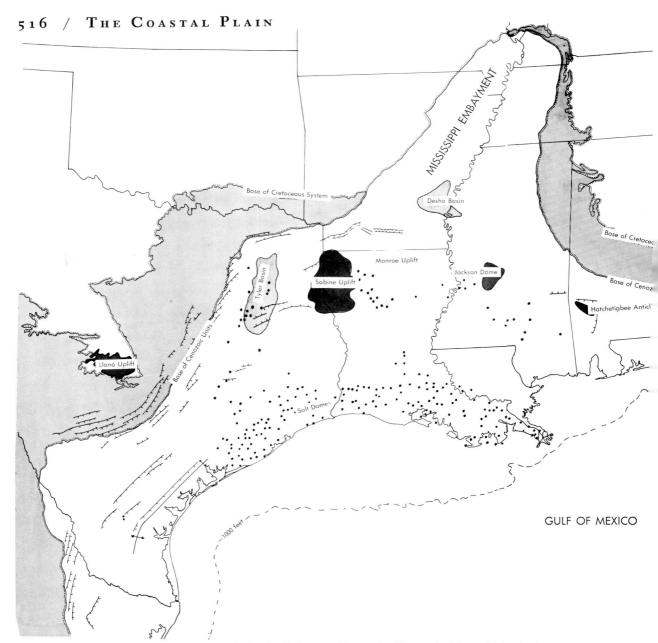

FIG. 32-7. / *Tectonic sketch of map of the Gulf Coast.* (*From the Tectonic Map of North America.*)

under Cenozoic sediments. Jurassic beds that have been reached by drilling in southern Arkansas contain salt, gypsum, and anhydrite, and appear to be a logical source for the salt. Because the source beds are so deep they have not been penetrated by wells drilled in the southern part of the Coastal Plain, even though some of these have been drilled over 20,000 feet deep. The main body of a salt plug is coarse crystalline salt. The top of the dome is covered by a cap, which contains gypsum, anhydrite, and brecciated sediments. Cap rock often contains sulfur, concentrated in sufficient quantities to make it commercially important.

Structures within the salt show that the salt has been strongly deformed. Internal crinkles and folds are nearly vertical and give the appearance of a mass squeezed upward through a constricted opening. These folds result from solid flowage. The salt recrystallized as it was forced upward, thus flowing without ever becoming a liquid. A complex structural

These resulted when the salt plug rose for a period, arching overlying strata, then ceased to move upward, allowing erosion to bevel the top of the dome. Subsequently sediments were deposited on the beveled surface. This process may be repeated many times. On the flanks of plugs strata are pushed aside and faulted as the plug pierces them. Such structures provide many potential sites for the accumulation of oil and gas, and many outstanding fields in the Gulf Coast region produce from strata near salt domes.

The question of how these plugs start to rise is best explained in terms of the relative density of salt and sediments over the source bed of the salt. Salt has a lower density than semiconsolidated and unconsolidated sediments covering the thick, salt source bed. An unstable condition already exists because the salt is lighter than the sediment and tends to rise. After overlying sediments reach a certain thickness, weight on the salt bed becomes great enough to make it flow. Once an upbulge in the source bed begins, salt assumes a streamlined shape to make passage through sediments easier. Upward movement of the plug may be stopped if the salt source bed becomes pinched off around the plug as overlying sediment sinks

FIG. 32–8. / Cross section of a salt dome showing a fault developed at the margin of the plug. (After Halbouty and Hardin, 1954.)

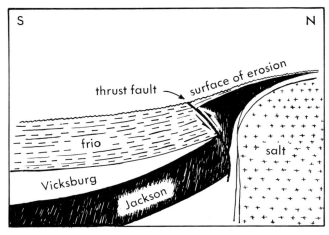

pattern surrounds the domes (Fig. 32–9). Over the top of a typical salt plug sediments are arched upward. Concentric outcrop patterns at the surface can be seen on air photographs even where the ground surface is almost flat. Strata over the dome are generally faulted as well as domed. Faults are normal and give rise to grabens and steplike blocks. Displacements along these faults are usually small, typically amounting to less than 100 feet. Many slight angular unconformities are found over some salt plugs.

into the space from which the salt has moved, or if the plug encounters a hard bed through which it cannot penetrate.

Recent Events in Coastal Plain History

PLEISTOCENE AND RECENT TIMES HAVE witnessed the emergence of the Coastal Plain as it is today. In company with the advance and retreat of ice sheets in the Northern and Southern Hemispheres in the last million years, sea level has been lowered and then raised. Fluctuations in sea level have been of sufficient magnitude to bring about great changes in position of the coastline. If enough ice now in existence melted, raising sea level by 100 feet, this would bring the coastline into the position shown in Fig. 32–10. In the past, similar inundations have flooded the coasts and created wave terraces. The Dismal Swamp is located on one of these terraces. These changes in sea level have also affected the gradients of major streams and in this way influenced their erosive capabilities. Terraces cut by the Mississippi are the best known evidence of these changes in gradient of the river during the ice ages. All along the coast rivers flowed out across the exposed continental shelf during periods of glacial advance, cutting canyons that have recently been extended by slumping and turbidity currents.

Most recently in the geologic past, following the last advance of ice, the modern coast has come to take its present shape. Offshore barrier beaches and bars, separated from the low-lying land by lagoons, have formed along great stretches of the coast from Long Island to Key West and along considerable stretches of the Gulf Coast. These are best developed where longshore currents move sand and silt. At Cape Hatteras, beaches assume a cusp-shaped form as a result of convergence of the northward-flowing Gulf Stream and southward-moving currents along the coast. At the mouth of the Mississippi deltaic deposits continuously build out into the Gulf.

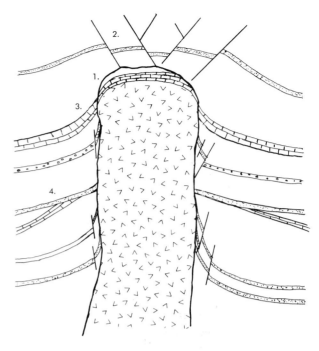

FIG. 32–9. / Gulf Coast salt dome shown diagrammatically in section. Consolidated and semiconsolidated sedimentary rocks through which the crystalline salt plug has penetrated are faulted and deformed. Faults form graben and horst structures in the domed strata over the salt plug. The top part of the salt is covered by a cap rock composed of dolostone, gypsum, anhydrite, and sulphur. Sulphur is produced commercially from a number of domes in the Gulf Coast, and many structures suitable for the accumulation of oil and gas are associated with the domes. These have been numbered in the diagram. What kind of trap is each?

FIG. 32–10. / *Position of the coast in the eastern United States if sea level rose one hundred feet.*

The long-established pattern of sedimentation continues along the continental margins. Extraordinary deposits of carbonate rock are forming today along the coast of Florida and in the Bahamas, as they have done for millions of years. Green sand deposits forming off the New Jersey coast may be similar to deposits from which the famous Lake Superior iron ores formed. In the Gulf region salt domes continue to force their way up very slowly through the sediment covering their source bed. In North Carolina a number of unusual, nearly perfectly-shaped elliptical bays are found. The shape of these bays suggests impact of a swarm of extremely large meteorites which may have hit this region in geologically recent times. In Florida porous Tertiary limestones have been arched to a position near the surface of the ground. The porosity of these units and their susceptibility to solution by ground water have made them world famous for the immense springs that flow from them.

33 /

Climatic History of Earth

Some recent thought on the origin of the atmosphere and oceans was presented in chapter 29, and modern climatic regions are outlined in chapter 7. Now let us turn to the question of what is known of past climates on earth, and how that knowledge is obtained. Past climates are revealed in a number of ways, but most of these must be evaluated qualitatively. Nevertheless, within the limitations imposed by the extent of outcrops of various ages, by the fact that most of these are marine sedimentary rocks, and by the ambiguity of many climatic indicators, it is possible to reconstruct climatic patterns in such broad terms as arid, humid, very hot, or very cold. In some instances it is possible to be much more specific. Such interpretations are based on the theory of uniformitarianism. Thus we can see what characteristics of modern plants, soils, rocks, natural processes, weathering products, or fauna are related to climate, and we can interpret past conditions on this basis.

Indications of Past Climates

Soils and Weathering

Among the best indicators of climatic zones today are soils and rock weathering products. Breakdown of certain minerals is closely related to chemical reactions between them and water. Feldspar, augite, hornblende, and olivine are common rock-forming minerals that decompose rapidly in weathering in humid climates. Thus soils containing these minerals most likely formed in either arid or frigid climates. Arkose, a sedimentary rock containing large quantities of feldspar, may be formed either by very rapid burial in water, or, if deposited on land, by very dry climatic conditions. Pebbles of clay or sand are found in glacial deposits which under humid–warm conditions would have been broken down.

Kaolin, a clay mineral, tends to form only

in soils in relatively hot and wet climates. Leaching of soil is likely to be most complete when moisture is abundant. Thus soils formed during interglacial stages have thicker leached zones than those formed during glacial advances.

In arid climates salts tend to form in the soil, and soils tend to be thinner and light in color. In climates where average temperatures are high (60° F.) and where moisture is relatively abundant (25–40 or more inches), red soils are common, but less moisture is necessary for red soils to develop on carbonate rocks than on silicate rocks.

Laterite soils, those enriched in aluminum and iron oxides and from which silica has been leached, are forming today in regions of savanna and tropical rainforest climates. In these areas there is abundant rainfall and hot weather. Ancient laterites presumably formed under similar conditions. A more complete description of this and other soils is given in chapter 16.

Sedimentary Rocks

THE CHARACTER OF SEDIMENTS now forming in a great variety of marine and transitional environments was discussed in chapter 9, and some of these environments are related to climates. Evaporites form in lakes, lagoons, and in soils in arid climates. A number of extensive salt and gypsum deposits of ancient age are known. High temperatures and rapid evaporation found in hot, arid climates favor deposition of evaporites. The significance of arkose and other feldspar-bearing sediments as indicators of arid climates has already been pointed out.

Limestones, especially reef limestones, are important. Solution and deposition of calcium carbonate depends on the carbon dioxide content of sea water. Water contains more carbon dioxide at low than at high temperatures. Thus, sediments from the deepest portions of the oceans have low carbonate content. It follows that thick and extensive limestones were formed in warm seas, particularly reef limestones.

Reefs

CORALS AND MANY OTHER of the common reef-forming organisms live under rather limited ecological conditions. Coral reefs today require clear seas with a minimum temperature of 68° F., normal salinity, and depths of less than 50 meters. With few exceptions all modern reefs are located between latitudes 30° N. and 30° S. In addition the number of species in reefs tends to be a function of temperature; more species are found in warmer waters.

Plants

PLANTS ARE EXCELLENT INDICATORS of climate, but they are not useful throughout the time scale because plants were not abundant until the Devonian Period, and the modern groups mainly appeared late in the Cretaceous. Plants are scarce in desert regions. Those that grow in arid climates tend to be small and to have poorly developed leaves. Density of veining of leaves is an indication of exposure to the sun. Leaves that are in the sun most have more dense veining.

The number of species of plants tends to increase toward the equator. This is reflected in the number of species of different types of plants —there are approximately 15 species of trees in central Europe, but nearly 600 species in Cameroon. Climate is indicated by certain types of plants. Nearly 90 per cent of the flora in Panama is made up of plants that have smooth-margined leaves without lobes. This same type makes up 56 per cent of the flora in the mountains of Hawaii, 30 per cent of the flora in England, and only 8 per cent of the flora in northern Japan.

Humid climates are indicated by peat bogs and formation of peat and coal. Tree ferns abound in humid regions, and their leaves commonly have elongated points called "drip points." Among Carboniferous plants tree ferns were particularly prominent and grew to extreme

FIG. 33–1. / *Important Carboniferous plants. Shown, from left to right, are* Sigillaria, Lepidodendron, Calamites *and* Cordaites.

sizes (Fig. 33–1). Many Carboniferous plants had no growth rings, suggesting warm climates all year. Palms also favor warm climates, and are relatively common among fossils.

Among plants indicating cold climates, two species, *Glossopteris* and *Gangamopteris* (Fig. 33–2) were associated with pre-Tertiary glacial deposits. In recent times the arctic willow and dwarf birch are common in high latitudes. Conifers grow in cool climates and are entirely absent from tropical regions.

Pollen analysis has proven to be a very valuable means of interpreting climates. When pollen is blown into a lake it settles along with other sediment, and may be preserved. Pollen can be identified, and this in turn gives an indication of the species of plants that grew around the lake at the time the sediments were laid down.

Animals

ANIMALS, LIKE PLANTS, GIVE some hint of climates, but not all species give clear pictures of climate. Mammals, for instance, have lived in all climates and, though their size tends to increase somewhat toward polar regions, they are poor climatic indicators. Reptiles and other cold-blooded land animals are among the best indicators. They live only in temperate and

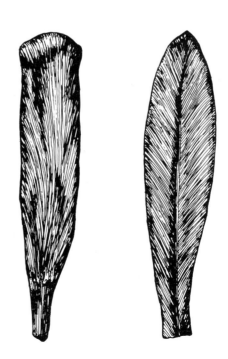

FIG. 33–2. / *Leaves of* Gangamopteris, *left, and* Glossopteris, *right.*

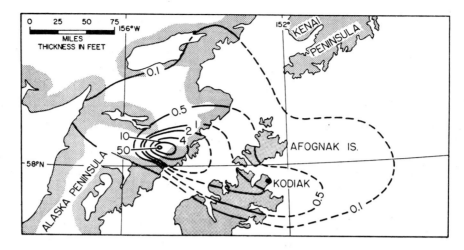

FIG. 33–3. / Distribution of ash fall from Mount Katmai. Thickness variations of the ash are shown by isopach lines. (From G. P. Eaton, Jour. Geol., 1964.)

tropical climates, and there is a definite increase in the size and number of species toward the equator. The giant reptiles of the Mesozoic lived in warm climates. Some fishes live only in water of certain temperature ranges, and the importance of reefs has already been indicated.

Miscellaneous Other Indicators

STUDIES MADE OF CAVE formations suggest that the type of calcium carbonate deposited is a function of temperature. It has been shown that in certain North American caves calcite is formed if the temperature is over 15.6° C. and that a similar mineral, aragonite, forms if the temperature is below 15.6° C.

Numerous sedimentary structures can suggest wind direction. Internal structure of sand dunes indicates the direction of wind, as does the shape of ventifacts. In cases of volcanic activity dust is spread downwind (Fig. 33–3). Directions of currents in water can be shown by the shape of ripple marks and the side of a reef on which coral debris is present.

One of the most modern indicators of paleo-temperatures is the use of *oxygen isotope ratios*. The ratio of two oxygen isotopes, O^{18}/O^{16}, in such common sediments as carbonates is related to temperature conditions under which deposition took place. Such carbonate is found in shells of fossils, but caution must be exercised in the use of these indicators, as in the use of all others. Most of a shell may be built during one season of the year, and the ratio of the two isotopes depends on the ratio of the amounts of the two isotopes in water in which deposition takes place as well as on temperature.

Résumé of Paleoclimates

Precambrian Climates

GLACIAL DEPOSITS, or tillites, of Precambrian age are known in Finland, Australia, in the region between Lake Huron and Lake Chibougamau (1 billion years old), Wyoming (1 billion years old), Michigan, Utah (600 million years old), South America, and South Africa (1 billion and 600 million years old). All of these extremely ancient deposits are slightly altered and not all are universally accepted as true tillites. But there is a strong suggestion of at least two periods of glaciation 1 billion and 600 million years ago in widely separated areas of the world.

Apart from the information provided by glacial deposits, we know relatively little of Precambrian climates. Red beds and mud cracks

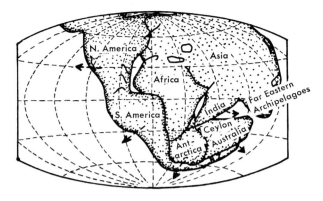

FIG. 33–4. / *Hypothetical arrangement of the world's continents according to Wegener. From a single mass like this the continents supposedly drifted apart. (After Wegener.)*

indicate that relatively arid climates existed for periods during deposition of Beltian units in Montana and during formation of Keweenawan deposits in the Great Lakes region, but no evaporite sequences are present anywhere.

Glacial deposits of Late Precambrian–Early Cambrian time are well-known in many parts of the world, including Scandinavia, Greenland, Australia, south-central Africa, eastern South America, and China, and some of questionable character occur in Utah. Explaining such widespread glaciation is difficult. Possibly the continents were closer to polar regions. It is also possible that the continents were not as far apart (Fig. 33–4).

Paleozoic Climates

PALEOZOIC ROCKS ARE fossiliferous, better exposed, and much more intensively studied than those of Precambrian age. Consequently a much broader and more accurate picture of Paleozoic climates can be reconstructed. Early and Middle periods of the Paleozoic (Cambrian through Devonian) were warm and sometimes arid throughout the Northern Hemisphere. Thick sections of limestone were deposited, and the Paleozoic seas often possessed extensive reefs (Fig. 33–5). Arid climates are indicated by evaporite deposits. Most famous of these are Silurian salt deposits of New York and Michigan

in the United States, but evaporites are known for other periods in many parts of the world. These deposits may be broadly outlined to indicate the arid belts (Fig. 33–6). The positions of these strongly suggest a long-term shifting toward the present equator. This aridity has been related to the mountain building of Late Ordovician Age.

In later parts of the Paleozoic (Carboniferous–Permian), glaciation was common in widely separated regions of the Southern Hemisphere. At the same time (Carboniferous), land areas of the north were warm and moist, almost tropical, and were dominated by extensive peat bogs and swamp areas densely covered by fern trees. Tropical conditions gave way to aridity in North America and Europe in the Permian.

Mesozoic Climates

MOST OF THE WORLD was warm during the Mesozoic. There were local cool periods but generally the world was much warmer. There was no glaciation in either hemisphere. Reefs were common and evaporites were deposited. It was in the Jurassic that salt now found in Gulf Coast salt domes was deposited. Dinosaurs and other reptiles were common in Montana, Wyoming, and other areas now too dry and cold for such large cold-blooded animals.

Cenozoic Climates

THE CENOZOIC opened with climates similar to those of the Mesozoic, but soon a cooling trend set in, which marked the approach of the Pleistocene. This change is evident from flora and fauna as well as oxygen isotope determinations on marine sediments. Locally the rise of mountains had great influence, particularly in changing the western interior of North America into an arid region.

Pleistocene History

WE ARE NOW LIVING IN THE ICE AGES, OR Pleistocene Epoch. Certainly this is not a period

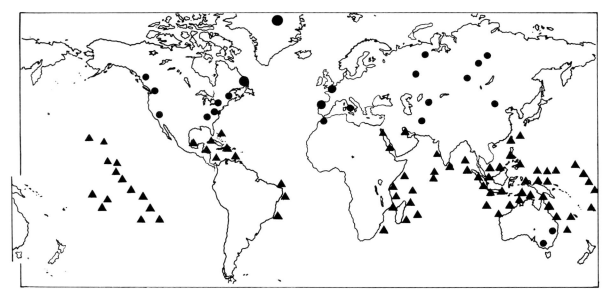

FIG. 33–5. / *Modern and early Paleozoic reefs. Modern reefs are represented by triangles, and circles indicate positions of early Paleozoic reefs. Note that the two lie essentially in belts, but at different latitudes. (Modified after Schwarzback, 1949.)*

of maximum glacial advance, but even so about 10 per cent of the land area of the world is covered by ice. In comparison, the maximum land area covered by ice during any one advance of continental glaciers amounted to about 30 per cent of the land area of the world. At present ice is concentrated largely in the Antarc-

tic and Greenland Ice Sheets, with minor amounts in mountain glaciers distributed on every continent on earth. The Pleistocene Epoch began when climates of the continents started to cool. This cooling caused changes to take place in faunas and floras of the world. These faunal differences serve as a guide to the bound-

FIG. 33–6. / *Generalized distribution of evaporite belts in the Northern Hemisphere for the early Paleozoic and modern times. Modern evaporites occur mainly in the area covered by the dashed pattern. (After Lotze, 1957.)*

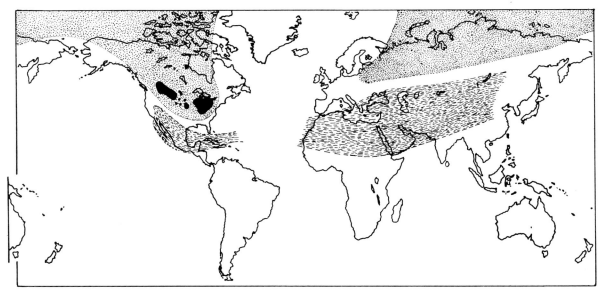

ary between the Pleistocene and Pliocene epochs. Indications of the date of the start of the Pleistocene put it between one and two million years ago.

This has been the time during which modern topography has evolved. Every feature of the world's physiography originated in the Cenozoic Age, but most of it took its present-day form during the Pleistocene. Volcanic activity and diastrophism as well as erosion and glaciation are important features of the history of the last two million years.

Volcanic Activity

THE PRESENT is a period of active volcanism. Volcanoes distributed around the Pacific Ocean form what is known as a "ring of fire," and there has been much activity within recorded time in the Mediterranean in East Africa, Asia, and in the Caribbean Sea. Apparently there is less volcanic activity in this most recent part of the Pleistocene than there was earlier. Within the last million years the belt from Alaska to northern California has been very active. Recent cones and flows are common in New Mexico, Arizona, Idaho, and over large parts of Mexico. Many of these could not have been exposed to erosion very long. They are composed of cinders and easily eroded materials that could not remain many thousands of years without considerable alteration. Volcanoes have been active throughout the length of the Andes. In Iceland and Spitsbergen lavas are interbedded with glacial drift.

Diastrophism

THERE HAS BEEN MUCH upwarping and block faulting in the Pleistocene. It is for this reason that so many mountains are still as high as they are today. The Tetons, the Sierra Nevada, the Central Rockies, and the Northern Rockies have all been uplifted in the Pleistocene. In fact, almost the entire region of the Great Plains has been warped upward during this time, and probably the Appalachians as well.

Glaciation

DURING THE PLEISTOCENE, ice sheets have formed in both Northern and Southern Hemispheres and advanced across extensive areas of the world. Continental ice sheets formed in Canada and moved down over the northern border of the United States. There have been several of these advances. At least four main stages can be recognized from drift deposits left by them. Each is separated by an interglacial stage during which ice sheets retreated, warmer conditions prevailed, old glacial deposits were eroded, and new soils developed. Even glacial advances can be subdivided into substages during which there were relatively minor changes in positions of sheets and deposits left by them. The most outstanding effects of these glacial advances have been:

1. Lowering of sea level with each advance of the ice, by as much as 400 feet. As a result of these fluctuations, terraces have been formed along continental borders, canyons have been cut across parts of emergent continental shelves, and gradients of streams flowing into oceans have been shifted, with consequent development of stream terraces.

2. Derangement of drainage. Stream courses were moved by each glacial advance. The drainage patterns of most major streams in the central United States have been brought into their present positions since the last glacial advance. Their courses were influenced by morainal deposits, and the positions of the lakes formed from meltwater.

3. Formation of the Great Lakes. These lakes are remnants of much more extensive and even larger lakes that were formed by glacial scouring and deposition of moraines.

4. Formation of periglacial lakes. Beyond the margins of ice sheets, water drained off into low areas and formed large and extensive lakes. In North America these developed in the Great Basin, where interior drainage prevented escape of the waters. Great Salt Lake is a remnant of one of these lakes. Many hundreds of others dotted the Basin and Range province during the Pleistocene.

5. The covering of Mississippi Valley by windblown deposits of loess derived from glacial deposits of outwash plains.

6. Development of some of our land's most beautiful scenery, for which erosion by mountain glaciers has been responsible. Arêtes, horns, cols, and U-shaped valleys that now characterize most high mountain ranges formed during the Pleistocene. Less rugged topography over which ice sheets moved tended to become suppressed and smoothed out.

7. Deposits from ice sheets, from lakes formed near their margins, and from windblown deposits, lie over more than half of the area of the United States. Modern soils have developed in these materials.

Evidence of Multiple Advances

FOR MANY YEARS the glacial erratics, moraines, till, stratified drift, and most other Pleistocene continental deposits were ascribed to the flood during the time of Noah. It was assumed that large erratics were blocks floated into their present position while frozen into icebergs. It was not until 1840 that Louis Agassiz pointed out that glacial deposits in valleys and plains below alpine glaciers were deposited there when glaciers were expanded. He postulated an ice sheet covering all of northern Europe to explain glacial deposits in that region. This became one of the most controversial questions of the time. The validity of his work has now been so well documented that no doubt about the origin of these and similar deposits in other parts of the world remains.

Soon after Agassiz made his first studies of glaciers it was recognized that there are two or more superposed sheets of glacial drift in Europe. Thus glaciation was early known to be multiple. Although we rarely find evidence of more than two sheets superimposed on one another in a single locality, there were at least four periods or stages of glacier advance during the Pleistocene in North America. Sequence of these stages has been determined by correlation and dating. Since glacial tills often resemble one another, regardless of age, they have limited value in establishing glacial history. Instead, use is made of deposits laid down in front of the ice sheets, and particularly sediments deposited during interglacial periods when ice sheets were retreating or nonexistent. Most common of these deposits are loess, glacier outwash, peat, and varved lake clays formed in marginal lakes. Within these units we can establish time equivalence by means of correlation of the varves, by use of fossil fauna and flora, or by use of carbon-14.

One effect of interglacial periods is weathering of deposits formed during the previous advance. Soil profiles have been used as the best means of identifying tills. Depth of oxidation, amount and kind of chemical weathering, or extent of decay may be used as a means of estimating relative ages of different tills. The most recent sheet of glacial till is very fresh, in comparison with older sheets, making it relatively easy to identify the last North American continental ice sheet, called the Wisconsin sheet.[1] Studies of these till sheets and the interglacial deposits have led to the following subdivision of the Pleistocene, in order from youngest to oldest:

Wisconsin Glaciation: defined on the basis of till in Wisconsin.
Sangamon Interglacial: for deposits in Sangamon County, Illinois.
Illinoian Glaciation: for deposits in Illinois.
Yarmouth Interglacial: for deposits in Yarmouth, Iowa.
Kansas Glaciation: for sections in northeastern Kansas.
Aftonian Interglacial: for deposits in Afton Junction, Iowa.
Nebraskan Glaciation: for deposits in Nebraska.

Various substages are known for some of the stages above. This is particularly true of the Wisconsin. One of these substages, the Iowan, may actually represent a separate period of glacier advance comparable to the Nebraskan, Kansas, and Illinoian.

In the type locality for each stage, lithologic characteristics may be used to help identify the stages, but variability of glacial deposits makes this of relatively little use for correlation over

[1] See a portion of the Glacial Map of the United States at end of book.

great distances. Criteria for identification of the stages are:

1. Topography. The Wisconsin till sheet may be distinguished from older sheets by development of drainage patterns on it. Older sheets tend to be more dissected by stream erosion. Some substages of the Wisconsin, and to a lesser extent the older stages, may be distinguished in this way.

2. Weathering. All of the till sheets with the exception of the Wisconsin have reached advanced stages of weathering. In the B horizon there is a layer of *gumbotil* (leached deoxidized clay), or *silttil* (unleached silty till), depending on the texture. Thicknesses of these zones are sometimes used as an indication of relative age of a till.

3. Carbon-14. Radiocarbon dating is the most exact means of dating and correlating deposits of the Pleistocene. It may be used on wood, bones, peat, and other organic materials. However, it is applicable only to the Wisconsin Stage, because the half life of carbon 14 is not long enough to make it useful in dating objects more than about 50,000 years old.

4. Pollen analysis. When angiosperms flower, grains of pollen are shed in great abundance. These pollen grains and spores are widely distributed by winds. Through careful study of various types of spores and pollen grains it is possible to identify the genus and even the species of plants from which the pollen came. Pollen grains found in a lake or bog deposit reflect the types of plants that were living near it at the time the sediment was laid down. By taking a section through a sequence of pollen- and spore-bearing sediments, the assemblage of plants that was nearby at successive times can be determined. Pollen reflects changes in relative abundance of different plants as the ice sheets advanced and retreated. Certain types of plants serve as climatic indicators.

5. Varves. These have been used in correlating lake deposits of glacier marginal lakes to one another.

6. Deep-sea sediments. Sediments deposited in the ocean during the Pleistocene are very simple, compared with terrestrial deposits. These can be recovered by means of coring devices. Many cores that are 40 to 50 feet long have been obtained in this way. Layers in the topmost parts of these cores may be dated by means of carbon 14; fossil content has been most useful in the lower parts of the cores. A great deal of work is being done on interpretation of these cores as a means of reconstructing paleoclimates during the Pleistocene. Among the interesting results obtained is the discovery that the rate of deep-sea sedimentation is related to the temperature of the surface water, and thus to climatic conditions of the region. Many Foraminifera are guides to water temperature, so variation in geographic distribution of these also serves as a climatic indicator.

History of the Mississippi Drainage System

THE MISSISSIPPI RIVER now drains a basin that extends from the Rocky Mountains to the Appalachian Highlands and northward to the Great Lakes. Virtually the entire southern perimeter of the continental ice sheets drained into the Mississippi River during and following their greatest advances, bringing about repeated shifts in northern parts of the river and its two main tributaries, the Ohio and Missouri rivers (Fig. 33–7).

Before advances of these ice sheets, the drainage pattern was strikingly different from that which we now find. The northern part of the Missouri River drained northward into Hudson Bay. That segment from Kansas City eastward has maintained its course. The source of the Mississippi was probably near its present head in Minnesota, but the part of the stream channel north of St. Louis was shifted a number of times during the ice ages. Northern and eastern parts of the Ohio River from central Ohio to West Virginia drained northward into the Gulf of St. Lawrence. The lower part of the Ohio drainage went into a preglacial stream known as the *Teays River*, which flowed across central Ohio and Indiana.

When the great ice sheets moved southward they blocked and filled valleys of many parts of the preglacial streams. The Teays River valley was filled with glacial till. Its position can now

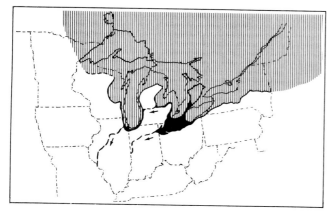

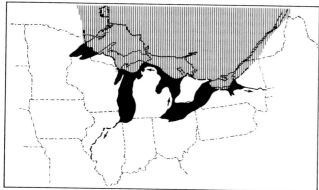

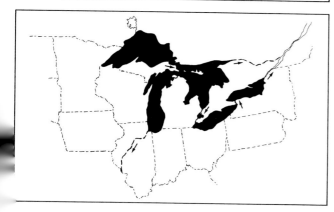

FIG. 33–7. / *Stages of the Great Lakes. Shown are three stages in the formation of the Great Lakes. The top map depicts the region during one phase of glacial advance when the lakes, shown in solid black drained into the Mississippi River. As the ice retreated, shown at center (post-Huron stage) drainage was into the Mississippi and the Hudson Rivers. At the bottom (Postglacial Great Lakes) drainage is similar to that at present except that the lakes drained into the Mississippi and there was a connection between the Ottawa River and Lake Huron. (Redrawn after Hough, American Scientist, v. 51, 1963.)*

be traced by the unusual thicknesses of glacial drift in it. Waters of the rivers became ponded or blocked by edges of the ice sheet, and new lines of drainage were established around edges of sheets. The greatest advances of ice sheets coincide approximately with the present positions of the Missouri and Ohio rivers. Thus the present drainage pattern was established by these channels formed near the margins of the ice sheet. Before this pattern became established there were many shifts in channel positions along the front of the ice.

Advances and retreats of the ice sheets have left other impressions upon the Mississippi Valley. During each glacial advance water was removed from the oceans, lowering sea level and increasing the gradient of the lower parts of the Mississippi Valley. At the same time, with the advance of ice, the upper parts of the valleys became clogged with a sediment load the streams could not possibly carry. Each time glaciers began to retreat, the reverse situation occurred. Upper parts of the river received great quantities of water from melting ice, the sea level rose, and the gradient along the lower reaches of the river was decreased.

Thus, during periods of glacial advance, upper parts of the Mississippi Valley became filled with sediment, while lower parts of the valley were cut more deeply as a result of steepened stream gradients. During glacial retreats, the upper valley was washed clear of debris by the increased flow from meltwater, and lower parts of the valley became filled with debris because sea level was rising and thus lowering the gradient of the stream. Evidence of effects of fluctuations of sea level in the lower parts of the valley are found in four river terraces, which correspond to the four major periods of glacial advance.

DEVELOPMENT OF THE GREAT LAKES. Before the Pleistocene there were no large lakes in the region of the Great Lakes. Instead, streams of that area drained northward. Lake Superior is now located in a structural basin of Precambrian rocks, and most of the other lakes are situated on sedimentary sequences that probably were depressions in the Pliocene topography. As Pleistocene ice sheets moved into the region, these earlier valleys were enlarged by scouring and were depressed under the weight of the ice mass. Lakes began to form in the last stages of the Wisconsin glaciation as the ice sheet began to melt and retreat. Meltwater was trapped between margins of the ice sheet and high ground along the drainage divide of the Mississippi basin.[2]

During the first part of the history of the lakes they actually drained into the Mississippi, but later, as the ice retreated farther, a new outlet was opened and waters from the southern margin of the ice front drained westward across Michigan. A sequence of positions of the lakes at different times is illustrated (Fig. 33–8). Note the changing shapes and the shifting outlets through the passage of time.

The sequence of known events in the development of the Great Lakes is extremely complex. The following are among the most important factors that have contributed to this course of development:

1. During glaciation the weight of the ice sheet caused the continent to be depressed, and as ice wasted away land rose. Old shorelines have become tilted by this isostatic rise which has been greatest in the central part of the Canadian Shield.
2. The ice front did not remain stationary during the evolution of the lakes. It oscillated back and forth, advancing and retreating in different places at different times.
3. The configuration of the land surface exposed as the ice sheet wasted has naturally partially determined the shape of the lakes.
4. With each advance of the ice sheet, morainal debris was pushed into new positions and partially removed from older ones, thus changing outlets and barriers to lake waters.

In spite of these complicating factors, the history of the lakes has been largely worked out. It is possible to trace the position of the lakes by means of mapping beaches, wave-cut cliffs, sand dunes, bars, and other shoreline features formed at each stage in the lakes' history. Along

[2] See the Glacial Map of the United States at the end of the book.

these old shorelines it is possible to find outlets used by the lakes in each position. It is not possible to outline exactly the position of each lake at every time during evolution of the Great Lakes, because the story has not been one of a gradually receding body of water. Some of the more recent lake shorelines cross and obliterate earlier shoreline features. In addition, most of the earlier lakes were marginal to ice, consequently no shoreline features are found where beaches ran into the ice sheet.

LAKE AGASSIZ. Largest of the former lakes was glacial Lake Agassiz. Remnants of this lake are Lake Winnipeg, Rainy Lake, and several other smaller bodies of water. We can now determine the position of Lake Agassiz by mapping the lake deposits that appear as an almost continuous thin cover over a large portion of southern Canada. This magnificent lake disappeared when the retreating ice sheet had moved far enough inland to permit waters to escape into Hudson Bay.

Causes of Ice Ages

GLACIERS HAVE NOT ALWAYS COVERED THE polar regions. Judging from the scarcity of glacial deposits in past times, periods of glaciation are very unusual. Remains of corals and other animals that ordinarily favor warm waters are found in rocks in the Arctic and Antarctic. What has caused glaciers to form is an intriguing question that has given rise to a great deal of speculation. Scientific literature abounds in hypotheses which try to answer the question. Some of them are based on assumptions that have proved to be fallacious, and the validity of others remains unestablished. No definitive answer can be given to the question.

What Must Be Explained

ANY ACCEPTABLE HYPOTHESIS must explain observed facts, or at least not contradict them.

Occurrences of till containing striated and grooved pebbles assure us that there have been

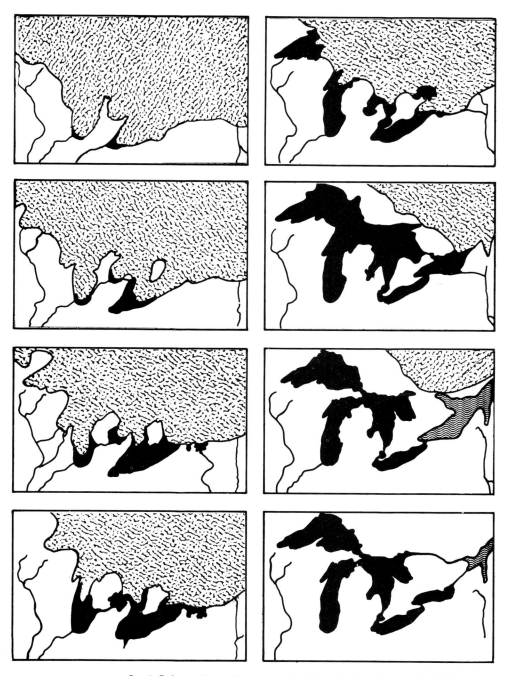

FIG. 33–8. / *Schematic evolution of the Great Lakes during the Pleistocene.*

several periods of glaciation. The oldest of these took place in the Precambrian, and it seems probable that there may have been more than one glaciation during the billions of years of Precambrian time. The oldest North American ice sheets occupied an area in the southern part of the Canadian Shield. Glacial sediments are also found in widely separated areas in rocks that lie just beneath the Cambrian system. They are scattered over the Canadian Shield, in Utah, Norway, Australia, eastern Greenland, and India. One of the most unusual things about these is the distribution of glacial debris in areas that now lie in temperate and even tropical climatic belts. A third major period of glaciation occurred during the Carboniferous and

Permian Periods. At this time, about 230 million years ago, glaciers covered parts of South Africa, Australia, and India. In Australia there are five separate sheets of till of this age interbedded with coal. This relation indicates cold periods of glacial advance separated by warm, moist interglacial periods during which plant life flourished.

The Pleistocene period of continental glaciation started about a million years ago. Since it started there have been at least four major intervals of glacial advance and three interglacial ages, not counting the present, which may or may not be an interglacial age. The last great resurgence of ice ended about 10,000 years ago. During periods of advance, ice sheets have covered most of Canada, the northern United States, Greenland, northern Europe, northern Siberia, Antarctica, and high mountains throughout the world. Each of these advances took place essentially simultaneously throughout the Northern Hemisphere. Thus whatever caused glaciation affected this huge region at about the same time. Even within each of the glacial advances there were minor advances and retreats of relatively short duration. There are not enough data to demonstrate conclusively whether or not major glacial periods occurred at regular intervals. Consequently, we cannot be sure if the cause of glaciation is one that occurs at fixed intervals.

There are several other observations which must be taken into account. Ice caps grow and decay rapidly—the last ice sheet covered the northern United States only 10,000 years ago. Sea level fluctuates with the amount of ice piled up as ice caps. Accumulation of ice and snow is favored in mountains and on land masses with high elevation. Variations in temperatures on earth of only a few degrees centigrade should be sufficient to cause glacial advances and retreats.

Many theories have been advanced to explain the cause of ice ages. Some are no more than speculations, but others have been worked out in great detail. Among these are cosmic theories in which radiation reaching earth from the sun has varied due to cosmic dust clouds and to the amount of radiation actually transmitted from the sun; planetary theories in which periodic changes in position of the earth in relation to the sun have produced unusually cold conditions; and geological theories in which volcanic activity, variations in carbon dioxide in the atmosphere, and variations in oceanic circulation are offered as causes. Two theories are here selected as representative of modern thought on this question.

Oceanic Circulation Hypothesis

GEOGRAPHY OF THE NORTH POLAR REGION is such that the Arctic Ocean is essentially surrounded by continental areas. The connections between the Arctic, the Atlantic, and the Pacific oceans are narrow, and water in these areas is relatively shallow. Thus circulation of water between the Arctic and Atlantic and Pacific would be greatly influenced by sea level. If the present ice caps melt, sea level will rise, and there will be better circulation between these oceans. This would cause waters in the Arctic to become warmer. Since warmer water evaporates more readily, atmospheric moisture content in the Arctic would increase, there would be more clouds, more precipitation, and more storm activity. Unless the temperatures were elevated above freezing, precipitation in the Arctic would be in the form of snow and ice. Thus new continental ice caps would begin to form. This process would continue until sea level was lowered to the point of greatly reducing circulation between the oceans. At this point Arctic waters would cool off again rapidly and precipitation would become low. The ice caps would stop building up on land and would gradually melt away as an interglacial stage approached. When the ice had melted sea level would again rise and the cycle would be repeated.

Studies during the International Geophysical Year have established the thickness of the Antarctica ice cap and therefore the shape of the underlying land. If the ice sheet melted there would be a mountain range exposed on one side and a large island on the other (Fig. 33–9).

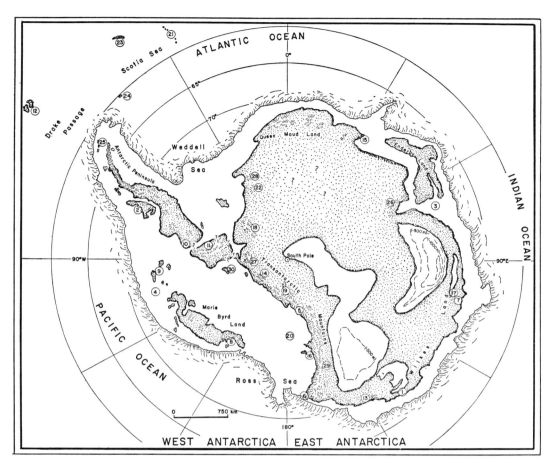

FIG. 33–9. / *Antarctica as it would appear if the ice ever were removed. (From Arthur Ford, U.S.G.S., Trans. Am. Geographical Union, v. 45, with permission.)*

Thus conditions similar to those in the Arctic exist at the South Pole, and the oceanic current hypothesis might explain glaciation in both areas. It is not so clear how this theory would apply to other more ancient periods of glacia-tion, such as those in the Permian and Precam-brian. Drifting continents and shifts of the en-tire crust over the mantle could have placed these other regions in polar positions, or changes in the earth's axis could have shifted the poles,

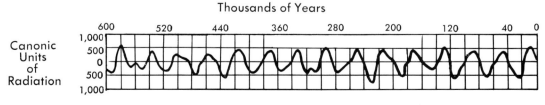

FIG. 33–10. / *Variation in solar radiation. This plot shows the amount of solar radiation plotted against time, in thousands of years. (After Milankovitch, 1938.)*

but too little is known to establish accurately what the geography of those times and places was like.

Variations in Solar Radiation

THE IDEA THAT output of solar radiation has caused glaciation is not at all new, but new evidence has been found to emphasize this as a probable factor in causing ice ages. The average amount of energy reaching the earth's surface is about two calories per square centimeter each minute. This value has fluctuated by about three per cent since 1918. Another fact which supports this hypothesis is that climatic fluctuations tend to be in phase in both hemispheres, and to follow essentially the same geographical pattern. It has recently been shown that there is a relationship between atmospheric pressure and sunspot activity. The theory no longer requires that the whole atmosphere be cooled, because it can be shown that the effect of certain wavelengths of solar emissions in the high atmosphere is accompanied by rearrangement of the hot and cold sources in the lower atmosphere. These in turn cause a significant response in the general circulation pattern. Sunspot ac-

tivity is known to vary in several established cycles. One of these is 11 years in length, and a long one is 80 years. High sunspot activity tends to create a pattern of circulation on earth similar to that of interglacial patterns, and low activity causes the type of pattern associated with glacial advance. This relationship suggests a possible cyclic nature to glaciation. Cycles can be demonstrated in weather patterns (Fig. 33–10). There were abrupt and notable reactions to periods of change from high to low sunspot activity in 1787, 1871, and 1947. Furthermore, our experience in measuring glaciers enables us to point out that the two periods of maximum rate of recession coincided with major sunspot maxima in 1917 and 1937. The strong possibility exists that the short-term variations in sunspot activity so familiar to us are but minor cycles superimposed on larger cycles of even greater period. Some geologists support the idea that glaciations on earth have cyclic occurrence.

It may well be that a combination of factors brings about ice ages. These might be expected to include, in particular, variations in solar emissions and certain types of geographic configurations.

X /

HISTORY OF LIFE

34 / The Origin of Life

No scientist pretends to be able to describe exactly how life began. Problems involved in bringing together just the right substances, in exactly the necessary amounts, and in arrangements necessary for formation of even the simplest living organism, almost exceed the imagination. The possibility that the earliest living forms could ever have come to exist at all in the "hostile environment" of the Early Precambrian may seem negligible. Yet combined efforts of chemists, biologists, and geologists have thrown much light on this fundamental problem. We shall see that the earth's early environments were less hostile to development of life than our present environment, and that what seems improbable in terms of man's history may become probable when considered against the background of geologic time.

Is it possible to explain the origin of life in terms of inorganic processes affecting materials that occur naturally on the surface of the earth? In seeking an answer to this question we must first find answers to the following questions:

1. What materials make up organisms?
2. What is the means by which these organic molecules may be produced by inorganic processes?
3. What forces act to bring these molecules together in arrangements found in organisms?
4. What sources of energy would be available to sustain the first forms of life?

Composition of Organisms

Organisms are composed of water, salts like those found in sea water, and organic carbon compounds. These are called organic compounds because they occur very rarely in nature except in organisms. Organic compounds are composed of four elements—carbon, oxygen, nitrogen, and hydrogen. These four combine in various ways to make up four classes of organic compounds—carbohydrates, fats, proteins, and nucleic acids. Fats and carbohydrates, which are simpler than proteins and nucleic acids, are used by organisms as sources of the energy necessary to carry on functions of living matter. *Nucleic acids* are larger and more complex structures capable of almost endless variety; they are believed to be the main constituent of *genes*, the units which control inherited traits in all living things. *Proteins* are still more complex. They include the largest and most complex molecules known in nature. Their structure is built up of *amino acids* strung together in long chains. Different amino acids may be attached in different orders to provide literally millions of combinations. No two species of living organisms possess the same assortment of proteins.

Formation of Organic Molecules

LIFE BEGAN BEFORE UPPER PRECAMBRIAN strata were deposited. Life of the Cambrian was so abundant, varied, and advanced that its forerunners must have existed far back into Precambrian time. When were the necessary constituents for living matter first present? Of these constituents water formed very early, and salts began to accumulate as soon as erosion of land by water started. But the question remains as to how organic compounds could have formed before any life existed.

For a little over a century chemists have been able to synthesize organic compounds in the laboratory, and they are now known to form by inorganic processes in nature. Volcanic emanations of metal carbides react with water vapor at the earth's surface to yield compounds of carbon and hydrogen. Dr. S. L. Miller successfully produced organic compounds by circulating a mixture of water vapor, methane, ammonia, and hydrogen over an electric spark. This experiment simulates electrical charges in the upper atmosphere in the presence of the constituents postulated for the primitive atmosphere of the earth according to the residual atmosphere hypothesis. Results of the experiment are impressive in that several amino acids were formed. This experiment makes spontaneous formation of amino acids, and therefore proteins, much more likely than had been thought. The amount of time covered by the Precambrian was three or four billion years. Over this span of time even the slowest processes of synthesis would yield great quantities of organic molecules.

If such an organic molecule should be formed today by inorganic synthesis, it would be short-lived indeed. It would almost immedi-

ately become the prey of some living organism, or it would be burned up through oxidation. Such would not have been the case in the early Precambrian, for there was no life, and oxygen was lacking in the atmosphere. Oxygen had yet to be released from compounds by photosynthesis and photochemical reactions in the upper atmosphere. For this reason there was plenty of time for organic compounds to become integrated into more stable aggregates.

Integration vs. Dissolution

SIMPLE ORGANIC COMPOUNDS are subject to the process of spontaneous dissolution, for processes by which organic compounds may be synthesized are reversible—actually, they are known to go backward much faster than they go forward. This poses a serious problem in the formation of living matter through inorganic processes. Living organisms are subject to this same process, and they are able not only to withstand it but to grow as well. This is done through expenditure of large quantities of energy. That integration should take place becomes more likely when we realize that attachment of several molecules together makes the aggregate more resistant to dissolution. Larger molecules tend to disintegrate much more slowly than small ones. Furthermore, organic molecules tend to form various structures spontaneously, and these structures give the aggregate even more stability. This tendency is so strong that proteins may orient themselves even while in solution. It would be through this tendency to form structures that organic molecules, once they had been synthesized, could combine in aggregates which would gradually become transformed into more complex structures.

We may visualize many thousands of millions of these structures forming, until one form produced possesses characteristics with which we associate life. Such a process almost certainly took place in the seas, for it is there that the necessary constituents are concentrated and in constant motion, bringing many combinations together. That such a process, plus the tendency of organic molecules to form structures, might be responsible for formation of a live organism is demonstrated by recent experiments. In these experiments pieces of cartilage and muscle were dissolved in a solution of water. The solution was stirred until a completely random orientation of molecules was assured. Then as the solution was precipitated the molecules realigned themselves to reproduce the original pattern of the tissues. If such an experiment is possible with a tissue as intricate in structure as muscle, then it does not seem unreasonable to explain the origin of much simpler structures in this manner. In the Precambrian there was certainly time and the necessary materials for many trials.

Once simple structures began to form, the process of natural selection might have begun to operate. As aggregates of molecules began to form in large numbers some were more favorably organized and situated for survival. As a result they grew while other forms less well suited to the environment failed in the competition. Once the most favored molecular aggregates had reached the threshold of life they were confronted with new problems—problems that confront all organisms. Organisms are dynamic structures constantly taking in matter and energy and disposing of that which is unsuited for their development.

Present-day living plants are able to obtain this energy through the process of photosynthesis, by which they produce sugar from carbon dioxide, water, and sunlight. Animals obtain the necessary energy through respiration, by which they convert sugar to energy. But at the time of development of the first living forms there were no plants, little or no oxygen in the air, and deadly ultraviolet rays penetrated to the land surface, killing off any living forms that were unprotected by waters of the seas. How then did these early organisms obtain energy?

Energy Sources

THROUGH THE PROCESS OF *fermentation* an organism can break down organic molecules into smaller parts with resultant yield of some energy. Fermentation of sugar by yeast to yield

alcohol is an example. How long early organisms obtained energy through fermentation is not known. Eventually, photosynthesis developed. This could not happen until there was carbon dioxide in the atmosphere, which might have been very early in the earth's history. It would have eventually developed through the process of fermentation, in which carbon dioxide is a waste product. Once photosynthesis started the problem of finding enough material to ferment was alleviated, for there was then an abundant supply of energy.

One by-product of photosynthesis is oxygen. As soon as this was available in quantity, organisms could develop a way of using it to produce energy—respiration, which is much more efficient than fermentation. This is a form of combustion in which sugar plus oxygen yields carbon dioxide, water, and energy. The main advantage that this offered organisms was that the amount of energy yielded from a like quantity of sugar through respiration was about 35 times that obtained through fermentation. This abundance of energy provided organisms with all they needed to carry on life processes. It was out of this surplus that future evolutionary developments took place.

With release of oxygen through photosynthesis and through photochemical reactions in the upper atmosphere, a layer of ozone formed. This layer of ozone in the upper atmosphere serves as a filter to remove ultraviolet rays. Once this layer had formed the first stages had been set for emergence of life from the seas.

The First Signs of Life on Earth

FOLLOWING INITIAL STAGES IN DEVELOPMENT of the crust, temperatures near the surface were much too high for living organisms. Development of oceans and atmosphere was followed by a period of millions of years during which the first organic compounds formed. This first part of the earth's history would have been a time of trial and error. In this time synthesis of various organic compounds took place in the seas. Eventually structures formed that resem-

FIG. 34-1. / Fossils in Precambrian rocks. This photograph is one of Conophyton Zone 2, Flathead County, Montana. (Photo by U.S. Geological Survey.)

bled living organisms. It may be that no organisms were present on the earth during the first half of its history. When living forms did appear they had no hard parts suitable for preservation, and so efforts to find them are frustrated attempts to find something that no longer exists.

Carbon

IN EARLY PRECAMBRIAN ROCKS the only thing we have been able to find that may be associated with living organisms is carbon. Carbon is a constituent of all living organisms. In fact, organisms are one of the few agents by which carbon becomes fixed in nature. Carbon is abundant in shales, schists, and limestones of Precambrian age. The ratio of carbon 12 to carbon 13 is higher in organic carbon than in carbon formed through inorganic processes. This test has been run on carbon of Precambrian rocks, and it is found that a large part of the carbon in these ancient rocks is of organic origin.

Fossils

BEFORE THE END OF THE PRECAMBRIAN sufficient time had elapsed for development of some organisms of a more complex nature. The fossil record bears this out. There is considerable evidence of life in Upper Precambrian units. In limestone units of the Grand Canyon small rodlike spicules characteristic of the walls of sponges have been found. The most abundant early fossil is calcareous algae, a simple plant. Together these form reeflike masses (Fig. 34-1); individually they are concentrically laminated structures that resemble a head of cabbage.

History of Fossils

THE GREEK HISTORIAN Herodotus was among the first to recognize the true significance of fossils. He realized that fossil shells found exposed in outcrops far inland were remains of marine organisms left in ancient seas. History

FIG. 34–2. / *Fossil ant preserved since the Miocene near Florissant, Colorado. (By courtesy of the U.S. National Museum.)*

FIG. 34–3. / *Cast of brachiopods. Many fossils are preserved as molds or casts. A mold is the impression left by the original parts in the sediment. A cast is a duplication of the original parts. The brachiopods in this specimen have the form of casts. (Photo by courtesy of the U.S. National Museum.)*

shows that this conclusion has not always been as obvious as it now appears. Even Aristotle failed to see the connection between "figured stones" and shells. He taught that these objects grew in place in the rock.

The period of greatest controversy over the true nature of fossils was in the Middle Ages. The Church held that these figured stones were placed in rocks by the Devil to mislead people. One interesting compromise solution to the origin of fossils was that they had been created at the same time as the earth, and were put there as a picture of great events to come, so it was no wonder that they resembled life of the present. Other speculations held that after the Creator formed various types of animals and plants He discarded those He didn't like. Fossils thus were the unsuccessful forms that were discarded.

Johann Beringer, a professor at the University of Wursburg in the early 18th century, was keenly interested in fossils at a time when the idea that fossils grew in place was popular. Some of his students decided to play a practical joke by planting a few home-made fossils in the outcrops Beringer took his students to visit. When Beringer fell for the hoax, to the delight of his students, they set about preparing all sorts of fossils. The first ones resembled usual fossils, but in time the students became more daring and made replicas of birds' nests, insects, beehives, and birds in flight. The more of these Beringer found the more delighted he became. Finally he decided to write a book and illustrate the extraordinary fossil find. After the publication had gone to press, in 1726, he discovered a fossil that contained Hebrew characters. He realized then that he was the victim of a hoax and spent the rest of his life trying to buy all the copies of the book, but his efforts were in vain, for his heirs sold the books as a novelty after he died.

By 1800 our present basic concepts concerning the origin of fossils had become well established.

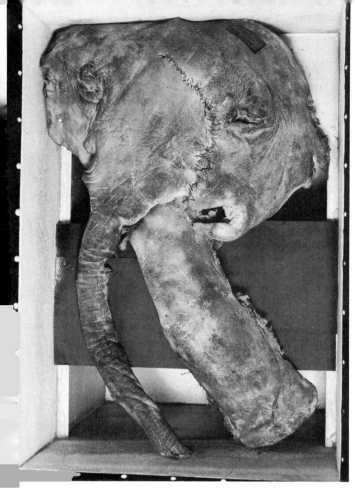

FIG. 34-4. / *Baby woolly mammoth, dug out of frozen ground in Alaska. (Courtesy of the American Museum of Natural History.)*

FIG. 34-5. / *Perfect preservation of an arthropod in resin. (Photo by courtesy of the U.S. National Museum.)*

Fossilization

BOTH ACTUAL REMAINS of organisms and traces of them are fossils. Direct evidences of past life include *actual remains, petrifactions,* and *prints.*

Indirect evidence of past life includes *molds* or *casts, coprolites, artifacts, trails, tracks,* and *burrows* (Fig. 34-3).

Conditions Favorable for Preservation

SPECIAL CONDITIONS FAVOR PRESERVATION of plants and animals. Organic matter decays; it is oxidized and broken down by bacterial action rapidly if left exposed to the atmosphere. Scavengers consume soft parts of plants and animals both on land and in seas, unless the parts are buried quickly or the environment of the sea floor is such that scavengers cannot live there. Consequently, fossilization is most likely to occur when there is quick burial in a protective medium, and if the organism has hard parts such as a shell or skeleton.

Soft remains of organisms are rarely discovered. Most such fossils have been recovered from oil seeps where animals became trapped in the sticky tar coverings, and from ice and frozen soils of the Arctic. One such discovery was an extinct woolly mammoth, an elephant-like beast that roamed the northern Siberian plains during the Pleistocene. When thawing remains of one of these mammoths were first discovered in 1900 the flesh of the animal was red—so fresh that wild dogs ate a considerable part of it before an expedition could reach the site (Fig. 34-4). Insects, complete with delicate appendages, have been found in amber resin of trees (Fig. 34-5).

Most fossils are shells, skeletons, and other hard parts of animals. Such parts are likely to be composed of calcite, phosphate, silica, or chitin, if they remain unaltered. Corals, mollusks, and many other marine invertebrates have calcite shells. A few have phosphate shells. Silica makes up hard parts of several groups of

FIG. 34–6. / *Specimen of petrified wood. (Washington and Lee Univ. collection.)*

FIG. 34–7. / *Fossil leaf impressions, common in rocks of late Paleozoic age. The organic matter is left on the rock as a thin film of carbon. (Photo by courtesy of Chicago Natural History Museum.)*

protozoans, sponges, and one of the most abundant plants—diatoms. Silica is the most resistant common substance found in fossils. Chitin is the rather soft material of which fingernails are composed.

Frequently actual remains are altered by slowly circulating ground waters carrying elements in solution. Organic matter may be replaced volume for volume by calcite, silica, or pyrite, or pore spaces in porous fossils may be filled by mineral matter as in petrified wood (Fig. 34–6). While original material decays the texture of the remains is preserved.

Prints of fossils are formed of carbon left after volatile and gaseous constituents of flesh or soft parts are distilled away. Such fossils look as if they were printed on the shale or mudstone in which they occur (Fig. 34–7). Many of the best fossil plants are of this type.

Law of Faunal Succession

WILLIAM SMITH, WHO WAS BORN IN 1769 in Oxfordshire, England, son of a farmer, grew up in a region where the strata are particularly fossiliferous, and these fossils attracted his attention early in life. Later, as he traveled throughout England he kept notes on occurrence of fossils, types present, rock types in which they were found, and their geographic locality. His studies continued for over 25 years. During this time he made and kept geologic maps showing strata and their fossils. Finally he came to the conclusion that the succession of strata exposed on the south coast of England is the same as that found on the east, and that

the sequences can be traced across the country. Furthermore, he concluded that each individual horizon could be recognized by its particular fossil content. Thus for the first time it was recognized that each fossil species is associated with certain stratigraphic horizons. This discovery opened up a whole new method of identifying chronological order in rock units and in turn made correlation and interpretation of earth history possible. This conclusion that the strata contain fauna that occur in the same succession everywhere (that fauna in different strata are recognizable and different) is one of William Smith's principal contributions to geology.

The qualities that made Smith famous deserve the attention of every man. They are keenly brought out in the following tribute (Zittel, 1901).

William Smith was a self-taught genius of rare originality and with exceptionally keen powers of observation. Without much intellectual cultivation, without any introductory teaching, without any means at his disposal, and at first even without the encouragement and sympathy of colleagues in the study which he loved, his own unflinching determination, noble enthusiasm, and remarkable insight enabled him to elucidate the structure of his native land with such clearness and accuracy that no important alteration has had to be made in his work. Smith confined himself to the empirical investigation of his country, and was never tempted into general speculations about the history of formation of the earth. His greatness is based upon this wise restraint and the steady adherence to his definite purpose; to these qualities, the modest, self-sacrificing, and open-hearted student of nature owes his well-deserved reputation as the "Father of English Geology."

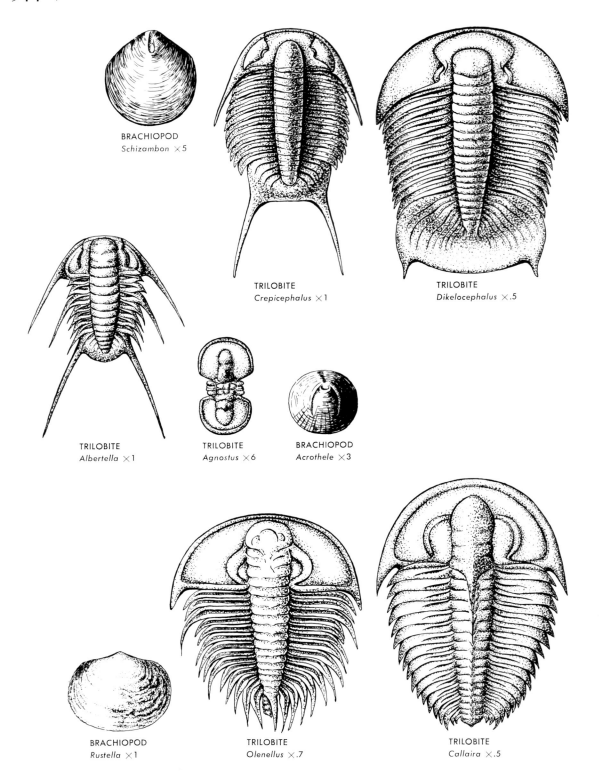

BRACHIOPOD
Schizambon ×5

TRILOBITE
Crepicephalus ×1

TRILOBITE
Dikelocephalus ×.5

TRILOBITE
Albertella ×1

TRILOBITE
Agnostus ×6

BRACHIOPOD
Acrothele ×3

BRACHIOPOD
Rustella ×1

TRILOBITE
Olenellus ×.7

TRILOBITE
Callaira ×.5

FIG. 35–1. / *Guide fossils for the Cambrian Period. Fossils depicted on this illustration are common guide fossils for the Cambrian. Those on the bottom row are guides to the Lower Cambrian, etc. While these are guide fossils the range of some far exceeded the part of the period they are here related to.*

A Brief History of Life on Earth

Precambrian

THE THREE TO FOUR BILLION YEARS THAT preceded the Cambrian Period was ample time for life to begin through synthesis of inorganic matter and for it to pass through the initial stages of differentiation and development. No record of this phase of life history on earth exists. In fact, there are very few widely accepted Precambrian fossils. Many so-called Precambrian fossils are disputed as inorganic markings of various types, but a few true fossils are known. These include primitive types of plants, blue-green algae found in southern Ontario, and trails and burrows presumably left by some type of wormlike animal. In addition, sponge spicules, jellyfish, bacteria, protozoans, and even arthropods have been tentatively identified.

Cambrian

ONE OF THE MOST FUNDAMENTAL BREAKS in the rock record occurs between Precambrian and Cambrian rocks. In many places this break represents a gap of millions, even billions, of years, but the significance of the break is best demonstrated by the conspicuous differences in fossil content of the units. Below are the vir-

tually unfossiliferous Precambrian units; above, layers in which a host of fossil invertebrates are found. Cambrian strata contain fossils of almost every invertebrate phylum. Some of these are minor constituents of Cambrian populations, and many of them are relatively primitive organisms by comparison with later members of their groups; but the initial diversification of organisms into many different structural groups had already taken place before the Cambrian. The first known fossil chordates (animals with backbones), fish, appear in Ordovician strata, but the remains are those of a highly developed animal. Thus we may eventually find chordate fossils in Cambrian rocks.

Among the most important groups of the Cambrian fauna and flora were trilobites, brachiopods, sponges, and calcareous algae. *Trilobites*[1] (Fig. 35–1) are a primitive class of

---

[1] Formal generic and specific names are ordinarily italicized in this text. Suprageneric and anglicized names are not italicized. The student should note that certain scientific terms have been placed in italics throughout this book to make them stand out so they can be easily located and learned. In this chapter the suprageneric names have been placed in italics for emphasis where they appear for the first time or at the place in the chapter where they are described most fully.

arthropods that inhabited shallow sun-lit waters of the continental shelves. Although they are now extinct they virtually dominated Cambrian seas. They molted, shedding an exoskeleton which was fragile and easily broken by wave action, producing local concentrations of trilobite fragments known as "trilobite hash." They crawled around on the sea bottom groveling in sediment for food.

A second group, next in importance to trilobites, were *brachiopods* (Fig. 35–2) (a phylum of marine invertebrate animals that have two unequal shells each of which is normally bilaterally symmetrical), marine *bivalves* (having a shell composed of two parts) that live attached to the bottom, generally in shallow water. They resemble modern clams, except that the plane of symmetry of the shells bisects rather than lies between the two shells. The earliest of these had shells composed of a chitino-phosphatic material similar to a fingernail, and, unlike those described above, did not have hinged shells.

Large reefs of *sponges* (Fig. 35–3) are found in Cambrian strata in New York and California as well as other parts of the world. One of the most commonly preserved parts of sponges are the spicules, hard supports in the soft walls. Glass or siliceous spicules that are small and shaped like jacks or little barbells are common.

Among the plants, *calcareous algae* were abundant. When well-preserved, these resemble large heads of cabbage (Fig. 29–10). Calcium carbonate became trapped within the algae, building them up as reefs.

Other less important groups of fossils include cystoids, a type of *echinoderm* (a phylum of marine invertebrate animals characterized by radial and five-rayed symmetry, a skeleton made of calcium carbonate plates, and many have spines) that resembles a plant attached to the sea floor and supporting a calyx, or head, on a long stem. A few small *gastropods* (mollusks that usually have a calcareous shell which is asymmetrically coiled and without internal partitions) have been found, both with coiled and with uncoiled shells. *Pelecypods* (invertebrates

FIG. 35–2. / *Cross section and break away of brachiopod shells, left, and illustrations of morphological parts of pelycopods, right. Although these two belong to different phylae they are often confused.*

characterized by a bivalve shell each of which is asymmetrical, but the two valves are mirror images of each other) were present, but very rare. *Cephalopods* (marine invertebrates characterized by a head surrounded by tentacles and, in most fossil forms, by a straight or coiled shell divided into chambers by partitions—a group which includes the modern nautilus) with straight, uncoiled shells lived in the seas, as did the now extinct graptolites. *Graptolites* (Fig. 35–5) lived in large colonies. The individuals were housed in small cup-shaped theca attached to a long string or stipe which hung from a float. Thus they drifted widely through the seas and fell into sediments at all depths and in many different types of environments, but they are best preserved in black shales and limestones. Even worms and jellyfishes have been preserved in Cambrian rocks in at least one remarkable fossil locality known as the Burgess Shale. This fauna is depicted in Fig. 35–4.

Ordovician

APPEARANCE OF THE FIRST FOSSIL FISH IS the most important development in Ordovician life. These first fish were jawless and covered by a hard, bony armor; thus the name *ostracoderm*—armor-skin (Fig. 38–2). Of these fish little more has been found than a few scales at several localities in the Rocky Mountains. Judging from the sediments in which they are found, the ostracoderms lived in freshwater streams. In any case they are the first vertebrates known to live on earth.

FIG. 35–3. / *Sponge and spicules. Cross section through a simple sponge, at the left, and an enlarged view of a variety of spicules, at the right. The shape and composition of the sponge spicules are used for classification of fossil sponges.*

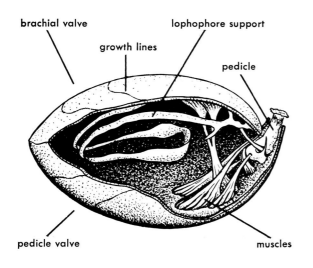

brachial valve

growth lines

lophophore support

pedicle

pedicle valve

muscles

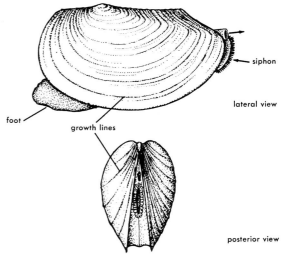

siphon

foot

growth lines

lateral view

posterior view

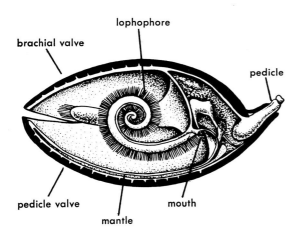

lophophore

brachial valve

pedicle

pedicle valve

mouth

mantle

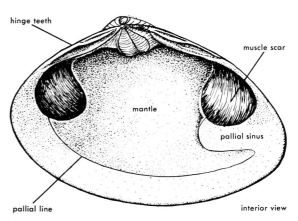

hinge teeth

muscle scar

mantle

pallial sinus

pallial line

interior view

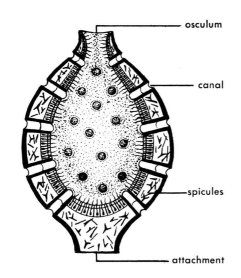

osculum

canal

spicules

attachment

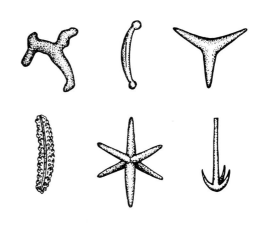

FIG. 35–4. / *Burgess shale restoration. These animals lived on the shallow sea floor in British Columbia, an area which now stands thousands of feet above sea level. This view includes colonies of branching sponges, trilobites, sea cumbers, jellyfishes, and an arthropod somewhat like modern crustaceans. (Photo by courtesy of the U. S. National Museum.)*

No evidence of land plants has been found in lower Paleozoic rocks. It is entirely possible that such life would not have been preserved even if it had been abundant. Almost certainly the lower, moist sections of the continents must have supported some of the simpler plants like lichens, but trees, grasses, and shrubs as we know them today were not present. Instead the continents were vast barren stretches of exposed rock. But life was flourishing in the seas of this time. None of the major groups found in Cambrian units became extinct in the Ordovician. Brachiopods and trilobites continued to be numerous and underwent further diversification with the appearance of many new genera. Algae continued to be prominent and the pelecypods became much more numerous.

A number of new classes of animals are found in Ordovician rocks. Up to this time the only *coelenterates* (a phylum of invertebrate animals characterized by simpler body organization than echinoderms and radial symmetry) were jellyfishes, but now true corals were present. These included the honeycomb coral, *Favosites* (Fig. 35–10), and horn corals (Fig. 35–6). These corals, unlike jellyfishes, build calcareous bases attached to the sea floor to house the soft parts of the animal. The horn corals contained a single animal, but whole colonies were built together by the honeycomb corals. The Cambrian echinoderms (meaning spiny skin), *cystoids*, were joined by several new and important classes, including *crinoids* (or "sea lilies"), *blastoids*, and starfishes. Both the crinoids and blastoids resemble the plantlike cystoids superficially, but they are readily identified when the calyx is examined in detail (compare in Fig. 35–19). Unlike the other echinoderms, the *starfishes* were not attached to the sea floor. They roamed the shallow sea bottoms, eating pelecypods and

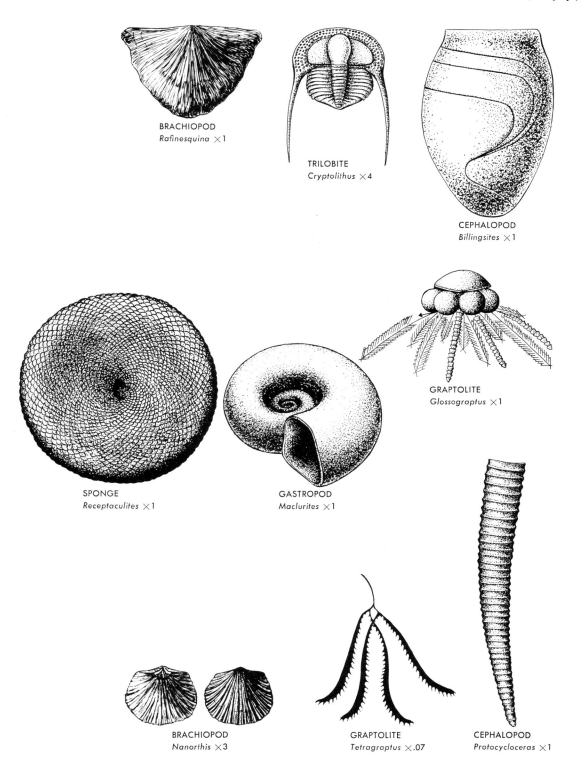

BRACHIOPOD
Rafinesquina ×1

TRILOBITE
Cryptolithus ×4

CEPHALOPOD
Billingsites ×1

SPONGE
Receptaculites ×1

GASTROPOD
Maclurites ×1

GRAPTOLITE
Glossograptus ×1

BRACHIOPOD
Nanorthis ×3

GRAPTOLITE
Tetragraptus ×.07

CEPHALOPOD
Protocycloceras ×1

FIG. 35–5. / *Guide fossils for the Ordovician System.*

FIG. 35–6. / *Cup corals, also called rugose corals.* (*Photo by courtesy of the U. S. National Museum.*)

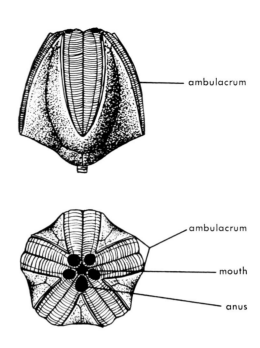

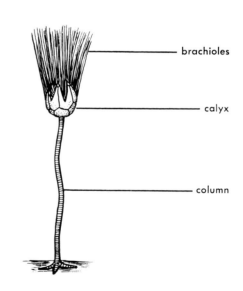

FIG. 35–7. / *Morphology of a blastoid. The brachioles waved in the water, creating currents directed along the ambulacral areas toward the mouth.*

probably brachiopods in much the same manner that modern starfish do, by using their tube feet to pull on a closed clamshell until the exhausted clam relaxed and the shell opened, laying the soft parts open to attack.

The Ordovician is known as the age of graptolites, now considered among the most structurally advanced invertebrates. They possessed a primitive *notochord* similar to that of the vertebrates. Until this was discovered they were variously classified as coelenterates and bryozoans, due to their colonial habit, their small size, and their generally poor preservation. Most specimens are no more than thin carbon films found in shale. The importance of the graptolites lies mainly in their great abundance, their floating habit, and the fact that they underwent rapid and easily discernible evolutionary changes. These characteristics make them exceptionally good guide fossils.

A new invertebrate phylum, *bryozoans* (Fig. 35–8), is found early in the Ordovician. These formed colonies in some ways resembling corals. They are among the important reef builders and are often associated with other shallow marine invertebrates. The giant of the Ordovician seas was a cephalopod that had a straight, uncoiled shell nearly fifteen feet long (Fig. 35–9). Although arthropods had been present since the

Cambrian, a new *crustacean*, the *ostracod*, destined to become geologically important, became abundant in the Ordovician. These are generally microscopic in size and have shells, shaped something like lima beans, in which the shrimplike animals live. They have become important for use in correlation.

Silurian

THERE WERE RELATIVELY FEW MAJOR changes in the Silurian fauna from those of the Ordovician. Invertebrates (Fig. 35–10) continued to be the most important groups of animals.

FIG. 35–8. / *A small section of a bryozoan colony. Two individuals are shown in cross section.*

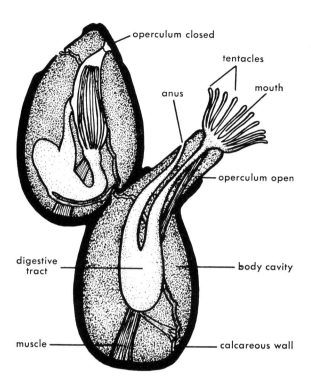

FIG. 35–9. / *Restoration of an Ordovician sea floor in the vicinity of Chicago. Seas which occupied the central United States contained the fauna and flora depicted here. They include trilobites, seaweeds, straight shelled cephalopods, "honeycomb" corals, gastropods, and nautiloids (swimming). (Courtesy of the Chicago Natural History Museum.)*

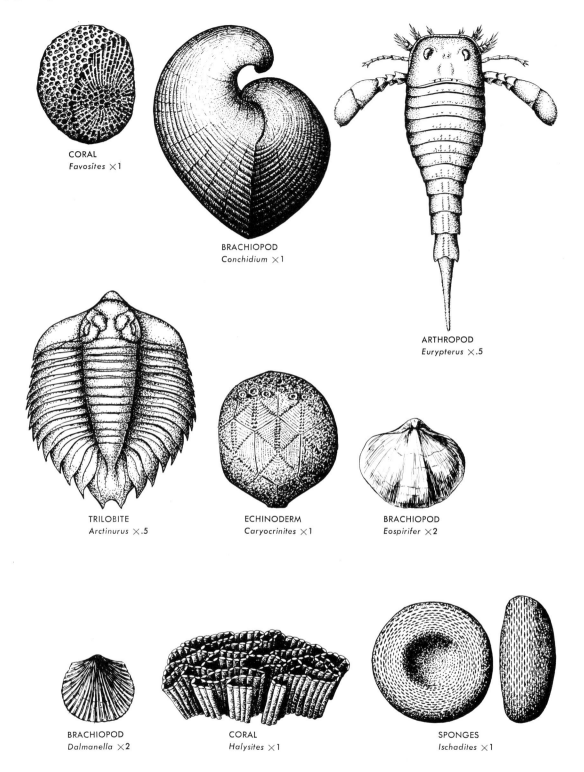

CORAL
Favosites ×1

BRACHIOPOD
Conchidium ×1

ARTHROPOD
Eurypterus ×.5

TRILOBITE
Arctinurus ×.5

ECHINODERM
Caryocrinites ×1

BRACHIOPOD
Eospirifer ×2

BRACHIOPOD
Dalmanella ×2

CORAL
Halysites ×1

SPONGES
Ischadites ×1

FIG. 35–10. / *Guide fossils for the Silurian.*

FIG. 35–11. / *Restoration of a Silurian sea floor near Buffalo*, N. Y. *Shown are algae, sea scorpions* Pterygotus (*center*) *and* Eurypterus (*left foreground*), *water scorpion* Eusarcus (*right background*), *worms, and "shrimp." (Photo courtesy of the U.S. National Museum.)*

Plants were scarce on land, although the first definite evidence of relatively large land plants is found in this system. These remains almost certainly do not represent the first plants to live on land, but they are the first that have been well preserved. Lands of the Cambrian and Ordovician and most of those of the Silurian were barren wastes. Only lowlands had much in the way of a vegetative cover, but plants that appeared at this time were forerunners of the greatest forests of all time in the Carboniferous.

A significant advance in plant life took place during the Silurian. Earlier plants had all been nonvascular, but at this time plants with leaves and stems and poorly developed root systems came into existence. With the evolution of roots it became possible for plants to live farther away from bodies of water and to grow to greater heights. These fossils are known as *lycopsid land plants* (Fig. 35–15).

Scorpion and milliped fossils have been found in Silurian strata. Soft parts of these are not well-enough preserved to reveal lungs or lunglike organs that might have been used to breathe air. But if they did have such organs, as do their modern counterparts, they are probably the first animals to obtain their oxygen supply directly from air.

Among the most unusual inhabitants of Silurian seas were arthropods called *eurypterids* (Fig. 35–11). These had long appendages similar to the claws of modern lobsters, and some of them grew to lengths of nine feet, making them the largest arthropods ever known.

Corals became a highly important group in Silurian seas. In the central United States there are many important Silurian coral reefs surrounding the Michigan basin and extending into New York (Fig. 35–12). These grew in shallow waters around an inland sea. Honeycomb, chain, cup, and compound corals all thrived in the shallow, warm waters. All Cambrian and Ordovician groups previously mentioned were still present, although the graptolites were not as important. One of the earlier groups, crinoids, became so abundant and widespread that whole rock units are composed of their remains.

Devonian

THE DEVONIAN IS KNOWN AS THE AGE OF Fishes. The first ostracoderms appeared in the Early Ordovician. More than 120 million years later fishes reached the climax of their development. The jawless ostracoderms were still abundant in Devonian freshwater streams, but there were many others. One notable variety, *placoderms*, contained platelike pieces of bone in their skin. One of the giants of the fish world was the arthrodire, a jointed-neck placoderm that grew to be 30 feet long (Fig. 35–13). These may well have been the most feared predators of the period. Sharks were abundant, but many of them were considerably smaller than those we know today.

The first bony fishes, forerunners of many modern varieties, also lived in the Early Devo-

nian. One of the bony fishes to evolve at this time was an ancestor of the African lungfish. We can learn a great deal about these early fish from habits of lungfish, which now live in upper parts of the Nile River valley. The climate is highly variable; there are warm, humid winters and dry summers. In winter lungfish live in water, breathing through gills, but in summer, as swamps begin to dry out, they embed themselves in mud. Each fashions a chamber in the mud and rests there until the next humid season. During this period it makes use of a swim bladder which is connected to the throat and functions like a lung.

The main group of Devonian lungfish is known as *crossopterygians*. They possessed a lobe-shaped fin for which they are named. They are important because they are the connecting link between fish and amphibians, which ap-

FIG. 35–12. / *Restoration of a Silurian sea floor near Rochester, N. Y. Shown are algae, chain coral (foreground), honeycomb coral (background), organ pipe corals (right side), bryozoans (lacy), feathery-armed flowerlike cystoids, brachiopods, straight-shelled nautiloid cephalopod, and trilobites. (Photo courtesy of the U.S. National Museum.)*

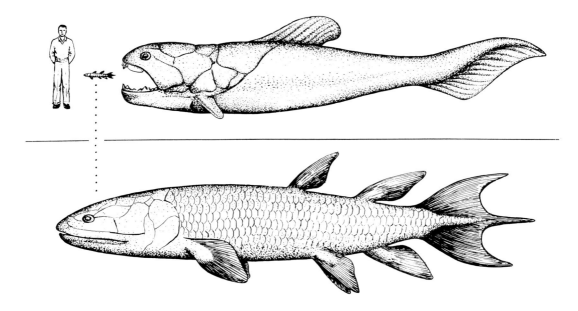

FIG. 35–13. / *Devonian fishes. At the top is a restored placoderm,* Dinichthys, *which grew to lengths of 30 feet. The head region was heavily armored with external bony plates that were jointed. Below is a Devonian crossopterygian. This fish was only about 2 feet long.*

peared late in this same period of time. The difference between these groups is relatively minor. Both breathe air through lungs. Amphibians, like fish, must lay their eggs in water, and both are closely linked to the aqueous environment in other ways. Most amphibians spend their lives near lakes, seas, or at least swampy lands. This close relationship is also indicated by the crossopterygian's strong muscular fins, which are similar in structure to the legs and webbed feet of primitive amphibians.

That land plants had become highly developed by this time is proven by an exceptional fossil forest, known as the Gilboa Forest (Fig. 35–15), which grew in the western part of New York State. Fossils here show us that seed ferns and scale trees, similar to those which were to become so common later, were present. Also fossils of the first known evergreen trees are in Devonian strata.

By this time a pattern of change and replacement among the invertebrates is discernible (Figs. 35–14 and 35–16). This continues through the geological record to the present. All of the phyla continued to be represented, but some of the early groups, like the trilobites, were becoming less important, while others, such as the brachiopods, became exceedingly abundant and diversified. In spite of their small numbers, Devonian trilobites are highly ornamented and huge, up to three feet long. In the case of the brachiopods, more than seven hundred species are known from rocks of this period. Corals also continued important, with some cup corals reaching the surprising height of nearly two feet. A group of coelenterates, called stromatoporoids, now extinct, were important reef builders of the Mid-Paleozoic. A new type of cephalopod appeared. These, called *ammonoids*, can be distinguished from *nautiloids* by the shape of the wall-like structure built within the shell behind the living chamber. This wall is smooth among *nautiloids*, but the structure is highly complicated and folded among ammonoids. The intersection of this partition with the exterior of the shell is called the *suture pattern* (Fig. 37–7).

FIG. 35–14. / *Restoration of a Devonian sea floor near Buffalo, N. Y. Shown are large colonial and solitary or cup corals, organ pipe corals (two kinds), staghorn corals, crinoids or sea lilies, blastoids, lacy bryozoa, straight-shelled nautiloid (striped), frilled and coiled nautiloid cephalopod, snails, and trilobites. (Photo courtesy of the U.S. National Museum.)*

Mississippian

BY THE BEGINNING OF THE CARBONIFEROUS all major phyla and most important classes of animals were present. Amphibians appeared before the Mississippian, and reptiles are found in the next overlying system, thus it is probable that reptiles lived in the Mississippian and that we will some day find their remains.

Sharks were the most important vertebrates of Mississippian seas. Their teeth are particularly well preserved. Some had teeth especially designed for crushing shells. These short rounded teeth lined the jaws, giving them the appearance of a stone pavement; hence the name *pavement teeth*. Several hundred species of sharks are known to have lived during this time, as compared with less than 100 species of sharks in periods which preceded and followed the Carboniferous.

Fusulinids (Fig. 35–18), microscopic-sized protozoans belonging to the group known as Foraminifera, have been exceptionally good guide fossils for the Carboniferous. In places they are so abundant that whole limestone units are made up of their tiny shells, shaped like grains of wheat. Fragments of crinoids (Fig. 35–17) are found widely distributed in Mississippian limestones, and a few limestones are composed almost entirely of their stems. They are among the most plentiful Mississippian fossils. Brachiopods continued to be abundant in shallow-water marine environments. Several new brachiopods appeared. *Productid brachiopods* (Fig. 35–20), which have spiny projections from

FIG. 35–15. *Early land plants. Abundant and widespread land plants are found first in rocks of the Devonian Period, dating from about 350 million years ago. They set the stage for the invasion of the land by animals, which are ultimately dependent upon plants for food. Shown here are one of the first ferns, a tree that grew 30 to 40 feet high; horsetail rushes; one of the most primitive plants, Psilophyton, which had no leaves; and a lycopod, the tall tree without leaves which is covered by short spikelike projections which served as leaves. (From a mural by C. R. Knight, courtesy of Chicago Natural History Museum.)*

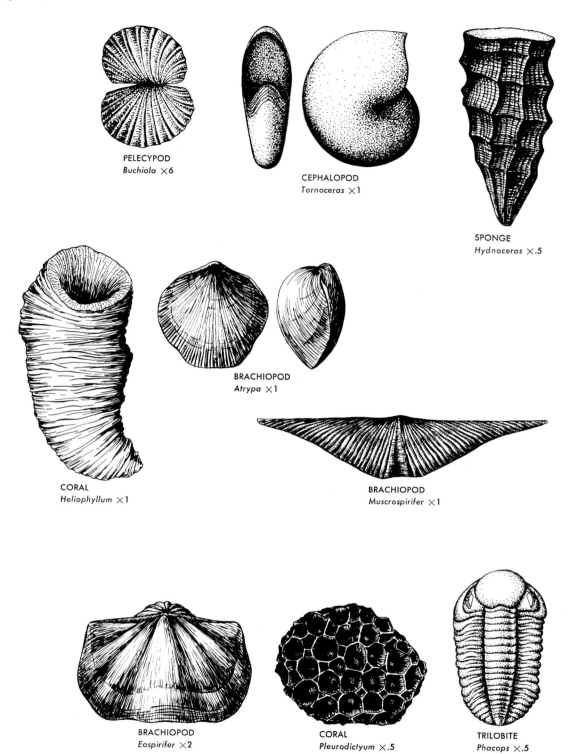

PELECYPOD
Buchiola ×6

CEPHALOPOD
Tornoceras ×1

SPONGE
Hydnoceras ×.5

CORAL
Heliophyllum ×1

BRACHIOPOD
Atrypa ×1

BRACHIOPOD
Muscrospirifer ×1

BRACHIOPOD
Eospirifer ×2

CORAL
Pleurodictyum ×.5

TRILOBITE
Phacops ×.5

FIG. 35-16. / *Devonian guide fossils.*

FIG. 35–17. / *Restoration of a Mississippian sea floor near northwestern Indiana. Shown are algae, sea lily "garden" with several kinds of crinoids, blastoid, and starfish (on bottom). (Photo courtesy of the U. S. National Museum.)*

their shells, were one of these. They continued to be important throughout the Carboniferous. A second group, *spirifers* (Fig. 35–16), are distinguished by the shape of the lophophore, the internal support that held up soft parts and was used to set up currents directed toward the mouth. These supports in spirifers are spirals. Blastoids (Fig. 35–19) were probably never as abundant as they were during the Mississippian, but before the end of the Carboniferous they became extinct.

Corals and trilobites were on the decline. Older corals, such as cup and honeycomb corals, finally died out, only to be replaced by other corals that have continued to be abundant to the present. Trilobites, on the other hand, gradually declined, until the last survivors of this magnificent species vanished during the Pennsylvanian. They may have become prey of sharks, but the cause of their extinction is still unknown.

FIG. 35–18. / *Fusulinids. (Photo courtesy of the U. S. National Museum.)*

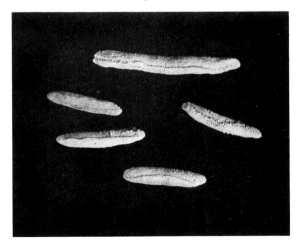

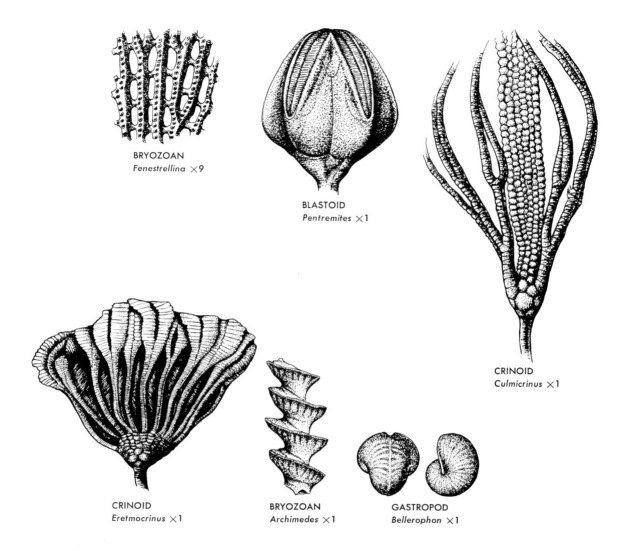

BRYOZOAN
Fenestrellina ×9

BLASTOID
Pentremites ×1

CRINOID
Culmicrinus ×1

CRINOID
Eretmocrinus ×1

BRYOZOAN
Archimedes ×1

GASTROPOD
Bellerophon ×1

CORAL
Hadrophyllum ×1.5

PELECYPOD
Mytilarca ×1

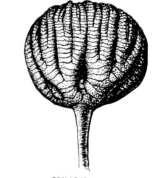

CRINOID
Parichthyocrinus ×1

FIG. 35–19. / *Mississippian guide fossils.*

Pennsylvanian

No feature of the life of the Pennsylvanian is as outstanding as the swampland forests (Fig. 35–22) that covered large areas in almost every part of the world. We have little record of life that may have thrived on higher lands, but the swamps provide us a record of profuse vegetation unlike any before or since. There were no flowering plants like those that make up most of the modern vegetation in lowland regions. Instead, there were seed ferns and giant scale trees. Scale trees, *Lepidodendron* and *Sigillaria* (Fig. 35–21), were the largest trees of the time. The largest is more than 100 feet tall and over five feet in diameter. The name "scale tree" is given to these groups because the bark looks as though it is covered by scales. Actually these are scars left after leaves were shed from branches and trunk. *Lepidodendron* bark is easily distinguished by diamond-shaped leaf scars arranged spirally around branches. Their leaves were similar to pine needles and 8 to 10 inches in length. *Sigillaria* leaf scars are oval in shape and arranged in vertical rows.

Under these trees there was a luxuriant growth of seed ferns and true ferns. Scouring rushes grew in dense thickets like modern cane-brakes. Largest of these rushes were the *calamites* (Fig. 35–22). These grew up to 30 feet tall and were almost a foot in diameter. Rushes are recognized by vertical ribs and regularly spaced joints in stems. On *calamites* a whorl of simple leaves grew at the joints. Like larger scale trees they contained a pithy center surrounded by a thick layer of woody matter.

Insects swarmed through the swamps. Of these cockroaches were notable, not only because of their great number but also because of their variety. Almost 1,000 different species have been described. Some of these grew to be as long as three inches (Fig. 35–24). This period is often called the "Age of Cockroaches." Besides cockroaches, almost 2,000 other species of insects lived in the Pennsylvanian. It was during this time that some of these species attained the largest sizes ever known. Dragonflies with a wingspread of nearly 30 inches were abundant, and several other insects grew to be a foot long (Fig. 35–22).

Of the Pennsylvanian amphibians, *labyrinthodonts* (Fig. 38–12) were particularly abundant, and several others were represented. The giant amphibians were approximately 15 feet long. They had large bodies with strong tails, but relatively small legs. There were others whose general appearance was very similar to that of modern snakes. One of the smallest grew no larger than angleworms. The ability of several forms to lay their eggs in soft sand instead of in water was perhaps the most outstanding advancement of this group as a whole. This adaptation was a big step toward occupation of the continents.

Remains of true reptiles first appear in this period. Most of these early specimens were only about a foot long and had an elongated, slender body. Because their skin could retain moisture it was possible for them to travel great distances away from streams and swamps.

FIG. 35–20. / *Productid Brachiopods. (Photo courtesy of the U. S. National Museum.)*

FIG. 35–21. / *Four important fossil plants:* Lepidodendron, Cordaites, Sigillaria, *and* Calamites. *All of these were abundant in the coal-forming swamps which covered the eastern interior of North America during the Carboniferous.*

FIG. 35–22. / *Coal forest restoration. A large dragonfly with a wing span of nearly three feet dominates the center of this view into a Carboniferous coal swamp. Also present are ferns:* Sigillaria, Lepidodendron, Calamites, *a large rush that grew to be as much as thirty feet tall, and smaller rushes,* Sphenophyllum. *(Photo by courtesy of the Chicago Natural History Museum.)*

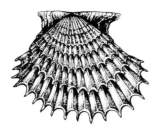

PELECYPOD
Acanthopecten ×2

GASTROPOD
Euconospira ×2

BRACHIOPOD
Dictyoclostus ×1

PELECYPOD
Monopteria ×1

CRINOID
Graphiocrinus ×1

CORAL
Lophophyllidium ×1.5

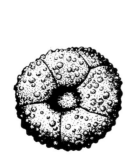

CRINOID
Ethelocrinus ×1

CEPHALOPOD
Gastrioceras ×2

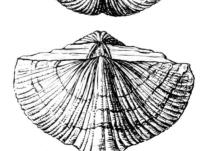

BRACHIOPOD
Neospirifer ×1

FIG. 35–23. / *Pennsylvanian guide fossils.*

FIG. 35–24. / *Cockroach fossil. Cockroaches were so abundant during the Pennsylvanian that the period is sometimes known as the "Age of Cockroaches." This fossil is* Dictyomylacris *from an Upper Carboniferous coal swamp.*

FIG. 35–25. / *Restoration of a Pennsylvanian sea floor near North-central Texas. Shown are algae, staghorn sponge and solitary sponge, large cup corals, sea lilies, brachiopods (spiny, light gray, and striped), a large spiny sea-urchin, scallops (background), mussels (left and right foreground), snails, large coiled nautiloid cephalopods (right and left foreground), and small ammonite (center). (Photo courtesy of U. S. National Museum.)*

FIG. 35–26. / *Mammal-like reptiles. Two hundred million years ago, reptiles of a kind destined to give rise to the mammals had come into existence. This scene, during the Triassic period in South Africa, shows a clumsy plant-eater* (Kannemeryeria) *being attacked by a group of active flesh-eaters* (Cynognathus) *believed to be close to the actual ancestors of mammals. (From a mural by Charles Knight, photo by Chicago Natural History Museum.)*

Permian

BY THIS PERIOD AMPHIBIANS WERE VERY abundant. One of these, *Eryops*, is fairly typical of late Paleozoic amphibians. These were heavily built, with a broad, flat skull of thick bone. The large bone structure suggests that they were well adapted to life on land. Most probably they lived an alligator-like existence along streams and swamps. Another group, *Seymouria* (Fig. 39–1), possessed characteristics intermediate between reptile and amphibian skull-bone structure. Although reptiles were already in existence at this time, it seems likely that they may have evolved from a *Seymouria*-like animal.

Specialization of reptiles is especially interesting. One of these groups, *theriodonts* (Fig. 35–26), developed teeth like those of mammals. One group of primitive reptiles had become diversified so that some ate meat; others fed on insects, and still others lived on plants. One of the most peculiar-looking reptiles of the period was the *Dimetrodon* (Fig. 35–28), which possessed a series of skin-connected spines that stood up on its back like a sail.

Evidence of Continental Drift

GLOSSOPTERIS FLORA: Two of the most characteristic plants of the Permian in the Southern Hemisphere are *Glossopteris* and *Gangamopteris*. Both have small, thick leaves from which the name "tongue ferns" was derived. Remains of these frequently occur with sediments deposited near margins of Permian glaciers. Apparently they lived under frigid conditions near ice sheets. One interesting aspect of this plant assemblage is that Permian fossils of them are found on continents now separated by thousands of miles of ocean water. The problem

BRACHIOPOD
Punctospirifer ×1

BLASTOID
Timoroblastus ×1

FUSULINID
Triticites ×8

CEPHALOPOD
Perrinites ×1

BRACHIOPOD
Meekella ×1

GASTROPOD
Bucanopsis ×2

CORAL
Lophophyllidium ×2

PELECYPOD
Myalina ×.5

CEPHALOPOD
Cooperoceras ×.3

FIG. 35–27. / *Permian guide fossils.*

FIG. 35–28. / *Reconstruction of a group of Dimetrodons, one of the mammal-like reptiles. (Painting by Charles Knight, Chicago Natural History Museum.)*

they raise is how such an otherwise geographically restricted group could suddenly appear in such widely separated regions as Africa, South America, and India. Spores of *Glossopteris*, which have a broad double-wing shape, might have been blown for long distances and might possibly have gotten across the oceans in this way or in ocean currents. Another suggestion has been that there may have been land bridges —one connecting the southern tip of South America with Antarctica and another connecting Antarctica with South Africa. Such a bridge between South America and Antarctica seems possible, since there are a number of islands between the two land masses, but the distance between South Africa and Antarctica is great. It has also been suggested that there were continental lands that simply sank, but geophysical studies reveal no sign of a true continental-type crust anywhere in the region.

FIG. 35–29. / *Restoration of a Permian sea floor near Western Texas. Shown are algae, large pipelike sponges, bead sponge (left background), compact sponges (foreground), cup corals, spiny brachiopods (on reef), oyster-like brachiopods (middle foreground), red-striped brachiopods, spire-bearing brachiopods, spiny oysterlike clams with slender cup corals (left foreground), coiled and spiny nautiloid cephalopods (on bottom), and ammonites on patch reef. (Photo courtesy of the U.S. National Museum.)*

FIG. 35–30. / *Restoration of a Cretacheous sea floor near Western Tennessee, east of Memphis. Shown are algae with numerous types of clams and snails, straight-shelled ammonite (left side), giant coiled ammonite (left side), cork-screw ammonite (right center background), boat-shaped ammonite (center foreground), and belemnites (swimming). (Photo courtesy of the U.S. National Museum.)*

Another long-debated idea is that India, South America, and Africa may have once been a single continental land mass. If this indeed was the case in the Permian, then it is easy to explain the distribution of glaciers and the peculiar associated flora. It would follow that after the Permian the land mass split and the segments drifted apart to their present positions. This theory is known as the *theory of continental drift*. Outlines of continental borders of South America and Africa are quite suggestive of this possibility. Tentative correlations of the geological frameworks of these areas have also been made. More recently some paleomagnetic studies have supported this view.

The colder climates of the Permian were unfavorable for the Carboniferous ferns and scale trees. True conifers, *Walchia*, better adapted to the cool climatic conditions, rapidly expanded to replace earlier plants.

The end of the Permian is one of the most significant breaks in the record of life on earth. The extinction of many earlier groups, the general restriction of favorable environmental conditions for life, and the remarkable changes in dominant groups that followed in the Triassic, are the basis for grouping the Permian and older periods in the Paleozoic, meaning "old life," and separating them from the following three periods, known collectively as the Mesozoic, "middle life." By the close of the Permian many of the earlier invertebrate groups had disappeared. Among these were the trilobites, fusulinids, honeycomb and tetra corals, crinoids, and many of the bryozoans; furthermore, many of the Carboniferous plants had dwindled almost to extinction.

Triassic

REPTILES BECAME EXCEEDINGLY ABUNDANT and varied in their adaptations during the Triassic. One group, *phytosaurs*, was similar in appearance and mode of life to alligators. Two important groups of reptiles returned to the seas from which their ancestors had come. These, *ichthyosaurs* and *plesiosaurs* (Fig. 35–31), were large, streamlined, and fishlike in appearance. They must have been very swift swimmers. Plesiosaurs were shaped something like a turtle with a long flexible neck. They were clumsy compared with ichthyosaurs, but used their long necks to good advantage in grabbing fish.

A number of mammal-like Triassic reptiles have been found in South Africa. Some of these are so similar to mammals that the only important differences appear to be in the number of bones in the lower jaw and in the feet. They may have had warm blood, hair, milk glands, and other mammalian characteristics. In general appearance these reptiles resembled modern opossums. Other mammal-like reptiles were much larger. They were heavy-boned animals with only two teeth in the upper jaws.

Dinosaurs, most spectacular of the reptiles, evolved in the Triassic, and before the end of the period they had established themselves as the dominant animals in the world. They began a rule that lasted throughout the Mesozoic Era and was shared only with other reptiles.

The petrified forest of northern Arizona contains remains of a forest of huge trees. These were preserved in clays of the Chinle formation. Most of the trees in the petrified forest were conifers, similar except in size to those that grow in the southwest today. Many of these had trunks over 100 feet long and up to 10 feet in diameter. Some of these cone-bearing trees may have been up to 200 feet high. In the same area are found a few ferns, which grew along banks of streams.

Ammonoids became the most important of the marine invertebrates. Suture patterns in these cephalopods became increasingly complex.

FIG. 35–31. / *Marine reptiles. The long-necked plesiosaurs propelled themselves with strong flippers. The fish-like ichthyosaurs fed on squids and drove themselves through the water with their powerful tails. (Painting by Charles Knight, Chicago Natural History Museum.)*

Some could swim, but apparently others simply floated in surface waters. Toward the end of the period ammonoids almost became extinct, but one group survived into the Jurassic, when they underwent a second evolutionary burst. It may be that they were nearly killed off by marine reptiles at the end of the Triassic.

Jurassic

THROUGHOUT THE MESOZOIC REPTILES dominated the world. The peak of their development was reached in the Jurassic, although they continued strong throughout the Cretaceous as well. Reptiles took to air and to water and dominated land environments (Fig. 39–1). The number and variety are remarkable. (Evolutionary development of the reptiles is described later.) Flying reptiles were unlike birds because they lacked feathers, but the two were related in that both descended from reptiles. Flying reptiles probably could not fly like birds, but were reduced to gliding. They ranged in size from several inches to almost four feet. Marine reptiles reached a peak in their abundance. Dinosaurs roamed the land masses, inhabiting swamps, river bottoms, and marshy alluvial plains. They ranged in size from one about the size of a rooster, found with its young in the Solenhofen limestone, up to giants like *Brontosaurus*, which sometimes grew to as much as 90 feet long and weighed over 50 tons. These spent most of their lives in swamps and fed on plants. One group of dinosaurs, *Camptosaurus*, had ducklike bills, which they used to search through sands and shallow-water sediments for food. Most ferocious dinosaurs of this time had jaws lined with sharp teeth. These huge beasts lived outside swamps and fed on their fat and less agile plant-eating relatives. *Stegosaurus*, a dinosaur armed with bony plates along its back and tail, lived out of the swamps but fed on plants.

The first definite mammal remains are found in rocks of this period. Jaws and teeth of these small mammals have been found in many parts of the world. Teeth are one of the best-preserved and most useful structures for classification of mammals, for mammalian teeth are differentiated into molars, premolars, canines, and incisors. These early mammals probably looked like small squirrels or other rodents.

Remains of feathers of some of the earliest birds, called *Archaeopteryx* (Fig. 39–15), have been found in the Solenhofen limestone of Bavaria. These birds, which were about the size of a crow, possessed sharp teeth and other reptilian characteristics that establish the connection between these groups.

Moths and flies were among insects that appeared for the first time. Insects were abundant and have been preserved in the remarkable deposits of the Solenhofen limestone and in the Purbeck beds of England, where dragonflies, locusts, grasshoppers, butterflies, ants, and even beetles are beautifully fossilized. About 19 species of mammals are found in these same beds.

Invertebrate faunas had by this time assumed very modern characteristics. With a few exceptions they resembled the life of present seas. Those exceptions are ammonites and belemnites. Ammonites flourished anew in the Jurassic after escaping extinction by a narrow margin at the end of the Triassic. *Belemnites* (Fig. 35–32) were cephalopods that probably resembled modern squid. They had an internal calcareous skeleton that looks much like a cigar. Although most of these are only a few inches long, some reach a length as great as five feet.

Cretaceous

WERE WE ABLE TO VISIT CRETACEOUS time, undoubtedly the most impressive aspect of the life would be dinosaurs. The mammals would probably have been rather hard to find, since most of them were small and probably remained hidden from the larger reptiles as much as possible. Aside from dinosaurs, however, we would probably be impressed by the forests, which were so changed from those of earlier geologic periods. *Deciduous* trees, those that shed their leaves during part of the year,

FIG. 35–32. / *Restored belemnites of the Jurassic seas. These squid-like cephalopods flourished in the Jurassic but they became extinct before the end of the Mesozoic. These cigar-shaped internal skeletons are all that remains. (Photo by courtesy of the Chicago Natural History Museum.)*

would be present for the first time. This characteristic almost certainly sprang up in response to climatic conditions—a seasonal variation in temperature and rainfall. Earliest of these trees are magnolias, fig trees, and poplars. Of course, there were also flowering plants at this time. This too was something new on earth, the advent of trees with flowers and seeds protected by a covering. By the middle part of the period there were birches, maples, oaks, walnuts, tulip trees, sweet gums, laurel, ivy, and holly. These trees had come to replace the evergreen cone-bearing trees as the dominant land plants. However, conifers were still present and abundant. Among them sequoias somewhat smaller than the giants of California were widespread.

At the same time many other new angiosperm plants (those that have seeds in a closed ovary) appeared. These included grasses, cereals, fruit-bearing trees, and vegetables. Try to imagine your diet without products of angiosperms, and you will see why it is thought that mammal evolution was tied in closely with evolution of

these plants. Birds for the first time found a food supply above the ground, where they could obtain it relatively free from danger. They no longer needed teeth to pick up small animals and fish, and thus many new varieties of birds began to evolve in succeeding periods. Likewise mammals found a new food source suitable for their needs, and they were able to sustain life through whatever the extremes were that killed the dinosaurs.

Two new groups of mammals appeared on the scene, although neither was a challenge to the dominance of reptiles. These new mammals were *marsupials* and *insectivores*. Marsupials carry their young in a pouch, like the kangaroo. The first insectivores resembled shrews and moles, which are later descendants of this same stock.

Dominance of reptiles continued through the Cretaceous. They had by this time become adapted to almost every mode of life and filled and dominated air, seas, and land masses. Most terrible of these was *Tyrannosaurus rex* (Fig.

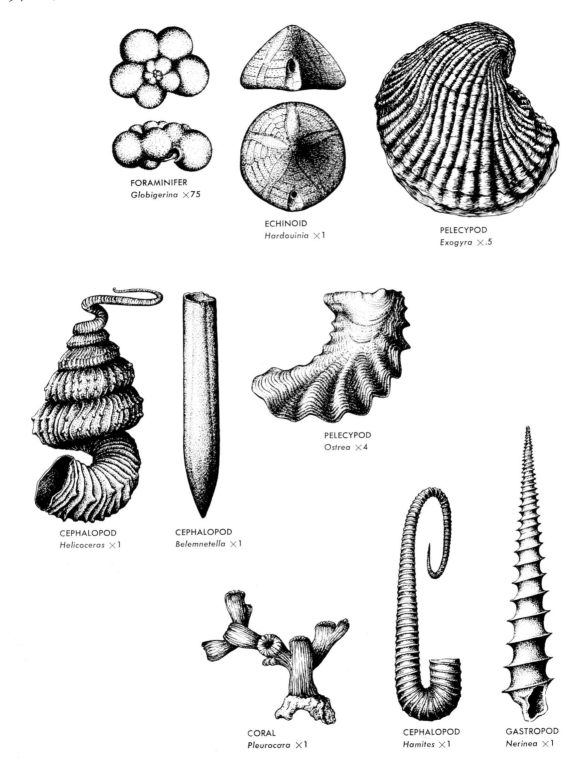

FORAMINIFER
Globigerina ×75

ECHINOID
Hardouinia ×1

PELECYPOD
Exogyra ×.5

CEPHALOPOD
Helicoceras ×1

CEPHALOPOD
Belemnetella ×1

PELECYPOD
Ostrea ×4

CORAL
Pleurocora ×1

CEPHALOPOD
Hamites ×1

GASTROPOD
Nerinea ×1

FIG. 35–33. / *Guide fossils for the Cretaceous.*

39–6), very likely the most voracious animal ever to roam the earth. They walked on their hind legs, like most smaller dinosaurs, and their front legs were small, and probably useless, vestiges. They stood up to 20 feet tall and had a four-foot head. Their long, powerful jaws were lined with sharp teeth. Others of the dinosaur clan of this time looked like large ostriches. They had no teeth at all and probably depended on eggs of other dinosaurs for their food.

The first skulls of the large, horned dinosaurs, *Triceratops* (Fig. 39–6), are found in the Cretaceous. They had two long horns that projected from their forehead and a shorter one over the nose and were further protected by a massive, bony shield that covered the neck. They probably needed such protection from the gigantic carnivorous dinosaurs with which they lived.

Duck-billed dinosaurs had been present in the Jurassic and were still abundant during the Cretaceous, as were plesiosaurs. Most notable of these has been found in Australia, where one plesiosaur skull measures 9½ feet. Similar giants flew over Cretaceous seas. These were the *pterosaurs*, which first appeared in the Jurassic, but those of Cretaceous age were much larger. Some had a wingspread of more than 25 feet. Reptiles had by this time attained the culmination of their reign on earth, and before the end of the period all of the most important groups died out, leaving only a few rather inconspicuous members of their race behind. What caused this great "dying-off" is one of the most baffling problems in historical geology.

Several groups of Foraminifera (Fig. 35–33) became exceedingly abundant during the Creta-

FIG. 35–34. / *A restored late Cretaceous sea floor. (Courtesy of the Chicago Natural History Museum.)*

ceous. In fact, the chalk deposits for which the period is named were formed of their minute remains and are common in many parts of the world. Notable among these chalk deposits are the cliffs of Dover.

Ammonites continued to be important among invertebrate groups. They attained their maximum sizes at this time, when some of the coiled ammonites were more than seven feet in diameter. If that shell had been uncoiled, as some ammonites were, it would have been more than 35 feet long.

Not a single dinosaur is known to have escaped the extinction which overtook the group at the end of the period. Many explanations have been offered for the disappearance of a group that had become so well adapted to life in all sorts of environments. Why did they suddenly lose the ability to adapt to any further changes? Mountain building, which occurred toward the close of the period, has been cited by many as the most probable cause. Mountains interrupt and change the circulation of air and the climate in regions near them; but mountains rose in the Jurassic also, with no such comparable result. It could be that these climatic changes were too much for the dinosaurs and other reptiles. It has also been pointed out that many reptiles had evolved to extremes in size and structure, and that these forms were unsuited to adaptations. We cannot be sure what happened, but the close of this period saw the decline and extinction of all dinosaurs, pterosaurs, ichthyosaurs, and plesiosaurs, and also all ammonites and belemnites.

Cenozoic

THE LIFE HISTORY OF THE CENOZOIC IS characterized by the replacement of older groups which accompanied the evolutionary emergence of modern fauna and flora. Drastic changes took place in a relatively short time between the Late Cretaceous and Early Tertiary. Mammals rapidly replaced reptiles in the position of dominance, and birds, insects, and bony fish underwent almost explosive evolutionary bursts.

Two major classes of mammals, *marsupials* and *placentals*, have been abundant in the Cenozoic. Marsupials have pouches in which the young are carried during early life. Placentals have a longer gestation period during which the young develop within a placenta. A third class, *monotremes*, has barely survived to be represented by such highly specialized but archaic forms as the duck-billed platypus and the spiny anteater. Like other monotremes, these retain various reptilian characteristics which make them the lowest order of all mammals.

Marsupials and placentals presumably lived together at the start of the Tertiary, but during this time the placentals began to multiply and diversify so fast that the marsupials were unable to compete effectively; consequently, they nearly disappeared from all but two isolated areas, South America and Australia. Both of these continents have been connected, as South America now is, by narrow "land bridges" with other continents. It was just at the close of the Mesozoic that Australia became separated from Asia. Similarly, South America was not connected to North America during most of the Tertiary. Thus, in isolation from the superior placentals, marsupials survived and underwent a remarkable evolutionary history. One of the most interesting aspects of this has been the evolution of animals that are closely similar in habits and appearance to placentals. Examples include the Tasmanian wolf, Koala bears, and marsupial "mice" and "moles." Only a very few marsupials, notably the opossum, inhabit regions where placentals are abundant.

There have been 28 orders of Cenozoic placentals, sixteen of which live today. These include:

Even-toed hoofed mammals—pigs, camels, deer, giraffes, sheep, and cattle.
Odd-toed hoofed mammals—horses and rhinoceroses.
Insectivores—shrews, moles, and hedgehogs.
Bats.
Edentates—anteaters, sloths, and armadillos.
Rodents—squirrels, beavers, porcupines, mice, and rats.
Rabbits.

Whales and porpoises.

Carnivores—seals, cats, dogs, skunks, wolves, foxes, weasels, minks, and bears.

Proboscideans—elephants.

Primates—lemurs, tarsiers, monkeys, apes, and man.

This list omits the now extinct mammals, but its length, the variety of animals represented, and the great differences in the habits and lives led by these animals suggests the nature and extent of Cenozoic mammalian history. Mammals have gradually expanded into all types of environments, just as reptiles did in the Mesozoic. There are also cases of trends toward increase in size and especially toward specialization of teeth and limbs.

One of the best-documented parts of the evolutionary development of mammals deals with horses. The first ones lived in the Eocene Epoch of the Tertiary, but they were miniature animals, about the size of a dog. They inhabited the Northern Rocky Mountains region. In succeeding periods the horses became larger and the bone structure of the hoofs became increasingly better adapted to running.

Primate history, though poorly documented, is of particular interest to man. The first primates, lemurs and tarsiers, lived in the Paleocene. Apes and monkeys came later, in the Miocene, and took advantage of a new environmental condition—the forests, with their abundance of food and safety. A manlike ape lived in the Pliocene, and true man emerged in the Pleistocene.

The histories of mammals and birds in the Cenozoic are linked to the development and abundance of flowering plants. Without the fruit- and nut-bearing trees and the grasses and cereals it is doubtful that most of the birds and mammals we know today would have survived long. Moreover, it is doubtful that they would have evolved at all. Grazing animals evolved and became abundant early in the Tertiary. This was likewise a time of abundance of grasses and cereals. Most Mesozoic birds had teeth. They presumably lived on small animals in much the same way that hawks do today. With the development of angiosperms and a new plentiful food supply the teeth were unnecessary. So it is not surprising that modern birds of the Cenozoic are toothless. There have been other changes among birds. Those that continue to live in the air have developed a lighter and stronger bone structure consisting of hollow or air-pocket-filled bones.

A group of fishes known as bony fish (teleosts) have also been exceptionally prominent among Cenozoic fauna. The teleosts lived in the Mesozoic, but they became the most abundant fishes in the Tertiary. Now there are an estimated 20,000 species, making up possibly half of all living vertebrates. Included among the bony fish are most modern fish, such as herring, sardines, shad, anchovies, salmon, trout, smelts, graylings, and catfish.

Changes which took place among the invertebrates are less spectacular than those among the land animals. Most of the modern genera either appeared very early in the Tertiary or were carried over from the Mesozoic. Virtually all of the classes of invertebrates had been in existence long before the start of the Cenozoic. Of the invertebrates, Foraminifera, or protozoans, stand out as important in the Cenozoic. They have been both abundant and highly varied, and their remains make up large portions of modern sediment. Foraminifera have been especially useful in making correlations and helping to establish environmental conditions of the sediments of which they are a part. Certain of them are known to inhabit fresh water; others live exclusively in marine waters of specific temperature ranges. Of the larger invertebrates, pelecypods and gastropods have been abundant and widespread. Their remains make up large parts of the shell fragments on beaches. A host of other invertebrates, including echinoderms, arthropods, and corals, are at least locally important.

36 / Theory of Evolution

FEW SCIENTIFIC THEORIES HAVE HAD AN IM-
pact, on scientists and nonscientists alike, comparable to that of the theory of evolution. The
theory precipitated a controversy between science and religion that has not yet completely
subsided. The idea that man, as well as all other
animals and plants, has through an extremely
long period of time evolved from lower forms
of life, and perhaps ultimately from inorganic
materials through inorganic processes, was totally
contrary to religious dogma of the 1800's. This
initiated an open "conflict between science and
religion." As a result, many religious faiths have
readjusted their ideas in such a manner as to
resolve the conflict. Others hold tenaciously to
their original dogma on grounds that, no matter
how conclusive scientific facts may seem, there
is always ample margin for error and misinter-
pretation. The theory of evolution did far more
than affect the relationship between science and
religion. Darwin's mechanism for the evolutionary process is natural selection, a process
that has often been misconstrued as meaning
"survival of the fittest," in a very strict sense
of the phrase. The Darwinian concept has even
become an underlying principle in some politi-
cal and economic philosophies.

Basis for Theory of Evolution

EVIDENCE FOR THE VALIDITY OF THE
theory of evolution now abounds on every side.
Various lines of evidence may be found in the
fields of embryology, genetics, and anthropology,
but we will confine our attention to evidence
obtained primarily from paleontology. The body
of geologic data revealing the fossil content of
successively younger rock strata is the most dramatic and conclusive proof of the changing
character of life through time. This record
formed the basis for many of the basic ideas
expressed by Darwin.

Because geologists use fossils as a basis for
recognition of the age of rocks, it is commonly
assumed that evolution is the basis for the
geologic time scale and that all historical interpretation is based on the assumption of systematic evolution of life through time. This is
most emphatically not true; if it were, geology
would indeed be on uncertain ground. Geologic
time cannot be based directly on evolution of
life, for the question of the rate of evolution is
largely unanswered. Also, there is no way to
predict exactly in which direction evolution is
likely to turn the development of a particular

organism—some species have not evolved through time, others have evolved toward higher forms, and still others have evolved toward extinction.

Instead, evolution is based on the rock record. One of William Smith's major contributions to geology was his recognition that each stratum of rocks contained a definite assemblage of fossils, and that it is possible to determine what part of a sequence is present by its fossil content. It is not possible to predict on the basis of evolution alone *what* fossil forms will be in the next higher or lower strata in a sequence. It took many years of detailed description and field investigation to establish a stratigraphic column that is applicable over large parts of the world. First the normal (right-side-up) sequence had to be established and intervals of erosion and nondeposition accounted for. This could only be accomplished through correlations based on physical criteria such as continuity of outcrop, lithology, and position in a sequence. Once these correlations were complete, it was then possible to compare and correlate faunas and floras of one unit of rocks with those of the same age in other places. It became obvious that assemblages of fossils were characteristic of certain units, and that, for purposes of correlation, they were as reliable as physical properties.

After the stratigraphic column had been established, it was apparent that some fossil faunas and floras within successively younger units showed remarkable progressive changes. Many types of changes could be noted. Instead of finding that man, horses, sharks, crinoids, and algae all appeared at one time in geologic history, we discovered that the simplest forms of life are found in the oldest rocks and progressively more advanced animals and plants came in later periods. In addition to these, we note that certain groups underwent changes in shape, and that there were shifts in the sizes of populations of animals and plants as well as in individuals. The study of these changes through time leads to the idea of evolutionary change. We have already reviewed the life of each of the periods of the geologic past. This record of change is the main evidence for evolution. Now we may turn to the mechanisms by which these changes took place.

The concept of the evolution of life was very much in the minds of men in the nineteenth century when Darwin set forth his renowned theory of the mechanism of evolution. Other naturalists had already suggested that life undergoes evolution. Jean Lamarck, an astute student of fossil invertebrates, had proposed that evolutionary changes he observed in the fossil record were due to *inheritance of acquired characteristics*. Even Darwin's own grandfather had proposed a theory of the "transmutation" of living things. In generations before Darwin one prevalent view was that life was created through a number of special creations. Differences in fossil content of different strata were explained as being due to widespread catastrophes that killed existing life, followed by new special creations. Such thought had been forced on scientists by the religious dogma which concluded that the world was created in 4004 B.C. To pave the way for a theory such as Darwin's this misconception concerning the age of the earth had to be eliminated. For this accomplishment we owe thanks to Charles Lyell, James Hutton, and others who, by establishing the theory of uniformitarianism, demonstrated that the earth has been modified slowly and through long periods of time by natural processes similar to those in action today. Once it was established that the earth's history encompassed hundreds of thousands, even millions of years, theories of slow mutation and modification of life could be visualized without bias.

Charles Darwin set out on the now famous voyage of the *Beagle* in 1831 at the age of 22. Oddly enough, the captain, Fitzroy, was a very religious man whose purpose in selecting a naturalist to accompany him was to put to rest the heretical views currently expressed by geologists. Perhaps Darwin's poor record as a student of natural science was a factor in his selection for this cruise. In spite of, or perhaps because of, his past record Darwin set out making very detailed notes and careful observations of rocks, minerals, plants, animals, and natural processes. The most significant stop of this journey for

Darwin was a visit to the Galápagos Islands of the southern Pacific. This group of islands lies isolated 600 miles west of Ecuador and nearly 3,000 miles east of Polynesia. Here Darwin found "a little world in itself, with inhabitants such as are found nowhere else." It was here that Darwin made many observations that were to lead him to his theory of the nature of evolutionary processes.

Among his observations Darwin noted the existence of thirteen species of finches in the Galápagos. All are similar enough to be classed in the same family, but different enough so that they do not interbreed. Included in this group were six species of ground finches, six species of tree finches, and one species of warbler finches. The ground finches lived in the arid coastal plain areas, where four of them ate seeds of different sizes, one with a longer and more pointed beak ate prickly pears, and the sixth ate cactus and seeds. Of the six species of tree finches found in the Galápagos, one which had a parrot-like beak ate buds and fruit, three of them differing from one another only in size ate various insects, one of them lived in mangrove swamps eating insects, and the last lived a woodpecker type of existence. This last species did not have the long tongue of woodpeckers, but manages to pick bugs out of holes in tree bark by using a cactus spine or small stick, one of the extremely rare instances in which an animal, other than man and apes, uses a tool to secure food. The thirteenth species resembled warblers in feeding and other habits. Here, then, Darwin found an instance of thirteen species of a bird living in close proximity far removed and isolated from other species of birds and animals. Here was an instance in which it appeared likely that numerous species had evolved from one or more species of finches that had somehow found their way to the islands a long time before. This conclusion is warranted because these species are unlike other finches known in South America. The principal way in which these finches differ among themselves is in the shape and use of the beak (Fig. 36–1). Each species has a beak specially suited for the size and type of food it eats.

It was twenty-two years after the cruise of the *Beagle* before Darwin wrote anything of his travel and observations. In this time he remained confined to his home, where he continued studying and thinking about what he had seen. Twenty-eight years after the cruise his book *On the Origin of Species* was published. Through his study of variation among populations of any given species, adaptation of certain physical characteristics of animals to certain types of living (as in the case of the finches' beaks), and the struggle for existence among the animal kingdom, he had come to the conclusion that *natural selection* was the probable mechanism by which evolution takes place. If changes take place in the environment, that portion of the animal population best suited to survive will live to reproduce and propagate the species. Weak and poorly adapted members of the population are eliminated. Thus physical characteristics of a population can evolve toward forms better adapted to the environment.

This theory of natural selection can be readily applied to the finches. All thirteen species may have evolved from one ancestral species. In such a case the original species became differentiated through adaptation of beaks for eating of specialized types of food. The initial population became split up as finches lived on a number of different islands or in different parts of an island. In each case the finches gradually evolved toward having beaks suited for the type of food available. Later, when mixing of the species took place, the finches did not interbreed; thus numerous, very similar, but distinct species now live side by side.

The Individual and His Heredity

UNTIL GREGOR MENDEL PERFORMED HIS now famous series of experiments in crossbreeding different varieties of peas, our present understanding of the mechanism of inheritance of traits could not be attained. Even Darwin apparently believed that we inherit our characteristics through the blood of our parents, and they in turn from their parents. Mendel's work

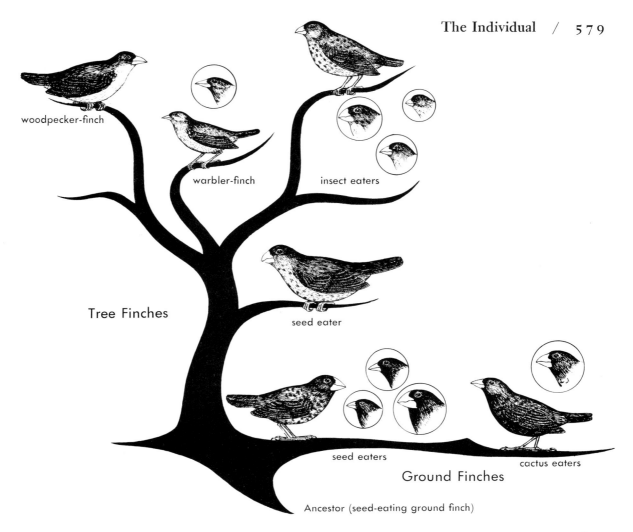

woodpecker-finch

warbler-finch

insect eaters

Tree Finches

seed eater

seed eaters

cactus eaters

Ground Finches

Ancestor (seed-eating ground finch)

FIG. 36–1. / *Darwin's finches. Shown are most of the species of finches studied by Darwin during his visit to the Galapagos Islands.*

led to the recognition that traits are carried by certain nucleic acids, called *genes*, which are transmitted as discrete units from parents through the egg and sperm to the new individual. Some traits tend to be dominant, while others are recessive. These genes do not fuse in the new individual; they remain discrete, and only half of them are passed on from one parent to the next generation. The halves passed on by each parent combine in the offspring to form one complete set. Some of these will determine physical traits of the individual, and others may remain recessive. However, recessive genes may be passed along to the succeeding generation, in which they may match recessive genes from the other parent and thus become active determinants of traits of the individuals. The laws de-

rived from Mendel's work are considered by many to be the most fundamental biological laws. They make it possible to predict traits that will appear in successive generations of offspring descended from a given pair of individuals.

Reaction Range

ALTHOUGH GENES RECEIVED by an individual from his parents determine his developmental pattern, actual development is not completely independent of environment. The individual possesses a certain "reaction range" within which these traits may vary as a result of environmental factors. For example, an individual's skin color may be white as a result of the combination of genes received from his parents, yet, on exposure to sunlight, the skin colors may vary within rather wide limits. Reaction ranges of different traits are highly variable and little known.

Genes passed on from one generation to the next are the same regardless of the extent to which individuals of the parent generation have adapted to a specific environment. In other words, acquired characteristics are not passed on from generation to generation through genes. What is passed on is the developmental pattern, which can function within a certain reaction range. If the new generation does not have a wide enough reaction range to enable it to adapt to environmental conditions into which it is born, it either moves into an environment to which it can adapt, or it dies out.

Mutation may occur in the genes. Alterations within genes that are passed on when reproduction occurs are called gene mutations. These alter physical traits and reaction ranges of individuals produced. In some cases mutants are better adjusted to environments in which they find themselves and are likely to flourish and pass on their genes to the next generation.

Populations

ALTHOUGH THE INDIVIDUAL IS THE BASIC unit of life, evolutionary processes must be understood in terms of populations. We are, after all, talking about changes in vast populations over long periods of time. While a mutation within one individual may suit that individual to live a more effective existence within its environment, this is of little significance for a population as a whole, unless the mutation becomes widespread.

One fundamental characteristic of populations is that variations are represented within them. Individuals within a population of any given animal or plant are not identical. They vary in size, shape, and to some extent in structure. For example, if we collect a large sample of leaves, or seashells, all of which belong to a certain species, and measure the ratio between length and width of shells or leaves, we can immediately obtain an idea of the magnitude of the variation. If the number of individuals having a certain length–width ratio is plotted, a bell-shaped distribution is usually obtained (Fig. 36-2).

This population has a certain pool of genes upon which to draw for the next generation. If no mutations are introduced within this gene pool, if environmental conditions remain fairly constant or at least within the reaction range of the organisms, and if all individuals of mating age breed, then we may predict that no change in the over-all gene pool or in patterns of variation within the population would occur from one generation to the next. Nevertheless, we may be sure that in a biparental population processes of mutation and recombination will maintain an enormous variation within the population as a whole. It is this variation that makes evolution possible. This variation is passed on from generation to generation and is maintained even when no evolutionary change is occurring. Changes in species may arise from differences in inherited reaction ranges, from differences in environmental conditions (even if the reaction range of all members of the population is the same), or from a combination of the two. Within the population there is always some variation in the genes resulting from mutations. Both environmental variations and inherited genetic variations may cause the population to have a bell-shaped curve of population variation.

Natural Selection

THE EFFECT OF EVOLUTIONARY PROCESSES is to bring the great diversity of animal and plant life into a better adjustment with the environment. It is not a mere coincidence that some fish are able to withstand the cold water and great pressures found at the bottom of the ocean, while others flourish in shallow, sunlit waters. Nor is it chance that a woodpecker has a pointed beak and is able to chip pieces of wood from a tree, while a hummingbird has a long delicate beak and the ability to hold its body almost motionless in air while it sips nec-

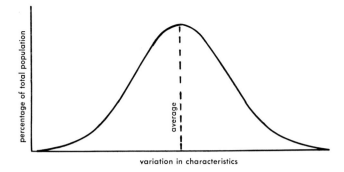

percentage of total population

average

variation in characteristics

FIG. 36–2. / A *normal distribution. This bell-shaped curve shows the theoretical distribution of some variables within a large population if the distribution is normal. The variable might be the height of individuals.*

tar from a flower. Variety of adaptation is evident in adaptations of modern mammals. The whale is more closely related to an ape than it is to a fish; both are mammals, adapted to different modes of life. Sometimes evolution of particular groups brings about adaptation of two or more unrelated forms to the same environment. In such a case the two may have similar outward appearance, as in the case of fishes and whales.

Natural selection is a simple process of nonrandom reproduction resulting in changes that tend to improve the ability of the population as a whole to survive and reproduce in the environment it inhabits. If animals exercise no choice in selecting partners for reproduction, then reproduction is random. Populations from generation to generation would maintain variants through mutation and recombinations of genes, but no evolutionary changes would be introduced like those that take place when selection of mates is nonrandom. Individual mate selection is of little significance in this connection. What does matter are group tendencies. If individuals possessed of certain characteristics are more desirable to the group as a whole, then a premium is placed on genes of that group, and they are likely to become more abundant in the population.

Perhaps more important is the fact that certain of the variants within a population may

possess certain physical traits which make it easier for them to get along in their environment or adapt to changes within the environment. When changes do occur these groups are more likely to survive than those variants which are not fortunate enough to have received a sufficiently wide reaction range. Thus through a long period of time a certain segment of the total population is able to produce more offspring carrying their genes. This brings about a shift in the norm, and the population as a whole has evolved slightly. A most important point in evolution is the fact that individuals which survive long enough to reproduce are the only ones that make a contribution toward continued existence of the group, and it is only their genetic heredity plus any introduced mutations that will be passed along to the next generation.

Factors that determine natural selection, adaptation, and, therefore, evolution include:
1. Nonrandom mating.
2. Change of the number of offspring to increase survival.
3. Ability to survive in the environment.
4. Ability to survive in competition with other organisms.
5. Ability to reproduce.

A good example of natural selection and adaptation is seen in adaptive skin coloration of certain animals. Some insects have become so perfectly adapted to their habitat that they closely resemble the plant stems and leaves on which they feed. This gives them the great advantage of being hard to see and reduces chances that they will fall prey to their natural enemies. This characteristic increases their ability to live and reproduce, and consequently those variants which most closely resemble a plant stem or leaf have a better chance to survive and reproduce. Their genes are likely to be passed along to the next generation. If this process continues for many generations, the cumulative effect is a considerable shift in physical appearance of the population as a whole.

As we study the history of the geological past it becomes apparent that some groups have been driven into environments which they had not previously occupied. There appears to be a certain pressure to diversify in such a way as to enable the groups to survive under new conditions. This may be explained in terms of natural selection. Any environment may become crowded, cutting down on food supply and on room to such an extent that some groups are forced to move into a new environment, either to escape consumption or to find food. Those variants which are particularly suited to live in the new environment are most likely to reproduce and survive within it. There are, however, a number of conditions that must be met before such a move can be made.

1. There must be access to a new environment.
2. The organism must have the necessary physical constitution to live in the new environment.
3. The new habitat must be such that the newly introduced organism can survive in it at least until a better adaptation can be effected.

Species

EXACTLY WHAT SPECIES MEANS HAS LONG been debated by biologists and paleontologists. The concept of species most often used by paleontologists defines it as a group of individuals essentially indistinguishable from some specimen selected as a standard of reference. Biologists consider a species to be made up of one or more usually highly variable populations which are capable of interbreeding and producing fertile offspring. Unfortunately, fossil records fail to supply the necessary information to satisfy requirements of the biologists' definitions. Paleontologists are forced to rely on:

Similarity of shape.
Association on the basis of proximity within a stratum.
Biogeography.
Paleoecology.

On the basis of the biologists' definition there are over a million different species living today. Each represents a population capable of interbreeding and producing fertile offspring. Each is unlikely to breed with any other species. If over a million species exist today one can understand the magnitude of the problem confronting the paleontologist, who is trying to describe and relate hundreds of millions of species which have lived since the beginning of Cambrian time.

Time Factor in Evolution

IT IS CONSIDERABLY MORE COMPLEX TO apply the concept of species to fossils than to living groups, because changes of great magnitude have occurred through time. In considera-

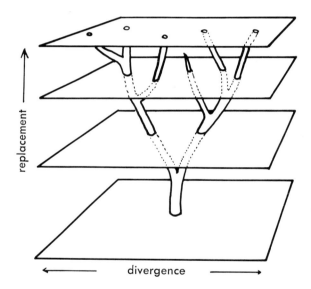

FIG. 36–3. / A simplified phylogenetic tree showing divergence of a population through time. The horizontal planes represent four times. Within each plane divergence of characteristics of the population is shown. Through time each generation is replaced by the next. The characteristics of each new generation are determined by the gene pool from which it was produced. Between the first and second time planes the initial population is split and after that divergence continues until by the time of the fourth plane there are five species, one having become extinct. (After N. D. Newell.)

tion of a population we have described the nature and cause of variations and some processes which give a population a tendency to evolve. Now we must consider the effect of time. Consider a species that starts initially as a simple, highly variable population capable of adaptation. If the species is now separated in such a way as to isolate certain parts of it in different environments, then through processes of natural selection and mutation the two groups may begin to undergo *morphological* (shape) and *genetic divergence* (the gene pool as a whole changes). The two populations may change in general physical traits and appearance.

If the two groups continue to be isolated long enough, changes may become so great that they no longer resemble one another. It is possible, even probable, that they would no longer be capable of interbreeding if they should be given the opportunity of freely mixing. Fig. 36–3 shows a simplified theoretical *phylogenetic tree* (a diagram that traces race history). Horizontal planes indicate stratigraphic horizons and time lines. Segments of limbs correspond to populations of this race present at one time. Each segment consists of a species population of almost identical individuals. Such species are transient in nature and may undergo change through time. A number of these cross sections of tree limbs combine to represent a succession of species. Any two adjacent sections would contain almost identical populations, but the farther apart segments are, the more diverse they would appear.

How truly does the picture above portray the record in stratigraphic sequences? There are few instances in which the history of successive changes in species can be traced very far through race histories. In general, data are inadequate. Only hard parts are preserved, which makes direct comparisons of groups of almost identical animals somewhat difficult. Studies of whole populations of fossil species have not often been made because the required number of specimens have not been found. There are many gaps in the rock record, some caused by nondeposition, others by erosion.

In spite of these shortcomings, which prevent complete piecing-together of phylogenetic trees for every group of animals and plants, our record is adequate to point out the general direction of most major evolutionary changes. Convincing connections can be made between many groups. There are well-documented cases of successive changes in species.

Modes of Evolution

THREE MAJOR STYLES OR MODES OF EVOLUTION, speciational, phyletic, and quantum, have been described by G. G. Simpson, who is one of the most prominent of modern students of evolutionary theory. All three are brought about by natural selection and mutation.

Speciation

SPECIATION IS THE SPLITTING of one species into two or more groups through isolation of groups of a widespread population followed by local differentiation of groups. For example, two groups of a marine population may separate so that one occupies slightly deeper water. Differences likely to arise at first may be so slight as to be unnoticed, but this may be a first step toward complete isolation and eventually complete differentiation.

A zone is "a definite paleontological horizon characterized by the constant occurrence in it of certain species which do not occur in the preceding or succeeding neighbor zones" (A.G.I. Glossary). A zone may be divided into subzones, which show minor lateral and vertical changes. Zones frequently reflect environmental conditions; therefore, two or more zones may be contemporaneous. As a result of evolution by speciation, the population of a certain species may become differentiated either by fanning out across adjacent subzones or by becoming widely spread into different zones. Both are adjustments of organisms to slight differences in ecological conditions under which they live. As a result of scattering of a population there may not be an even distribution of variants within that population. This may give rise to minor differences within species after a few generations. Of course, there may be mutations in the process of fanning out and adaptation to new conditions each segment of the population encounters. If the population is able to accumulate characteristics that are favorable to existence under the new conditions, evolution proceeds, but if nonadaptive characteristics are accumulated the group is headed for possible extinction.

Phyletic Evolution

A SECOND MODE of evolution involves a sustained directional shift of average characters of the populations. It is not so much a splitting up of the species as a general, over-all change in the population's mean characteristics. *Phyletic evolution* leads to *successional species*, whereas speciation leads to evolution of several contemporaneous species. Most paleontological data fall into patterns of phyletic evolution.

Within phyletic evolution three patterns are found (Fig. 36–4). In the first of these the population is more or less in a state of equilibrium. The norm for the group is such that the organism is well adapted to the environment. Some variants may be less well adapted, but these make up a small part of the group. Through time, there is an adequate response to slight changes in environment. Responses are such

FIG. 36–4. / *Phyletic evolution. At the left is a species which is well adapted to a zone in which no changes are taking place. Successive generations show little change in characteristics. In the middle the population becomes more specialized with each new generation until the adaptation is so narrow that survival is threatened. As the tendency continues the species becomes extinct. At the right the successive generations show a slowly changing norm in the population characteristics. This is in response to a gradual shift in the environmental conditions (adaptive zone). (After G. G. Simpson, Tempo and Mode in Evolution.)*

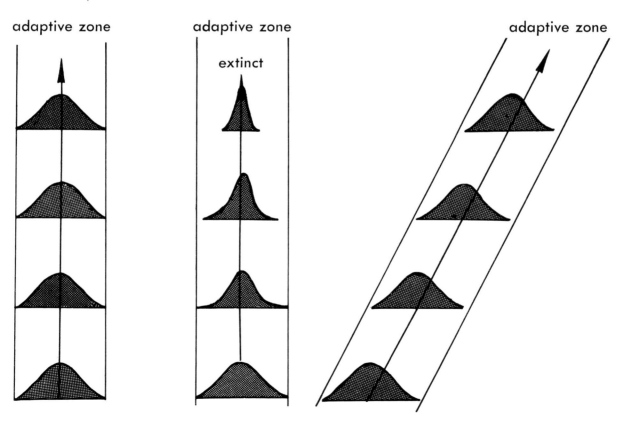

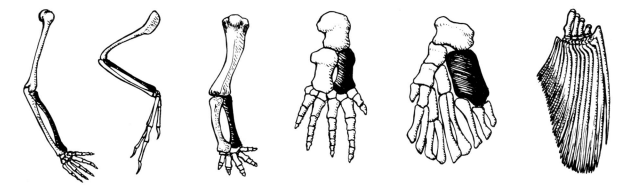

FIG. 36–5. / *Homology of forelimbs. Homology is correspondence between structures of different organisms due to their inheritance of these structures from the same ancestry. Compare here the forelimbs of man, an early bird, a dinosaur, a whale, a lobe-finned fish, and a modern fish.*

that the group as a whole is maintained in a state of equilibrium.

A second pattern is that of a population becoming more narrowly adapted to its environment. Organisms, through a long series of changes, become more and more specialized in order to carry on their life functions within special restricted conditions. As a result, the group may be headed for extinction, because environmental conditions are likely to change eventually and the species will have so limited its adaptability that it can no longer accommodate itself to these changes.

A third pattern is that of a slow change in response to shifting ecological conditions. Here the environment is undergoing a more or less steady change. Progressively warmer climates or continually increasing salinity of sea water are examples. As these changes continue, the group as a whole adjusts to them by natural selection leading to survival of those members of the population that have the necessary genetic makeup and reaction range to survive and reproduce.

Quantum Evolution

SELECTION AND ADAPTATION are also responsible for *quantum evolution*, which differs from the first two modes in rapidity of change and apparent temporary failure of the state of equilibrium to continue through the process. In quantum evolution there is a sudden change in the type of conditions to which the group is best adapted such as might give rise to new families, orders, and classes. By comparison, speciation gave rise to subspecies and new species, and phyletic evolution to species and perhaps families. Quantum evolution is discontinuous; there is a change by a certain quantity or amount.

Evidence that quantum evolution does occur is found. There are many sudden small changes in group characteristics. Much indirect paleontological evidence indicates that major transitions take place at great rates over short periods of time. Some groups have left scanty remains in the fossil record for long periods of time, during which they were relatively simple and restricted forms. Suddenly these groups seem to diversify and multiply at such a great rate that the changes are best described as "explosive evolution."

The initial stage in the quantum evolutionary process is thought to be development of a condition to which the population cannot readily adapt itself. For a period the species is inadaptive and the population loses equilibrium. The usual thing at this point is for the population to move into a new environment or suffer extinction, but in a few rare cases the apparent reaction of the species is to select extreme variants (such as mutants), and these multiply rapidly. Then, through successive generations of sustained highly selective pressures, the population begins to move toward a new equilibrium stage. The final step is realization of equilibrium again, but when this is reached, changes that have taken place are of such great magnitude that structure, size, and organization of the organisms are different from their former state, and we recognize the new form as a member of a new order or class.

Trend of Evolution

Does man represent the culmination of evolution throughout all of geological time? Is he, in fact, the last and most advanced form that will ever inhabit the earth? Some biologists agree with this assumption. They think that a final state of completion of evolution has now been reached. However, change has been the dominant theme of evolution in the past. It has been slower at some times than at others, and it has been slower among some groups of organisms than it has among others, but there is no evidence that evolution tends to approach a state of equilibrium. There is no evidence that it has, as a whole, slowed down, nor is there any evidence to support the contention that it will reach a final completion. There is hardly any basis for the assumption that evolution has stopped. Other biologists and geologists contend, moreover, that there has been an acceleration in the rate of evolutionary change. They hold that this has been a tendency since life first appeared on earth and that the rate of change at the present time is the greatest in the history of the world. Only time will determine which of these opinions is correct.

We will confine our attention to the evolution of life in the past and up to the present.

Nothing characterizes life in the past billion years more than "change." This has been the essence of evolution. What we know of the past comes mainly from the fossil record, and an abundant record it is. Fossil species of plants and animals that have inhabited the earth number in millions. Even so, they represent only a part of all forms that have lived on earth. Others without hard parts to be preserved must also have lived in the past. The fossil record is sufficiently complete to give us a very accurate picture of relative abundance and principal types of organisms that lived in marginal seas and in and around swamps during the major divisions of geologic time since the beginning of the Cambrian Period. However, some important parts of the record have been lost during periods of emergence, when older fossil-bearing sequences were eroded and gradually worn away. Thus the record is replete with gaps of time forever lost. These gaps are extremely important because they make it impossible to achieve a complete reconstruction of the evolution of life in detail. A second important handicap in attempting such a reconstruction is the fact that life had become quite advanced, and many steps in the evolution of higher forms had already

FIG. 37–1. / *Burgess shale restoration. Some of the plant and animal life of the Middle Cambrian which has been preserved in detail in the Burgess shale are shown. These animals lived on the shallow sea floor in British Columbia, an area which now stands thousands of feet above sea level. This view includes colonies of branching sponges, trilobites, sea cumbers, jellyfishes, and an arthropod somewhat like modern crustaceans. (Photo by courtesy of the U.S. National Museum.)*

taken place, before the first fossils were preserved. For all practical purposes the fossil record begins with the Cambrian Period. Rock units of that age confront us with a rather advanced and complex group of organisms such as the trilobites. Until fossils are found in abundance in Precambrian rocks we cannot hope to reconstruct accurately the earliest stages of evolution. It is possible that we will someday find fossils in Precambrian rocks. Likely sites for them are in slates in which we may find a Precambrian counterpart of the Burgess shale (Fig. 37–1).

Although the two limitations described above—lack of any fossil record for the Precambrian and lost intervals—form important obstacles in solving detailed steps in evolutionary sequences, they have by no means prevented detection of major trends or tendencies in the evolutionary process. These major trends provide a background against which the description of more detailed evolutionary trends among invertebrates and vertebrates may be viewed.

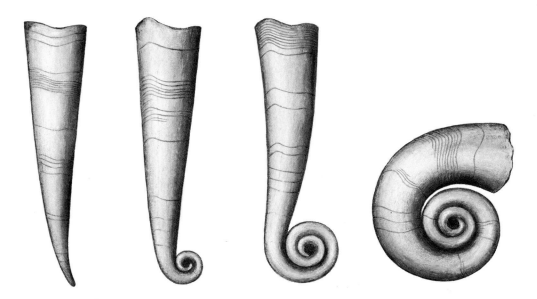

FIG. 37–2. / *Evolution of coiling in cephalopods. (After Schindewolf.)*

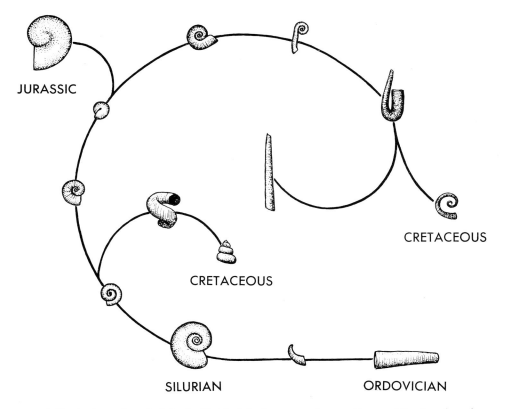

JURASSIC

CRETACEOUS

CRETACEOUS

SILURIAN

ORDOVICIAN

FIG. 37–3. / *Evolution of cephalopods. Cephalopods are marine molluscs with chambered, cone-shaped shells. Straight at first, the shells became in time more and more tightly coiled. Several stages of coiling can be recognized, each of which continued for millions of years after the next was developed. Gas within the chambered shell made the animal buoyant under water. The various types of coiling brought the lifting force above the animal's body— a compact and efficient design. (Drawn from exhibit at the Chicago Natural History Museum.)*

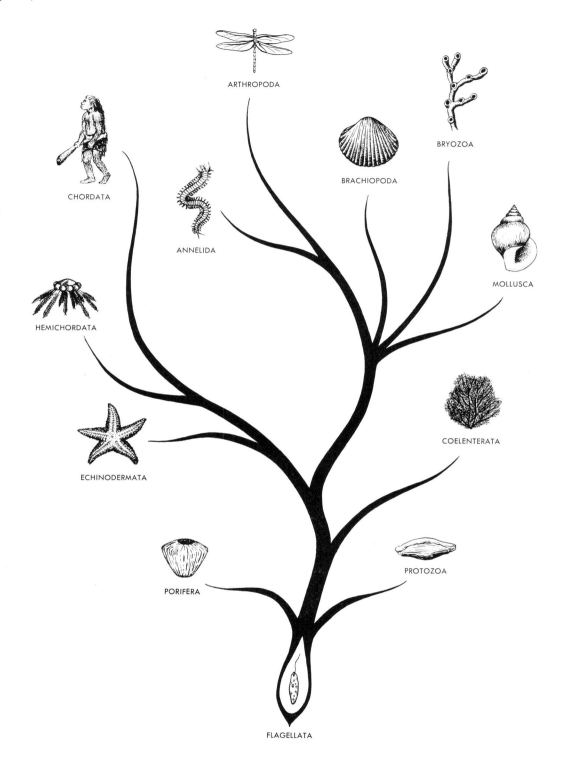

ARTHROPODA

BRYOZOA

BRACHIOPODA

CHORDATA

ANNELIDA

MOLLUSCA

HEMICHORDATA

COELENTERATA

ECHINODERMATA

PORIFERA

PROTOZOA

FLAGELLATA

FIG. 37–4. / *Schematic diagram showing generalized trends of evolution and phyletic relationships. (After Hyman.)*

General Trends

MOST POSITIVE AND DIRECT EVIDENCE OF evolution comes from observable changes in structure of hard parts of fossils. The following trends have characterized evolution of most organisms at one time or another:

Divergence of form. Out of the population emerges single species of two or more groups that initially are similar in structure but become more differentiated with time. Eventually structures of the two become so divergent that they cannot be considered as the same species.

Increased complexity of structure. This may be illustrated by such tendencies as coiling of shells (Fig. 37–2), increased complexity of partitions within shells, and accentuation of special structures—such as spines or shell ornamentation.

Trend toward extremes. Some animals have developed extreme sizes or structures. The latter have included elaboration of ornaments on the shell or body. In some cases these changes have enabled the organism to achieve a better adaptation to its environment, but others have resulted in extinction.

Changes in structure or function. Such changes have in some instances opened up new ways of life for groups previously blocked to them. One of the most important examples is development of an enclosed egg in reptiles. This made possible new modes of life on land and in turn provided the opportunity for a great variety of new divergences and changes of structure which led to explosive evolution and expansion of reptiles.

Changes in Level of Organization

ALL LEVELS OF ORGANIZATION FROM THAT of the amoeba to that of man exist today. One of the major trends of evolution has been toward development of higher levels of organization. The single cell accomplishes all the life functions of the protozoans. These cells are organized as tissues among coelenterates and sponges. Specialized organs appear in brachiopods and echinoderms. These organs become increasingly complex and more specialized among higher animals (Fig. 37–4). The fossil record dramatically documents these trends. The oldest fossil plants are among the simplest in structure. The most advanced, the angiosperms, appeared very late. Likewise, progression of important animal groups may be traced.

Lower Paleozoic—Invertebrates
Mid-Paleozoic—Fishes
Late Paleozoic—Amphibians
Mesozoic—Reptiles
Cenozoic—Mammals and Man

Changes in level of organization and structure have in general made possible a better and more precise adaptation of organisms to their environments. The mechanism responsible for the development of many changes has been natural selection. Natural selection has usually led to an improvement of the organism in the sense that it has become better adapted to a particular environmental niche. While this has been a common tendency through the past, we have but to consider the great number of extinct forms to see that it has not been universal. Long-range effects of this generalized improvement through structural modifications and changes in levels of organization have been:

More intensive and extensive occupation of environments.

Over-all expansion of life.

Replacement of older orders by newer and usually better-adapted organisms.

Over-All Tendencies

Environments

IF WE COULD HAVE an opportunity to go back in time to the Cambrian Period to follow the gradual development of life, we would find ourselves in a world with no trees, shrubs, or grasses anywhere. There would be no birds or reptiles, nor even any of our familiar pests such as ants or rats. The only signs of life would be in the seas, and even that would be unfamiliar to us. As millions of years passed we would witness a gradual change in distribution and types of life. At first marine organisms would expand in numbers and diversity. The first fishlike organisms would appear. Until the Silurian Period there would be no life on land. At about that time a general movement toward a land environment started. This required certain special new modes of life, and we would have to wait for the trial and error of evolutionary development to provide satisfactory adaptations to this new realm. In the succeeding hundreds of millions of years adjustment to land and its great variety of environmental niches becomes a reality. Plants and animals now inhabit almost every environment, and in great numbers. These include conditions ranging from those at margins of glaciers to caves, deserts, plains, swamps, and even sand dunes.

Expansion

EXPANSION OF LIFE has taken place in several ways. The over-all number of organisms has become greater. The total number of different species has tended to increase. There has been increased diversity of form and structure, and even more phyla have appeared through time. Little is known about the rate of expansion during initial stages in the development of life. Signs of life first appeared in the Precambrian. Early diversification may have required more time than all of that which has passed since the start of the Cambrian. However, there was rapid, almost explosive diversification early in the Paleozoic Era. Throughout the record some groups were on the decline, while others expanded, but on the whole life expanded until the Silurian, when the rate of increase stabilized somewhat. Only once, toward the end of the Paleozoic, did it appear that expansion of life was stopped and even reversed, but following that period there has been another great expansion, which has continued up to the present.

Replacement

THERE ARE SOME rather remarkable instances in which species that developed in the early part of the Paleozoic have persisted and may even be found in present-day seas. Such an example is *Lingula*, a brachiopod. If you were given shells of a fossil of the animal and a recently dredged Lingula you would find almost no difference in the form of the two. Most organisms that have had such a history are simple in structure, apparently well adjusted to their environments, and capable of maintaining that adjustment even as the environment undergoes slow changes. Such instances are rather rare. While it is true that many of the same groups that lived in the Cambrian Period are represented today, modern forms are replacements of older forms of the same group. Replacement is prompted by development of a new, better-adapted form.

Examples of Evolution of Invertebrates

Micraster

MICRASTER IS A SEA URCHIN, an echinoderm (Fig. 37-5). The population was most abundant in seas off the western coast of Europe some 70 million years ago. Like other echinoids before and since, they lived on the bottom in marine waters. They were gregarious animals; great numbers lived together, scavenging the sea floor for bits of food. When food was abundant they consumed that found on the sea floor, but when it became more scarce they ate some sea-bottom sediments for their organic content.

Many other forms of life existed at the same time and in the same region with *Micraster*. In fact, protozoans were so numerous that when echinoids died their remains were buried in sediment composed of shells of protozoans. Thus, over a long period of time in the Late Cretaceous, the unbroken chalk formations of England were deposited. Parts of this sequence are exposed in the famous chalk cliffs of Dover. Be-

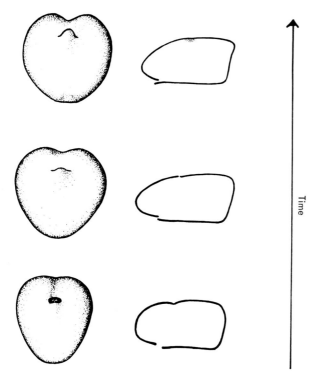

Time

1. Increase in size.
2. Shift of the widest portion of the test toward the middle.
3. Development of a plate to cover the mouth, and a shift in the position of the mouth.
4. A gradual increase in ornamentation.
5. Development of a larger subanal fasciole, a hole in the top of the test connected with the water circulatory system.
6. Development of a deeper anterior notch.
7. Development of more complex plates in the test.

These evolutionary changes represent the main line of development, but within zones there are several divergent lines. One leads to development of an echinoid that is taller than the main line and in which the subanal fasciole becomes smaller and disappears, rather than becoming larger.

Interpretations of these changes are made in terms of environmental adaptations. The main stock underwent a series of changes leading to a progressively better adaptation to a life of burrowing in sediments. Many echinoids live this sort of life today. They burrow through loosely consolidated sediments obtaining food from organic debris. The plate over the mouth greatly increases efficiency of the mouth as an organ of ingestion. It may well have been that large populations of echinoids in the Late Cretaceous caused a short supply of food. Those that could burrow effectively were better able to prosper and reproduce. In living echinoids the subanal fasciole is surrounded by a dense mass of hair-like appendages which move rapidly and produce strong water currents directed toward the back of the animal. These would be most effective in discharging water from the burrow, and probably explains the large size of the hole in the more advanced forms.

The offshoot from this main stock appears to have become adapted for living on the bottom rather than in the sediments. For this mode of life the subanal fasciole is unnecessary, and therefore it decreased in size.

FIG. 37–5. / *The evolution of Micraster. The record of the small evolutionary changes which took place in these echinoderms during the Cretaceous is one of the most complete we have. It is possible in this case to see an unbroken series of changes in morphological features which lead to the evolution of several species. (After Neaverson.)*

cause the chalk is soft, it is a simple matter to remove the fossils without seriously damaging them. The echinoid skeletons possess many structural features that are readily identified, and functions of these may be interpreted by analogy with living echinoids. Thus these fossils make ideal material for the study of evolutionary changes.

Large numbers of these fossils have been collected, and their structural features have been carefully analyzed. A number of changes in form can be noticed. So reliable is the sequence of changes that six zones in the Cretaceous are identified by this means. It is possible for a student of these units to take a collection of fossils from any one zone and predict the form of the fossil echinoids that will be found above and below it. As is shown in Fig. 37–5, changes include:

Gryphaea

GRYPHAEA IS THE NAME OF an extinct genus of pelecypods, in a sense ancestors of the present-day oysters. They were most abundant during the Mesozoic, when they lived a life similar to that of the oyster. The shell was attached to the bottom of the sea, to a stone, or to some other shell. Like other pelecypods, Gryphaea had two shells, but unlike most other pelecypods the two shells are not symmetrical nor even nearly alike. There is no plane of symmetry either within or between shells. The shell attached to an object was typically much larger and heavier and grew in a tight coil at one end; the other shell was small, light, and flat. Gryphaea thrived in the Cretaceous in southern England, and from studies of these sequences some evolutionary trends have been traced.

Gryphaea thrived on the surface of muddy sea bottoms. This is a very difficult environment for an animal that is attached so that it cannot move and stay out of dirty water. The problem is accentuated by the fact that as the animal grew larger the shell became heavy enough to break loose from its attachment and fall to the bottom. In response to this sort of environment there was a general decrease in size of the area of attachment, the size of the shell increased, and the rate of coiling increased with development of tighter and heavier coils.

These trends may be simply explained in terms of special habits of the animal and its need to stay out of the mud. The increased size and odd shape of the shell evolved in such a way as to keep the opening into the shell pointed upward so the animal could receive food and clean water. The end of the shell that developed into a tight heavy coil would tend to become oriented downward when the shell broke loose from its attachment. This left the opening to the shell upward, above the bottom.

Coiling continued throughout the life of the animal. This, combined with a trend toward increased coiling, eventually led to development of coils that were so large and tight that in later stages of life the small top shell became wedged into a closed position. This, of course, brought on death by starvation. This condition affected mainly oversized adults and was not responsible for eventual extinction of the group.

Graptolites

NOT ALL EVOLUTIONARY CHANGES can be directly related to environment or habits of the animals. This is especially true of extinct forms that have no closely related modern counterparts. Such is the case with the graptolites (Fig. 37–6). Fossil remains are abundant in black shales and slates from lower Paleozoic rocks of many parts of the world. The abundance of the record allows delineation of several distinct trends, but the nature of the remains leaves us without a good explanation of the function of some parts or the reason for the changes. Unfortunate as this is, it does not necessarily detract from the value of graptolites for purposes of stratigraphic correlation. They have proved to be one of the most important groups for world-wide correlation of the lower Paleozoic shales and slates.

The established trends in the evolution of graptolites include:

1. Progressive simplification of the branchings of the stipes (Fig. 37–6). In the Early Ordovician some of the graptolites had between 32 and 80 stipes, but by the end of the period the number had been reduced to a single stipe.

2. Change in direction of growth of the stipes. From a downward position they progressively shifted toward a horizontal orientation and finally in the later forms extended straight up. Both of these trends seem to have developed together in successful forms. Those in which the trend toward reduction in numbers of stipes proceeded more rapidly than the change in growth direction tended to die out, for some unexplained reason.

FIG. 37–6. / *Evolutionary trend among the grap-tolites. Early in the Ordovician the stipes of the graptolites hung down, but through time these tended to grow in positions that became progressively turned up. Another evolutionary trend among the graptolites was toward a reduction in the number of stipes. Early forms had as many as thirty-two or more stipes. (After Ruedemann.)*

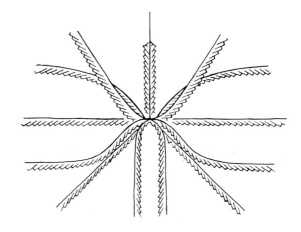

Ammonoid Suture Patterns

AMMONOIDS ARE AN EXTINCT group of cephalopods. They inhabited the seas in large numbers from the Devonian until they died out about the end of the Mesozoic. Ammonoids are easily identified by the suture patterns formed where *septa,* partitions, built behind the living chamber intersect outside walls of the shells (Fig. 37–7). Most, but not all, ammonoids were coiled. Toward the end of the Paleozoic and in the Mesozoic they became highly diversified. The most remarkable diversification occurred in shapes of the suture pattern. This underwent progressive evolutionary change from a relatively simple pattern toward increasingly complex and intricate designs. In early forms the pattern is a smooth-flowing curve not very different from the pattern of many nautiloids. But later the smooth curve becomes crumpled, and a large number of folds are formed. By the end of the Paleozoic many forms began to show even more intricate patterns. Sutures became folded until patterns became dendritic, and finally after millions of years the ammonoids disappeared.

FIG. 37–7. / *Evolutionary changes in the suture patterns of the ammonoids.*

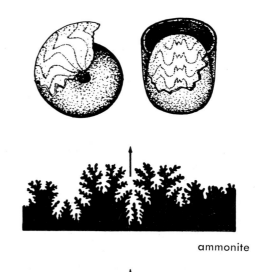

ammonite

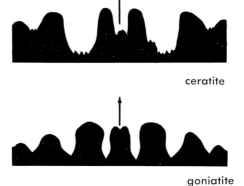

ceratite

goniatite

38 /

Evolution of Fishes and Amphibians

Earliest Vertebrates: Fishes

SO LITTLE EVIDENCE REMAINS OF THE FIRST animals with backbones that it is impossible to tell accurately what they were like. The only indication of these early fishes is a few scales of bony structure, found in freshwater sediments of Ordovician age in Colorado. But this is enough to establish their presence and to give rise to the hope that better-preserved specimens will be found in time. A recently described fossil from Silurian rocks of England supports the idea that these early fishes bore a strong resemblance to modern *lampreys*. The lamprey is a jawless vertebrate (class *Agnatha*). It has a round, cup-shaped mouth which enables it to attach itself to the side of another fish. Its tongue has a rasplike surface used to scrape the side of the victim, allowing the lamprey to lead the life of a parasite, feeding off the blood of its prey. It is quite probable that the first fish had a somewhat similar mouth, which was used to suck up food from the sea and lake bottoms. The lamprey has no bones—its body is supported by cartilage. It has neither scales nor paired fins (Fig. 38–1).

Ostracoderms: Jawless Fish

THE FIRST FISHES TO BE well documented in the fossil record are the ostracoderms (Fig. 38–2). Like lampreys they are jawless vertebrates. They resembled lampreys in their lack of paired fins and a bony skeleton, but the ostracoderms did have bony scales as an outside covering. The earliest trace of ostracoderms is from Upper Silurian deposits. It is probable that they were in existence long before that time. In the Devonian an explosive radiation occurred in the evolutionary history of the fishes. Many new species appeared, and they became much better adapted to life in the oceans. From the Devonian to the present the fossil record abounds with a great variety of fishes.

The name "ostracoderm" is applied to a variety of primitive fishes characterized by absence of a lower jaw. One of the best-known genera is *Cephalaspis* (Fig. 38–3), a heavily armored fish one foot long. Its head was covered by a single, solid, rather flat shield, and its elongated body was protected by heavy scales. The body tapers back to the base of the tail where it bends upward, forming strong dorsal

FIG. 38–1. / *Lamprey. The lampreys probably resemble the early fishes. Note the rasplike projection in the mouth. These are used by the lampreys to attach themselves to their prey.*

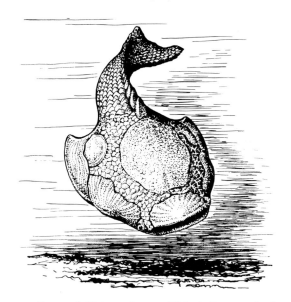

FIG. 38–2a. / *Ostracoderms. This is* Psammolepis, *one of the flat-bodied members of the group. This specimen grew to be about a foot long. Note the bony plates arranged in the skin. (After Mark and Bystrow.)*

FIG. 38–2b. / *The Ostracoderms were abundant in the Late Silurian and Early Devonian, but disappeared before the end of the Devonian. Pteraspis is one of the best known of these jawless vertebrates. It was only about 2¼ inches long. (After A. S. Romer.)*

support for the tail. Movements necessary for swimming were accomplished by flexing the body from side to side, setting up waves which traveled down the body to the tail. Scales were arranged in vertical rows, making this flexibility possible.

Placoderms: Fish with Jaws

AN EXTREMELY IMPORTANT evolutionary development took place when the first jaws were formed. The first fossil fishes known to have jaws have been found in Upper Silurian sediments. Although it might seem probable that these evolved from ostracoderms, there is no evidence to suggest such a connection. The two lived side by side for millions of years in the Silurian and Devonian seas, but during the Devonian Period the placoderms, far better prepared to dominate life in the seas, apparently killed off the ostracoderms.

The importance of the development of jaws and the great advantage held by those animals possessing them is immediately apparent. The way they formed can be seen in the structure of gill arches. These bony supports for gills are roughly V-shaped, the V pointing toward the tail. Transformations that took place in evolution of gill arches were essentially enlargement of the lower side of the forward arch, development of teeth, and a hinge at the pointed end of the V.

A great variety of placoderms inhabited Middle Paleozoic seas. Although one order survived into the Permian, most became extinct as the Devonian Period drew to a close. As in other instances, it was the most primitive form (Fig. 38–4) that survived the longest. Only a few inches long, this early fish, except for its blunt head and a tail supported by the upward-bent body, had the appearance of many modern fishes.

Other placoderms bore no resemblance to living fishes. In this group is the huge Late Devonian fish, *Dinichthys* (Fig. 38–5). The heads and shields of some of these were 10 feet long. Sharp, bony plates functioned as teeth, and the structure of the head–shield at-

FIG. 38–3. / Hemicyclaspis, *a representative of the early ostracoderm group,* Cephalaspis.

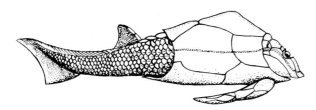

FIG. 38–4a. / *A mid-Devonian placoderm,* Pterichthyodes, *which was about six inches long. The placoderms were the first group to have well defined jaws. This gave the group a great advantage over the jawless vertebrates. (After Traquair.)*

FIG. 38–4b. / *This specimen of* Dinichthys, *an Upper Devonian placoderm, has a head which is over 10 feet long. It could open its mouth both by raising the upper jaw and lowering the lower jaw. (After Heintz.)*

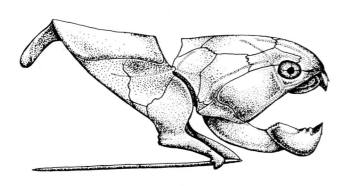

tachment allowed *Dinichthys* to open its mouth not only by dropping its lower jaw, but by raising the upper one as well—a distinct advantage for a carnivorous fish. These were the giants of Devonian seas, and it is likely that they dominated the waters of that time.

Still another placoderm resembled Devonian sharks. They were small fish and had broad, flat heads, a tapering body, and a mouth lined with pointed teeth. Fins were greatly enlarged, as are those of modern rays.

Sharks

A THIRD MAJOR group of fishes that evolved in the Devonian seas were those whose bodies are supported by cartilage, as are sharks and their close relatives. The most unfortunate aspect of this structure is the absence of hard parts that are likely to be preserved. Sharks did have hard teeth and, in some cases, hard spines, and these make up most of the available record. One of the best preserved specimens comes from Upper Devonian shales south of Lake Erie. This nearly perfect preservation has made it possible for us to form a reasonably accurate picture of the appearance of early sharks. They bear a remarkable similarity to small modern sharks. Differences become apparent in details such as structure of the jaw hingement and teeth. All sharklike fishes, such as rays, modern sharks, and skates, evolved along two major

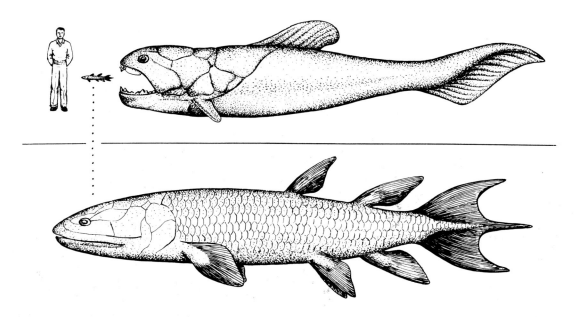

FIG. 38–5. / *Devonian fishes. At the top is a restored placoderm,* Dinichthys, *which grew to lengths of 30 feet. The head region was heavily armored with external bony plates that were jointed. Below is a Devonian crossopterygian. This fish was only about 2 feet long. The crossopterygians were probably the connecting link between the fishes and the first four-legged, air-breathing vertebrates. The basal lobe is the forerunner of the limb of the tetrapods. Other fish did not have such a lobe.*

lines from the primitive forms. One line, similar to many modern sharks, became extremely well adapted for a predaceous life. They were stream-lined and torpedo-shaped for fast motion; their tail and fins allowed great freedom of movement. Their mouth and head structure adapted in a way permitting the sharp, teethlike jaws to open widely. The other evolutional line led to rays and skates, which are peculiarly suited for life on the sea floor. Some modern rays are 6 feet long and a few measure 20 feet. The pectoral fins are greatly enlarged, and their motion is controlled through movement of these fins. The mouth has very stout, platelike teeth suited for crushing and grinding, a feature essential for an animal living primarily on shellfish.

A remarkable thing about sharks is the similarity between Devonian and modern sharks. Rarely does an animal become so particularly well adapted to a mode of life and fit so well into its ecological niche that it is able to main-tain its position through so many millions of years.

The modern mackerel sharks, including the most aggressive and fastest, the white sharks, are the largest predatory fish in modern seas, but their 20- to 30-foot lengths seem small compared with some of the large Paleogene sharks. These grew up to 50 feet long, and their jaws opened wide enough to allow a man to walk through them erect. Not all sharks have been predators. This is especially true of the largest sharks. One of these less dangerous groups is the modern whale shark, which reaches lengths of 50 feet and lives on small floating and swimming organisms in the upper reaches of the sea.

Bony Fishes

BY FAR THE LARGEST and most varied group, bony fishes represent the culmination of this phase of evolution and make up the largest part of the fish population found in lakes, streams,

FIG. 38–6. / *Bony fishes. (Courtesy of the Chicago Natural History Museum.)*

FIG. 38–7. / *Lungfish. These fish are found in South America and in Africa. They have the ability to burrow into the bottom sediments and spend the dry seasons in the mud breathing through lungs during these periods when they are not surrounded by water. (Photos by courtesy of General Biological Supply House.)*

and seas today. First representatives of this group made their appearance in the Devonian. Their distinguishing characteristics are bony structures, highly developed both internally and externally. The body is completely covered by scales, and there is a covering over the gill opening (Fig. 38–6). Vertebrae are harder than the body supports found in other fishes. Primitive bony fishes had lungs that functioned to enable them to breathe air, but through time this feature has evolved to become an air bladder that helps control buoyancy.

Air-Breathing Fishes

Two PRIMITIVE GROUPS of bony fishes were able to breathe air and thus survive periods out of water. These were lungfishes and lobefin (crossopterygian) fishes. Lungfishes are represented by three living genera, which inhabit fresh waters in Africa, Australia, and South America (Fig. 38–7). Two varieties have two lungs and are able to live for several months in stream beds and pond bottoms after water is completely evaporated. Australian lungfishes are even able to walk a little, using their fins for locomotion. This certainly suggests the method by which the first amphibians must have evolved.

Lungfishes and crossopterygian fishes have never been abundant since they first appeared in the Devonian. It had long been thought that crossopterygians became extinct in the Cretaceous, but in 1938 one was brought up alive off Madagascar (Fig. 38–8). Since then others have been caught. The excitement that surrounded these discoveries was great because it was from Devonian ancestors of this line that amphibians almost certainly evolved. Among features of crossopterygians that indicated this connection were internal nostrils and lungs. Their fins were exactly the kind from which amphibians' legs might evolve. Not only was their skull pattern like that found in the first amphibians, but there was also a striking similarity in structure of the backbone (Fig. 38–9).

Evolution of Bony Fishes

The FIRST BONY FISHES appearing in freshwater deposits of Middle Devonian time were small. Their scales were diamond- or rhombic-shaped. They had large eyes, long mouths extending the length of the skull, and paired fins in front and back. Their vertebrae were not

FIG. 38–8. / Latimeria. *The only lobefin which still survives, Latimeria was long thought to be extinct until one was caught near Madagascar. It was from a fish very similar to this one that the first amphibians are thought to have evolved. (Photo by courtesy of the American Museum of Natural History.)*

FIG. 38–9. / *A restored Eusthenopteron, one of the lobe-finned crossopterygians. This fish is known from Devonian strata in the United States. The fins are stout enough to support the animal out of water; however, it probably could not move far away from water. (Modified after W. K. Gregory.)*

hardened. Among trends that are typical of successive stages in the evolution of bony fishes are change in shape and thickness of scales from heavy, rhombic scales to thin, rounded ones. The internal skeleton, which was initially cartilaginous, because increasingly harder. In the most primitive group lungs were not transformed into an air bladder, but in the later groups this became an effective means of maintaining balance. Other changes involved jaw hingement, tail structure, and position of fins.

Amphibians

THE FIRST GROUP OF ANIMALS TO ENcroach upon the land areas of the world and become adapted to a terrestrial life were the amphibians. This major step forward in the evolutionary story was to lead to eventual conquest of the land by reptiles and finally by mammals (Fig. 38–10). Amphibians were present in the Devonian, and until the close of the Carboniferous they represented the most ad-

vanced form of life on earth. Their greatness was soon overshadowed by the better adaptation of reptiles to life on land. By the end of the Triassic amphibians had dwindled to a relatively small and unimportant class represented then, as now, by three groups—frogs, salamanders, and several wormlike forms.

The frog, a typical amphibian, lays small eggs covered by a jellylike mass in water. When they hatch, the embryo is a tadpole which must swim around to find its own food. For this life in water the tadpole is equipped with a flexible tail, and it uses special gills for breathing. As maturity is approached, metamorphosis occurs, and the life of the tadpole changes remarkably. Lungs develop, gills disappear, limbs grow rapidly, and the young frog is soon adapted to a life on land. It must return to water only for breeding.

The amphibians that have survived are a highly specialized and rather degenerate group. The remarkable thing about the class as a whole is its early development from fishes and its adaptation to problems of living on land. The first

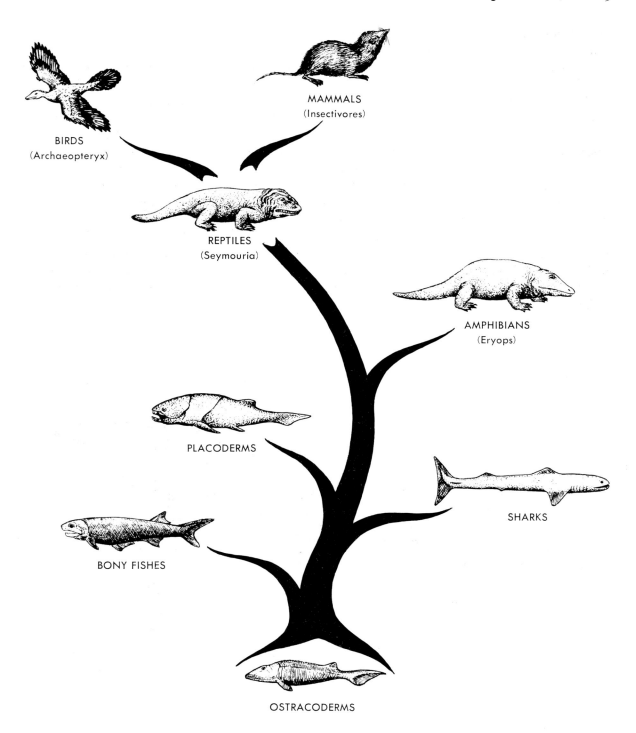

FIG. 38–10. / *Generalized evolutionary connections among the various major groups of fishes and the amphibians, reptiles, birds, and mammals.*

amphibians were beset by all sorts of problems which no previous animal had been forced to face. They had to depend on lungs and *respiration* for oxygen, and on strong limbs to support the body when its weight was not buoyed up by water; they needed a way of preventing the drying out of the body; and finally they required a new means of locomotion. Amphibians evolved in such a way as to solve all of these problems. Among the most important characteristics of crossopterygian fishes was their development of lungs suitable for breathing on land. The main difference between these and the first amphibians was the way in which the two made use of their lungs. The lungfish depend almost solely on gills for oxygen and use lungs relatively little, while amphibians depend almost exclusively upon their lungs. Legs of early amphibians have a structural pattern similar to that which is characteristic of most later land animals. These had evolved from the paired fins of fish. Another important structural change took place in the backbone. Vertebrae of amphibians altered to form much stronger structures better suited to support the weight of the animal out of water. Another necessary structural adaptation concerned hearing. Fishes had no specialized mechanism for transmission of sounds to the inner ear, since they are not needed in a water environment. An effective amplifying system evolved in amphibians, making it possible for them to hear sounds propagated through air, an important feature for any land dweller.

FIG. 38–11. / *One of the most primitive amphibians from the Upper Devonian of Greenland. The limbs are no longer finlike in appearance, but the tail still resembles the fish tail fin.*

Ancient Amphibians

AMPHIBIANS WHICH LIVED in the Paleozoic and early part of the Triassic had skulls completely covered by an armorlike mass of bone. On this account they are known as stegocephalians (roof-headed amphibians). The largest group of these were the labyrinthodonts, a name derived from the structure of their teeth (grooved and infolded in a complex pattern) (Fig. 38–11).

Until recently the oldest amphibians had been found in swamp deposits of the Carboniferous. Many diversified forms were present in these deposits, indicating a long period of development before the Carboniferous. The gap in our knowledge has now been closed by a discovery of amphibian remains in Devonian beds of Greenland. These earliest remains reveal an amphibian with a head and a tail fin much like those of the crossopterygian fishes, but they also possessed short, stubby limbs. Early amphibians resembled present-day salamanders, although some varieties were eight feet long. One of these, *Eryops* (Fig. 38–12), is a fairly typical Late Paleozoic amphibian. *Eryops* was heavily built, with a broad, flat skull of irregularly thick bone. They were well adapted to life on land because they had an unusually strong and large bone structure. They probably lived an alligator-like existence along streams and lakes of Carboniferous coal swamps. Its sharp teeth suggest that *Eryops* may have lived on fish and smaller land-dwelling animals.

FIG. 38–12. / Eryops, *one of the early labyrinthodont amphibians. This genus was one of the most abundant late Paleozoic amphibians.*

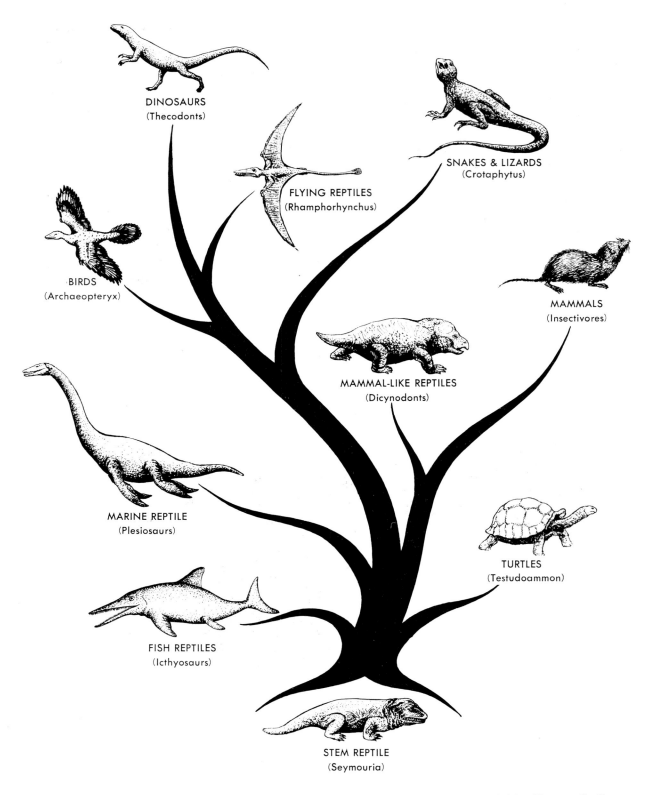

FIG. 39–1. / *Family tree of the reptiles showing their relationship to the amphibian-like reptile Seymouria, the birds, and mammals.*

39

Rule of the Reptiles

THERE IS NO MORE FASCINATING STORY IN the history of the earth than that of the rise, spread, and eventual fall of reptiles as the dominant form of life on earth. They ruled for a period of more than 130 million years, during which they became adapted to and dominated life on land, in deep seas, in marshes, and in air. Most prominent members of the reptile family during the Mesozoic were dinosaurs, which eventually vanished, leaving only scattered remains preserved for later discovery in the sediments of the era.

The first evidence of reptiles has been found in Carboniferous rocks. They closely resemble Permian amphibians, the labyrinthodonts. Since reptiles are now known to have evolved from labyrinthodonts, it is not surprising that the initial branchings from amphibian patterns are only slightly different. An almost perfectly intermediate fossil between reptiles and amphibians, known as *Seymouria*, has been discovered (Fig. 39–1).

Amphibians had made a tremendous step forward in developing a means of living effectively on land. However, one weak link existed in their pattern of life, and this probably caused them to be overcome eventually by reptiles. That weak link was the necessity of amphibians to lay eggs in water. Evolution of a hard egg covering, the shell, made it possible for reptile young to hatch far from water (Fig. 39–2).

The first reptiles appeared shortly after the first labyrinthodonts. For a time they co-existed, competing with one another, but eventually the reptiles won the struggle. As the history of the labyrinthodonts drew to a close they retreated back into the sea and after a short time became extinct.

Characteristics of the Reptiles

DEVELOPMENT OF A SHELL COVERING OVER the reptile egg should be emphasized as one of the most important differences between two otherwise similar classes, and as a significant step in the evolutionary history of organisms toward higher degrees of development. The shell protects the egg from physical harm and contains the necessary food for development of the embryo. At the same time it frees the reptile from an early youth in water.

Reptiles, like amphibians, contain no system for regulation of body heat. This is important in that it confines them to warm, temperate, or

FIG. 39–2. / *Reptile leaving the egg. The hard egg covering was first evolved among the reptiles. It is one of the most important steps in the spread of life onto the land areas of the world. For the first time animals were free to roam far from water.*

tropical climates. In all respects reptiles developed to a higher degree than amphibians. They are superior in the manner of organization of their skeletons, muscles, and circulatory systems. Although the reptile brain is small compared with that of mammals, its capacity still exceeds that of amphibians. Reptiles were the first animals to have even the most elemental forms of higher brain centers.

Forerunners of Dinosaurs

MAMMAL-LIKE REPTILES, fishlike mammals, dinosaurs, and turtles all radiated from a primitive group of reptiles called *cotylosaurus*. This reptile evolved along slightly different lines into several groups during the Permian and Triassic periods before they died out in the Triassic. They had long, low bodies and awkward, sprawling limbs like those of *Seymouria*.

One branch of cotylosaurs were small, lizard-like reptiles with a pointed head, sharp teeth, and two openings in the back of the skull. These reptiles, known as *thecodonts* (Fig. 39–4), were the first dinosaurs, and all others radiated from them. Unlike many dinosaurs that were to follow, thecodonts were only about four feet long. They were adapted to bipedal locomotion, an important advance over the first land-living vertebrates, which walked on all fours. Bipedal locomotion was made possible by a hinged pelvis and development of a long tail

which functioned as a counterbalance for the weight of the front of the body. The pelvis acted somewhat like a fulcrum. With two front feet off the ground, they soon became able to use them to grasp objects. The hind legs, which had to support the body weight and enable them to run, became stronger and longer, while the front feet diminished in size.

Dinosaurs

DINOSAURS WERE ONLY ONE OF THE IMportant groups to radiate from the early reptiles. When dinosaurs were first discovered, an argument arose as to what they were. "Dinosaur," meaning "terrible lizard," was applied to the first fossil remains. Unfortunately it was not until many years later that it was realized that two distinctly different groups of fossil remains had been classed together under this name. As a result, the term "dinosaur" is now applied in somewhat the same context as the name "ungulate," which refers to all animals with hoofs although they may be as different as horses and cows. The basic distinction between the two orders of dinosaurs is the structure of the pelvis.

SAURISCHIA. Dinosaurs of this order have a pelvis similar in structure to that of other reptiles (Fig. 39–3). Otherwise the group is quite diversified and includes many of the most widely known dinosaurs, such as *Tyrannosaurus* (Fig. 39–6) and *Brontosaurus* (Fig. 39–7).

FIG. 39–3. / *Pelvic structure of the two major orders of dinosaurs,* Saurischia *and* Ornithischia.

reptile-like pelvis   birdlike pelvis

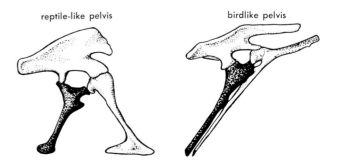

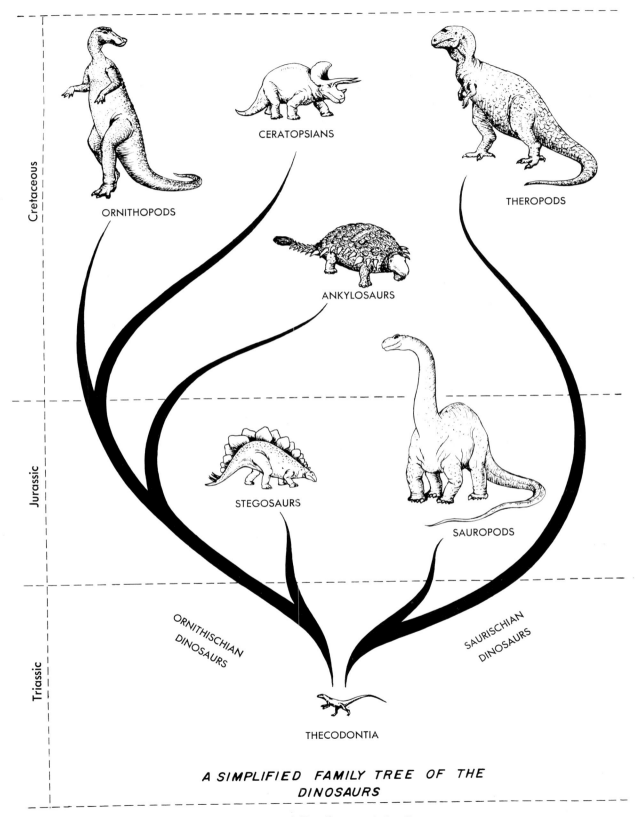

A SIMPLIFIED FAMILY TREE OF THE DINOSAURS

FIG. 39–4. / *Family tree of the dinosaurs.*

Comparison of the lives of *Brontosaurus* and *Tyrannosaurus* serves to illustrate this diversity, although both of them were giants, even among dinosaurs. *Brontosaurus* walked on all four legs, fed on plants, and lived in swampy areas where it could get in the water, possibly for protection and probably to take some of the load off its feet. The largest of these was nearly 80 feet long and seems to have reached just about the maximum size that its type of bone structure could reasonably support. The head was extremely small compared with the rest of the body, and its brain could have weighed no more than a few ounces. Motion of the rear end was probably governed mainly by a concentration of nerves near the end of the backbone. *Tyrannosaurus* walked on the two back legs, which were large and strong, used the forelegs to grasp objects, fed on meat, and lived on somewhat dryer land. Though the brain was not much larger than that of other dinosaurs, *Tyrannosaurus* did have a large head, powerful jaws, and many sharp teeth. They were well suited for the carnivorous lives they led. Some of these grew to be 50 feet long and stood up to 20 feet high.

ORNITHISCHIA. The second order of dinosaurs has a pelvis similar in structure to that of birds. They lived later in the Mesozoic and ate plants, but they too were a highly varied group. The *ornithopods* (Fig. 39–5), known as the duck-billed dinosaurs, lived in marshes and swamps. Some were bipedal, while others walked on all fours. One group was rather small, only eight feet tall; others of this suborder developed unusual bony skulls (Fig. 39–8), like the *Troodon*, which had a nine-inch-thick skull and therefore is called the bone-headed dinosaur.

Stegosaurus (Fig. 39–9) lived at the same time and in the same environment as *Tyrannosaurus*. These reptiles were able to survive because of a heavy armor of large finlike plates of bone down the back, and a tail equipped with spikes on the end. *Stegosaurus*, whose brain was

FIG. 39–5. / *Duck-billed dinosaur*, Anatosaurus annectena Marsh. *From the upper Cretaceous Lance formation of Niobrara County, Wyoming.* (*Photo by courtesy of the U.S. National Museum.*)

FIG. 39–6. / Triceratops *and* Tyrannosaurus. *Tyrannosaurus, one of the last of the dinosaurs, was the greatest land-living flesh-eater known. Standing 19 feet high, its jaws were armed with large saber-like teeth. The plant-eating Triceratops on the left was protected by its three horns and by the bony frill covering its neck. Both of these dinosaurs lived in North America at the end of the Cretaceous period, 78 million years ago. (Painting by Charles Knight, Chicago Natural History Museum.)*

FIG. 39–7. / Brontosaurus, *a huge plant-eating dinosaur. The sauropod dinosaurs that lived at the end of the Jurassic Period, 145 million years ago, were the largest land animals of all time. Brontosaurus attained a length of 67 feet and an estimated weight of 30 tons. It probably spent most of its life in swamps, where there was plenty of vegetation for food. Supporting its great weight would have been less of a problem in the water than on land. (Painting by Charles Knight, Chicago Natural History Museum.)*

about the size of a peanut, must be ranked as the most mentally deficient dinosaur. Nerves in an enlargement of the spinal cord probably controlled most movement of the rear end.

Another solution by armament is found among the *ankylosaurs* (Fig. 39–10), which came close to resembling a tank. They were low-slung, medium-sized, and had bony plates that fitted together over most of the body surface. These plates were hinged to allow some movement. The skull was broad and flat with a thick bone covering, and the tail was heavy, stiff, and contained a large mass of bone.

The *ceratopsian dinosaurs* (Fig. 39–11) also had to cope with flesh-eating enemies. Their solution to the defense problem was a massive bony shield around the neck and head and long pointed horns. They were the last major group of dinosaurs to evolve. From the fossil record

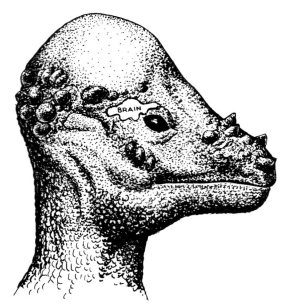

FIG. 39–8. / *The "bone-headed dinosaur," the* Troodon. *This dinosaur lived in the late Cretaceous. It was kin to the* Camptosaurus *and other ornithopods.*

FIG. 39–9. / Stegosaurus. *The bony plates of his back served as protection against the flesh-eating dinosaurs. (Photo by courtesy of the U.S. National Museum.)*

FIG. 39–10. / *Late Cretaceous dinosaurs. The peak of dinosaur evolution was reached shortly before the extinction of the group. Prominent in North America 90 million years ago were the duck-billed dinosaurs, such as* Edmontosaurus *on the right and the hooded* Corythosaurus *and crested* Parasaurolophus *in the swamp on the left. Other contemporary dinosaurs were the heavily armored* Palaeoscincus *in the center and the ostrich-like* Struthiomimus *in the background. (Painting by Charles Knight, Chicago Natural History Museum.)*

FIG. 39–11. / *Horned dinosaur,* Triceratops prorsus *Marsh. From the upper Cretaceous Lance formation of Converse County, Wyoming. (Photo by courtesy of the U.S. National Museum.)*

left by them we find one of the best-documented records of progressively better morphological adaptation found among vertebrates.

Aquatic Reptiles

REPTILES INVADED AND ADAPTED TO LIFE in almost every type of environment. Some evolved in such a way as to become adapted to water, like amphibians, spending part of their life in water and part on land. Others spent their entire lives in the water. *Ichthyosaurs* and *plesiosaurs* (Fig. 39–12) are two of the best known of these. These reptiles were not true dinosaurs; however, some dinosaurs did live in water at least part of the time, and a number of the largest of them like *Brontosaurus* sought refuge in water from their adversaries.

The oldest ichthyosaur remains are found in marine Triassic deposits. By that time they were fully adapted to life in the water. They were shaped much like a modern porpoise—bodies were streamlined for fast swimming, limbs were altered to form fins (a reversion to the original use of fins), and jaws formed a tapering, pointed beak armed with a large number of sharp teeth used to catch and chew fish. The ichthyosaurs propelled themselves as fish do, by a side-to-side movement of the body. They had no neck, and the head simply made up a part of the front of the body. They reached the height of their development in the Jurassic and Cretaceous. One interesting change occurred in the tails of the ichthyosaurs as they became more perfectly suited to life in water. The end of the tail evolved into a fishlike tail, which served to stabilize the animal in swimming. Early ones were not so well adapted for this purpose as were those that lived toward the end of the Mesozoic. Development of the tail, head, feet, and other morphological features into fishlike organs makes the ichthyosaurs an excellent example of convergence in evolution. *Conver-*

FIG. 39–12. / *Reptiles that invaded the seas. The several groups of reptiles that became aquatic trace their ancestry back to land forms. In the seas of Early Jurassic times, 170 million years ago, two types of reptiles were abundant. The long-necked plesiosaurs were fish eaters that propelled themselves with their strong flippers. The fish-shaped ichthyosaurs fed mostly on squids and drove themselves through the water with their powerful tails. (Painting by Charles Knight, Chicago Natural History Museum.)*

gence is the term used when two or more unrelated forms evolve into very close resemblance.
In Fig. 39–13, compare the ichthyosaur (a reptile), the shark (a fish), and the porpoise (a
mammal). All adapted to the same environment, and each evolved to forms particularly
suited to a successful life in that environment,
demonstrating marked convergence.

Another pattern of adaptation to the marine
environment began to develop during the Triassic. These were small to medium-sized reptiles
with long flexible necks and limbs which took
on the form of paddles. These limbs were strong
and probably enabled the animal to crawl out
of water in much the same fashion as a present-
day seal or sea lion does. The heads were small,
but jaws were equipped with sharp teeth suitable for catching and holding fish. Plesiosaurs
evolved from this earlier stock in Jurassic time,
and they survived until the end of the Cretaceous. The main change through this time
was an increase in size. Some Cretaceous plesiosaurs were 40 feet long. Studies of muscle attachments and bone structure suggest that
plesiosaurs were able to operate their paddles
like oars, rowing forward or backward or working them in opposite directions to make a fast
turn. Since the animal had to rely on its ability
to catch fish for food, it evolved in such a way
as to do this effectively. One group evolved
longer necks—so long, in fact, that they were
over twice as long as the rest of the body. These
long flexible necks could move from side to
side as the animal caught fish. Another line
evolved to form large heads. The extreme in this
line was reached when some possessed heads
over 12 feet in length.

Origin of Birds

The fossil record contains remains of
birdlike reptiles which developed toward the
middle of the Mesozoic Era. The birdlike existence of these creatures required adaptations
and specializations in a more sensitively bal-

FIG. 39–13. / *Convergence, an evolutionary trend
toward similarity of outward appearance in unrelated groups. Compare the ichthyosaur, a reptile
(bottom), with the shark, a fish (top), and the porpoise, a mammal (middle).*

anced system than any other trend in reptilian
evolution. Requirements for flight are rigorous:
the organism must overcome the gravitative pull
on it, which requires a special lightness in
structure usually effected by hollow bones and
a light skeleton; and the structure and amount
of wing area must be adjusted to compensate
for and balance the weight, even for soaring.
For true flight even greater specialization is required. Flying animals need some effective guid-
ance system, either good eyes or a mechanism
like the "radar" of bats.

Unfortunately the record of fossil birds is
incomplete. This might be expected, since most
birds live on land, their remains are apt to be
devoured by scavengers, and their small delicate
bones are not so well suited for preservation.
We are very fortunate, however, in having almost perfectly preserved fossil remains of two
bird skeletons from the Jurassic Solenhofen
limestone in Bavaria.

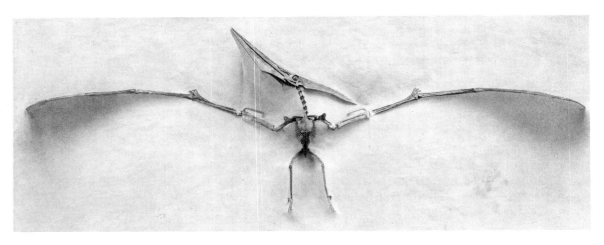

FIG. 39–14. / *Restored skeleton of the flying reptile* Pteranodon ingens. *From the upper Cretaceous Chalk deposits of western Kansas. (Photo by courtesy of the U.S. National Museum.)*

Birdlike Reptiles

ONE OF THE JURASSIC REPTILES that became adapted to flight is *Rhamphorhynchus* (Fig. 39–14). They were about two feet long. Jaws and skull became elongated and contained sharp, pointed teeth which were probably used for catching fish. The tail was relatively long and flared out into a rudder-like structure at the end. The fourth finger was elongated to form a support for a large wing, and the first three fingers were shaped like small hooks, with which they could hang on trees or rock ledges. The back limbs appear to have been very weak and might have served as wing attachments.

Late in the Jurassic another flying reptile branched from *Rhamphorhynchus*. This was *Pterodactylus*, which reached the peak of its development in the Cretaceous. This awkward-looking reptile had a wingspread of more than 25 feet, but the body was not substantially larger than a modern turkey or goose. These groups became extinct at the close of the Cretaceous. One important factor in their extinction must have been the evolution of true birds, which through their superior adaptation were able to predominate over the food sources of the flying reptiles.

First Birds (Archaeopteryx)

THE OLDEST FOSSIL BIRDS are found in the Solenhofen limestone, and are beautifully preserved. Were this not the case, their remains probably would have been classified as those of another flying reptile, for the structure of the skeleton is extremely reptile-like. But in the calm, scavenger-free waters of the Solenhofen Sea even feathers were preserved. *Archaeopteryx* (Fig. 39–15) was a little over a foot long. It had a long neck and tail, and its hind legs appear well adapted to walking or running. It probably walked somewhat like a chicken. Jaws were elongated and contained teeth. The long tail was characteristic of reptiles. Three digits of the feet were elongated to support the wing. Feathers extended out from the hand and lower arm bones, and some apparently were on the body. Other feathers were arranged along either side of the tail. Besides having feathers, the first bird differed from reptiles in having an expanded brain capacity, denoting a complex central nervous system.

By Cretaceous time birds were rapidly becoming more modern in aspect. Some steps in modernization of birds included fusing of bones of the hand and development of a lighter body and a beak suited for picking berries and fruit. Birds of the Paleogene Period were probably very similar to some present-day birds. Among evolutionary trends of the birds has been return to the ground, which characterizes such birds as the ostrich, but this has in general proved unsatisfactory, since mammals have controlled lands of the Cenozoic. The most notable characteristic in the evolution of birds in modern times is their adaptation to life in so many different ecological niches. Consider the different adaptations of the owl, snipe, hummingbird, sea gull, and hawk.

FIG. 39–15. / *Cast and restoration of* Archaeopteryx. (*Courtesy of the American Museum of Natural History.*)

FIG. 40–1. / *Dimetrodon, one of the mammal-like reptiles. This pelycosaur is characterized by a lizard-like appearance and the sail. The purpose of this sail has been a subject of much debate. One of the most reasonable explanations is that it was a crude mechanism for the regulation of body temperatures, a need of warm-blooded animals such as the mammals. (Photo by courtesy of the U.S. National Museum.)*

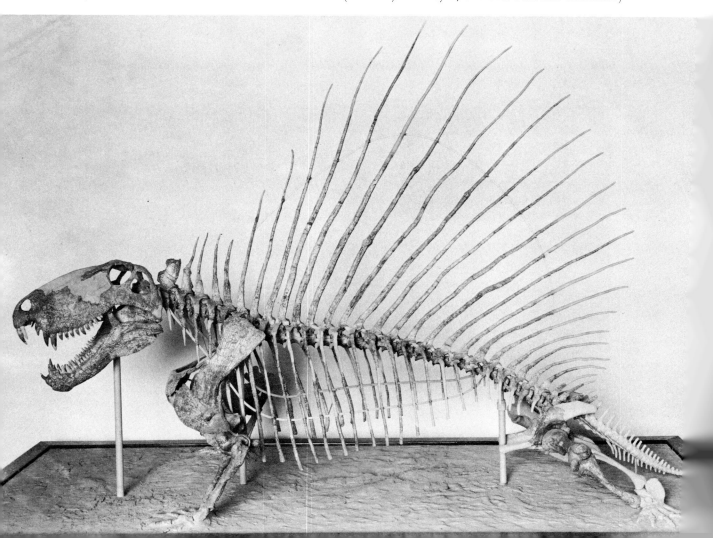

40

Rise of the Mammals

MAMMALS ARE NOW RULERS OF THE EARTH IN the same sense that reptiles were in the Mesozoic. Like Mesozoic reptiles, mammals live in seas, they dominate land areas, and they have become adapted to a great variety of modes of life. Their origin and development are of peculiar interest because man is a mammal. Although mammals hold an exalted position now, they evolved from reptiles in the Jurassic and did not come to be important for many millions of years.

Mammal Characteristics

MOST NOTABLE DISTINGUISHING CHARACteristics of the mammals are:

The size of the brain. This is the most outstanding mammalian attribute. Even the most stupid mammals possess much larger brains than reptiles, especially if considered in relation to the animal's total size. This enlargement in the brain size has been largely confined to one particular area, a part known as the cerebral hemispheres. This part governs thought processes. It is the area in which sensory impressions are received, stored as memories, and later used in thought processes. Brains of all mammals are not alike, nor is size a direct measure of intelligence. More progressive mammals have brains in which the cerebrum is folded in a complex manner. Intelligence seems somewhat related to the surface area of this part of the brain.

A high body temperature. Mammals, like birds, are warm-blooded. This enables them to have a high rate of metabolism, which in turn makes possible some of the complexities of organization of the body. Associated with warm blood is a system of cooling and maintaining body temperature, such as sweat glands and hair covering. Other highly specialized systems include the circulatory system and mechanisms for respiration.

Reproduction. Mammals bear their young live. Young are nourished within the body of the mother, then taken care of after birth until they have developed enough to take care of themselves.

Structure of the skull. One of the main bases for classification of the reptiles is the structure of the skull, particularly with reference to the temporal openings that characterize most reptilian skulls. There is no opening in the top of the skull of mammals such as is found among some reptiles. The jaw is changed considerably, with the seven bones of reptiles being represented in mammals by a single bone. Reptiles have a single bone connecting the head to the backbone, while mammals have two. The mammal brain case is much enlarged to hold larger brains, and structure of the temporal region includes an arch at the edge of the cheek.

Teeth. Teeth provide one of the more important means of differentiating mammals. Teeth of reptiles are comparatively simple, are replaced many times during the life of the animal, and are generally about the same shape throughout the jaw. In general terms, mammal teeth include four sharp teeth suited for nipping; two large piercing teeth, canines; six premolar teeth; and four molars, used for grinding. A similar number occur in the other jaw.

Reptile-Like Mammals

The first mammal-like reptiles came from the most primitive reptile stock, not from one of the more advanced reptiles. One radiation from cotylosaurs led to the dominant forms of life in the Mesozoic, dinosaurs; another line of radiation led to mammal-like reptiles, *pelycosaurs*; and a third led to *therapsids*. This last group and their survivors lived more or less as onlookers throughout the 150 million years of the reign of the reptiles. But at the end of that reign, in the Early Cenozoic, these therapsids, which had evolved as mammals, took over and their descendants have ruled the animal kingdom ever since.

Pelycosaurs (Mammal-Like Reptiles)

Pelycosaurs branched from animals like *Seymouria.* The first of this group were so much like reptiles that they almost certainly would be classified as reptiles, but later they came to resemble true mammals more and more closely, until the two cannot be distinguished. A well-known genus of the pelycosaurs is *Dimetrodon* (Fig. 40-1). They walked on all fours in a rather clumsy fashion, with legs protruding to

the side, and with an outward resemblance to lizards. Their mammal-like features included differentiation of teeth into incisors, canines, and molars, and structure of bones of the cheek was distinctly mammal-like. One of the more peculiar features of *Dimetrodon* was a row of spines on its back which supported a sail-like skin covering. This is thought to be a primitive type of mechanism for regulation of body heat. Blood vessels in the skin covering the spines could absorb heat from the sun or lose it, like a radiator, when extended. Heat flow would be reduced by lowering spines along the back.

Therapsids

Dimetrodon and other pelycosaurs were dominant carnivores of the Permian, but another form branched off from them in the middle of the Permian, and these, the therapsids, lived on into the Triassic. Therapsids (Fig. 40-2) have been best preserved in beds of the Karroo in South Africa. They were about the size of a large dog, and among the more important changes from reptiles represented in them is bone structure of the legs, which indicated that they were adapted to a fast, four-footed gait. Another important feature is the shape of the skull, which is intermediate between reptile and mammal. Some of the reptilian bone structures that are absent in mammals were much reduced in size in therapsids. Two bones connected the head with the backbone, teeth were much like those of mammals, and the penial opening had practically disappeared. Therapsids were meat-eaters, and their bone structure must have given them a considerable advantage over their prey, the awkward reptiles. This advantage was soon lost to the larger dinosaurs, which the mammal-like reptiles were unable to kill. By the early Jurassic they were gone.

Mammals of the Jurassic

The remains of mesozoic mammals are rare. Most of them are little more than fragments of teeth, jaws, and other skull pieces. From such a sparse record it is hard to re-

create a very good picture of what mammals of the Jurassic and Cretaceous were like, but we know from the size of the teeth and jaws that they must have been very small, probably about the size of rats, and they may have resembled the modern rat or squirrel rather closely. It is not hard to understand why so little remains. As dinosaurs radiated rapidly in the Mesozoic, mammal-like reptiles were destroyed, and when mammals finally reached the scene they too were under constant threat of destruction. During this period of trial mammals apparently developed their brains rather than their bodies, and when dinosaurs became extinct mammals were ready to assume leadership and to move into environments left vacant by their adversaries.

Despite the scarcity of remains, four orders of mammals have been described from Jurassic sedimentary rocks. One of these possessed a long jaw with many teeth, differentiated as in modern mammals and showing a much greater specialization in this respect than mammal-like reptiles. Three cusps in the molar teeth gave these animals their names—the *triconodonts*. Another group, *multituberculates*, was the most probable forerunner of herbivorous mammals. Their front teeth were a pair of large, elongated incisors specialized to assist them in clipping. The other teeth were arranged in two parallel rows. The last premolar was enlarged into an effective shearing blade. They may have lived a life somewhat like that of modern rodents.

A third group, *pantotheres*, is thought to be the forerunner of most of the higher mammals because the arrangement of the molars is exactly like that of later mammals. A fourth group, *monotremes*, has survived to be represented among the most primitive mammals living today by the duckbilled platypus (Fig. 40-3) and the spiny anteater. The duckbill is adapted to burrowing in mud in search of soft animals for food. Because it lives on such soft material, teeth are lost, and two hard pads replace them in the adult. The feet are adapted to this environment as webbed paddles. Like the most primitive mammals, the duckbills lay eggs, and their structure bears a strong resemblance to the reptiles.

FIG. 40–2. / A therapsid from the Permian of South Africa restored by J. C. Germann under the direction of E. H. Colbert. Notice how the skull has many mammal-like characteristics and the legs are adapted to enable the animal to run rapidly. The typical reptiles had sprawling legs which made them awkward. (After J. C. Germann.)

Cretaceous Mammals

REMAINS OF CRETACEOUS MAMMALS ARE also hard to find, but it has been established that two of the largest groups of mammals made their first appearance in the Cretaceous. These were marsupials and placentals.

Marsupials

MOST PROMINENT OF MARSUPIAL characteristics are the short gestation period and the pouch in which newly born animals are placed, where they develop further. The opossum and kangaroo are members of this group. Marsupials

FIG. 40–3. / Duckbilled platypus. (Courtesy of the American Museum of Natural History.)

FIG. 40–4a,b, and c. / *Note the dominance of mammals in these murals of Tertiary fauna from the Miocene (top), Oligocene (bottom), and Eocene (opposite page). (Courtesy of the U.S. National Museum.)*

are more primitive than placentals. They have smaller brains, more teeth, and other more subtle differences in bone structure, particularly in the skull, pelvis, and feet. Although marsupials may be thought of as second-class mammals, they have undergone an adaptive radiation that enables them to live many different modes of life. Evidence of this is found among living forms in Australia today, where various marsupials closely resemble mice, moles, wolves, woodchucks, squirrels, rabbits, and many others.

Placentals

THIS GROUP INCLUDES most of the modern mammals. Radiation of placentals has been so extensive that they are classified in 28 orders, which compose over 2,500 genera and make up about 95 per cent of the mammals. Placentals are those mammals in which young go through a long period of gestation before they are born at a rather advanced stage in their development. In some cases young are quite active soon after birth. Their most important feature is an enlarged brain case, which is covered by a solid bony plate. For purposes of classification, however, the most important feature is their teeth. Teeth are so specialized in each group that almost the same classification of placentals would exist if nothing but teeth remained as fossil evidence.

Reconstruction of skulls found in Mongolia indicates that the first placentals were insectivores. Some placentals living today have a similar existence as, for example, shrews, moles, and hedgehogs. Of these, shrews come closest to approximating the size and shape of the first placentals.

Primates

OF THE 28 ORDERS OF PLACENTAL MAMmals (Fig. 40–4), primates are of greatest interest to man since he belongs to this group, along with lemurs, tarsiers, monkeys, and apes. It is the part of the story of evolution that deals with this order that has caused the greatest amount of controversy over the theory of evolution. If man had a unique body structure completely unlike that of any other animal, it is likely that the theory of evolution would have received little attention except from scientists. However, the fact remains that the bone structure of man strikingly resembles that of other members of the primate group (Fig. 40–5). Furthermore, there is enough evidence available now to demonstrate many stages in the gradual evolution of man from more primitive forms.

The fossil record of man is far more extensive than that of many other vertebrates, but it will probably never be as complete as we might wish. This is especially true of the early origin of primates. We know that almost all of these lived in trees. The forested areas of the world are usually in temperate or tropical climates. The tropical terrestrial environment is least favorable for preservation of fossils because there is a rapid rate of decay of dead organisms. Burial by natural causes is too slow, and there are many scavengers present to destroy remains. The first primate probably appeared in the Cretaceous, and was much like the modern tree shrew. From this primitive insectivore there were two periods of radiation—one in the early part of the Paleocene Epoch when lemurs and tarsiers branched off, and a second in the Eocene when anthropoids—man, apes, and monkeys—evolved from lemuroid ancestors.

Characteristics of Primates

MANY OF THE CHARACTERISTICS that distinguish primates are thought to be associated with their life in trees. Of the primates only two, man and baboons, have abandoned trees to live on the ground. Five features are of particular importance among the primates:

1. They developed a prehensile hand with an opposable thumb. This mechanism enables primates to grasp tree limbs and branches, making it much easier for them to move about in trees. The ability to grasp soon became important in their feeding habits and opened the way for many other advances, including close inspection of objects and the ability to manipulate objects with precision.

FIG. 40–5. / *Comparison of several important primates.* (*Modified after A. H. Schultz.*)

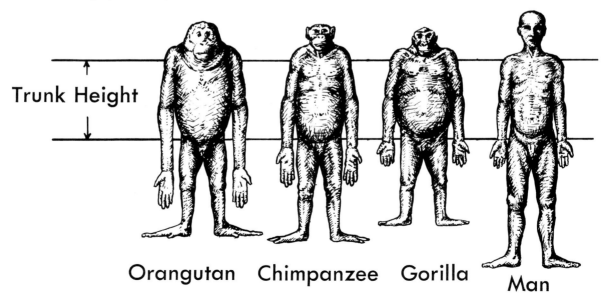

Trunk Height

Orangutan   Chimpanzee   Gorilla   Man

2. Primates developed the ability to move with agility and rapidity. This flexibility in body movements gives them another great advantage over other animals. It was necessary for climbing about in trees.

3. Sight is greatly improved in primates. They have large eyes which at first were needed to detect food and to assist movement in trees. One unusual adaptation of the visual apparatus is stereoscopic vision, whereby primates can see in three dimensions. To make this possible an advance in the structure of nerves governing sight had to be effected. This structure has to be sensitive enough to bring about, within the brain, a superposition of images seen in each eye. Another development is the highly developed area in the center of the retina, which makes it possible to see small details. Most of the eye is incapable of such great resolution.

4. Teeth in primates are not very specialized, but are suited for an omnivorous diet. Their structure and arrangement is such that the group has a short jaw and consequently a short face.

5. Their brains are the largest developed among mammals. This brain power probably evolved in part because of natural selection of those forms that were best suited for life in trees. Such a life requires agility, muscular co-ordination, good eyesight, and other characteristics that depend in part on capabilities of the brain. Such great advantages came to those groups with superior brain power that much pressure was exerted toward their continued evolution to superior forms.

Lemurs

THE HIGHER PRIMATES, the anthropoids, evolved from an earlier primate which closely resembled the modern lemurs (Fig. 40–6). Lemurs are small, arboreal animals with a bushy hair covering, a long tail, moderately long limbs, and a shortened face with a muzzle somewhat resembling that of a fox. The name "lemur" was applied by Romans to the souls of the dead which haunted the night. Similarly, lemurs have nocturnal habits.

Tarsiers

THESE SEEM TO represent a form intermediate between lemurs and monkeys. The tarsier is definitely more advanced than the lemur in that its vision is stereoscopic, its eyes are rotated forward rather than to the sides, the foxlike muzzle is gone, and the brain is larger. There is not enough fossil evidence to establish clearly the relationship between lemurs, tarsiers, and monkeys. It is most probable that the Anthropoidea evolved from lemurs to an ancestral form of tarsiers and then branched into manlike creatures.

Anthropoidea

THE MORE ADVANCED primates include monkeys, apes, and man. These three belong to a single suborder because they are structurally similar. That man evolved from apes or monkeys is a common misconception. Similarities be-

FIG. 40–6. / *The lemur. Lemurs probably evolved from a primitive insectivore like the modern tree shrew. The lemur, like man and the ape, is a primate. The anthropods evolved from lemuroid ancestors in the Eocene Epoch.*

tween members of this group do not mean that one evolved from the other, but simply that they had a common ancestry if traced far enough back. We may be sure that man did not evolve from any living types of apes or monkeys, for each represents a separate branch from a common stock.

Monkeys

The first monkeys appeared in the Oligocene Epoch. It is most probable that they evolved from a lemur-like animal. Two distinctly different groups of monkeys are found in South America on the one hand, and in Africa, Asia, and Europe on the other. They are known respectively as the New World and Old World monkeys. Both developed about the same time and have had about the same geographic distribution since the Oligocene. Among features that distinguish them as members of the anthropoids are their brains, eyes, and hands, and the general framework of their skeleton. The face of the monkey is short and flattened. Both eyes are directed forward, and fields of vision overlap considerably, giving them good stereoscopic vision. Both their hands and feet are prehensile. The monkey brain is larger than that of the lemur. This is particularly true of the upper part of the cortex. Thus the monkey has more brain than its ancestors and undoubtedly can use it more effectively.

Apes

Modern apes include the orangutan of Sumatra and Borneo, the gorilla and chimpanzee of central Africa, and the gibbon of southeastern Asia. Judging from the distribution of known fossil remains, apes have inhabited warmer parts of Africa and Asia since the first ape appeared in the Oligocene Epoch. Either they evolved from some line of Old World monkeys, or there was a common ancestor. Apes have never been particularly abundant, and relatively few fossil remains of them are found. They must have been much more highly varied and probably more numerous during the Miocene than dur-

ing any other time. It was at that time that the immediate ancestors of the modern apes arose.

One of the most interesting but least specialized of early Miocene apes is *Proconsul*. These probably were forerunners of all modern apes, with the exception of gibbons. Unlike modern apes, they were comparatively lightweight, agile, and not nearly as specialized as the orangutan, chimpanzee, or gorilla.

Several trends have characterized evolution of apes, such as increase in size, development of the brain, change in structure of teeth, and brachiating (the feat of swinging from branch to branch). This became necessary for an animal that was evolving to larger sizes. With increased size apes found it increasingly difficult to walk along tree limbs and thus developed the ability to swing from one part of the tree to another. Gibbons are the most skilled brachiators of all primates. They are relatively small and have long arms that facilitate their acrobatic jumps and swings through trees. Orangutans and chimpanzees are somewhat less talented along this line, and gorillas have given it up altogether. Undoubtedly the size of the gorillas has been an important reason in their abandonment of trees as a way of life. Some of them climb trees, but none live there. They are the largest of the apes, and some are the largest of all primates. They are larger than man and much stronger than the strongest men. Even so, modern gorillas were surpassed in size by a giant gorilla that lived in the Early Pleistocene.

Man-Apes: Australopithecus

Fragments of skulls, teeth, and skeletons of a peculiar manlike ape have been found in Pleistocene cave deposits of South Africa. These remains are those of an animal that falls in an intermediate position between structures typical of men and those associated with apes (Fig. 40-7). The skull is comparable to that of modern apes. The animals had a brain case that is much smaller than that of men and about the same size as that of an ape, but the teeth are much more like those of men than apes. The head was set on the shoulders instead of thrust forward, as in apes, and the structure of the pelvis indicates that these creatures were able to walk in an upright position. Gibbons walk on their hind legs, holding their arms up for balance, but all other modern apes normally walk on all fours. Thus this primate possessed a peculiar mixture of manlike and apelike characteristics.

We might immediately conclude that this is a definite intermediate form showing the connection between man and apes, but this appears improbable because of the age of the remains. They are much too recent to represent an early man or an early ape. Instead they must be a separate line that evolved independently of apes or men. However, it is probable that their forerunners were ancestors of both apes and men.

Ape-Men: Pithecanthropus

SEARCH FOR THE OLDEST MEN, the "connecting links," continues and undoubtedly will continue as long as our civilization lasts. Each new discovery tends to clarify certain anatomical relations among fossil men already known to us. There are already so many remains of animals that possessed varying degrees of manlike characteristics that the question of which we shall call true men is strictly a matter of definition. Generally the *Australopithecines* are excluded as men, although it is likely that their ancestors back in the Miocene or Pliocene were the stock from which *Homo sapiens* evolved.

Fragments of skulls, teeth, jaws, and other bones found in Java and near Peking, China, are most commonly accepted as remains of the first fossil men. Java men are known as *Pithecan-*

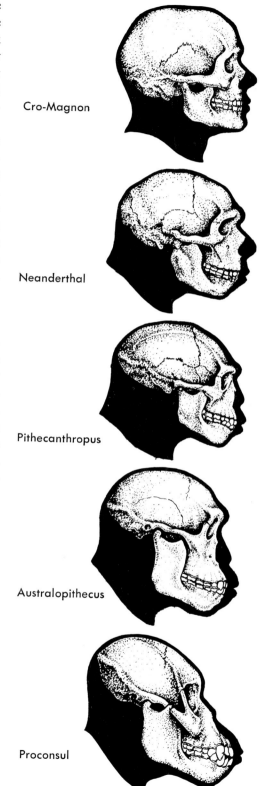

Cro-Magnon

Neanderthal

Pithecanthropus

Australopithecus

Proconsul

FIG. 40–7. / *Apes, manlike apes, and man. Proconsul was one of the less specialized apes of the Miocene Epoch. Australopithecus, a manlike ape, has been found in Pleistocene cave deposits of South Africa. Pithecanthropus is most frequently accepted as the first fossil man. Neanderthal man is the most primitive member of the genus,* Homo. *Cro-Magnon man was so similar to modern man that he would easily be mistaken for modern man.*

thropus, and although those found near Peking are given another name, *Sinanthropus,* they were probably no more different from one another than the modern races are from each other. Other fossils of these men have been found in Africa and in other parts of Asia, although none have been turned up in the New World. These men resembled apes in some features, but were much more manlike than *Australopithecus.* Their brain case was large enough to hold a brain of 800 to 1,300 cubic centimeters. In contrast, modern men have brains on the order of 1,200 to 2,000 cubic centimeters in size. Like modern man, they walked upright, and their teeth were similar, although they protruded in front. Protruding teeth, retreating chins, and heavy ridges above the eyes gave them a distinct apelike appearance.

Neanderthal Men

THE MOST PRIMITIVE member of the genus *Homo,* is *Neanderthal man.* Neanderthal remains are quite abundant in Europe, Asia, and Africa. There are variations in the skeletal remains, but none that cannot be attributed to individual and racial differences. These men lived during the third of the four periods of glacier advance. They were sufficiently developed to make tools, draw, and bury their dead. We even find offerings or sacrifices in graves of some of these people, suggesting that they had a religion.

They were short, stocky, and powerful people, and undoubtedly depended on their strength and superior mental abilities to trap and kill their prey. They differed in appearance from modern man primarily in that they had a heavy brow ridge and a large head. The forehead retreated more than that of most modern men, but the capacity of the brain case was about equal to that of modern man.

Cro-Magnon Men

NEANDERTHAL MAN WAS OF THE Old Stone Age. One of the last of the groups whose culture was based on chipping of flint for weapons and tools was *Cro-Magnon man.* These were truly modern men and belong to the species, *Homo sapiens,* of which we are members. They resemble modern man in all respects. The forehead was high and wide, and the backbone formed an elongated S, giving the man an upright posture; he was tall and had a large brain.

These men lived in caves during the last stages of the Pleistocene glaciation. Their drawings of the animals around them in the last ice age are now famous for their accuracy and beauty (Fig. 40–8). They were skillful toolmakers and highly intelligent in other ways as well.

We cannot be sure yet if the various Pleistocene men were of different species or if they all belonged to the same species. It seems very probable that they were all of a single species that split up into a number of widely separated populations. Within each of these populations there may have been some variants that retained more archaic characteristics than others. In addition, the norms of different populations evolved in slightly different ways through the Pleistocene. But during this time natural selection within the groups tended to eliminate the archaic variants and to produce types more nearly characteristic of modern man.

The alternative hypothesis is that Neanderthal man was a different species from that of early *Homo sapiens.* When the two came into direct competition the modern man won out and eliminated his adversary.

FIG. 40–8. / *Cro-Magnon artist painting in the cave of Font de Gaume. (Photo by courtesy of the American Museum of Natural History.)*

Selected References

THE FOLLOWING REFERENCES have been selected as suitable for parallel reading with this book. The list is far from comprehensive, and includes primarily books that are currently and readily available. More specific references to various subjects may be found in the bibliographies of volumes listed under "General References."

General References

DUNBAR, C. O., 1960, *Historical Geology*. New York: John Wiley & Sons, Inc., 500 p.

EMMONS, W. H., *et al.*, 1960, *Geology: Principles and Processes*. New York: McGraw-Hill Book Company, 490 p.

GILLULY, JAMES, *et al.*, 1959, *Principles of Geology*. San Francisco: W. H. Freeman & Co., 534 p.

HELLER, R. L., 1962, *Geology and Earth Science Sourcebook*. New York: Holt, Rinehart & Winston, Inc., 496 p. (paperback).

KING, P. B., 1959, *The Evolution of North America*. Princeton, N. J.: Princeton University Press, 190 p.

LEET, L. D., and SHELDON JUDSON, 1958, *Physical Geology*. Englewood Cliffs, N. J.: Prentice-Hall, Inc., 502 p.

LEET, L. D., and F. J. LEET, 1961, *The World of Geology*. New York: McGraw-Hill Book Company, 262 p. (paperback).

LONGWELL, C. R., and R. F. FLINT, 1962, *Introduction to Physical Geology*. New York: John Wiley & Sons, 504 p.

MOORE, R. C., 1958, *Introduction to Historical Geology*. New York: McGraw-Hill Book Company, 638 p.

PUTNAM, W. C., 1964, *Geology*. New York: Oxford University Press, Inc., 479 p.

SPENCER, E. W., 1962, *Basic Concepts of Historical Geology*. New York: Thomas Y. Crowell Company, 504 p.

SPENCER, E. W., 1962, *Basic Concepts of Physical Geology*. New York: Thomas Y. Crowell Company, 472 p.

STOKES, W. L., 1960, *Essentials of Earth History*. Englewood Cliffs, N. J.: Prentice-Hall, Inc., 502 p.

STRAHLER, A. N., 1963, *The Earth Sciences*. New York: Harper & Row, 681 p.

WHITE, J. F., 1962, *Study of the Earth*. New York: Prentice-Hall, Inc., 408 p. (paperback).

ZUMBERG, J. H., 1963, *Elements of Geology*. New York: John Wiley & Sons, Inc., 342 p.

Crust and Interior of Earth

(See also the physical geology texts listed under "General References" above.)

AIRY, G. B., 1855, "On the computations of the effect of the attraction of the mountain masses as disturbing the apparent astronomical latitude of stations in geodetic surveys": Roy. Soc. London, *Transactions*, ser. B., v. 145.

BULLARD, F. M., 1962, *Volcanos.* University of Texas Press: Austin, 441 p.

CHADWICK, G. H., 1944, "Geology of the Catskill and Kaaterskill Quadrangles": *New York State Museum Bull.* 336 p.

DANA, J. D., 1856, "On the plan of development in the geological history of North America": *American Journal of Science*, v. 22.

DUTTON, C. E., 1889, "On some of the greater problems of physical geology": *Wash. Phil. Soc. Bull.* ser. B., v. 11.

DYSON, J. L., *The World of Ice.* New York: Alfred A. Knopf, Inc., 292 p.

EATON, AMOS, 1818, *An Index to the Geology of the Northern States,* Albany, 286 p.

EATON, J. P., and MURATA, K. J., 1960: "How Volcanos Grow," *Science*, v. 132.

HACK, JOHN, 1960, "Interpretation of erosional topography in humid temperate regions": *American Journal of Science*, v. 258-A.

HEDBERG, HOLLIS, 1963, "The Mohole Project", *University: A Princeton Magazine*, Spring.

HODGSON, J. H., 1964, *Earthquakes and Earth Structure.* Englewood Cliffs, N. J.: Prentice-Hall, Inc., 166 p. (paperback).

LYELL, CHARLES, 1853, *Principles of Geology.* New York: D. Appleton Co., 834 p.

MOORE, RUTH, 1956, *The Earth We Live On.* New York: Alfred A. Knopf, Inc., 416 p.

OAKESHOTT, GORDON, 1964, "The Alaska earthquake": *Mineral Information Service* v. 17, p. 119.

PEARL, R. M., 1956, *Rocks and Minerals.* New York: Barnes & Noble, Inc. 275 p. (paperback).

POUGH, F. H., 1953, *A Field Guide to Rocks and Minerals.* Boston: Houghton Mifflin Co., 333 p.

SHIMER, JOHN A., 1959, *This Sculptured Earth.* New York: Columbia University Press, 255 p.

WOODBURY, D. O., 1962, *The Great White Mantle.* New York: The Viking Press, 214 p.

History of Life on Earth

(See also the historical geology texts listed under "General References" above.)

BEERBOWER, J. R., 1960, *Search for the Past.* Englewood Cliffs, N. J.: Prentice-Hall, Inc., 562 p.

CLARK, W. E., 1959, *History of the Primates.* Chicago: University of Chicago Press, 186 p. (paperback).

COLBERT, E. H., 1955, *Evolution of the Vertebrates.* New York: John Wiley & Sons, Inc., 479 p.

MATTHEWS, W. H., III, 1962, *Fossils.* New York. Barnes & Noble, Inc., 337 p. (paperback).

SIMPSON, G. G., 1953, *The Major Features of Evolution.* New York: Columbia University Press.

SIMPSON, G. G., 1949, *The Meaning of Evolution.* New Haven: Yale University Press, 364 p. (paperback).

STIRTON, R. A., 1959, *Time, Life, and Man.* New York: John Wiley & Sons, Inc., 558 p.

History of Geology

ADAMS, F. D., 1938, *The Birth and Development of the Geological Sciences.* New York: Dover Publications, 506 p. (paperback).

ALBRITTON, C. C., JR., et al., 1963, *The Fabric of Geology.* Reading, Mass.: Addison-Wesley Publishing Co., 372 p.

BAILEY, EDWARD, 1963, *Charles Lyell.* Garden City: Doubleday & Company, Inc., 214 p.

GEIKIE, ARCHIBALD, 1905, *The Founders of Geology.* Reprinted 1962, New York: Dover Publications, 486 p. (paperback).

Place of Earth in Space

ALTER, DINSMORE, et al., 1963, *Pictorial Astronomy,* 2nd rev. ed. New York: Thomas Y. Crowell Company, 312 p.

HOYLE, FRED, 1962, *Astronomy.* Garden City, New York: Doubleday & Company, 320 p.

HURLEY, P. M., 1959, *How Old Is the Earth?* Garden City: Doubleday & Company, 160 p. (paperback).

SHOEMAKER, E. M. 1964, "The Moon Close Up," *National Geographic Magazine* (November).

YOUNG, L. B., *et al.*, 1963, *Exploring the Universe.* New York: McGraw-Hill Book Company, 457 p.

Atmosphere

SPAR, JEROME, 1962, *Earth, Sea, and Air.* Reading, Mass.: Addison-Wesley Publishing Co., 152 p.

STUMPFT, KARL, 1959, *Planet Earth.* Ann Arbor: University of Michigan Press, 191 p. (paperback).

Oceans

CARSON, R. L., 1951, *The Sea Around Us.* New York: Oxford University Press, Inc., 230 p.

KING, C. A. M., 1963, *An Introduction to Oceanography.* New York: McGraw-Hill Book Company, 337 p.

MAURY, M. F., 1855, *Physical Geography of the Sea.* New York: Harper & Bros., 287 p.

SHEPARD, F. P., 1959, *The Earth Beneath the Sea.* Baltimore: Johns Hopkins Press, 275 p.

SHEPARD, F. P., 1963, *Submarine Geology,* 2nd ed. New York: Harper & Row, 557 p.

Index

QUESTIONS:

1. What evidence indicates that the present glaciers are only small remnants of much larger glaciers?
2. Locate: a hanging valley
      a cirque
      an arête
3. What is the shape of the profile of Tenmile Creek Valley near the word Tenmile?
4. Why does it change toward the south?
5. Explain the origin of the shape of Spectacle Buttes.

KINGSTON QUADRANGLE

RHODE ISLAND

U. S. Geological Survey

scale 1:62,500   1 inch equals 1 mile

The central portion of this map is a morainal deposit from a continental ice sheet.

QUESTIONS:

1. Explain the probable origin of the ponds on the moraine.
2. How do you explain the enclosed depressions in the southern half of the map?
3. What differences would you expect to find in the rocks or soil if you dug test pits at Matunuck Pt., north of Matunuck Sch., and on a ridge at Cedar Swamp Pond?
4. Compare the enclosed depressions on this map with those on the Mammoth Cave map and on the Voltaire map.

ANTELOPE PEAK QUADRANGLE

ARIZONA

U. S. Geological Survey

scale 1:62,500   1 inch equals 1 mile

NOTES:

1. Many characteristic features of the arid and semiarid southwest are shown. Note the beautifully developed alluvial fan in Sections 16, 17, 18, 7, 8, and 9.
2. Note the intermittent stream flowing north out of Table Top Mountain. Water from this stream evaporates or infiltrates into the alluvium.

QUESTIONS:

1. What are the principal geomorphic agents responsible for the landforms found here? Outline areas where each is in operation.
2. What has caused the numerous V-shaped indentations along contour lines?
3. Why do these indentations point toward the mountains?

PORTAGE QUADRANGLE

MONTANA

U. S. Geological Survey

scale 1:62,500   1 inch equals 1 mile

NOTES:

1. The drainage pattern shown here is a typical dendritic pattern.
2. Rock units in the area are nearly horizontal.
3. The region has features of youth. Note the V-shaped valleys, broad uplands, and evidence of headward erosion.

QUESTIONS:

1. What rock product is quarried in this area?

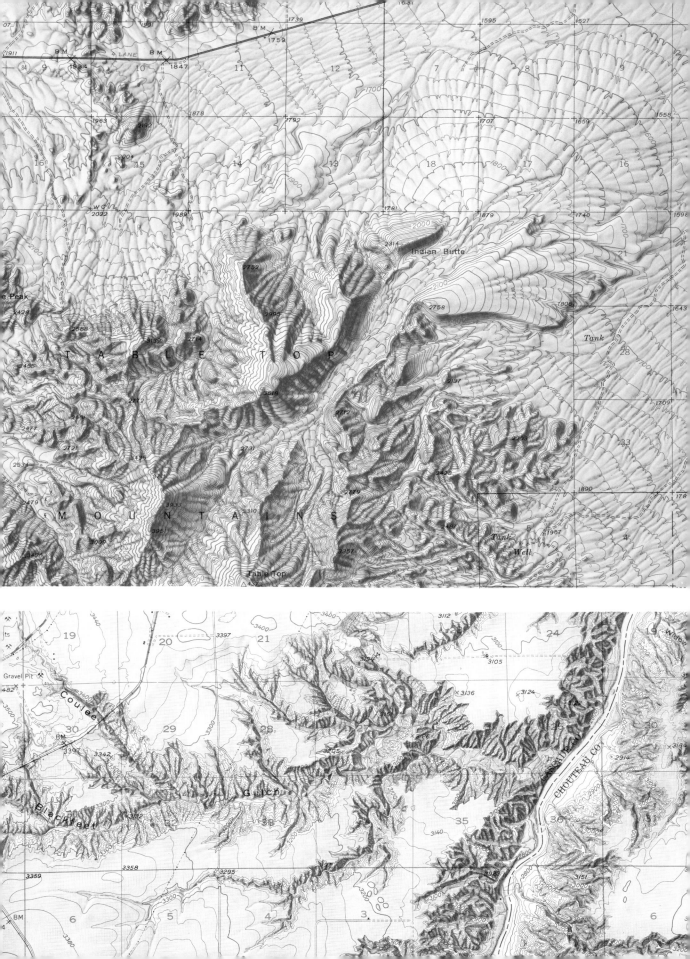

PAXTON SPRINGS QUADRANGLE

NEW MEXICO
U. S. Geological Survey
scale 1:24,000

QUESTIONS:

1. What types of volcanic materials can be identified by their topographic expression?
2. What factors have influenced the shape of the lava flow at Paxton Springs?
3. Explain the probable cause of the springs shown on this map.
4. What are some of the causes of the rough surface of the lava flows?
5. Are the streams on the map younger or older than the lava flow?
6. What are the relative ages of the cone and the lava flows?

MAMMOTH CAVE

KENTUCKY
U. S. Geological Survey
scale 1:62,500   1 inch equals 1 mile

Two nearly horizontal rock units, a sandstone and a limestone, outcrop in this area. The sandstone overlies the limestone.

QUESTIONS:

1. In which part of the area is the limestone exposed at the surface?
2. What are the small depressions in the southern half of the map?
3. Explain the origin of the drainage system in Cedar Spring Valley.
4. How would you describe the surface drainage in the southern part of the map?
5. What is the pattern of the large stream at the northern margin of the map?
6. Explain the probable relationship between the ground water and the surface drainage in this area.

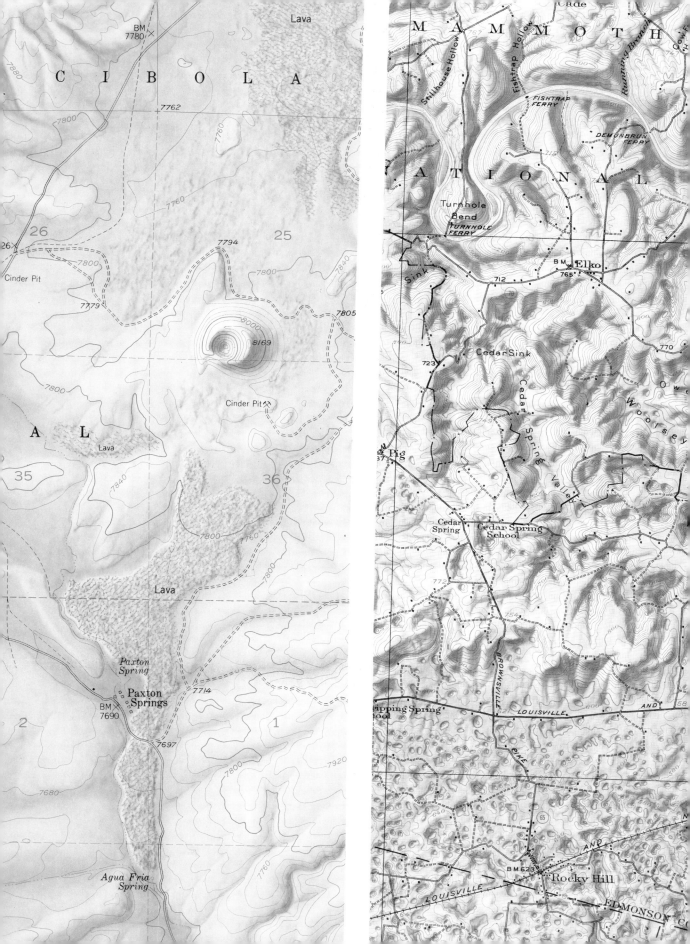

MAVERICK SPRING QUADRANGLE

WYOMING

U. S. Geological Survey

scale 1:24,000

NOTES:

1. A structural dome is reflected in the topography of this area.
2. Each of the ridges and valleys shown is underlain by a different rock stratum. All of the strata are sedimentary.
3. At numerous points along the ridges where streams cut through the ridges V-shaped notches indicate the direction of dip of the strata.
4. In Section 6 a small plunging fold is reflected as a zigzag ridge in the topography.
5. Many of the streams have an annular pattern.

QUESTIONS:

1. What is the direction of strike of the strata in Section 33? What is the direction of dip?
2. What is the strike and dip of the strata at the point marked 6662 in Section 36?
3. Compare the angle of dip of the strata in the southwest corner of Section 36 with that of the strata in Section 30 (north of Section 31).
4. Compare the probable relative ages of the strata exposed in Section 36 with those in Sections 31, 32, and 33.

Geologic Maps

MAPS ARE PREPARED BY GEOLOGISTS to show a variety of types of information. One of the most useful types of map is a geologic map, showing the areal distribution of sedimentary and metamorphic formations and igneous intrusions. A *formation* is a mappable rock unit consisting generally of a single rock type or a group of closely related rock types. Such maps are usually prepared on a topographic map base if one is available. Lines on the map separating formations or intrusions are called lines of contact. These lines are drawn in solid if the contact is exposed at the ground surface. They are dotted or dashed if the contact is covered by thick soil or forest. Faults are also shown. They may be differentiated as to type by use of symbols. Arrows are used to indicate relative movement along strike slip faults, "U" and "D" are used to indicate upthrown and downthrown sides of normal or reverse faults, and barbs or "T" is used to indicate a thrust fault. Such maps always contain a legend showing formations represented on the map and color patterns or symbols used to differentiate them. The legend is arranged so that the youngest formation is at the top of a column and others are arranged below in order of increasing age. Igneous and metamorphic rocks may be set aside in a separate column. In summary, a geologic map shows the surface distribution of rock bodies of different types, the structure of the rocks, and the distribution of rocks of different ages. The ages and rock types are found through use of the map legend. The structure can be interpreted from the map patterns.

Map Interpretation

IGNEOUS intrusions usually have different outcrop patterns (i.e., dikes, stocks, etc.) from sedimentary and metamorphic bodies on geologic maps. Sedimentary rocks are normally stratified, extend for great distances laterally, and are relatively thin. They may be flat-lying, tilted, broken and displaced by faults, or folded. Igneous intrusions cut across the rocks which were present when the intrusion took place. Their contacts are likely to be irregular, and dikes or sills or other related features are evident when the mapping is done in detail. Intrusions may be seen on the geologic map of the northeastern United States in the Triassic lowlands, in the Adirondacks, and in the New England area.

The patterns that sedimentary rocks have on geologic maps depend on the original shape of the layer, the present structure or shape of the layer, and the effects of topography. If the layer is flat in a region of low relief it will cover a large area on the map. The Tertiary deposits on the Wyoming map are gently dipping in the northeast corner of the map for this reason. Where the units outcrop in a very narrow belt it likely indicates that they are steeply inclined. Compare the Cambrian-Ordovician units on the Wyoming map in the northwest and around the edge of the Bighorn Mountains.

In general the direction of inclination of a rock unit can be determined from a map at points where streams cross the contact of the unit. A V-shaped pattern is formed in the contact. The V points in the direction of dip of the contact in almost all cases.

If layers are folded and later eroded the pattern and relative ages of rocks in the different portions of the pattern are diagnostic of the type of fold. If an anticline is eroded so that the top is removed older rocks will be exposed in the center of the structure. In a syncline younger rocks will occupy the central portion of the structure. Study the folded pattern in the Appalachian Valley and along the flanks of the Bighorn Mountains.

Angular unconformities are indicated on geologic maps where the line of contact of one sedimentary layer crosses the contacts of other older units. Notice the contact between the Cretaceous sedimentary layers in the Coastal Plain where they lie unconformably on Piedmont metamorphics and Triassic sediments. What is the nature of the contact between the Triassic sediments and the Piedmont metamorphics?

Among the other types of maps used by geologists are *isopach maps*. These are contour maps showing lines of equal thickness of a formation or group of formations. Some formations are nearly uniform in thickness over large areas, but others vary greatly in thickness, and some variation is usually found. *Structure contour maps* contain lines showing the elevation and configuration of some particular contact completely independent of the topography. Contacts between units often extend below the ground. A structure contour map shows what the shape of the contact is over a large area. A considerable amount of subsurface control is needed to draw such a map accurately. Other maps may be prepared to show what a geologic map of an area would have looked like at some time in the geologic past before deposition of some units or perhaps before the units were folded and faulted.

WYOMING GEOLOGICAL MAP

U. S. Geological Survey, Wyoming Geological Survey, and University of Wyoming Geology Dept.

scale 1:5,000,000

SYMBOLS:

Quaternary (Pleistocene and Recent):
  Qg–glacial, Qal–alluvium
Tertiary (yellows): Tf, Twm, etc.
Cretaceous (greens): Kif, Kmv, etc.
Jurassic (blue-green): Ju, etc.
Triassic (blue):
  ℞Pu (Triassic-Permian together)
Carboniferous (grays): Cta, Cm, etc.
Ordovician-Cambrian (reds): O€u, etc.
Precambrian (tan): p€u

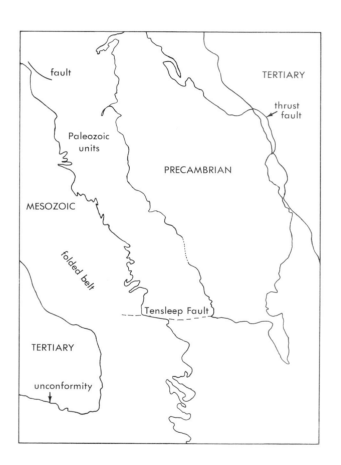

QUESTIONS:

1. What age are the youngest rocks broken by the Tensleep Fault?
2. What age are the youngest rock units unbroken but showing effects of movement along the Tensleep Fault?
3. Explain why the outcrop belt of Paleozoic units is so narrow on the east side of the Bighorn Mountains as compared with the belt on the west side.
4. Silurian and Devonian units are not present on this map. Are they missing as a result of an angular unconformity, a disconformity, or faulting?
5. Locate and name the age of several angular unconformities on the map (for example, the one existing between Twl and Tf in the lower left part of the map).
6. Explain why the Ctd has such an unusual outcrop pattern, lower center of map.

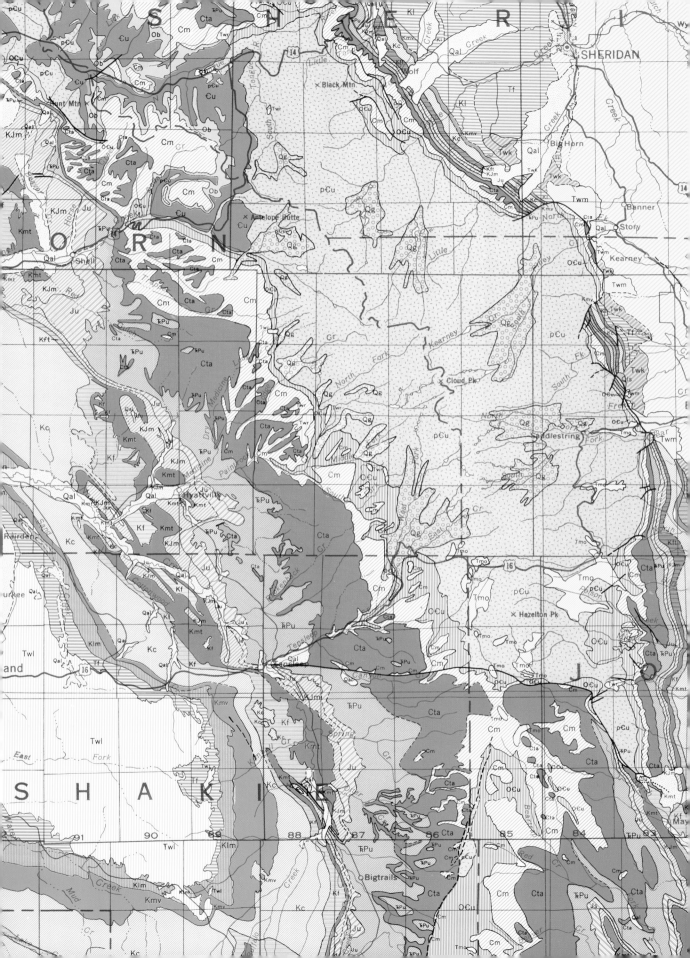

SYMBOLS:

Quaternary (blue): **Qs**
Tertiary (yellows): Ms, Mc, etc.
Cretaceous (greens): Ku, Kl
Triassic (blue-red): ℞b, etc.
Carboniferous (blue): Cm, etc.
Devonian (gray-purple): Du, Dm, etc.
Silurian (lavender): S
Ordovician (pink): O
Cambrian (brown): €u, etc.
Precambrian (various colors):
  AR i, Awl, etc.

Heavy solid lines show major faults,
  undifferentiated as to type.

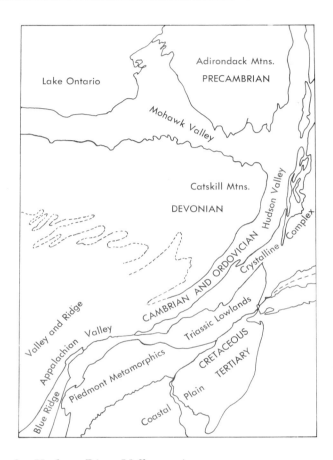

FEATURES TO NOTE:

1. Note the complex fault outcrop pattern in the Hudson River Valley region.
2. The red units in the Triassic lowlands are basalt sills and flows.
3. There is an angular unconformity between Coastal Plain sediments and older sedimentary and metamorphic units.
4. Notice the finger lakes formed by glacial erosion south of Lake Ontario.

QUESTIONS:

1. What evidence indicates that the units marked As east of the Hudson Valley are remnants of large thrust sheets?
2. Describe the relation between the Triassic and other units along (a) the western edge of the lowland and (b) the eastern edge of the lowland.
3. The faults in the Hudson Valley were formed before what period of time? Cite evidence.
4. Why would you expect to find waterfalls on the Potomac River at Washington, D.C.?

GLACIAL MAP OF THE UNITED STATES
EAST OF THE ROCKY MOUNTAINS
Geological Society of America
By Committee of National Research Council, R. F. Flint, Chairman

SYMBOLS:

yellow: Pleistocene stream deposits
blue: Lake deposits including varved clays
dark green: Moraines formed during the Wisconsin glaciation
light green: Drift deposits formed during the Wisconsin glaciation
pink and orange: Pre-Wisconsin glacial deposits

Dots with lines through them indicate the direction of ice movement as shown by striations and grooves.

Small black arrows indicate spillway outlets of glacial lakes and channels cut by meltwater streams.

Red lines mark positions of strandlines including beaches, bars, etc.

Barbed lines indicate outer limits of glacial advance.

EXERCISES:

1. Without reference to the key to the colors determine the relative age of the various deposits by noting which units lie on and partially cover others.
2. How do you explain the breaks in some of the morainal deposits such as those in the Mississinewa and Bloomer moraines?
3. Explain why the spillway outlets were directed south in Ohio.
4. Explain why there are so many well-defined moraines of Wisconsin age instead of just one terminal moraine.
5. Cite one probable reason why there are not numerous moraines of Illinoian or Kansan age.